θ

x

$$\tan\theta = \frac{5/32}{1\,3/4 + x}$$

AIR POLLUTION

VOLUME I

AIR POLLUTION

Edited by

ARTHUR C. STERN

United States Public Health Service
Robert A. Taft Sanitary Engineering Center
Cincinnati, Ohio

VOLUME I

1962

ACADEMIC PRESS · New York and London

ACADEMIC PRESS INC.
111 Fifth Avenue
New York 3, N. Y.

United Kingdom Edition
Published by

ACADEMIC PRESS INC. (London) Ltd.
Berkeley Square House
Berkeley Square, London, W. 1

Library of Congress Catalog Card Number 61–18293

PRINTED IN THE UNITED STATES OF AMERICA

This volume is dedicated to
DICK, BETTY, AND BOB

CONTRIBUTORS TO VOLUME I

BERNARD D. BLOOMFIELD, *Division of Occupational Health, Michigan Department of Health, Lansing, Michigan*

C. STAFFORD BRANDT, *Agricultural Research Service Liaison, United States Public Health Service, Cincinnati, Ohio*

LESLIE A. CHAMBERS, *Los Angeles County Air Pollution Control District, California**

JOHN R. GOLDSMITH, *Air Pollution Medical Studies, Bureau of Chronic Diseases, California State Department of Public Health, Berkeley, California*

A. J. HAAGEN-SMIT, *California Institute of Technology, Pasadena, California*

E. R. HENDRICKSON, *Air Pollution Research Laboratory, University of Florida, Gainesville, Florida*

E. WENDELL HEWSON, *Department of Engineering Mechanics, The University of Michigan, Ann Arbor, Michigan*

MORRIS B. JACOBS, *Division of Occupational Medicine, School of Public Health and Administrative Medicine, Columbia University, New York, New York*

ELMER R. KAISER, *College of Engineering, New York University, New York, New York*

JAMES P. LODGE, JR., *Chemical Research and Development Section, Division of Air Pollution, United States Public Health Service, Robert A. Taft Sanitary Engineering Center, Cincinnati, Ohio†*

N. A. RENZETTI, *California Institute of Technology, Pasadena, California‡*

ELMER ROBINSON, *Stanford Research Institute, Menlo Park, California*

AUGUST T. ROSSANO, JR., *California Institute of Technology, Pasadena, California*

B. J. STEIGERWALD, *Department of Civil Engineering and Engineering Mechanics, Case Institute of Technology, Cleveland, Ohio*

HERBERT E. STOKINGER, *Toxicology Section, Division of Occupational Health, United States Public Health Service, Department of Health, Education, and Welfare, Cincinnati, Ohio*

GORDON H. STROM, *New York University College of Engineering, New York, New York*

* Present address: Scientific Director, Allan Hancock Foundation, and Professor of Biology, University of Southern California, Los Angeles, California.

† Present address: National Center for Atmospheric Research, Boulder, Colorado.

‡ Formerly: Air Pollution Foundation, San Marino, California.

BERNARD D. TEBBENS, *University of California, Berkeley, California*
R. C. WANTA, *Allied Research Associates, Inc., Boston, Massachusetts*
JOHN E. YOCOM, *Bay Area Air Pollution Control District, San Francisco, California**

* Present address: Arthur D. Little, Inc., Research and Development Group, Western Laboratories, San Francisco, California.

PREFACE

This book is concerned with the cause, effect, transport, measurement, and control of air pollution. It is intended for professionals. However, by professionals are meant those trained in as wide a variety of callings as are represented among its authors: engineers, chemists, physicists, physicians, meteorologists, lawyers, agronomists, and toxicologists.

Since this is a two-volume work, it may be helpful to the reader who does not find the subject of his interest in Volume I to outline briefly the contents of Volume II. It covers four major areas: the emissions to the atmosphere from the principal air pollution sources; the control techniques and equipment used to minimize these emissions; the applicable laws, regulations and standards; and the administrative and organizational procedures used to administer these laws, regulations, and standards. The concluding chapter of Volume II discusses air pollution literature resources and gives guidance in locating information not to be found in either volume. Volumes I and II were prepared simultaneously and the total work divided into two volumes to make it easier for the reader to use.

Altogether, the two volumes represent the work of forty-five separate authors. It was my responsibility, as planner and editor of the book, to define the subject area to be covered by each author. Therefore, gaps in the coverage of the over-all subject of air pollution are my fault, not that of the authors. Some of the gaps are intentional. For instance, during the time this book was being written, there has been intensive development of instrumental methods of chemical analysis. Because it was felt that discussion of these developments was in the domain of analytical chemistry rather than air pollution, it was omitted from the book. We also debated the desirability of including detailed lists of air pollutant levels in a number of cities. These, too, were intentionally omitted because of their rapid obsolescence. Appendix I of Volume II lists industrial processes capable of causing emission of pollutants. It is admittedly an incomplete list. Since it was obviously impracticable to cover all such processes, only a few were selected for detailed discussion in Volume II.

Two very common shortcomings of multi-authored books are repetition of the same material in several chapters and unevenness of treatment of the subject matter among the several chapters. I have attempted to control repetition by initially requiring detailed chapter outlines from each author and then eliminating like material from all but one chapter outline.

To maintain uniformity of technical level among the chapters, the authors were asked to write for a scientifically advanced reader and to assume that any further mathematical or other scientific background information that might be required by a reader could be obtained from other sources.

Authors were initially assigned chapter lengths. It is interesting to note that most authors felt that to achieve the desired level of sophistication, they required more space than was originally assigned them, some exceeding their initial quota by a considerable margin. In each case where a longer-than-intended chapter was allowed to remain, it was because I believed that severely cutting it would deprive the reader of valuable information. My reluctance to cut these chapters back to their preconceived length has resulted in expanding a book originally planned as a one volume work of 500 pages to the present two volume work of 1,200 pages.

The principal problem of the editor of a work of this nature is the race between the time it takes the slowest author to complete his chapter and obsolescence that has accumulated in all the previously completed chapters. The authors of all chapters were given the opportunity of last minute updating of their material. Despite this, the astute reader will spot some differences in the relative amounts of very recent material included in the various chapters.

The subject index for both volumes was prepared by Esther E. Norton and Marion G. Curry.

As editor of a multi-author book, I thank each author for both his contribution and his patience. For each author, there is also a family to be thanked for their forbearance and a secretary for her help in preparation of the manuscript. In my particular case, as not only editor but also chapter author, I acknowledge to my family and thank my secretary, Celia G. Barlow, who carried forty-five times the burden of all the other authors' secretaries combined. In this task, Carolyn S. Froelich helped her carry the load. Special thanks are due my superiors in the Public Health Service for permitting the participation of myself and so many of my Public Health Service colleagues.

ARTHUR C. STERN

Cincinnati, Ohio
November, 1961

CONTENTS

Part I: Air Pollution and Its Dispersion

Part II: The Effects of Air Pollution

CONTENTS OF VOLUME II

Part IV: Air Pollution Sources

Part V: Control Methods and Equipment

Part VI: Air Pollution Control

PART I

Air Pollution and Its Dispersion

CHAPTER 1

Classification and Extent of Air Pollution Problems

LESLIE A. CHAMBERS *

Los Angeles County Air Pollution Control District, California

I. Historical Perspective

A. AIR POLLUTION PRIOR TO THE INDUSTRIAL REVOLUTION

The quality of the atmosphere, on which all terrestrial forms of life are dependent, has been recognized as an important variable in the environment only during the past few decades. It may be supposed that smoke and fumes from forest fires, volcanoes, and crude "domestic" heating and cooking arrangements were troublesome or lethal in discrete localities even before our human ancestors became organized in fixed communities, and that the odors of decaying animal and vegetable refuse, attested to by existing residues of prehistoric garbage dumps in and near Stone Age dwellings, were cause for protesting comment in such language as may have been available to the temporary residents.

However, it is unlikely that such circumstances can have been regarded as more than incidental to devastating natural cataclysms, or as

* Present address: Scientific Director, Allan Hancock Foundation, and Professor of Biology, University of Southern California, Los Angeles, California.

cause for transfer to another dwelling site, until social evolution reached the husbandry level involving association of family units into more or less fixed communities. Only then could human activities in the aggregate have produced sufficient effluvia to affect an occupied neighborhood. To what extent they did so is entirely conjectural with respect to all of prehistory and can be guessed only by tenuous inference with respect to most of the ancient and medieval periods. The embodiment in folk knowledge of the middle ages, and in prescientific belief, of the concept of "miasmas," or poisonous airs, as etiological agents of certain diseases, may indicate a deduction from ages-old survival experience related to recognized sources of unwholesome air, but is more likely a mistaken association of "malarias" with the odors of swamps rather than with their mosquitoes.

Historically oriented writers on air pollution occasionally have cited classic references to blackened buildings and monuments as evidence that the smoke nuisance has a reality spanning thousands of years. But the grime of antiquity, while a reasonable expectation, does not suffice to indicate a contemporary recognition of its impact on ancient communities or their members. In fact, accumulated knowledge of domestic heating practices, and of the available primitive metallurgical and other limited industrial processes utilized during the first 13 or 14 centuries of the Christian era, leads to the inference that generalized air pollution could not have been an important problem in the villages and towns of the time; cities, in the sense of modern magnitudes, were nonexistent. The frequently cited references to deaths caused by toxic atmospheres, e.g., the suffocation of Pliny the Elder by volcanic fumes as recorded by Tacitus, seem not to be pertinent except in the sense of demonstrating that the human species was then, as now, physiologically responsive to anoxia or to excessive amounts of poisonous gases.

Throughout the earlier periods of history wood constituted the prime source of energy; dependence on it undoubtedly slowed the evolution and use of industrial processes, and eventually limited the per capita availability of heat as the depletion of nearby forests proceeded. The discovery of the energy potential of coal and its gradual replacement of wood took place in Europe about the time of Marco Polo's return from his travels through the more technologically advanced civilizations of Asia. But in spite of its abundance in the West and its retrospectively apparent advantages, the European adaptation to its use, which culminated in the Industrial Revolution, proceeded slowly and against all the resistance normal to economic readjustments. Coal was an "unnatural" fuel; its sulfurous combustion products confirmed its suspected association with anticlerical forces at a time much too closely related to the ascendancy of strict orthodoxy; above all, as a matter of record, it caused neighborhood "action committees" to protest against its evident pollution of the atmosphere.

In England, Germany, and elsewhere on the continent various limitations and prohibitions relative to the use, importation, and transport of coal were proclaimed officially, and in isolated instances there is evidence that capital penalties were imposed. Nevertheless the overriding necessities for domestic heat and industrial power made these efforts useless generally and assured their disposal in the limbo of unenforceable law. Coal—the revolutionizer—made possible the Industrial Revolution. And then there was smog.

B. Air Pollution as Related to Coal Smoke and Gases

From the beginning of the 14th century to the early part of the 20th, air pollution by coal smoke and gases has occupied the center of the stage almost exclusively, and in many industrialized areas of the world is still the dominant concern. That it is still a community problem, in spite of a repeatedly demonstrated technological capability for its control, would be surprising if public and official hesitance to pay the price were not so characteristic a factor in the historical evolution of all types of health protection programs. Positive action has seldom been anticipatory; instead it has occurred only after dramatic disasters or large-scale sensory insults have aroused public clamor based on fear. We build levees only after floods have devastated whole regions; we abate pollution of water supplies only after typhoid epidemics or similarly impressive episodes; and we take necessary action to control air pollutants only after their killing or irritating potentials have been realized on a large scale as in London in 1952, or in Los Angeles around 1945.

In no case is the very early recognition of a public health problem, and the failure to take any effective action until it threatened personal survival, better illustrated than in the case of air pollution produced by the unrestricted use of coal in Great Britain. During the reign of Edward I (1272–1307) there was recorded a protest by the nobility against the use of "sea" coal; and in the succeeding reign of Edward II (1307–1327) a man was put to the torture ostensibly for filling the air with a "pestilential odor" through the use of coal.

Under Richard III (1377–1399) and, later, under Henry V (1413–1422) England took steps to regulate and restrict the use of coal, apparently because of the smoke and odors produced by its combustion. The earlier action took the form of taxation, while Henry V established a commission to oversee the movement of coal into the City of London.

Other legislation, parliamentary studies, and literary comments appeared sporadically during the following 250 years. In 1661 a most remarkable pamphlet was published by royal command of Charles II. It consisted of an essay entitled "Fumifugium; or the Inconvenience of the Aer and Smoke of London Dissapated; together with Some Remedies Humbly Proposed," written by John Evelyn, one of the founding members of the Royal Society. It is unfortunate that the author's 17th century style has attracted more attention in the 20th century than has the content of his paper. Evelyn clearly recognized the sources, the effects, and the broad aspects of the control problem, to an extent not far surpassed at the present time except for detail and for chemical and physiological terminology. Thus it is clear, not only that the London of 1661 was plagued by coal smoke, but also that the problem and its content were recognized by at least one of the leading scientists of the period.

Some evidence exists that methods for abatement of the smoke nuisance were being sought immediately after the appearance of Evelyn's pamphlet. In 1686 a person named Justel presented before the Philosophical Society "An Account of an Engine that Consumes Smoke." The nature of this and other very early control devices is unimportant, since the rapid increase in smoke density through the next century and a half indicates that they were, like many more recent procedures, either ineffective or not widely used.

By the beginning of the 19th century the smoke nuisance in London and other English cities was of sufficient public concern to prompt the appointment (in 1819) of a Select Committee of the British Parliament to study and report upon smoke abatement. Immediately available sources do not include the substance of any resulting publication, but the effect of the study is suspected of having been similar to that of dozens of other committee recommendations made during the ensuing 133 years. The gradual development of the smoke problem was culminated in the action-arousing deaths, within a few days, of 4000 persons in London in December, 1952.

Records of lethal air pollution concentrations during the 19th century are not definitive; in fact, recognition of their occurrence seems to have resulted largely from retrospective examination of vital records and contemporary descriptive notes. In 1873 an episode having the characteristics of the 1952 event occurred in London, and more or less severe repetitions have affected metropolitan life at irregular intervals up to the present time.

The term "smog" originated in Great Britain as a popular derivation of "smoke-fog" and appears to have been in common usage before World War I. Perhaps the term was suggested by H. A. Des Voeux's 1911 report to the Manchester Conference of the Smoke Abatement League of Great Britain on the "smoke-fog" deaths which occurred in Glasgow, Scotland in 1909. During two separate periods in the autumn of that year very substantial increases in death rate were attributed to smoke and fog and it was estimated that "1063 deaths were attributable to the noxious conditions."

With few isolated exceptions, the extreme atmospheric concentrations of pollutants produced by coal burning in Britain have not been duplicated elsewhere. Nevertheless, coal-based industrial economies on the continent of Europe and in the United States have caused discomfort, public reaction, and regulatory action. A generation before the dramatic incident which killed 20 and made several hundred ill in the industrial town of Donora, Pennsylvania in 1948, public action and protest groups had appeared in several American cities. In some, such as St. Louis, Cincinnati, and, more recently, in Pittsburgh, popular movements have resulted in substantial elimination of the smoke nuisance, by substitution of less smoky fuels and by enforced employment of combustion practices designed to eliminate smoke. It has thus been demonstrated that high smoke densities are preventable, although the cost may be great. London and other English cities are handicapped in their current smoke abatement effort by a lack of domestic low volatility coal supplies, almost complete dependence on imports for other fossil fuels, and a centuries-old pattern of household heating, the physical characteristics of which can be changed only gradually and at a very high price.

No rigorous identification of the constituents of coal smoke responsible for the respiratory illnesses with which it has been associated has been produced, although the effects have been generally attributed to sulfur dioxide and trioxide. Recently the probability of a role of tar, soot, and ash particles in the total irritative effect has been the inspiration for several investigations. But the information available to us on the relationship of coal smoke to human health has been insufficient to explain the death and discomfort it has caused.

Smoke and gases from the burning of coal have been the chief atmospheric pollutants in all parts of the industrialized world for more than 400 years. In spite of the recent rapid shift to petroleum and natural gas, coal smoke still is a major contributor to poor air quality in all but a few metropolitan areas.

C. POLLUTION BY SPECIFIC TOXICANTS

While pollutants resulting from use of the dominant energy sources —coal and petroleum products—generally arise from a large number of points within a community and therefore often cause a general deterioration of the air supply over large areas, more restricted regions closely adjacent to individual sources may be even more seriously affected. Many localized events have emphasized that critical concentrations of pollutants other than smoke, having proven toxic properties, can adversely affect air quality. A large number of substances used in manufacturing and commerce have been recognized officially by the American Conference of Governmental Industrial Hygienists as hazards to industrial workers, and maximal limits of acceptable concentration for eight-hour exposures have been established. While the MAC's (maximum acceptable concentrations) are not applicable where intermittent exposure of an unselected population is the concern, they do indicate the classes and species of substances potentially hazardous.

Perhaps the most publicized recent example of serious air pollution by an identified toxicant was the episode at Poza Rica, near Mexico City, in which numbers of people were affected and a few died, from exposure to hydrogen sulfide. Metallic fumes and acid mists from metallurgical processing have occasionally rendered downwind regions wholly uninhabitable for plants as well as man. Fluorides escaping from aluminum processing and other industrial sources have been the cause of losses to cattle farmers. Malodorous pollutants from a wide variety of source types have produced responses ranging from public irritation to overt and wholesale illness.

But such unquestioned local reactions to specific pollutants are fortunately rather infrequent. Usually, dispersive processes reduce the concentrations of emitted toxic materials to levels below the probability of immediate or acute biological response. Under such circumstances the pollutants may provide a more or less continuous low dosage to occupants of an extended area, providing the possibility of slow concentration of substances such as lead, or a continuum of low grade physiological insults which may eventually overpower physiological defenses. The whole area of potential knowledge of the effects of low dosages of pollutants long continued is virtually unexplored; and the possibilities of synergism among two or more substances simultaneously breathed at subacute concentrations for extended periods of time have been suggested but scarcely examined, even theoretically.

D. Emergence of Petroleum Products

It is possible that future historians may recognize a Second Industrial Revolution born in the years following the successful completion (1859) of Drake's first oil well in Pennsylvania. Subsequent release of a flood of fossilized energy in the form of petroleum and natural gas not only has transformed industrial and domestic heating practices, but has made possible wholesale changes in transportation, and has provided the raw materials for petrochemical products in almost infinite variety.

Combustion of oil and gas has diminished the nuisance and hazard of coal smoke to the extent that the use of these fuels has displaced coal. With more than one type of mineral energy source available the magnitude of the change has varied markedly among geographical regions, in a manner closely related to propinquity of oil and gas fields, extension of pipeline networks and other transport facilities, relative local costs of delivered fuel, and other logistic factors. Within the United States, for example, large areas of the southwest now consume negligible quantities of coal, while portions of the eastern seaboard, the southeast, and the midwestern industrial complexes exhibit mixed patterns of coal, oil, and natural gas use.

Throughout the United States and in many other parts of the world the use of petroleum products, in the forms of gasoline and oil, has been tremendously accelerated, especially since World War II, by the almost exclusive employment of internal combustion engines in highway, railway, and marine transport. Thus, even in those regions unfavorably situated for the rapid adoption of oil and gas for heating and manufacturing, the combustion residues of petroleum products have become a factor in community air pollution.

The contribution of automobile engine exhausts to the atmosphere was pointed out as a potential hazard at least as early as 1915, and the objectionable fumes from diesel power plants have been a matter of concern at least as long, but it was not until about 1945 that the first acute community air pollution problem, definitely attributable to petroleum products and their use, forced itself into public and official recognition. The Los Angeles type of air pollution (hereafter referred to as "smog" in deference to local usage, although it is actually not identical to the smoke fog of Great Britain from which the term is derived) has become the infamous prototype of similar developments appearing with increasing frequency in metropolitan areas of the United States and in some other countries.

As a matter of fact, the physical system underlying the obvious manifestations of smog in Los Angeles includes neither smoke nor fog. Early in the hastily organized effort to abate the air pollution which became irritatingly evident during the wartime industrialization of southern California, Professor A. J. Haagen-Smit demonstrated that the eye irritation, damage to green leaves, and light-scattering characteristic of smog could be produced by ultraviolet irradiation of a mixture of hydrocarbon vapors and nitrogen dioxide. This, as well as much subsequent work, has proved that the "new" kind of air pollution results from exposure to sunlight of mixtures of olefins and other reactive products of petroleum manufacture and use, mixed with oxides of nitrogen. The variety of intermediate and terminal products formed under different conditions of relative concentration, humidity, temperature, solar radiation intensity, and admixture with other reactive gases and particles is certainly very great. Among them are ozone, organic hydroperoxides, peroxyacyl nitrites or nitrates (PAN or Compound X), several aldehydes and other irritants which have been positively identified, a wide variety of free radicals not experimentally demonstrated but necessary intermediates in the photochemical transitions from primary reactants to more stable products, and a host of possibly troublesome substances whose occurrence is still hypothetical.

Subsequent chapters of this volume will deal especially with the reaction mechanisms and their consequences.

Most of the pollutants related to petroleum production, processing, and use have intrinsic toxic or irritative potentials of a rather low order. By contrast, their photochemical reaction products may affect biological systems at extremely low concentrations. Thus, the control of the primary reactants must be based on their identification and their regulation to atmospheric levels at which they are incapable of generating effective amounts of secondary products. Ozone, for example, is not known to be produced in significant quantity from direct sources within the Los Angeles area; yet it occurs frequently at levels greater than 0.25 p.p.m. as the result of photoenergized reactions involving hydrocarbons at the level of 1 p.p.m. or less and NO_2 in the same range of concentration. To prevent toxic accumulations of ozone, it is necessary to control sources of both hydrocarbon vapor and nitrogen oxides which, except for the intervention of reaction in the general atmosphere, would be harmless.

Current economic trends and knowledge of proven world petroleum resources indicate that air pollution due to hydrocarbons, petrochemical products, and engine exhausts will become increasingly evident in most metropolitan areas for many years to come. Eventually, of course, retarding pressures generated by depletion of supplies will become operative, but the present and at least one or two future generations will find it necessary to protect local air supplies against contamination by gasoline vapors and exhaust gases.

E. Relationship to Energy Sources

The material which a biological system utilizes as its source of energy determines the characteristics of its waste products. Similarly, the fuel used by a community governs the kinds, amounts, and properties of its refuse to a major degree. The aerial excreta of a city may be modified by local patterns of industry, solid waste disposal practices, or occasional counteracting "perfumes" such as paper mill mercaptans, but the products generated in energy transformations constitute the core of the community air pollution problem.

It is not necessary to discount the importance of localized nuisances in order to accept this primary thesis. Odors, toxic dusts and fumes, and corrosive acid mists are of great importance to the locality directly affected. But the primary threat to the air resources of modern cities may be firmly attributed to the kinds of stuff they use for fuel and to the ways in which they use it.

A major change in the nature of the air pollution problem could occur only with a major change in energy sources. It is interesting, but probably of little immediate import, to speculate on what may occur if nuclear power, or direct utilization of solar energy, become practicable and economically competitive. In the one case a totally different kind of air pollution will require careful control; radioactive by-products of nuclear fuels could be troublesome to an extent not foretold by any previous experience with products of fossil fuels. In the present state of nuclear power technology the magnitude and quality of the potential air pollution problem cannot be defined, but it can be hoped that power packages will be so constructed as to minimize emission of active wastes.

Since about the beginning of the 20th century world-wide atmospheric concentrations of carbon dioxide have been increasing steadily in a manner related to the increased global use of fossil fuels. Carbon dioxide is not often considered to be an air pollutant since it produces adverse physiological effects only at relatively high concentration, and because biological and geochemical processes are known to provide a sufficient natural disposal system. Its atmospheric increase apparently reflects an accelerating disparity between the CO_2 production rate and the rate of approach to equilibrium with marine and terrestrial sinks. Unchecked increase in the rate of combustion of carbon fuels apparently will increase general CO_2 levels eventually to meteorologically and physiologically significant levels. Perhaps it may, within a few generations, compete with radioactive wastes for the dubious distinction of being a world-wide air polluter.

Any substantial shift of energy dependence from fossil fuels to nuclear or solar power plants will tend to re-establish the planetary CO_2 equilibrium. It is especially exciting to consider the air conservation potential of solar energy, certain types of fuel cells, and related non-polluting power sources now being explored. Should these prove capable of displacing current combustive transformations, the community air pollution problem would be reduced to more or less routine policing of localized sources.

II. Primary Concepts of Air Pollution

A variety of definitions of air pollution have been devised, each expressing more or less completely the individual philosophical, theoretical, practical, or protective motivation of its author. Any circumstance which adds to or subtracts from the usual constituents of air may alter its physical or chemical properties sufficiently to be detected by occupants of the medium. It is usual to consider as pollutants only those substances added in sufficient concentration to produce a measurable effect on man or other animals, vegetation, or material.

Pollutants may therefore include almost any natural or artificial composition of matter capable of being airborne. They may occur as solid particles, liquid droplets, or gases, or in various admixtures of these forms. Pollution of the air by a single chemical species appears to be a most unusual event; certainly, most community problems involve a very large number of kinds and sizes of substances.

In an effort to classify the pollutants thus far recognized, it is convenient to consider two general groups: (1) those emitted directly from identifiable sources and (2) those produced in the air by interaction among two or more primary pollutants, or by reaction with normal atmospheric constituents, with or without photoactivation. But any taxonomic system based on available sampling and analytical methods is almost certain to fall short of a complete description of the qualities of a polluted air supply. This is true because few, if any, of the polluting entities retain their exact identities after entering the atmosphere. Thermal and photochemical reactions, often catalytically facilitated by gases or solid and liquid surfaces, provide a dynamic, constantly changing character to the total system, and to its individual constituents. Eventually it may be possible to characterize a polluted air mass in space and time by a complex integration of reaction pathways and rates as governed by fluctuating free energy levels. But that capability is only a present dream.

A. Primary Emissions

Fortunately, it is usually possible to determine with reasonable assurance the kinds and amounts of primary pollutants emitted from each source in a community. Much information is available as to the chemical species and physical states of discharges from most types of artificial and natural generators. While the end effect of the emissions cannot be predicted with certainty from these data alone, they do define the primary reactants, and after other troublesome reaction chains have been identified, enable retroactive abatement with respect to the primary species contributing to the chains.

Primary emissions are often categorized, quite illogically because of our imperfect knowledge, under a mixture of headings defining chemical properties, physical phases, and magnitudes. For purposes of generalization a listing of the following type is probably as inclusive as any:

Fine solids (less than 100 μ in diameter)
Coarse particles (greater than 100 μ in diameter)
Sulfur compounds
Organic compounds
Nitrogen compounds
Oxygen compounds
Halogen compounds
Radioactive compounds

In one form or another, each of these groups of pollutants will be considered in detail in the following chapters.

The finer aerosols include carbon particles, metallic dusts, silicates, fluorides, tars, resins, some pollens, fungi and bacteria, solid oxides, nitrates, sulfates, chlorides, aromatics, and a host of other species obviously overlapping all of the more specific categories. As particles, they scatter light in conformance with well-established physical laws relating wavelength and particle size. As suppliers of large specific surfaces they afford opportunity for catalysis of normally slow interactions among adsorbed pollutants. As charged entities they govern to a substantial degree the condensation and coalescence of other particles and gases. As chemical species per se some of them exhibit high orders of toxicity to plant and animal species, or are corrosive to metal structures and other materials. To the extent that they are radioactive they increase the normal radiation dosage and are suspected of being factors in abnormal genetic processes. And finally, as plain dust, deposited in accordance with the physical laws governing precipitation and electrostatic attraction, they soil clothing, buildings, and bodies, and constitute a general nuisance.

The coarser particles, 100 μ and greater in diameter, present the same types of problems in greatly diminished degree. This is true because their mass assures rather prompt removal from the air by gravitational attraction, because physiological defensive mechanisms prevent their penetration into human or animal lungs, and because the same mass of substance in such large units affords substantially less opportunity for interaction with other components of the polluted air supply. On the other hand, their soiling effect may be more evident simply because they are readily deposited without opportunity for wide dispersal after leaving a source.

Interest in the sulfur compounds has been prolonged and intense because of their suspected role in the London disasters of 1952 and other years, and because of the extreme toxicity of hydrogen sulfide. Combustion of sulfur-containing fuels contributes large amounts of SO_2 and some SO_3, many industrial processes and waste disposal practices generate H_2S, and the nauseous odors of mercaptans are well-recognized associates of some paper-manufacturing and petrochemical processes. All of these affect plants and animals adversely at different, but generally low, concentrations. There is substantial evidence that the full air-polluting potential of SO_2 is realized only after it has reacted with other substances in the atmosphere.

Organic compounds released to typical community air supplies include a very large number of saturated and unsaturated aliphatic, and aromatic hydrocarbons together with a variety of their oxygenated and halogenated derivatives. They are emitted principally as vapors, but the less volatile compounds may occur as liquid droplets or solid particles. Some have odors which are characteristic and often objectionable. A number, notably the polynuclear aromatics, have been associated with carcinogenesis. But the majority have relatively low potential for serious air pollution effect so long as they retain their specific identities. Outstanding exceptions may be found, e.g., formaldehyde, formic acid, acrolein, and some compounds containing phosphorus and fluorine.

The nitrogen compounds most abundantly generated and released are nitric oxide, nitrogen dioxide, and ammonia. The first two of these are produced in high temperature combustion and other industrial operations by the combination of normal atmospheric oxygen and nitrogen. While NO_2 is irritating to tissues at relatively low concentration, the major interest in both the oxides is related to their participation in atmospheric photochemical reactions.

Carbon dioxide and carbon monoxide arise in huge amounts from the complete and incomplete combustion of carbonaceous fuels. In Los Angeles County the daily production of CO is estimated to exceed 10,000 tons daily, with more than 80% of it resulting from incomplete utilization of the carbon content of gasoline in automobile engines. CO is not known to participate in secondary atmospheric reactions, but its ability to impair the oxygen-carrying capacity of hemoglobin gives it special status as a primary pollutant. Carbon dioxide in very high concentration affects the cardiac control mechanism, but the quantity required is too great to be of much concern. Mention has already been made of the possible long-range influence of the general rise in atmospheric CO_2 on world temperatures and related phenomena.

Certain inorganic halogen compounds, among them HF and HCl, are produced from metallurgical and other industrial processes. Both are corrosive and irritating per se, and the metallic fluorides have toxic properties which have precipitated some intricate and costly legal actions among operators of producing factories and neighboring residents whose crops and cattle have been severely damaged.

It is not within the scope of this discussion to elaborate on the very specialized nature, sources, or properties of radioactive pollutants. Except for fallout of nuclear weapon residues, these materials have not yet presented a major practical problem beyond the vicinities of Atomic Energy Commission operations. That they will do so with increasing use of nuclear power and industrial applications of isotope techniques is unquestioned.

B. Secondary Pollutants

It was suggested earlier that the total polluted air mass over a populated area is chemically and physically unstable. As a whole, the system tends, like everything else in nature, to approach a state of minimal free energy. The rates, reaction routes, and intermediate steps involved in the process are influenced by many factors such as relative concentration of reactants, degree of photoactivation, variable meteorological dispersive forces, influences of local topography, and relative amounts of moisture.

In the simplest case two species may react thermally, as in the formation of a halide salt by combination of acid mists with metallic oxides. When water droplets are airborne, solution reactions may occur, as in the formation of acid mists by reaction of dissolved oxygen and SO_2.

The formation of sulfuric acid in droplets has been shown to be enormously accelerated by the presence in the droplets of certain metallic oxides such as those of Mn and Fe. This illustrates the well-established role of catalytic processes in affecting step rates in the over-all system.

Surface of liquid and solid particles contribute variously to the energy degradation processes. They may be able to adsorb gases from very dilute mixtures, thereby accelerating normal reactions by providing discrete sites of high reactant concentration. In the adsorbed form the retention of toxic gases in the respiratory system of man may be enhanced, and the apparent irritative effect of the gas may be greatly increased. This kind of phenomenon is well illustrated by Amdur's work relating NaCl aerosols with SO_2 and certain other irritating gases in their effect on pulmonary function. Some species of particles provide sites for surface catalysis of simple and complex reactions, and at least a few cases have been studied in which semiconducting metallic oxide surfaces are active in the catalysis of photoenergized events.

Photochemical reactions involved in air pollution have been studied enough in recent years to prove their major role in smog manifestations of the type experienced in Los Angeles. The primary photochemical event appears to be the dissociation of NO_2, providing NO and O radicals which are able to initiate sustained free radical reaction chains. The number and kinds of transient radicals and semistable compounds formed is then governed by the relative abundance and susceptibility of other chemical species in the system, and by environmental energy factors.

The secondary pollutants produced during events of this type are among the most troublesome that air pollution control agencies are required to abate. They include ozone, formaldehyde, organic hydroperoxides, and other very reactive compounds, as well as potentially damaging concentrations of short-lived free radicals, so long as photoactivation is maintained in the presence of a sufficient supply of primary and secondary reactants. It will be recognized that free radical mechanisms do not preclude the participation of O_2, H_2O or other normal atmospheric constituents in the formation of end products.

To unravel so complex and temporally variable a system will challenge air pollution research for a long time to come, and the precise prediction of the characteristics of the system one hour ahead may never be more reliable than a probability function. On the other hand, it is clear that the simple process of collecting and analyzing stable chemical species and physical entities as is now practiced cannot provide much knowledge of the continually changing assemblage of transient entities which are prime factors in the effects produced by air pollution.

C. Recognized Atmospheric Processes

In addition to chemical recombinations, several other major factors regulate the impact of primary and secondary pollutants. Principal among these are processes of nucleation and condensation, sedimentation, and other air-cleansing phenomena which tend to remove substances from the atmosphere, and meteorological processes that may dilute the reactants or tend to concentrate them.

Condensation nuclei released from many sources both natural and artificial, under appropriate circumstances can induce the accumulation of vapors into aerosols. These in turn may coalesce with other particles to an extent great enough to permit their eventual deposition on exposed surfaces. As in the case of chemical reaction, such physical processes are rate-related to concentrations; it is questionable whether aggregation and sedimentation play a significant role in air purification except under unusual circumstances, or with respect to coarse particles.

The energy-degrading mechanisms discussed in the previous section may be regarded as natural purification processes, in the sense that their end products are less reactive and therefore usually less troublesome than the primary or intermediate pollutants. The mechanism is analogous in its effect to the biological oxidation of organic pollutants in sewage and water supplies; in each case the oxidized products are relatively ineffective physiologically. Thus, the development of a large excess of ozone during a Los Angeles "alert" usually signals an ensuing rapid decline in eye irritation, presumably because the primary organic reactant in the air mass is near exhaustion and the ozone itself assures final oxidation of the irritating intermediate compounds.

Much closer analogies between water pollution and air pollution problems are apparent when physical dispersive factors are considered. In each case the volume of medium available for dilution of contaminants, and the speed of mixing, are dominant in determining the capability of the stream or air mass of accommodating a given output without presenting localized or general affronts to users of the water or air.

Air supplies are affected, in this quantitative sense, by the degree of containment beneath inversions, the magnitude of horizontal and vertical wind movements, and by the degree of turbulence induced by convection and nonlinear flow. As is the case with all types of meteorological phenomena these factors are governed by both external, synoptic forces, and by localized topographic and thermal influences.

It is possible, given sufficient data to establish wind direction and velocities, local and regional thermal variations, and other pertinent factors, to develop equations expressing the most probable concentrations of pollutants likely to occur in relation to a source of known characteristics. Hypothetically, it is also possible to relate these influences to future air pollution events in, and adjacent to, a large community of different sources. Some suggestive elementary models have already been proposed. But as practical tools for the regulation of regional problems, meteorological analyses have not been used effectively except in relation to localized emissions and their effects in the immediate vicinity.

The existence of usual patterns of air movement over specific geographical areas has suggested to many the possibility of affecting favorably the quality of air supplies by some form of zoning or regulated placement of sources. Sites in deep valleys and elsewhere, subject to frequent inversion entrapment, can be recognizd as unfavorable to maintenance of good air quality. However, it is unfortunately true that the acute air pollution episodes in affected localities occur when the meteorological pattern is not "usual." For this reason, a question may reasonably be raised as to the ultimate usefulness of regional zoning as a means of controlling air pollution. The whole matter of the relationship between meteorological probability and the relatively infrequent atypical pollutional occurrences associated with unusual air movement, or lack of it, is intensely interesting. But it is currently a mathematical exercise in topologic nonlinear differential equations, the number of solutions of which may well approach infinity.

Meterological factors are the chief diluters and dispersers of pollution. Where and when they fail to perform these functions adequately, the sources of pollution must be controlled.

III. Types of Effects Associated with Air Pollution

In the following sections detailed attention is devoted to the kinds and magnitudes of effects known and suspected of being produced by air pollution. They may be grouped under five general headings:

A. Visibility Reduction

Historically the earliest noted, and currently the most easily observed, effect of air pollution is the reduction in visibility produced by the scattering of light from the surfaces of airborne particles. The degree of light obstruction is a complex function of particle size, aerosol density, thickness of the affected air mass, and certain more subtle physical factors. Particulates responsible for the phenomenon may be either primary pollutants, e.g., coal smoke, or secondary, e.g., Los Angeles photochemical smog. At times London and cities in the eastern United States have been so seriously affected by pollutional reduction in visibility as to have experienced severe curtailment of transport and other municipal activities. It has frequently been pointed out that the attenuation of ultraviolet and other radiations reaching the surface through layers of aerosols may be associated with adverse physiological effects in men and vegetation.

B. Material Damage

Direct damage to structural metals, surface coatings, fabrics, and other materials of commerce is a frequent and widespread effect of air pollution. The total annual loss from these and incidental increases in cleansing and protective activities in the United States is not accurately known but has been estimated at a level of several billions of dollars. The destruction is related to many types of pollutants but is chiefly attributable to acid mists, oxidants of various kinds, H_2S, and particulate products of combustion and industrial processing. Secondary pollutants contribute a substantial share. For example, O_3 is known to cause rapid and extensive damage to all kinds of rubber goods in Los Angeles and elsewhere in the United States.

C. Agricultural Damage

A large number of food, forage, and ornamental crops have been shown to be damaged by air pollutants. The curtailed value results from various types of leaf damage, stunting of growth, decreased size and yield of fruits, and destruction of flowers. Some plant species are so sensitive to specific pollutants as to be useful in monitoring air supplies. *Poa annua,* the pinto bean, spinach, and certain other forms are so employed in southern California.

Again, no satisfactory estimates of dollar loss due to air pollutants are available. California places agricultural damage at a current annual rate of about $6,000,000 but this figure seems to exclude losses incidental to the enforced total abandonment of certain commercial crops such as spinach and orchids in the Los Angeles area.

Substances thus far identified as responsible for the damage include ethylene, SO_2, acid mists, fluorides, O_3, and a number of organic oxidants. Research on the etiology, physiology, and biochemistry of air pollution pathologies in plants is proceeding at a pace which promises early contributions to knowledge of related phenomena in man.

D. Physiological Effects on Man and Domestic Animals

Donora, Poza Rica, London, and the Meuse Valley of Belgium have given dramatic proof that air pollution can kill; together with other evidence, they have implied less shocking but more extensive effects of air pollutants on the health of affected populations. Long-continued exposure to sublethal concentrations of many substances, and combinations thereof, are suspected of having physiological effects, but in most cases the quantitative aspects of the relationships remain undefined.

The high incidences of "chronic bronchitis" in British cities, of nasopharyngeal and optic irritation in Los Angeles, and the rapid rise in lung carcinoma among metropolitan populations appear to be closely associated with air pollution. Fluorosis in cattle exposed to fluoride-containing dusts has been proved to be related to emissions from certain industrial operations. More subtle physiological effects of air pollution are suggested by laboratory observations of suppression of ciliary action, alterations in pulmonary physiology, specific enzymatic inhibitions, and changes in blood chemistry.

E. Psychological Effects

Since fear is a recognizable element in public reactions to air pollution, the psychological aspects of the phenomenon cannot be ignored. Psychosomatic illnesses are possibly related to inadequate understanding of a publicized threat. Little effort has been directed toward evaluation of such impacts in relation to general mental health of affected groups, or determination of their role in individual neuroses. Only in practical politics has any significant action been based on recognition of the psychological attitudes induced by periodic public exposure to an airborne threat.

IV. Air Pollution as a Problem of the Future

In spite of its long history of development, community air pollution must be looked upon as a problem of the future. Only a few of the largest population concentrations of the present day are occasionally using their air supplies faster than natural processes can replenish them. Such overuse must be expected to occur with increasing frequency as populations increase, since per capita demands for air cannot be expected to decline.

So long as the air resource was almost infinitely large with respect to its daily withdrawal and use, its pollution caused discomfort and illness only in areas immediately adjacent to individual sources. As regional and world populations increase exponentially, a time must come when human occupation of the medium will threaten the quality of the total air resource. On a world scale, residues of nuclear weapon testing and huge outpourings of CO_2 from fossil fuel combustion are already demonstrating the extent to which human activity can affect the total gaseous milieu.

Air pollution shares with all other threats to public health and welfare the certainty of becoming more and more severe as long as the population increase remains unchecked. Unless some effective population control is permitted to intervene, the monetary cost of maintaining an acceptable air quality can be expected to rise in some exponential relationship to the numbers of people and associated activities requiring it. This will be true regardless of the speed with which fossilized energy sources are replaced by thermonuclear or solar power plants. Nevertheless, such substitutions can be expected to delay, perhaps for generations, the development of large-scale completely intolerable and economically uncontrollable situations.

The emergence of air pollution as a regional, or even global phenomenon, has already had some impacts on governmental and administrative procedures. Air masses recognize no political jurisdictions, and in their movements frequently do violence to democratically evolved concepts of local autonomy. As the geographic breadth of air resource problems increases there will be a need to develop administrative mechanisms capable of dealing with them as regional, national, or international entities. Since they involve aspects of transportation, refuse disposal, industrial zoning, and power utilization, it is difficult to believe that future jurisdictional adjustments, made to meet the regulatory need, will conform with traditional governmental concepts.

Water, food, and air must forever constitute the survival bases of human and other populations; we will pay for them whatever they cost in time, money, and effort, since without them we die. It is therefore shortsighted to consider the air resource as a competitively priced commodity; it is priceless. In 1962 it may be appropriate to consider which of several alternative air pollution control measures may be imposed without their affecting the public purse unduly; this is true because there are still not enough of us to pose more than a marginal threat to air quality. However, the quadrupled population anticipated by the year 2062, if realized, may force consideration of basic resources as fundamental limits to survival, rather than as dollar-valued items affecting the cost of comfort.

References

NOTE: Because of the generalized and somewhat philosophical nature of the foregoing introductory discussion of the whole field of air pollution, and because each of its components will be dealt with in detail in the following chapters, no specific literature references have been cited. To attempt complete coverage would obscure the intent of the writer to sketch a broad outline of subsequent content; to cite a few sources and omit the hundreds of others necessarily drawn upon directly or indirectly would be misleading. To assist the reader in developing a more complete grasp of the general subject matter the following bibliographic listing is offered:

1. Anonymous, Ministry Health Rept. No. 95. Her Majesty's Stationery Office, London, 1954.
2. Anonymous, *A.M.A. Arch. Ind. Health* **20,** 266–270 (1959).
3. C. H. Bosanquet and J. L. Pearson, *Trans. Faraday Soc.,* **32,** 1249 (1936).
4. P. Drinker and T. Hatch, "Industrial Dust," 2nd ed. McGraw-Hill, New York, 1954.
5. J. Evelyn, Fumifugium: or the Smoke of London Dissapated (etc.) 1661. Reprinted by Natl. Abatement Soc., London, 1933.

6. W. L. Faith, "Air Pollution Control." Wiley, New York (1959).
7. W. L. Faith, N. A. Renzetti, and L. H. Rogers, *Air Pollution Foundation (San Marino, Calif.) Rept.* **21** (1957).
8. J. Firket, *Bull. Roy. Acad. Med. Belg.* **11,** 683ff. (1931).
9. A. J. Haagen-Smit, *Ind. Eng. Chem.* **44,** 1342–1346 (1952).
10. A. J. Haagen-Smit, C. E. Bradley, and M. M. Fox, *Ind. Eng. Chem.* **45,** 2086 (1953).
11. H. F. Johnstone and D. R. Coughanowr, *Ind. Eng. Chem.* **50,** 1169–1172 (1958).
12. J. P. Lodge, *Anal. Chem.* **33,** No. 5, 3–13 (1961).
13. P. A. Leighton and W. A. Perkins, *Air Pollution Foundation (San Marino, Calif.) Rept.* **24** (1958).
14. P. A. Leighton and W. A. Perkins, *Air Pollution Foundation (San Marino, Calif.) Rept.* **14** (1956).
15. *Air Pollution Control District Co. of Los Angeles, Calif., Second Ann. Rept.* 1950–51 (1951).
16. P. L. Magill, F. R. Holden, and C. Ackley (eds.) "Air Pollution Handbook." McGraw-Hill, New York, 1956.
17. F. S. Mallette (ed.) "Problems and Control of Air Pollution." Reinhold, New York, 1955.
18. T. F. Malone (ed.) "Compendium of Meteorology," Am. Meteorological Soc., Boston, Massachusetts, 1951.
19. L. C. McCabe (ed.), "Air Pollution," Proc. 1st U. S. Tech. Conf. McGraw-Hill, New York, 1952.
20. L. C. McCabe and G. D. Clayton, *Arch. Ind. Hgy. Occupational Med.* **6,** 199–213 (1952).
21. A. R. Meetham, "Atmospheric Pollution," 2nd ed. Pergamon Press, New York, 1956.
22. J. T. Middleton, E. F. Darley, and R. F. Brewer, *Proc. Am. Petrol. Inst. Sect. III* **37,** 184–191 (1957).
23. *Proc. Natl. Air Pollution Symposium. 3rd Symposium, Pasadena, Calif.* (1955); *First Symposium, Pasadena, Calif.* (1949); *Second Symposium, Pasadena, Calif.* (1952).
24. *Proc. Natl. Conf. Air Pollution, Washington, D. C., November, 1958.* U. S. Department of Health, Education and Welfare, Washington, D. C. (1959).
25. N. A. Renzetti (ed.) *Air Pollution Foundation (San Marino, Calif.) Rept.* **9** (1955).
26. Rept. Com. Investigation Smoke Abatement and Electrification of Railway Terminals. Chicago Association of Commerce, Chicago, Illinois, 1915.
27. H. H. Schrenk, H. Heimann, G. D. Clayton, W. M. Gafafer, and H. Wexler, "Air Pollution in Donora, Pennsylvania," Public Health Bulletin No. 306. U. S. Public Health Service, Washington, D. C., 1949.
28. O. G. Sutton, "Micrometeorology." McGraw-Hill, New York, 1953.
29. E. C. Tabor and W. V. Warren, *A.M.A. Arch. Ind. Health* **17,** 145–151 (1958).
30. M. W. Thring (ed.) "Air Pollution." Butterworths, London, 1957.
31. "Meteorology and Atomic Energy," U. S. Weather Bureau Dept. for U. S. Atomic Energy Commission. Govt. Printing Office, Washington, D. C., 1955.
32. J. E. W. Wallin, *Smoke Invest. Bull. Mellon Inst. No.* **2** (1913).

CHAPTER 2

Residual Pollution Products in the Atmosphere

BERNARD D. TEBBENS

University of California, Berkeley, California

I. Normal Air

Extensive and rapidly accumulating data are now available from a variety of sources concerning quality of air both in metropolitan centers and in other less densely populated areas. An understanding of existing air contamination can best be gained against a background knowledge of normal uncontaminated air, partly because of the large contrast between the amounts of material comprising normal clean air and the minute concentrations of materials which vitiate it.

A. GASES

Oxygen and nitrogen are the major gases making up the atmosphere. In dry air these constitute about 99% of the mixture by volume, i.e., $O_2 = 20.94\%$ and $N_2 = 78.09\%$. Argon ($A = 0.93\%$) and carbon dioxide ($CO_2 = 0.03\%$) comprise practically all of the remainder of the normal dry gas mixture, these four components totaling 99.99% of the mixture by volume.

Associated with these gases is water vapor, whose concentration is variable. In the usual range of absolute humidity, water vapor makes up about 1 to 3% by volume of the total mixture. Clearly, the other gaseous constituents are present in lower concentrations than cited above when normal water vapor is present. However, their proportions are constant; when the moisture percentage is known, the others may be readily calculated from this constant proportionality. For purposes of air pollution calculations, this is true up to altitudes of many thousands of feet and therefore within the few hundred feet above ground level where pollution problems are of main interest—this being the thin layer of atmosphere in which man and most of his works are totally immersed.

Of these gases, i.e., O_2, N_2, A, CO_2, and H_2O, only carbon dioxide is present in a relatively low concentration, and it normally constitutes over 0.03% by volume of the mixture. For purposes of comparison it is notable that an air-contaminating gas such as SO_2 would rarely be found in a concentration of 0.0001% by volume, i.e., at least two orders of magnitude less than the amount of that significant normal gas present in smallest amount. To re-emphasize this point, the concentrations of these several normal gases, in units more convenient for designating concentrations of contaminating gases, are shown in Table I. A usual

TABLE I

CONCENTRATIONS OF MAJOR GASES OF NORMAL DRY AIR PLUS SO_2

Gas	Concentration (p.p.m.)
N_2	780,900
O_2	209,400
A	9,300
CO_2	300
SO_2	1

expression for this purpose is parts per million by volume (p.p.m.). In these units, a rather high level of contamination by SO_2 would be 1.0 p.p.m. or:

$$\frac{1 \text{ vol. } SO_2}{10^6 \text{ vol. (air} + SO_2)}$$

B. Particulate Material

In addition to gases, normal air contains particulate materials whose number concentration varies over a large range but whose weight concentration is small in nearly all cases. Such particulate material, having a tendency to settle or to be washed out of air, is not homogeneous in concentration or composition, either from place to place in the lower atmosphere or from time to time. Naturally occurring particulates, or aerosols, include such materials as sea salt from the oceans; smoke from forest fires; mineral dusts from volcanic action or wind erosion of the earth's surface; organic fragments from eroded vegetation; living organisms such as spores and pollens; and constituents of heat haze which F. W. Went (*1*) has described as arising from volatilized essential oils of growing vegetation. Excluded from consideration are the particulate forms of water that make up rain, fog, ice crystals, etc.

Spatial variation of natural particulate concentration may be illustrated with some information on sea salt concentrations from data published by Moyerman and Shuler (*2*). Expressed in the usual weight to volume units, micrograms of particulate material per cubic meter of air (μg./m.^{3}), salt concentrations varied from about 4 μg./m.^{3} to about

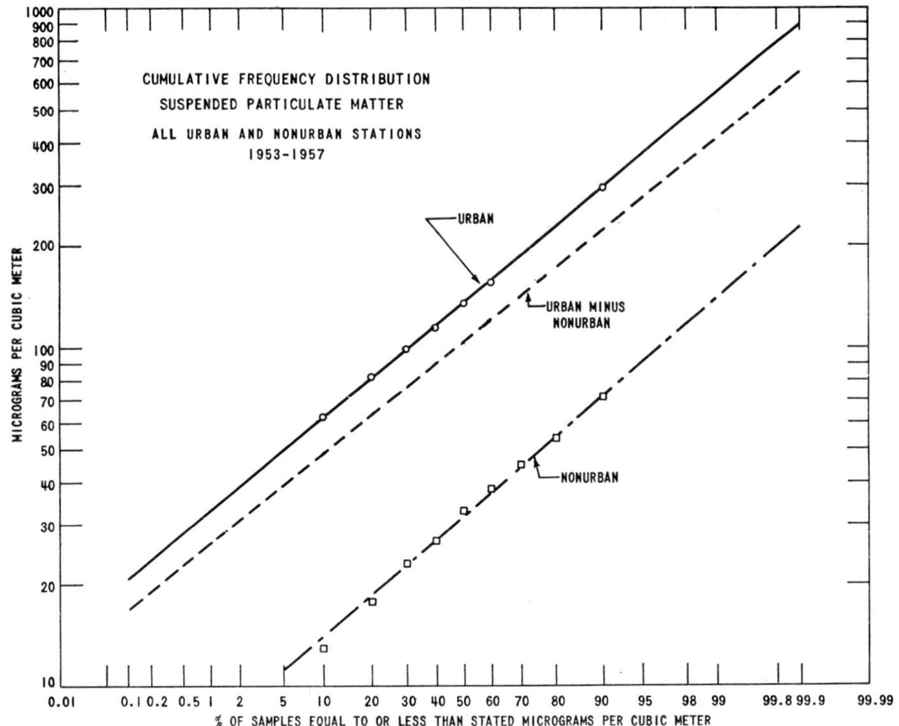

FIG. 1. Frequency distribution of total suspended particulate material in urban and in nonurban atmospheres. (From *U. S. Public Health Serv. Publ.* **637**.)

22,000 μg./m.^{3}, the latter quantity being found at a coastal site. The average concentration for a group of inland sites was 14 μg./m.^{3} which is considerably below the amount of total particulate material in clean, nonurban air, as indicated by Zimmer *et al.* From data accumulated in a series of measurements during 1957 and 1958 in the United States, the arithmetic average of particulate loadings in 1252 samples from rural sites was 39 μg./m.^{3} (*3*). Included in this particulate material were organic as well as inorganic (nonaqueous) constituents.

A compilation of data from the National Air Sampling Network in the United States (*4*) shows not only results of ten thousand air samples for particulate material obtained during the period 1953–1957 but also the range of concentrations for nonurban and for urban samples. Figure 1, taken from the publication, is a graphic representation of the data, which indicates that urban particulate concentrations are about four times as great as nonurban on the average. The statistical data from which the graph was plotted emphasizes this point but also shows that the maximum measured urban concentration was about one thousand times the minimum nonurban amount.

By contrast with gases, the difference in concentration of particulate material between normal air and polluted air is moderate, probably basically within two orders of magnitude on a weight per unit volume basis, whereas the difference between contaminating gas and normal major gas concentrations covers from five to eight or more orders on a volume per unit of volume basis.

II. Contaminated Air

From this basis of information concerning the composition and variation of normal air, we may review some of the data concerning the character of contaminating materials in the atmosphere and the variations in pollution that may exist. If one were to catalogue all air contaminants in some chemical frame of reference, the resulting list of chemical entities that have been observed would be very extensive. Only enough detail along this line is given here to demonstrate that such a procedure would be praiseworthy, but probably futile.

A. Character of Contaminants

1. *Organic Gases*

In a series of studies and publications appearing over several years' time, Weaver, Shepherd, and others (*5, 6*) of the National Bureau of Standards have demonstrated the presence in contaminated air of several cities of a large number of more or less volatile organic chemical compounds. By freezing the organics at liquid oxygen temperature, the material was separated from air. On subsequent observation of the condensate by mass spectrometry, so many chemical entities were found in the mixture as to lead to the statement, ". . . in every case there has been evidence that these peaks [mass spectrometer] represented many more than 80 compounds, and their complete identification was obviously impossible." A list of some of the identified compounds includes: cresol, phenol, xylene, ethyl benzene, toluene, benzene, styrene, pinene, 3-

methyl-1-pentene, 3-hexyne, 2-pentene, isohexane, ethanol, and 6 different chlorohydrocarbons. In several samples obtained in this way, the average concentration of the above and other volatile organics totaled to an estimated 0.18 to 1.0 p.p.m. of the mixed contaminant gases.

2. *Organic Particulates*

In another approach to separation and identification of organic materials from polluted atmospheres, Tebbens, Thomas, and associates have obtained samples by filtration of particulates, with subsequent separation of high molecular weight compounds by chromatographic procedures (*7, 8*). In one discussion of results, it is pointed out that more than ninety individual chemical entities were separated among the classes of polynuclear hydrocarbons, phenolic compounds, and carboxylic compounds of high molecular weight. The list of identified chemicals includes: anthracene, phenanthrene, pyrene, fluorenone, 1,2-benzanthracene, naphthacene, 3,4-benzpyrene, 1,2,5,6-dibenzanthracene, α-naphthol, and others.

Not only have the above types of organics also been found by many other investigators but the same chemicals have been discovered in the polluted air of cities all over the world (*9–11*). This of itself strongly suggests that the same types of sources lead to this large array of organic air contaminants wherever the activities of mankind lead to disposal of waste effluvia in the atmosphere.

3. *Photochemical Products*

To these incomplete lists of organic chemicals injected into the atmosphere from primary sources, we need only add another list, also incomplete, to emphasize the exquisite chemical complexity of polluted atmospheres. This is the group of compounds thought to be products of photoreactions in the atmosphere, which includes not only unknown free radicals but also organic peroxides, peracids, hydroxy peracids, and such nitrogen-containing compounds as peroxyacyl nitrite. Considering the tremendous variety of possible sources, the mechanisms of organic chemistry such as hydrocarbon synthesis in combustion as suggested by Tebbens *et al.* (*7*), and free radical intermediation, it seems reasonable to estimate that with refinement of observation, many hundreds if not thousands of individual organic chemicals could be isolated from polluted air. Adding to the complexity of this situation is the fact that the sum of all of these organic ingredients is only rarely greater than 5 p.p.m. (0.0005%) by volume, or a few micrograms per cubic meter by weight.

4. *Inorganic Particulates and Gases*

The possible list of inorganic air contaminants is probably smaller than that of organics. Nevertheless, many of the metallic ions and a large number of nonmetallic ions have been found in air in a variety of places and times. For example, Tabor and Warren (*12*) have reported on the concentrations of 17 metals found in the air of 20 communities in the United States. The range of concentrations was from a maximum of 49.0 μg. of zinc per cubic meter of air to a minimum of less than 0.002 μg. of chromium and some other metals per cubic meter. Table II,

TABLE II
RANGE OF MAXIMUM METAL CONCENTRATIONS IN ATMOSPHERE

Metal	Low level (μg./m.³)	High level (μg./m.³)
Zinc	0.4	49.00
Iron	0.23	30.00
Copper	0.05	30.00
Lead	0.33	17.00
Manganese	0.01	3.00
Barium	0.005	1.50
Tin	0.004	0.80
Vanadium	0.002	0.60
Titanium	0.01	0.24
Nickel	0.005	0.20
Chromium	0.002	0.12
Cadmium	0.002	0.10
Bismuth	0.002	0.03

extracted from reference (*12*), shows amounts of some of the metals found. While these are all in particulate form, Weaver *et al.* (*5*) have noted mercury in a vapor phase in many freeze-out samples. An extension of the same data, with considerable detail, is included in the National Air Sampling Network publication (*4*).

Another indication of the variety of inorganic as well as of organic chemicals found in air may be inferred from the Analytical Review on Air Pollution by Kay (*13*) and Lodge (*40*) showing 1356 references to methods of analysis from 1952 to 1960, including methods for such specific chemicals as zinc ammonium sulfate, ammonium chloride, carbon monoxide, ozone, nitrogen oxides, hydrogen fluoride, sulfur dioxide, and hydrogen sulfide, to mention some; additionally, methods for fluorides, chlorides, arsenic, and other ions are referred to.

B. Range of Amounts of Some Classic Contaminants

From this large and growing list of chemicals known to be present in polluted air, investigators who have wished to monitor the pollution level at a given time and place have been forced to choose for analysis a limited number of individual chemical compounds or undifferentiated combinations of mixtures, the concentrations of which were thought to be representative of the extent of the contamination. This choice of

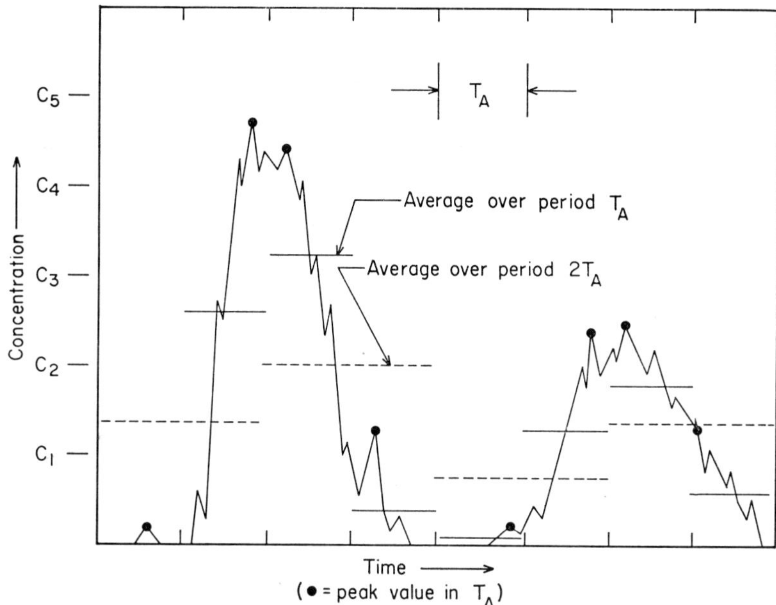

Fig. 2. Graphic representation of effect of instantaneous measure of concentration and time averaging of concentration. [From *Am. Ind. Hyg. Assoc. Quart.* **18,** June (1957).]

method usually revolves around the air pollution effect in which the observer is interested (see Chapter 1): for example, visibility reduction, material damage, agricultural damage, or physiological effects on man or animals. Because of convenience of measurement, adaptability of method, or possible relation to effects, the airborne concentrations of some chemicals have been measured or monitored widely for many years.

The concentrations found and the range of concentrations are dependent in part on the averaging time employed in sampling, whether inherent in the monitoring technique or arbitrarily chosen to relate to an effect. Wanta and Stern (*14*) have discussed this subject, generalizing the effect of averaging graphically as in Fig. 2 (see also Chapter 11). It is evident that in the dynamic air environment system, where contaminant concentrations may change rapidly owing to meteorological or source variations, a momentary peak concentration is not likely to be the same as an average concentration over one minute, one hour, one day, or any other time interval.

1. *Sulfur Dioxide and Carbon Monoxide*

Early and still continuing measurements of sulfur dioxide have been made in many locations. Meetham, for example, indicates a range of SO_2 concentration measured in London and other British localities as early as 1924 (*15*), while Greenburg and Jacobs indicate concentrations measured in New York in 1955 (*16*). The impetus for monitoring this particular gas phase contaminant results from some of its known irritating, corrosive, and phytotoxic properties. While measurement of sulfur dioxide concentrations is a widespread practice, its concentration has been established during only one of the well-known dramatic air pollution disasters. During the height of the London smog of December, 1952, the *average* concentration of SO_2 over a 2-day period was 1.34 p.p.m. (*17*). It is possible, indeed probable, that higher concentrations existed for shorter periods of time. This concentration is well below the maximum that has been measured in some other cities. Cholak indicates a range of concentrations at several locations in the United States of 0.0 to 3.2 p.p.m. (*18*). The higher concentrations were noted in commercial and industrial sections of solid fuel-using cities such as Chicago and Pittsburgh, where mean concentrations were below 0.1 p.p.m.

Another gas whose concentration has been of interest because of known human toxic properties is carbon monoxide. Measurements of this ubiquitous but nonirritating chemical have been remarkably rare until recent years. As an indication of range of concentration, however, DallaValle (*19*), citing data from the United States Public Health Service in 1936, states that amounts up to 65 p.p.m. had been found. Cholak (*18*) has listed ranges in a few locations of from 0 to 55 p.p.m. and a mean concentration of 20 p.p.m. at a business intersection in Cincinnati during a time of relatively heavy automobile traffic.

The fact that more data on CO concentrations has not been accumulated earlier is probably related to the failure of CO to impinge on any of the human senses. Illustrative of increasing current attention to the subject is the recent report of Clayton *et al.* (*20*) concerning CO concentrations in a residential area, in a shopping area, at a downtown street intersection, and at an express highway, all in Detroit, Michigan. At all sites except the residential, the maximum instantaneous concentration found during the several months of observation was over 100 p.p.m. (the recorder limit), with median concentrations as follows: residential, 2 p.p.m. during 18 weeks; shopping area, 10 p.p.m. during 58 weeks; downtown street, 9 p.p.m. during 21 weeks; express highway, 8 p.p.m. during 27 weeks. The maximum residential site concentration was 29 p.p.m. Generally, the fluctuation of concentration during daylight hours coincided with automotive traffic fluctuation and was influenced by meteorological variations.

2. *Particulates*

An example of nonspecific measure of air pollution, which has had a fairly long history of use, is that of dust and sootfall. This index is related to particulate material and especially to that which sediments onto horizontal surfaces where it may be an aesthetic nuisance. The method has had long use because of the relative simplicity of both instrumentation and analysis. Meetham (*15*) lists such measurements in London and other British locations as early as 1914, and continuous data since that year indicate trends of deposited matter in several locations. Similar data for many urban areas of the United States are available. As an example, Hemeon (*21*), in a systematic survey of air pollution in New Haven, Connecticut, found among other variations that individual measurements of dustfall within the city limits ranged from a low of 5 tons per square mile per month to a maximum of 62 tons per square mile per month. His general observations were in accord with those of other similar studies, that urban dustfall is less in summer than in winter and is higher in commercial and industrial areas than in residential sections of a city.

The maximum dustfall mentioned above has been exceeded in many such measurements; for example, Wohlers and Bell (*22*), in a compendium of data, show a maximum dustfall measurement in Pittsburgh, Pennsylvania of 291 tons per square mile per month. It is doubtful whether many measurements of less than 5 tons per square mile per month have been reported, since there would be no reason to make observations under such circumstances. The character of material collected in fallout is diverse but in general includes organic tars, mineral components both water-soluble and insoluble, and carbon.

C. Trends of Particulate Contamination

Another undifferentiated measurement of particulates is that of filter darkening. Unlike dustfall observations, the technique is used to determine material that remains airborne, i.e., the actual concentration of aerosols. Because of the relative simplicity of instrumentation, measurement of airborne particulates with various "smoke samplers" has been widespread and has been practiced since the original device of Owens was developed in London in 1918 (*15*). The darkness of a stain on filter paper has been correlated with weight of particulates per unit volume of air, or has been interpreted in arbitrary units such as the COH of Hemeon (*23*). The greatest use of such measurements is to indicate trends of particulate loading of the air over periods of the day, week, month, season, or year.

A discussion of such trends resulting from many years of observations appears in Meetham's book (*15*). The trend of smokiness in the London area was downward over the course of many years preceding 1948 (winter months only), possibly reflecting a reduction in smoke output. This observation coincides with the fact pointed out by Stern (*24*) that in several cities in the United States, soot and dustfall have been markedly reduced on the average during the past 25 to 30 years, reflecting a change in fuel usage, improved technology, and other factors.

Seasonally in London, particulate pollution reaches a maximum in the winter months and a minimum in summer. This phenomenon is probably more pronounced in a community utilizing coal as a fuel than in one using petroleum fuels, and would be affected also by specific climatic conditions. Meetham states that the average airborne smoke concentration at most stations is two to three times higher in winter than in summer. Considering data published by Tebbens (*25*) for similar smoke measurements in Berkeley, California, the average air-soiling potential there is also higher for winter months than for summer months by a factor somewhat less than 2. Additional data covering 5 years of observations in Berkeley indicate that this is consistently true, four winter months being about 1.8 times as smoky as four summer months, the data being summarized in Fig. 3. It is notable that both Davidson in New York (*26*) and Koshi in Tokyo (*27*) found similar seasonal variations.

The weekly cycle shows consistent variations by day of the week. As Meetham points out, the concentration of particulate pollution on week ends is considerably less than on weekdays. In London the decrease on the week ends is 20 to 40%. Tebbens found about 40% less on Sundays than on weekdays in Berkeley. That this is probably a universal phenomenon and measurable by other methods of observation than smoke sampling is indicated by data published in the booklet *Clean Air for California* (*28*). There the data for 17 days of "alerts" in Los Angeles during the calendar year 1955 showed no alerts on Sundays, whereas from one to four alerts occurred on other days of the week. An alert was called when ozone concentration exceeded 0.5 p.p.m. Haagen-

Smit (*29*) has also pointed this out. Although these and other data are remarkably consistent, Stern (*24*) noted, from the National Air Sampling Network data collected during 1957, only a small decrease of particulates on Sundays below the average of all other days of the week. These facts, however, indicate the probability that lower particulate pollution on week ends, and especially on Sundays, is a universal phenomenon, at least in cultures where Sunday is a day of rest. There seems no likelihood that meteorologic variations account for this particular fact.

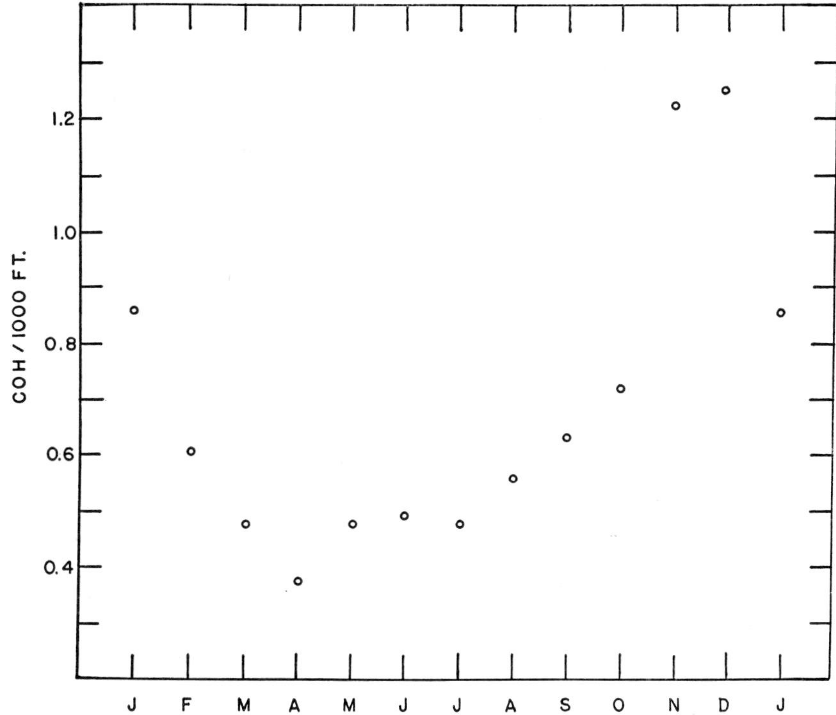

FIG. 3. Monthly averages of air-soiling potential in Berkeley, California.

The pattern of daily variation in particulate content of air is shown in Fig. 4, taken from a partial record in Berkeley, California. This graphical summation is notably similar to that shown by Meetham for London, by Davidson for New York, and by Koshi for Tokyo. Thus in widely separated geographical locations; namely, England, the east coast of the United States, the west coast, and Japan, the variation of time concentration of air pollutants as measured by staining on filter paper shows a diurnal minimal pollution at night and two maxima during the hours of major human activity. These daytime peaks are separated by 10 to 14 hours in time. London, New York, and Tokyo have a daily maximum near 8 A.M., while Berkeley, California, shows a peak near noon. The second peak, a smaller one in most cases, occurs between 8 and 10 P.M. The first three cities named are coal-burning communities, while Berkeley is in a large metropolitan center in which coal is practically unused, the major fuels being gaseous and liquid. This difference

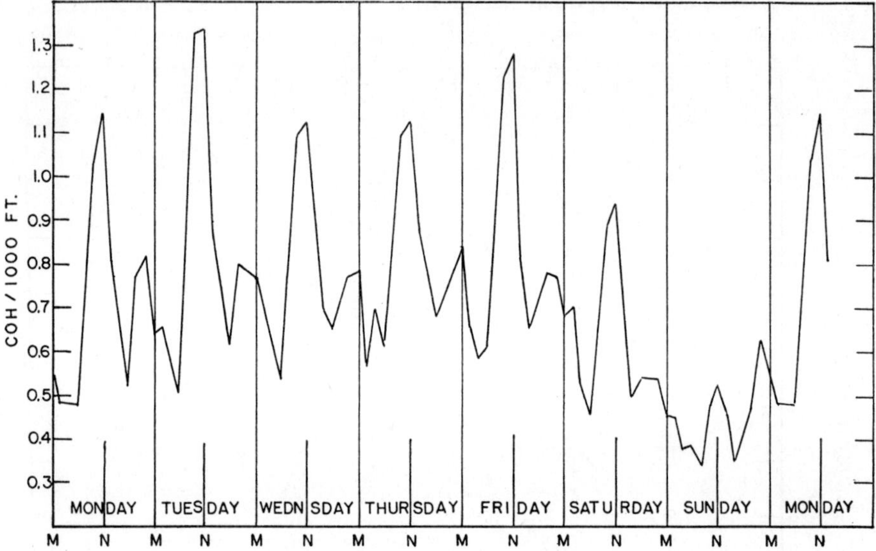

FIG. 4. Average air-soiling potential by hour of the day and day of the week. [From *J. Air Pollution Control Assoc.* **5,** February (1956).]

in fuels apparently leads not only to a significant degree of difference in total pollution loading by smoke particles but also may account for a difference in the timing of the maximum smokiness of the atmosphere. As Meetham points out, it should be possible, by careful analysis of the results of smoke-stain sampling, to estimate the significance of fuel consumption and meteorologic variables such as wind and turbulence to air pollution levels.

III. Recently Measured Gaseous Contaminants

Events of the last 15 years have given impetus to increasingly intensive measurement of several contaminants concerning whose concentration only fragmentary information was available before 1950. The interest, discussed elsewhere in this book, was essentially in the growing smog problems in Los Angeles, California after 1940; the correlation of vegetation damage and smog by Middleton in 1944; and the propounding of a mechanism of photochemical smog formation by Haagen-Smit in 1950.

A. Ozone and Oxidants

Texts on meteorology point out the importance of ozone and of nitrogen oxides in the upper atmosphere where those gases are known to be produced by solar irradiation. There is additional scattered information concerning trace amounts of ozone in the lower atmosphere, the quantity normally occurring being estimated in the range of 0.02 to 0.03 p.p.m. (*30*). Recent information obtained during the International Geophysical Year from a truly remote site, Antarctica, shows 0.01 to 0.03 p.p.m. (*31*).

The maximum content of ozone detected as an urban contaminant in outdoor air was 0.99 p.p.m. during a smog episode in Los Angeles in 1956 (*32*). Routine monitoring for ozone has been carried out in that community since 1955 because of the known irritating effect of ozone. It is typical of the ozone measured in Los Angeles and in some other west coast communities that it is only a part of the total oxidizing agent found in polluted atmospheres. Renzetti and Romanovsky (*33*) point out that the total oxidant content of polluted atmospheres is greater than the content of ozone, the magnitude of the difference depending in part on the method of analysis. The mechanism of oxidant and ozone formation is discussed in Chapter 3. In a review of monitoring results during several months of the fall of 1953, Larson *et al.* (*34*) show a maximum amount of total oxidant for the Los Angeles area of 1.00 p.p.m. Probably somewhat higher results than this have been recorded.

The amount of total oxidant has been approximately correlated with the eye-irritating characteristic of west coast smog. Littman, Ford, and Endow (*35*), in a discussion of the occurrence of oxidant and ozone in the Los Angeles atmosphere, indicate that at an oxidant concentration of 0.20 p.p.m. there was light smog—presumably visible, but not irritating—while at 0.39 p.p.m. a heavy smog with eye irritation and a typical odor existed. It is a reasonably good rule of thumb that the irritating characteristics of the west coast smogs are noticeable at oxidant concentrations greater than about 0.25 p.p.m. (*28*).

Diurnal fluctuation of oxidant and/or ozone concentration is one of the characteristics of the smog in Los Angeles. Littman states, for data obtained as early as 1951, and Renzetti confirms with 1955 data, that there is a typical pattern: low concentration at night, increasing to a maximum around noon, and practically disappearing at sunset following gradual decrease during the afternoon. Few major differences from this pattern occur in the Los Angeles smogs. The concentration during the hours of darkness rarely exceeds 0.05 p.p.m. Larson shows confirming data for 1953 and 1954, and many subsequent observations make it almost certain that this is a nearly invariant phenomenon. Figure 5 is taken from Renzetti's work (*33*) to indicate the phenomenon.

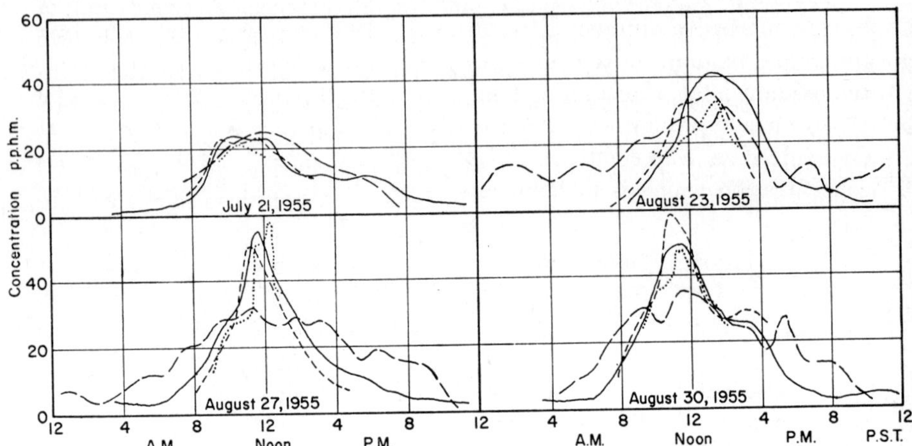

FIG. 5. Typical diurnal variations in oxidant and ozone concentrations in Los Angeles smog analyzed by several different methods. Key: - - - -, phenolphthalin; ———, potassium iodide; . . . . . ., rubber cracking; — — —, ultraviolet spectrometry. [From *A.M.A. Arch. Ind. Health* **14** (1956).]

A slightly different diurnal characteristic has been found for oxidant concentration in other localities, as demonstrated by Cholak (*36*). During the summer months of 1956, in Cincinnati, Ohio, he found maximum concentration during the afternoon and a lower level during the night. The concentration of oxidant was at a much lower level generally in Cincinnati, and probably at most other locations, than in Los Angeles. The range of concentrations measured during the summer period only (the season of highest oxidant concentration in Cincinnati) was 0.01 to 0.06 p.p.m. Later data from the same source (*36a*) show occasionally higher concentrations of oxidant to have occurred between 1956 and 1959. The maximum reached for a brief period of time was 0.29 p.p.m.

B. HYDROCARBONS AND ORGANICS

Because of the close association between oxidizing components in polluted air and the organic photochemical reactions leading to their presence (see Chapter 3), great interest has developed in the volatile hydrocarbon content of polluted air. More specifically, the measurement of "precursors" has been carried out with some regularity, as has the measurement of "hydrocarbons." The observation of nonspecific precursors (to oxidants) is probably useful as a measure of potential daylight oxidant concentration since, as Haagen-Smit has pointed out (*29*), the total organics in polluted air contain a variety of hydrocarbons capable of forming ozone in the presence of NO_2 and sunlight.

Littman (*35*) pointed out that potential oxidant or ozone precursors have a markedly different time distribution on any given day than does the actual oxidant on that day. As previously mentioned, in Los Angeles the oxidant is at a maximum near noon, whereas precursors show double peaks on a typical smog day, one near 8 A.M. and a second near 6 P.M. On some days this condition may be replaced by an elevated precursor concentration which is more or less constant during a 24-hour period.

TABLE III

MAXIMAL CONCENTRATION OF CONTAMINANTS IN CALIFORNIA

Contaminant	Air Pollution Control District, Los Angeles, 1949–1957 (p.p.m.)	Other California sources (p.p.m.)	Eight-hour averages[a] (p.p.m.)
Total aldehydes	1.87	—	0.2–0.8
Carbon monoxide	88.0	—	20–25
Fluorine	—	0.3	—
Total hydrocarbons	4.66	—	0.2–0.4
Hydrogen sulfide	—	0.9	—
Nitrogen dioxide	1.74	—	—
$NO + NO_2$	1.86	—	0.1–0.2
Total oxidant (potassium iodide)	0.69	—	—
Ozone (rubber-cracking)	0.99	—	0.15–0.2
SO_2 (autometer)	2.49	—	0.1–0.3
Arsenic	—	0.65 μg./m.^{3}	—
Lead	—	42.0 μg./m.^{3}	6–15 μg./m.^{3}

[a] Estimated from monitoring data for days with severe air pollution.

One of the early estimates of total organics (including hydrocarbons) in polluted air was reported by Shepherd *et al.* (*6*). A maximum concentration noted was nearly 0.5 p.p.m. total organic concentration. Subsequent observations using the same techniques of air analysis have indicated amounts up to about 1.0 p.p.m. More recent measurements, shown in Table III (*32, 37*), which lists both maximum officially recorded concentrations in Los Angeles and a few data from other sources in California, indicate up to 4.6 p.p.m. of total hydrocarbons. The effect of 8-hour time averaging of data, as shown in the estimates of the final column of Table III, is evident; i.e., the time average must be lower, and often much lower, than single peak measurements.

C. Oxides of Nitrogen

A final type of gaseous pollutant to be discussed is the nitrogen oxide-nitrogen dioxide combination. The presence of these gases in air has long been known, but intensity of monitoring them has expanded greatly since 1950, with the result that higher quantities have been observed recently. For example, Cholak (*18*), summarizing data in 1952, showed a maximum concentration for 5 different cities of 0.79 p.p.m., with Baltimore, Maryland reporting that figure. As shown in Table III, however, a maximum observation in Los Angeles (in 1957) was 1.86 p.p.m.

Recently available equipment has made it possible to monitor both gases individually, with the resultant fact becoming evident that, during periods when oxides of nitrogen are present in air in probably significant

TABLE IV
Ranges of Concentrations of Gaseous Pollutants

Pollutant	Range of average concentrations (p.p.m.)	Range of maximum concentrations (p.p.m.)	Number of cities
Aldehyde (as formaldehyde)	0.02–0.2	0.03–2.0	8
Ammonia	0.02–0.2	0.05–3.0	7
Carbon monoxide	2.0–10.0	3.0–300	8
Hydrogen fluoride	0.001–0.02	0.005–0.08	7
Hydrogen sulfide	0.002–0.1	Up to 1.0	4
Nitrogen oxides	0.02–0.9	0.3–3.5	8
Ozone	0.009–0.3	0.03–1.0	8
Sulfur dioxide	0.001–0.7	0.02–3.2	50

concentrations, nighttime is characterized by a predominance of NO, while during the day, NO_2 is more abundant. This situation is apparent at least in the case of the oxidizing type of pollution which characterizes the west coast smog. Chemical reasons for the phenomenon are discussed by Rogers (*38*).

As a final tabulation, Table IV is adapted from data gathered together by Wohlers and Bell (*22*) to show the range of several contaminant concentrations in cities. Additional information concerning specific contaminants undoubtedly resides in the files of the many agencies that make more or less continuous observations of air contamination. Correspondence with such agencies may be facilitated by reference to the Register of Air Pollution Analyses (*39*), which lists organizations in 400 cities of the United States which have collected data on airborne materials.

REFERENCES

1. F. W. Went, *Sci. American* **192,** 62 (1955).
2. R. M. Moyerman and K. E. Shuler, *Science* **118,** 612 (1953).
3. C. E. Zimmer, E. C. Tabor, and A. C. Stern, *J. Air Pollution Control Assoc.* **9,** 136 (1959).
4. *U. S. Public Health Serv. Publ. No.* **637** (1958).
5. E. R. Weaver, E. E. Hughes, S. M. Gunther, S. Schuhmann, N. T. Redfearn, and R. Gordon, Jr., *J. Research Natl. Bur. Standards* **59,** 383 (1957).
6. M. Shepherd, S. M. Rock, R. Howard, and J. Stormes, *Anal. Chem.* **23,** 1431 (1951).
7. B. D. Tebbens, J. F. Thomas, and M. Mukai, *A.M.A. Arch. Ind. Health* **13,** 567 (1956).
8. B. D. Tebbens, J. F. Thomas, E. N. Sanborn, and M. Mukai, *Am. Ind. Hyg. Assoc. Quart.* **18,** 165 (1957).
9. P. Kotin, H. L. Falk, P. P. Mader, and M. Thomas, *A.M.A. Arch. Ind. Hyg.* **9,** 153 (1954).
10. R. L. Cooper and A. J. Lindsey, *Chem. & Ind. (London)* p. 1177 (1953).
11. B. P. Gurinov, V. A. Zore, A. A. Il'ina, and L. M. Shabad, *Gigiana i. Sanit.* **8,** 10 (1953).
12. E. C. Tabor and W. V. Warren, *A.M.A. Arch. Ind. Health* **17,** 145 (1958).
13. K. Kay, *Anal. Chem.* **29,** 589 (1957); **31,** 633 (1959).
14. R. C. Wanta and A. C. Stern, *Am. Ind. Hyg. Assoc. Quart.* **18,** 156 (1957).
15. A. R. Meetham, "Atmospheric Pollution, Its Origins and Prevention," 2nd ed., Pergamon Press, New York, 1956.
16. L. Greenburg and M. B. Jacobs, *Ind. Eng. Chem.* **48,** 1517 (1956).
17. P. Drinker (ed.), Editorial, *A.M.A. Arch. Ind. Hyg.* **7,** 275 (1953).
18. J. Cholak, *Proc. Natl. Air Pollution Symposium, 2nd Symposium, Pasadena, California* p. 6 (1952).
19. J. M. DallaValle, "The Industrial Environment and Its Control." Pitman, New York, 1948.
20. G. D. Clayton, W. A. Cook, and W. G. Fredrick, *Am. Ind. Hyg. Assoc. J.* **21,** 46 (1960).
21. W. C. L. Hemeon, "The Nature of the Air Pollution Problem in the City of New Haven," Survey of Ind. Hyg. Foundation Am., 1952.
22. H. C. Wohlers and G. B. Bell, Stanford Research Inst. Proj. No. SU-1816 (1956). Reproduced with permission by U. S. Dep't. Health, Education, and Welfare.
23. W. C. L. Hemeon, G. F. Haines, Jr., and H. M. Ide, *Air Repair* **3,** 22 (1953).
24. A. C. Stern, Proc. Natl. Conf. on Air Pollution, *U. S. Public Health Serv. Publ. No.* **654,** 86 (1959).
25. B. D. Tebbens, *J. Air Pollution Control Assoc.* **5,** 233 (1956).
26. W. F. Davidson, *Monthly Weather Rev.* **70,** 225 (1942).
27. S. Koshi, *J. Meteorol. Soc. Japan* **34,** 327 (1956).
28. "Clean Air for California," Calif. State Dept. Public Health, 2nd Rept. Berkeley, California, 1956.
29. A. J. Haagen-Smit and M. M. Fox, *Ind. Eng. Chem.* **48,** 1484 (1956).

30. A. J. Haagen-Smit, C. E. Bradley, and M. M. Fox, *Ind. Eng. Chem.* **45,** 2086 (1953).
31. H. Odishaw, *Science* **129,** 14 (1959).
32. L. A. Chambers, Private communication (1958).
33. N. A. Renzetti and J. C. Romanovsky, *A.M.A. Arch. Ind. Health* **14,** 458 (1956).
34. G. P. Larson, J. R. Taylor, and W. J. Hamming, *Proc. Natl. Air Pollution Symposium, 3rd Symposium, Pasadena, Calif.,* 1955, p. 33.
35. F. E. Littman, H. W. Ford, and N. Endow, *Ind. Eng. Chem.* **48,** 1492 (1956).
36. J. Cholak, L. J. Schafer, D. Yeager, and W. J. Younker, *A.M.A. Arch. Ind. Health* **15,** 198 (1957).
36a. J. Cholak and L. J. Schafer, *Am. Ind. Hyg. Assoc. J.* **21,** 452 (1960).
37. M. H. Merrill, Air Quality for California Communities, *West Ind. Health Conf., Los Angeles, 1959.*
38. L. H. Rogers, *J. Air Pollution Control Assoc.* **8,** 124 (1958).
39. *U. S. Public Health Serv. Publ. No.* **610** Volume 1 (1958) Volume 2 (1961).
40. J. P. Lodge, Jr., *Anal. Chem.* **33** 3R (1961).

CHAPTER 3

Reactions in the Atmosphere

A. J. HAAGEN-SMIT

California Institute of Technology, Pasadena, California

I. Principles of Atmospheric Reactions

A. PRIMARY AND DERIVED AIR POLLUTANTS

Substances emitted to the atmosphere are subjected to a variety of physical and chemical influences that may lead to the formation of objectionable products or, on the other hand, objectionable products may be converted into harmless ones. Investigations of these reactions are helpful in establishing the nature of the precursors of the substances found in the air; consequently, a great deal of research has been carried out to explore in detail the mechanism of these reactions and the effect of the resulting products on physiological and toxicological phenomena in plants and animals.

The emissions undergoing these changes are products of human activity, from industrial as well as individual sources, and represent a variety of inorganic and organic materials. Evaporation of gasoline alone accounts for a mixture of hundreds of species of organic molecules. Even more complicated are the secondary transformation products found in automobile exhaust and in the emissions from incineration, which comprise a mixture of dry distilled, steam distilled, and destructively distilled products from essentially every material used by people. These thousands of compounds are then mixed with the natural components of the air and remain in the atmosphere for a considerable time. During this residence time unstable molecules will rearrange or couple with other substances. Both primary and secondary products are exposed to further changes through oxidation and photochemical reactions.

The over-all tendencies toward the formation of atmospherically stable products are seen in a practical example of the effect of atmospheric reaction on concentrations of pollutants emitted in the Los Angeles area (*1*). Using known emission of nonreactive carbon monoxide as a reference, the atmospheric concentrations of other pollutants were calculated from source-testing data and then compared with actual measurements of the atmosphere. This study showed that oxides of nitrogen, sulfur dioxide, and hydrocarbons found are less than the amounts calculated from the emission of known sources. On the other hand, aldehydes and organic acids, both oxidation products of hydrocarbons, have increased above their calculated concentrations.

A recent example of an air pollution balance comparison of automobile emissions before and after exposure to atmospheric influences is found in the work of Weaver *et al.* (*2*). From their mass spectrographic data analysis of smog condensates, a gradual oxidation of hydrocarbons, and disappearance of the more fragile olefins with formation of oxygen-containing carbonyl compounds and acids can be deduced.

B. Atmospheric Assimilation and Removal of Pollutants

Speculations about the ultimate result of the reactions of inorganic and organic materials in the atmosphere can be made with reasonable certainty. Through turbulence and diffusion, substances released at ground level will eventually be exposed to conditions in the upper atmosphere and become accessible to high energy photons which break up even the most stable molecules. It is in these regions that molecular oxygen is dissociated, and at heights above 50 miles oxygen exists almost exclusively in monatomic form. At lower levels, where concentrations are higher, the monatomic, quite reactive atoms partially combine to form di- and triatomic molecules of oxygen. The region of greatest ozone concentration is located between 10 and 20 miles above the earth (*3*). The reactions of oxygen in the upper atmosphere are summarized in the following equations (M represents an energy accepting third body):

$$O_2 + h\nu(\lambda 2000) \rightarrow O + O \quad (1)$$

$$O + O + M \rightarrow O_2 + M \quad (2)$$

$$O + O_2 + M \rightarrow O_3 + M \quad (3)$$

$$O_3 + h\nu(\lambda 2900\text{–}2000) \rightarrow O_2 + O \quad (4)$$

It is generally assumed that through the continuous mixing taking place in the atmosphere, some of the ozone is carried downwards to establish the concentration of 0.03 p.p.m. of ozone normally found in the lower atmosphere. In higher atmospheric regions several oxides of nitrogen—N_2O, NO, and NO_2—occur. Their reactions with ozone have received considerable attention because of their relation to the phenomenon of airglow. In order to reach ground level the oxides must pass the ozonosphere, which results in a complete oxidation to nitric acid. It is not expected that nitrogen oxides formed in the upper atmosphere will materially increase the concentration due to industrial and man-made pollution (*4*). Conversely, these man-made oxides of nitrogen, when reaching the upper atmosphere, will adjust themselves to the equilibrium conditions prevalent at the higher regions.

At lower altitudes photochemical effects are less drastic, owing to the filtering effect of the ozone layer on ultraviolet radiation and the sharp termination of the solar spectrum at 2900 Å. For these lower regions we can predict that under the milder conditions inorganic materials will be converted to stable salts—mostly sulfates, nitrates, and chlorides—which will eventually be added to the soil. Organic compounds will end up as carbon dioxide and water. Their nitrogen will be found in ammonium salts and nitrates.

In this assimilation process the composition of the earth and its atmosphere is not changed qualitatively. Noticeable quantitative changes in the atmosphere do occur, however, through the years, by the release of billions of tons of carbon dioxide in the burning of fossil fuels. The concentration level of carbon dioxide is rising slowly, and has been estimated to increase by approximately 0.1–0.5 p.p.m./year. Its effect on living conditions on our planet has been a matter of speculation. Appreciable effect on the SO_2 concentration, amounting to an increase of 0.01 p.p.m. per year, would be calculated on the basis of the known emission of SO_2—an estimated 20 million tons per year for the United States alone. Removal as sulfate probably reduces this figure considerably, and no analytical measurements of sufficient accuracy or over a long enough period are available to decide whether an increase in the SO_2 content of the air actually occurs.

C. Formation of Intermediate Reaction Products

For air pollution control purposes we are usually more interested in the chain of events that precedes the formation of stable end products. The investigation of the intermediates formed from an exceedingly complex mixture of substances present in minute quantities is very difficult. Fortunately, we can establish some restrictions or simplifications in the discussion of atmospheric reactions. One of the first requirements is that the reaction rate be reasonably fast, so that the reactions will have significantly advanced during the time that the pollutants are still in the area being studied, and are present in concentrations sufficiently high to affect us in some way.

The large preponderance of some atmospheric constituents over others is another factor which guides us in predicting the probability of certain reactions. For example, the relatively high concentration of oxygen (209,400 p.p.m., V/V) makes it one of the most important participants in various reactions with air pollutants. Since rates of reactions are dependent on the concentrations of the participating reactants, reactions with oxygen, present at concentrations often a million times greater than that of the pollutant, are more likely to occur than when both substances are present in concentrations of only a fraction of a part per million. For example, when a bimolecular reaction with participants in the concentration range of 10% (100,000 p.p.m.) requires 0.0036 sec. to go halfway to completion, it will take 10^6 times as long, or a whole hour, to reach the same point with concentrations of 0.1 p.p.m. If such reactions are to be at all significant, their rate must be quite high as compared with those with oxygen. The same holds true, although to a far lesser degree, for reactions with water and carbon dioxide, which are present, respectively, in concentrations of 1000–50,000, and 300–500 p.p.m., V/V.

D. Photochemical and Photosensitized Reactions

1. *Energy Requirements*

For chemical reactions to take place it is necessary to add a certain amount of energy derived from molecular collisions or from radiations. In atmospheric reactions the temperature is usually limited to a narrow range which does not supply enough energy for most reactions. The light-activated processes, on the other hand, take a most important place in atmospheric reactions, and may be considered initiators of most dark reactions by endowing atoms and molecules with the necessary activation energy. The limitations set to the photochemical reactions are contained in the two fundamental laws of photochemistry.

The first law requires that light must be absorbed by the reacting atoms or molecules. For example, when visible light shows some photochemical activity there is a colored substance involved. In plants it is the green chlorophyll which makes the energy of the sun available for photosynthesis. In air pollution problems it is often the orange-colored nitrogen dioxide that plays the role of light energy acceptor.

The second law of photochemistry states that one molecule of a reacting substance may be activated by the absorption of one light quantum. A light quantum is the smallest amount of energy that can be removed from a beam of light by any material system. A molecule therefore can absorb several of these quanta, but not less than one. The size of this energy unit is directly proportional to the frequency of the light, and is usually expressed as $h\nu$, where ν is the frequency of the light, and h a constant (Planck's constant) having the value of 6.62×10^{27} erg sec. As seen in Fig. 1, the energy contained in quanta in the long wavelength area of infrared is relatively small as compared with that needed for the breaking of bonds between atoms such as the carbon-

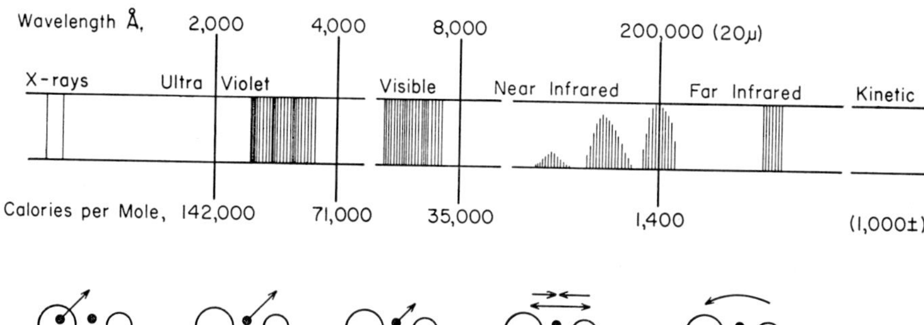

FIG. 1. Schematic representation of different types of spectra, showing wavelength ranges and energy ranges in which they occur, and the corresponding electronic, vibrational, and rotational motions. (F. Daniels, Physical Chemistry, 1st ed., p. 595, Wiley, New York, 1951.)

carbon or carbon-hydrogen bonds, respectively, 84 and 100 kcal. per mole (*5*). In this region, quanta will influence vibration and rotation and will heat the molecule, but they cannot supply enough energy to an individual molecule to overcome the forces which hold its atoms together. In the visible and especially the ultraviolet range of the spectrum, chemical bonds can be broken, and the only limit set is due to the presence of the ozone layer in the upper atmosphere which does not permit radiation of wavelengths below 2900 Å to reach the earth's surface.

A typical example of a photochemical primary reaction is given by the photodissociation of the common air pollutant, nitrogen dioxide. The bond strength between the nitrogen and oxygen is in the order of the energy corresponding to wavelengths smaller than 4500 Å. The photodissociation actually takes place at wavelengths smaller than 3800 Å; above this region, the "excited" molecule retains the energy without dissociating until it loses the extra energy by emitting light in fluorescence or phosphorescence. In other cases atoms and molecules endowed with the extra energy may transfer this to other molecules. Familiar examples of this light-sensitizing action of substances are the action of organic pigments in sensitizing the photographic plate to certain spectral regions, or the dissociation of the hydrogen molecule with mercury and light, whereby the excited mercury transfers its energy to the hydrogen and then returns to its original state. This same principle appears to be of importance for atmospheric reactions with oxygen. Although absorbing only faintly in the red end of the visible spectrum, the high concentration at which oxygen occurs will supply a relatively large number of excited oxygen molecules. The excitation energy gained with this irradiation is in the order of 40 kcal. per mole, while the dissociation requires 117.3 kcal. These excited molecules may possibly react with ozone and with hydrocarbons to form alkyl radicals. Both reactions are of special importance in air pollution studies. The maximum rate of reaction between excited oxygen molecules and a pollutant present at concentrations of 50 p.p.h.m. has been estimated at 1 to 7 p.p.h.m./hr. (*6*). In these reactions the excited oxygen returns to its normal state after it has functioned as a temporary carrier of light energy.

2. *Light Source*

In addition to the limitations set by the absorbing materials, there is an important factor in the variable intensity of the light. This factor has been discussed in extensive theoretical reviews by Leighton and Perkins (*6, 7, 7a*). In their calculations the cyclic effects of direct and scattered light at ground level have been considered. The sunlight passing through the atmosphere is subject to molecular and particulate scattering, reflection, refraction, diffraction, and absorption. The intensity depends further on the lengths of the path of the direct solar radiation and is a function of the zenith angle and surface reflection. At conditions favorable to scattering, the absorption at short wavelengths may be greater than that of direct sunlight. The scattering within the polluted layer may cause the absorption rate at the top of the layer to be several times greater than at the bottom, and at noon the average absorption rate within the layer may be 20 to 30% greater than it would be in the absence of scattering. At ground level, Renzetti (*8*) determined that over the period August–November, 1954, the average total daily radiation (sun + sky at all wavelengths) in downtown Los Angeles was some 10% below what it should have been in the absence of pollution. Spectroradiometer measurements conducted in Pasadena by Stair (*9*) showed that at times of intense pollution solar radiation was reduced in the ultraviolet by more than 80%.

3. *Primary Photochemical Reactions in Air Pollution*

Absorption rates and estimated upper limits for the rates of primary photochemical processes in urban air under certain radiation conditions and absorber concentration of 10 p.p.h.m. have been calculated by Leighton and Perkins (*6*, pp. 95–96). By comparing these rates with those actually observed in stationary or moving air pollution clouds, we obtain some information regarding the major contributing reactions. For the Los Angeles area the photodissociation of nitrogen dioxide into nitric oxide and atomic oxygen seems to be the most important primary photochemical process. Next in importance is the photodissociation of aldehydes into free radicals (Eqs. 5 and 6):

$$NO_2 + h\nu \rightarrow NO + O \qquad (5)$$

$$R\text{—}C(=O)H + h\nu \rightarrow \dot{R} + H\dot{C}O \qquad (6)$$

While this is probably true for most modern urban areas, there is a distinct possibility that under different circumstances and different patterns of emissions, the dominant role of nitrogen dioxide may be taken over by other primary absorbers—organic compounds of many types, halogens and other inorganic compounds, as, for example, particulate metal oxides.

A case was reported at Midland, Michigan (*10*) in which an eye irritant was formed by the chemical combination of two effluents—styrene and halogens—both occurring at concentrations of a few parts per million or less. The formation of the irritant in laboratory experiments was catalyzed by ultraviolet radiation, and in practical circumstances seemed to be dependent upon the presence of sunlight. The role of ultraviolet radiation in these tests suggests that some reaction product other than the direct substitution product may be the actual irritant.

4. *Free Radical Formation*

An important feature of atmospheric reactions is the formation of free radicals. The great dilution of the radicals—in the order of 0.1 to 1 p.p.m.—results in half-lives of minutes, and even hours, as Johnston (*11*) has calculated. A possibility that these reactive intermediates may play a role in eye irritation reactions has been suggested (*7*, p. 195). Free radicals are produced in the photodissociation of aldehydes, as shown in Eq. 6, but they also are formed by a great number of other compounds which absorb solar radiations. These compounds include aldehydes, ketones, alkyl, acyl, peroxyacyl nitrates, hydrogen peroxide and organic peroxides, nitrous and nitric acid (Eqs. 7–12) (7, p. 119). Free radical formation may be indicated as follows:

$$\begin{matrix} R_1 \\ \quad\diagdown \\ \quad\quad C{=}O + h\nu \rightarrow \dot{R} + R\dot{C}O \\ \quad\diagup \\ R_2 \end{matrix} \qquad (7)$$

$$H_2O_2 + h\nu \rightarrow 2\dot{O}H \qquad (8)$$

$$RONO + h\nu \rightarrow R\dot{O} + NO \qquad (9)$$

$$\searrow \dot{R} + NO_2 \qquad (10)$$

$$HNO_2 + h\nu \rightarrow \dot{O}H + NO \qquad (11)$$

$$\searrow H + NO_2 \qquad (12)$$

A nonphotochemical reaction leading to free radicals—alkyl, acyl, and alkoxy radicals—occurs when ozone reacts with olefins (Eq. 13):

$$O_3 + \;\rangle C{=}C \langle\; \rightarrow \dot{R},\ R\dot{O},\ R\dot{C}O,\ ROH,\ ROOH,\ R\overset{O}{\overset{\|}{C}}OOH,\ \text{Polymers} \qquad (13)$$

The reactive free radicals find themselves surrounded by oxygen molecules, and peroxyl radicals are therefore readily formed. Equation 14 shows this reaction, in which R could be a hydrogen atom as well as an alkyl or acyl group, forming the corresponding peroxy radicals.

$$\dot{R} + O_2 \rightarrow RO\dot{O} \qquad (14)$$

The peroxy radicals readily react further with oxygen (Eq. 15), with nitrogen oxides (Eq. 16), with olefins (Eq. 17), and with other radicals, to yield a variety of products—ozone, peroxyalkyl and peroxyacyl nitrates, polymers, alcohols, acids, ethers, and peroxy acids. A selection of these postulated secondary reactions is presented in Eqs. 15–19.

$$RO\dot{O} + O_2 \rightarrow R\dot{O} + O_3 \qquad (15)$$

$$RO\dot{O} + NO \rightarrow ROONO \rightarrow R\dot{O} + NO_2 \qquad (16)$$

$$RO\dot{O} + \;\rangle C{=}C \langle\; \rightarrow ROO{-}C{-}C\cdot \rightarrow \text{Polymers} \qquad (17)$$

$$O + O_2 + M \rightarrow O_3 + M \qquad (18)$$

$$O_3 + NO \rightarrow O_2 + NO_2 \qquad (19)$$

The secondary reaction products are again subject to chemical and photochemical attack. For example, photochemical decomposition of a peroxyacyl nitrite may result in the formation of acylate and nitrogen dioxide, thereby accomplishing an oxygen transfer from oxygen of the air through a peroxy radical to nitrogen dioxide (Eq. 16). Such mechanisms could contribute to the reoxidation of nitric oxide, a key step in the formation of high ozone concentrations in urban atmospheres, and may explain the chain reaction type of ozone formation yielding concentrations of ozone higher than that of either one of the reactants. An illustration of this kind of reaction sequence is represented as follows (Eq. 20).

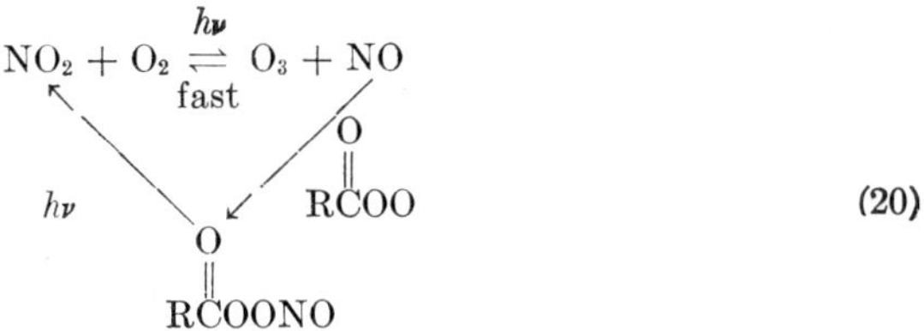

(20)

Although several theories have been advanced to explain the excess ozone formation, none has progressed beyond the speculative stage (*7a, 11a–g*).

E. Heterogeneous Reactions

The presence of solids and liquids introduces a new set of conditions leading to reactions in aqueous solution, absorption, catalytic, and photochemical phenomena. The chemical reactions are for the most part neutralization reactions, but may cover any reaction, such as the oxidation of SO_2 to SO_3 under influence of catalysts, or the hydrolysis of nitrogen oxides to nitric acid. Also, the decomposition of intermediate organic oxidation products to more stable acids and polymers continues in the liquid state, although it started as a gas reaction. Droplets collected from air polluted with organic material show the presence of a film of polymeric material filled with an aqueous solution containing organic and inorganic constituents. The catalytic effect of charcoal and metal oxide dusts on oxidation is well known, and labile substances such as ozone are decomposed. On the other hand, the oxidation of organic material is accelerated.

A special field of heterogeneous reactions is the one where light plays an important role (*12*; *6*, p. 62). For example, it has been shown that zinc oxide surfaces and water form hydrogen peroxide upon irradiation. Zinc oxide is therefore photosensitized for peroxide formation. In this process photoconduction electrons are formed, which results in electron transfer and subsequent oxidation-reduction phenomena at the crystal surface. The photosensitized formation of hydrogen peroxide and the oxidation of organic compounds by zinc oxide are not limited to liquid water medium, but have also been established for nonaqueous media and gases (*13, 14*).

From the preceding discussion of different aspects of atmospheric reactions it is evident that there are no clear-cut boundaries between thermal, photochemical, and heterogeneous inorganic and organic reactions. Once a substance has been released to the air it is subjected to many types of chemical attack, and the best we can do at the present time is to ferret out of the multitude of reactions a few of the major trends. For this reason, several pollutants common to many industrial and urban areas are selected for a more detailed discussion.

II. Atmospheric Reactions in Air Pollution Problems

A. Inorganic Pollutants

1. *Reactions of Oxides of Sulfur*

One of the most common types of pollution, the emission of sulfur dioxide, provides a typical example of a set of reactions leading toward atmospheric stability. When sulfur, present in reduced form in metal sulfides or in complex organic molecules in oil or coal, is roasted or burned, most of it escapes as sulfur dioxide. Almost immediately an oxidation to sulfur trioxide sets in, probably catalyzed by ash constituents. The sulfuric acid formed with the abundantly available water is largely responsible for the bluish smokes typical of "sulfur dioxide" emissions. After the sulfur dioxide has been released, the oxidation continues at a greatly reduced rate, for turbulent diffusion lowers the SO_2 concentration quite rapidly to only a few p.p.m. at a few hundred feet from the source. Under these conditions the gas phase dark oxidation is immeasurably slow. Although light absorption by SO_2 extends to the near ultraviolet, the photochemical oxidation is also slow, and it has been estimated that in intense natural sunlight the reaction rate is in the order of 0.1 to 0.2%/hr. (*15*). Recent investigation indicates higher rates of 0.4% per minute (*15a*). In this oxidation sulfuric acid droplets of 0.19 to 0.45 μ are formed, contributing to the general haziness of inhabited areas. This rate is only slightly increased by the presence of nitrogen dioxide (*16*).

In areas where strongly oxidizing materials such as nitrogen dioxide, ozone, peroxides, and peroxy- free radicals are present, we may expect a more rapid reaction. Automobile exhaust, and also olefins in the presence of oxides of nitrogen, have been shown to cause a more rapid oxidation of SO_2 by the photochemically produced oxidants (*16, 16a, 17, 17a*).

As soon as some oxidation of SO_2 has taken place, droplets are formed, and the stage is set for reactions in the liquid phase. This phenomenon has been studied in an ingenious manner on single droplets by the University of Illinois workers (*18*). They found that the rate of oxidation of SO_2 was materially increased by the presence of iron and manganese salts. This accelerated oxidation may perhaps be realized in fogs and stack plumes. The end result of the combined effect of these different types of reaction is the formation of sulfuric acid, which is soon converted to sulfates such as ammonium and, especially, calcium sulfate.

2. *Reactions of Oxides of Nitrogen*

The oxides of nitrogen present in the atmosphere are N_2O, NO, and NO_2. In addition, nitrous and nitric acids have been found, free, or in the form of their salts. Nitrous oxide (N_2O) is present as a regular atmospheric component at concentrations on the order of 0.5 p.p.m. (*4, 19*). Its stability makes it appear unlikely that it plays an important role in low level atmospheric reactions. The higher oxides of nitrogen are formed in chemical processes such as nitrations, but by far the largest contributor is combustion at high temperature, whereby nitric oxide is formed.

Nitric oxide (NO) reacts with oxygen to form nitrogen dioxide (NO_2), according to Eq. 21:

$$2NO + O_2 \rightarrow 2NO_2 \qquad (21)$$

At equilibrium conditions most of the NO is oxidized to NO_2. At a concentration of 1000 p.p.m. colorless NO is seen to turn brown with the formation of NO_2, in a matter of seconds. At the low concentrations occurring in the atmosphere the oxidation rate is much slower. For example, at 1 p.p.m. 100 hr. are needed for a 50% conversion of NO to NO_2. At 0.1 p.p.m. the half-life is 1000 hr. In the presence of ozone this oxidation is greatly accelerated (Eq. 19) (*20, 21*), and it is calculated that at a concentration of 1 p.p.m. the half-life of NO is 1.8 sec. in this reaction. If both reactants are present at 0.1 p.p.m., only 18 sec. are needed for virtually total oxidation.

Photochemically, nitrogen dioxide is strongly active and absorbs light over the entire visible and ultraviolet range of the solar spectrum available in the lower atmosphere (*22, 23*). From 6000 to 3800 Å, the spectrum indicates about the formation of excited molecules. Below 3800 Å, NO_2 dissociates to produce NO and oxygen atoms, according to Eq. 5. When atomic oxygen combines with molecular oxygen (Eq. 3), ozone is formed. In this process equal amounts of NO and O_3 would be produced and, as we have seen previously, the rapid reaction between

NO and O_3 will greatly decrease the total amount of ozone found. When nitrogen dioxide is present in a concentration of 1 p.p.m., the ozone formed in this process is 0.1 p.p.m.; at 0.1 p.p.m. of NO_2 it is 0.03 p.p.m., indicating that the high levels of ozone found in Los Angeles and some other places are not explained by this process (*24*).

In areas where the ozone concentration is high, rapid oxidation of NO_2 to N_2O_5 and, subsequently to nitric acid, occurs. At a nitrogen dioxide concentration of 1 p.p.m., we estimate the half-life of ozone to be only 8 minutes. The same end results will be obtained in fog droplets, whereby hydration and oxidation lead to nitrous and nitric acids, according to Eqs. 22–24.

$$2NO_2 + H_2O \rightarrow H^+ + NO_3^- + HNO_2 \qquad (22)$$

In acid solution the nitrous acid decomposes:

$$3HNO_2 \rightarrow H^+ + NO_3^- + H_2O + 2NO \qquad (23)$$

The over-all result is therefore a complete conversion into nitric acid:

$$4NO_2 + O_2 + 2H_2O \rightarrow 4HNO_3 \qquad (24)$$

A similar fate awaits any nitrosyl chloride which could possibly have been formed from sodium chloride.

Both nitric and nitrous acid may be photochemically decomposed, re-forming the lower oxides according to Eqs. 11, 12, 25, and 26, and their importance is therefore questionable.

$$HNO_3 + h\nu \rightarrow \dot{H}O + NO_2 \qquad (25)$$

$$\searrow H + NO_3 \qquad (26)$$

The reactivity of the oxides of nitrogen leads to many reactions with organic pollutants. These reaction products will be discussed later in more detail.

In general, we observe that the atmospheric processes tend to bring the oxides of nitrogen to the nitric acid stage. These oxidations may take place in hours or days, and during this time the nitrogen oxides participate in a number of complicated reactions in which they are switched back and forth between the various oxidation stages (*25*). Eventually, however, they end up largely as nitrates, which are removed from the nitrogen oxide atmospheric pool by rain (*4*). A smaller percentage is found in aerosols as nitro derivatives of high molecular organic polymers.

3. *Other Inorganic Pollutants*

Other common inorganic pollutants such as fluorides, ammonia, hydrogen sulfide, and carbon monoxide are removed from the atmosphere by similar processes. Hydrogen fluoride and the hydrolyzed silicofluorides readily attack a wide variety of materials—carbonates, silicates, and organic compounds. Neither ammonia nor its unpleasant-smelling organic homologues, the amines, absorb light in the range of 2900 to 8000 Å, and they are removed from the atmosphere by reaction with acids or acid-forming oxides. Consequently, ammonium sulfate is a common pollutant in urban areas. Hydrogen sulfide, transparent to the spectral range available at ground level, readily participates in chemical reactions, as, for example, in the combination of hydrogen sulfide with white lead in paint. The sulfides and their organic homologues, the mercaptans, as well as the amines, are subject to the oxidizing action of the atmosphere. These reactions are of importance in daylight when photochemically active components degrade the amines and mercaptans. In laboratory experiments their unpleasant odors disappear when these compounds are exposed to irradiation in air in the presence of a few tenths of a part per million of oxides of nitrogen. Hydrogen sulfide, itself, is probably oxidized to sulfates, although small amounts of elemental sulfur found in polluted atmospheres indicate that relatively stable intermediates may be formed.

Carbon monoxide is a transparent and comparatively inert substance. Its fate in the atmosphere is unknown but, since there is no evidence that it accumulates over the years, it is probably slowly oxidized to carbon dioxide; it has been suggested that this oxidation occurs for the most part at high altitudes where carbon monoxide absorbs radiant energy of short wavelength, and where atomic oxygen and ozone are plentiful.

B. Organic Pollutants: Los Angeles Smog

1. *Oxidation of Organic Materials*

Most organic substances oxidize slowly when exposed to atmospheric influences. On a large scale, these oxidations take place in the drying of paints, deterioration of foods, disintegration of rubber, gum formation in petroleum products, and bleaching of pigments. The mechanism common to these reactions is the removal of a hydrogen atom, leaving a hydrocarbon radical. The next step is the addition of oxygen to the radical. The peroxide radical is able to remove a hydrogen atom from another hydrocarbon molecule, and in this way the reaction, once set in motion, keeps going until it terminates by a process whereby free radicals and peroxides are removed. This sequence of reactions, called a chain reaction, is schematically presented as follows:

Initiation: Production of $\dot{R}$ and other radicals (7)-(13)

Propagation: $\dot{R} + O_2 \rightarrow R\dot{O}O$ (27)

$R\dot{O}O + RH \rightarrow ROOH + \dot{R}$ (28)

Termination: $2\dot{R} \rightarrow RR$ (29)

$\dot{R} + R\dot{O}O \rightarrow ROOR$ noninitiating, nonpropagating products (30)

$2R\dot{O} \rightarrow ROOR$ (31)

A recent infrared study of the reaction of aldehydes with oxygen, ozone, and light established the formation of a peroxyacid formed from the peroxyacetyl radical as follows (*26*):

$$CH_3{-}\overset{O}{\overset{\|}{C}}{-}H + O_2 + h\nu \rightarrow CH_3{-}\overset{O}{\overset{\|}{C}}\cdot + HO\dot{O} \quad (32)$$

$$CH_3{-}\overset{O}{\overset{\|}{C}}\cdot + O_2 \rightarrow CH_3{-}\overset{O}{\overset{\|}{C}}{-}O{-}\dot{O} \quad (33)$$

$$CH_3{-}\overset{O}{\overset{\|}{C}}{-}O{-}\dot{O} + CH_3{-}\overset{O}{\overset{\|}{C}}{-}H \rightarrow CH_3{-}\overset{O}{\overset{\|}{C}}{-}OOH + CH_3{-}\overset{O}{\overset{\|}{C}}\cdot \quad (34)$$

Fortunately for the continued existence of the organic world the initiation step, the formation of the radicals, is a difficult one, and outside energy is needed to start the reaction. This may be accomplished by any means which increase the rate of production of more free radicals, such as light and heat. Also, foreign substances may be added, which function in the formation of free radicals by removing hydrogen atoms. Such materials are found in metal catalysts used in the drying of paints and oils, and peroxides used in the polymerization of unsaturated hydrocarbons in the production of plastics and rubbers.

Oxidation of pure organic substances is usually quite slow until, after a certain time lapse called the "induction period," a much faster oxygen consumption sets in, owing to the formation of initiators. In air there are usually enough traces of these substances present, e.g., peroxides, ozone, and oxides of nitrogen, to shorten the induction period in the oxidation of organic material; thus we find that the otherwise stable paraffins will be degraded completely.

2. *Symptoms of Los Angeles Type Smog*

An interesting example of a large-scale oxidation, with NO_2 functioning as light-sensitizer, has appeared in Los Angeles. The result of this photochemical oxidation process is known as "Los Angeles smog," a phenomenon accompanied by eye irritation, plant damage, haze, ozone formation, and characteristic odor. The typical smog symptoms generally occur simultaneously with high oxidant values, due largely to a high level of ozone concentration plus smaller amounts of organic peroxides and oxides of nitrogen. Oxidant measurements show a definite daily rhythm, with a maximum during the daytime. At night the oxidant values are virtually reduced to zero—a strong argument for the photochemical origin of the smog.

The symptoms of Los Angeles smog can be reproduced in fumigations wherein pure hydrocarbons or gasoline fractions are exposed to solar radiation in the presence of oxides of nitrogen. Similar results are obtained in a fumigation with olefins and ozone, without irradiation, and subsequent research has shown that ozone is in fact formed during the photochemical oxidation of hydrocarbons in the presence of nitrogen dioxide (*27–31*). The formation of ozone accounts for the intense rubber cracking noted in the Los Angeles area. The high ozone concentration is also responsible for plant damage in areas with Los Angeles smog (*31a*). More frequently a different type damage appears, referred to as oxidant damage, which is reproduced in fumigations with olefins and ozone. Intermediate products responsible for this toxic action may be ozone-olefin addition complexes or degradation products, such as zwitter ions ($R\overset{+}{C}O\overset{-}{O}$), or products with peroxide groupings. Similar damage is obtained in fumigations whereby olefins are photo-oxidized in the presence of nitrogen oxides (*32, 33, 33a–b*). Peracyl nitrates are contributors to the phytotoxic complex of oxidant type. Their synthesis allows study of the toxic reactions with pure compounds (*11f–g*). The eye-irritating material should also be regarded as a mixture of several irritants. This complex is more stable than the plant toxicant and its half-life has been estimated to be of the order of half a day (*34*). Since neither starting products nor end products such as acids show eye-irritating effects at the concentrations used in the fumigations, intermediate oxidation products are again suspect as eye irritants. A part of the irritating effect, but not all, can be explained by the presence of formaldehyde and acrolein (*17a*). Other lachrymators mentioned are peroxides of various types, free radicals, peroxyacyl nitrates, diketene, and nitro olefins. The presence of aerosols may enhance the physiological reaction or, since some of the polymers formed are strong oxidants, aerosols themselves may contribute to the total eye irritation response.

Aerosol formation, usually accompanying fumigations with photochemically oxidized hydrocarbons, has been studied in connection with automobile exhaust (*36*). These studies confirm the photochemical aerosol formation observed with cyclic olefins and with olefins in the presence of sulfur dioxide (*27, 37*). The chemical composition, as well as the infrared spectra of these materials obtained by irradiation of gasoline or olefins in the presence of oxides of nitrogen, is similar to that obtained from ether-soluble aerosols collected from Los Angeles air. The composition of these aerosols is given in Table I. The empirical

TABLE I

COMPARISON OF AVERAGE ELEMENTAL ANALYSES OF AIR SAMPLES, SYNTHETIC AEROSOLS, AND GASOLINE GUMS, PER CENT BY WEIGHT

	Air samples		Synthetic aerosols[a] (NO_2 + cracked gasoline)	Gasoline gums[c]
	(*a*)	(*b*)		
Carbon	67.9	34.0	69.1	69.8
Hydrogen	9.2	5.3	9.0	8.7
Nitrogen	1.2	1.4	—	—
Oxygen	20.7	59	21.9	21.1
Sulfur	0.6	—	—	0.4

[a] Mader *et al.* (*37*).
[b] Faith *et al.* (*34*), p. 43.
[c] Ellis (*38*), p. 908.

formula roughly corresponds to $(CH_2O)_n$, indicating a far advanced state of oxidation of the original hydrocarbon material.

3. *Chemical Nature of Smog Components*

As a result of the work of many investigators, the reactions leading to unusually high ozone concentrations in urban areas have been studied intensely and have focused attention on chemical reactions in the atmosphere, as described earlier. Long path infrared studies have contributed to the finding of several degradation and intermediate oxidation products. An example of a spectrogram obtained from the irradiation of 3-methylheptane in the presence of NO_2 is shown in Fig. 2. This spectrum gives abundant evidence of the strongly oxidizing effect of the atomic oxygen produced in the primary photochemical reaction $NO_2 \rightarrow NO + O$. Fragments of the hydrocarbon are found as carbon dioxide, formic acid, and ketones. Indication of the temporary presence of free radicals is seen in the organic nitrates and nitrites. Of special interest is the appearance of bands belonging to a peroxyacyl nitrate, also found in infrared spectrograms of Los Angeles type smog.

In a study of the photolysis of isobutene, Schuck, Doyle, and Endow (*11c*) have measured the rates of formation of the numerous degradation products. Found in addition to the expected major oxidation products, acetone and formaldehyde, were carbon monoxide, peracetylnitrate, isobutene oxide, acetaldehyde, isobutyraldehyde, propionaldehyde, ethyl nitrate, methyl nitrate, ethyl nitrite, propylene oxide, and methanol.

Formation of irritating substances, as well as of ozone, is limited to a well-defined area of low concentrations of oxides of nitrogen (*34*, p. 8; *39, 40*). This area is shown for ozone formation in Fig. 3, and for eye irritation in Fig. 4. Optimum conditions for both reactions are

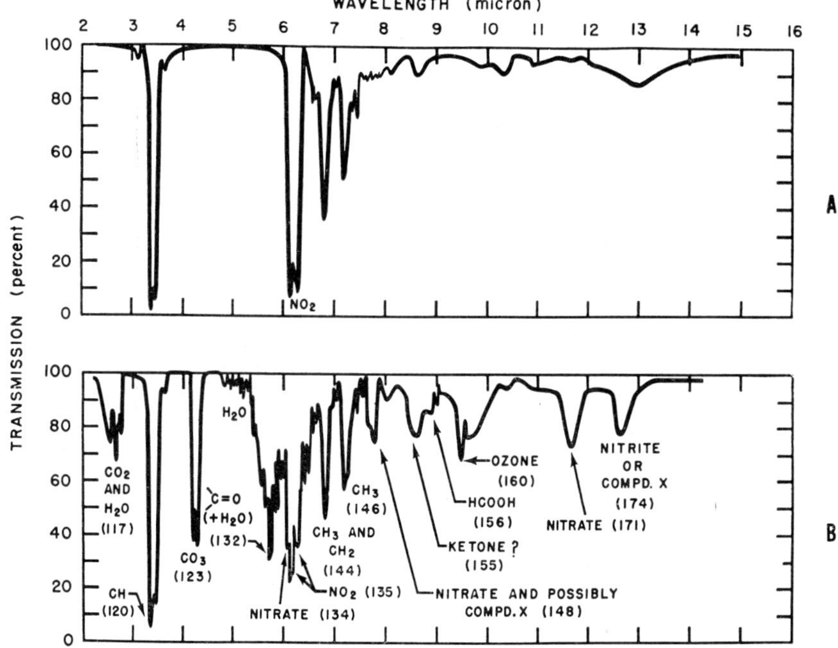

FIG. 2. Infrared spectra—10 p.p.m. 3-methylheptane and 5 p.p.m. nitrogen dioxide in 1 atmosphere of oxygen. (*A*) Before irradiation by AH-6 mercury arc; path lengths 240 meters. (*B*) After irradiation. [E. R. Stephens, P. L. Hanst, R. C. Doerr, and W. E. Scott, *Ind. Eng. Chem.* **48,** 1500 (1956).]

related not only to the absolute concentration, but also to the relative proportion of the reactants.

In general, the ozone measured during irradiation is the resultant of a light reaction leading to the formation of ozone (Eqs. 18 and 20) and dark reactions which destroy it (Eqs. 13 and 19). Among these are oxidation of nitric oxide to nitrogen dioxide and nitric acid, the formation of nitropolymers, and the reactions with olefins and other hydrocarbons. The competition between formation and destruction of ozone is readily seen in experiments in which any ozone formed is immediately removed from the reaction mixture by an ozone acceptor such as rubber. Under these conditions it is found that the capacity for producing ozone is several times greater than would be suspected from the concentration of the reactants (Fig. 5). It has been calculated that during a severe smog day, reaching concentrations of 0.5 p.p.m. O_3, 500 tons of ozone are present in the air over the Los Angeles basin at any one moment, below the inversion layer. To maintain this concentration over a period of hours, several thousand tons of ozone must have been formed.

Figure 6 shows the small difference between the rates of formation and decomposition of ozone in the case of irradiation of 3-methylheptane

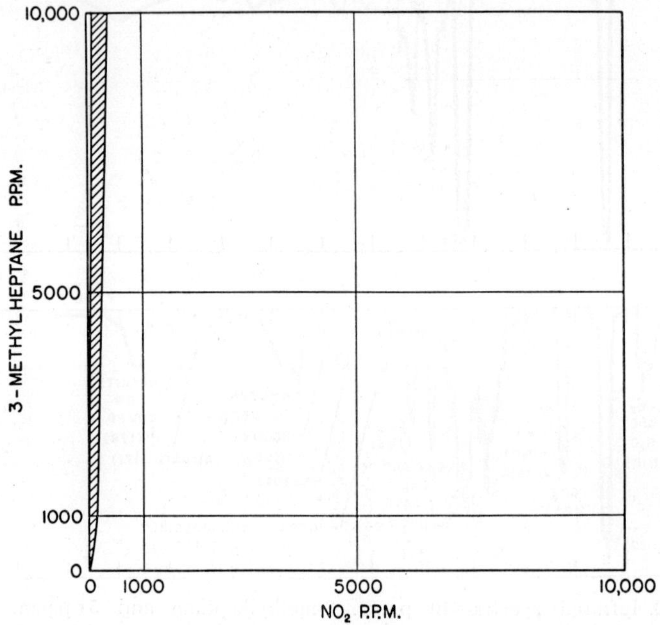

FIG. 3. Area of ozone formation with 3-methylheptane and NO_2. Linear chart. [A. J. Haagen-Smit and M. M. Fox, *J. Air Pollution Control Assoc.* **4,** 106 (1954.)]

and nitrogen dioxide. The initial rate difference of about 0.2 p.p.m. per hour establishes a concentration of 0.9 p.p.m. in 5 hr. By that time both rates have become equal, and a steady state of 1.0 p.p.m. is maintained until, after 25 hr., the decomposition rate takes the upper hand and the ozone gradually disappears. This combination of light and dark reactions explains the limited area of concentrations at which ozone formation may occur, as shown in Fig. 3. It is also a clue to the controversial statements regarding correlations between oxidant and irritation. The slightly faster rate of the light reaction decreases markedly when less light is available, whereas the dark reaction leading to the irritating products is not affected. The excess of ozone is rapidly consumed in these dark reactions, and its half-life is only one hour, as compared with half a day for the irritating reaction products. As a result, irrita-

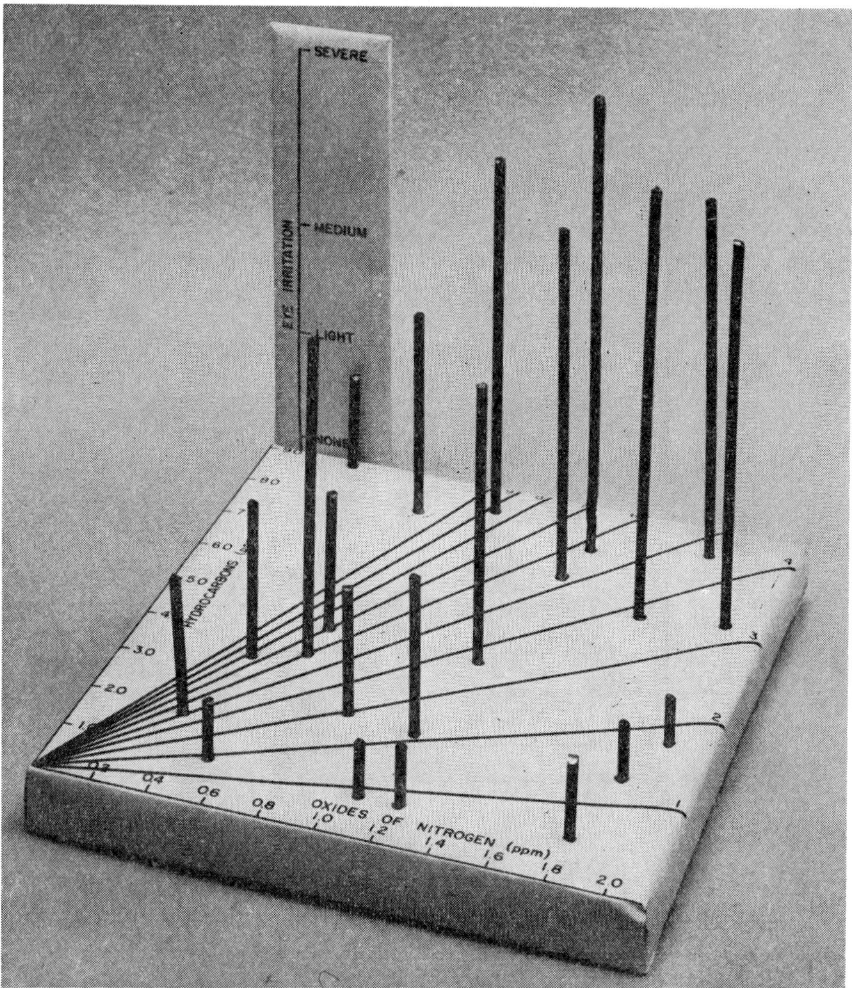

FIG. 4. Eye irritation as a function of hydrocarbons and oxides of nitrogen concentrations. [*Air Pollution Foundation (San Marino, Calif.) Rept.* **22,** 8 (1958).]

tion is often noticed many hours after sundown, when the ozone, and consequently the oxidant, is practically absent.

A systematic testing of a number of hydrocarbons plus their derivatives has demonstrated that ozone formation in the photochemical oxidation is quite a general phenomenon, shown by alcohols, aldehydes, ketones, acids, and different types of hydrocarbons (Fig. 7), (*28, 41*). Especially good ozone formers are diolefins, olefins, aldehydes, and alcohols. The lower saturated hydrocarbons from methane to pentane do not form any appreciable quantity of ozone in this nitrogen dioxide-catalyzed photochemical reaction. A similar study on eye-irritating properties of various compounds also showed the olefins to be superior to other hydrocarbons in the formation of eye irritants (*42*). As seen

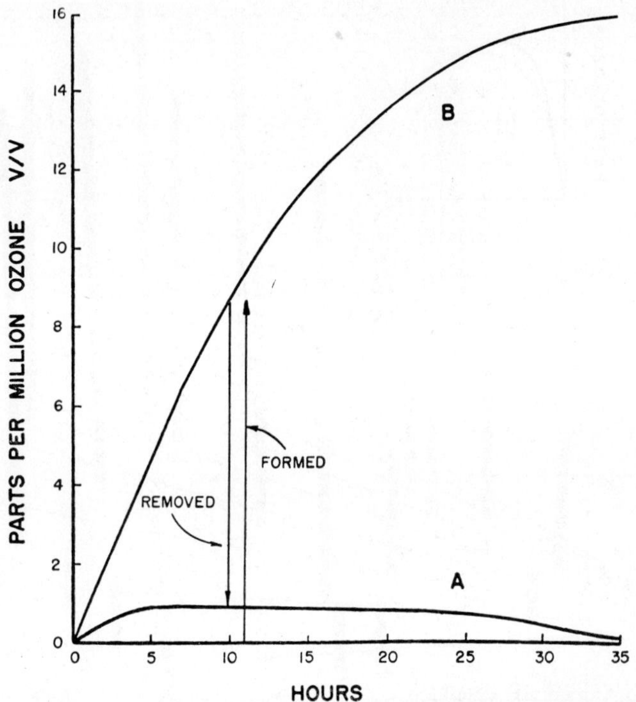

FIG. 5. Photochemical formation of ozone with 3-methylheptane and nitrogen dioxide. (*A*) Observed concentrations of ozone after irradiation. Net result of ozone formation and simultaneous destruction. (*B*) Formation of ozone measured by continuous removal, bent strips of rubber as ozone acceptors. [A. J. Haagen-Smit, *Ind. Eng. Chem.* **48,** 66A (1956).]

in Fig. 8, the times at which optimum ozone concentrations are produced with different hydrocarbons and their derivatives are widely varied. After emission, a mixture of these compounds is selectively oxidized, with olefins being most rapidly attacked. Pollution clouds therefore gradually lose their most rapid ozone formers, whose function is then taken over by aldehydes, ketones, slow reacting olefins, such as ethylene, and saturated hydrocarbons (*31a*). Thus a high ozone level is estab-

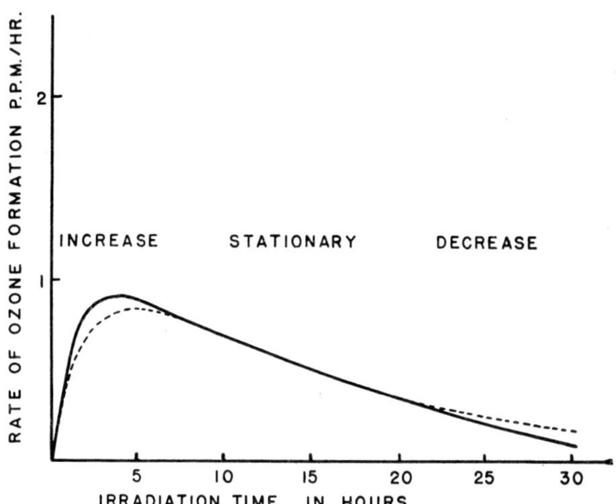

FIG. 6. Rates of formation and decomposition of ozone during irradiation of 3-methylheptane (3 p.p.m.) and NO_2 (1 p.p.m.). Note shift in equilibrium with time. Key: ———, formation rate; - - - -, decomposition rate.

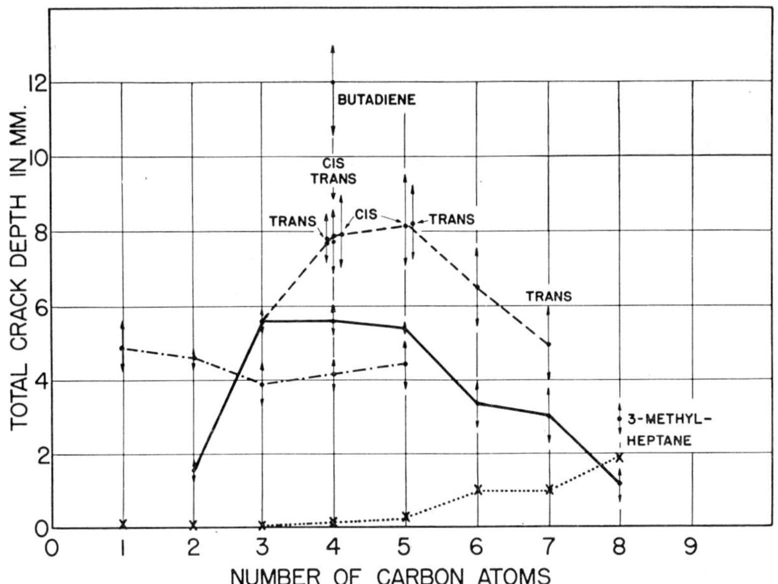

FIG. 7. Photochemical rubber cracking with organic compound (3 p.p.m.) and NO_2 (2 p.p.m.); 10 hours exposure. Key: . . . . ., *n*-paraffins; ———, 1-*n*-olefins; - - -,2-*n*-olefins; .—.—.—, *n*-aldehydes. [A. J. Haagen-Smit and M. M. Fox, *Ind. Eng. Chem.* **48,** 1486 (1956).]

lished and maintained over a long period of time. The rates of formation and decay of the objectionable reaction products of the organic emissions determine to a large extent the type and severity of Los

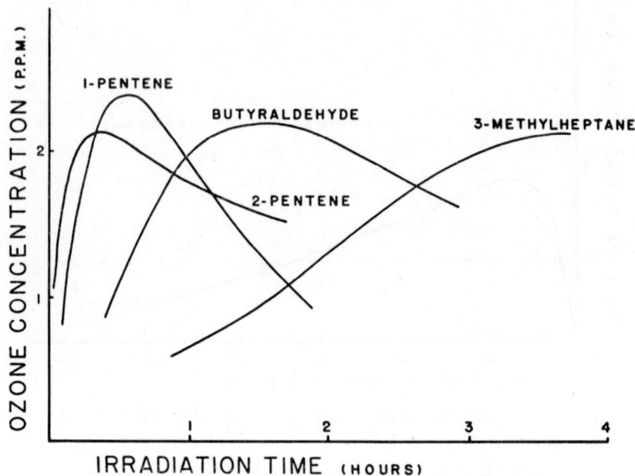

FIG. 8. Ozone formation with 5 p.p.m. NO_2 and 10 p.p.m. organic compounds [E. R. Stephens, P. L. Hanst, R. C. Doerr, and W. E. Scott, *Ind. Eng. Chem.* **48,** 1502 (1956).]

Angeles smog attacks. Such precise knowledge of the behavior of pure organic substances is presently available in only a few instances, and a systematic program of research is needed to provide a firm basis for future control measures.

REFERENCES

1. Second Technical and Administrative Report on Air Pollution in Los Angeles County, *Air Pollution Control Dist., Co. of Los Angeles, Calif., Ann. Rept. 1950–51* p. 41 (1952).
2. E. R. Weaver, E. E. Hughes, S. M. Gunther, S. Schuhmann, N. T. Redfearn, and R. Gorden, Jr., *J. Research Natl. Bur. Standards* **59,** 383 (1957).
3. F. E. Blacet, *Ind. Eng. Chem.* **44,** 1339 (1952).
4. L. E. Miller, *J. Air Pollution Control Assoc.* **8,** 138 (1958).
5. F. Daniels, "Outlines of Physical Chemistry," 1st ed. Wiley, New York, 1951.
6. P. A. Leighton and W. A. Perkins, *Air Pollution Foundation (San Marino, Calif.) Rept.* **14** (1956).
7. P. A. Leighton and W. A. Perkins, *Air Pollution Foundation (San Marino, Calif.) Rept.* **24** (1958).
7a. P. A. Leighton, "Photochemistry of Air Pollution." Academic Press, New York, 1961.
8. N. A. Renzetti (ed.), *Air Pollution Foundation (San Marino, Calif.) Rept.* **9,** 200 (1955).

9. R. Stair, *Proc. Natl. Air Pollution Symposium. 3rd Symposium, Pasadena, Calif.*, p. 48 (1955).
10. A. M. Adams and E. J. Schneider, *Proc. Air Pollution and Smoke Prevention Assoc. Am.* **45,** 61–63 (1952).
11. H. S. Johnston, *Ind. Eng. Chem.* **48,** 1488 (1956).
11a. H. W. Ford, *Can. J. Chem.* **38,** 1750 (1960).
11b. E. A. Schuck and G. J. Doyle, *Air Pollution Foundation (San Marino, Calif.) Rept.* **29,** 33 (1959).
11c. E. A. Schuck, G. J. Doyle, and N. Endow, *Air Pollution Foundation (San Marino, Calif.) Rept.* **31** (1960).
11d. S. Soto and R. J. Cvetanović, *Can. J. Chem.* **36,** 279 (1958).
11e. P. A. Leighton, Advance Papers, *Intern. Symposium on Chem. Reactions in the Lower and Upper Atmosphere, San Francisco 1961* in press.
11f. E. R. Stephens, E. F. Darley, O. C. Taylor, and W. E. Scott, *Proc. Am. Petrol. Inst. Sect. III* **40,** 111 (1960); also *Intern. J. Air Pollution* **4,** 79 (1961).
11g. E. R. Stephens, Advance Papers, *Intern. Symposium on Chem. Reactions in the Lower and Upper Atmosphere, San Francisco, 1961* in press.
12. J. G. Calvert, *Air Pollution Foundation (San Marino, Calif.) Rept.* **15,** 89–112 (1956).
13. M. C. Markham and K. J. Laidler, *J. Phys. Chem.* **57,** 363 (1953).
14. G. V. Elmore and H. A. Tanner, *J. Phys. Chem.* **60,** 1328 (1956).
15. E. R. Gerhard and H. F. Johnstone, *Ind. Eng. Chem.* **47,** 972 (1955).
15a. N. A. Renzetti and G. J. Doyle, *Intern. J. Air Pollution* **2,** 327 (1960).
16. M. J. Prager, E. R. Stephens, and W. E. Scott, *Ind. Eng. Chem.* **52,** 521 (1960).
16a. G. J. Doyle and N. A. Renzetti, *J. Air Pollution Control Assoc.* **8,** 23 (1958).
17. E. A. Schuck, H. W. Ford, and E. R. Stephens, *Air Pollution Foundation (San Marino, Calif.) Rept.* **26** (1958).
17a. Sixth Technical Progress Report, *Air Pollution Foundation (San Marino, Calif.) Rept.* **30** (1960).
18. H. F. Johnstone and D. R. Coughanowr, *Ind. Eng. Chem.* **50,** 1169 (1958).
19. A. Adel, *Science* **113,** 624 (1951).
20. H. S. Johnston and D. M. Yost, *J. Chem. Phys.* **17,** 386 (1949).
21. H. S. Johnston and H. J. Crosby, *J. Chem. Phys.* **19,** 799 (1951).
22. J. K. Dixon, *J. Chem. Phys.* **8,** 157 (1940).
23. T. C. Hall, Jr. and F. E. Blacet, *J. Chem. Phys.* **20,** 1745 (1952).
24. R. G. Cadle and H. S. Johnston, *Proc. Natl. Air Pollution Symposium. 2nd Symposium, Pasadena, Calif.* pp. 28–34 (1952).
25. L. H. Rogers, *J. Air Pollution Control Assoc.* **8,** 124 (1958).
26. L. M. Richards, *J. Air Pollution Control Assoc.* **5,** 216 (1956).
27. A. J. Haagen-Smit, *Ind. Eng. Chem.* **44,** 1342 (1952).
28. E. R. Stephens, P. L. Hanst, R. C. Doerr, and W. E. Scott, *Ind. Eng Chem.* **48,** 1498 (1956).
29. Third Technical Progress Report, *Air Pollution Foundation (San Marino, Calif.), Rept.* **17,** 97–99 (1957). (Report on project with Armour Research Foundation on Effect of Trace Materials in Air on Photochemical Formation of Oxidant by C. Brown, K. Franson, and A. Miller.)
30. R. D. Cadle, *Air Pollution Foundation (San Marino, Calif.) Rept.* **15,** 29–59 (1956).
31. B. E. Saltzman, *Ind. Eng. Chem.* **50,** 677 (1958).

31a. J. T. Middleton and A. J. Haagen-Smit, *J. Air Pollution Control Assoc.* **11,** 129 (1961).
32. A. J. Haagen-Smit, E. F. Darley, M. Zaitlin, H. Hull, and W. M. Noble, *Plant Physiol.* **27,** 18 (1952).
33. E. F. Darley, E. R. Stephens, J. T. Middleton, and P. L. Hanst, *Proc. Am. Petrol. Inst., Sect. III* **38,** 313 (1958).
33a. N. N. Arnold, *Intern. J. Air Pollution* **2,** 167 (1959).
33b. E. F. Darley, E. R. Stephens, J. T. Middleton, and P. L. Hanst, *Intern. J. Air Pollution* **1,** 155 (1959).
34. W. L. Faith, N. A. Renzetti, and L. H. Rogers, Fourth Technical Progress Report, *Air Pollution Foundation (San Marino, Calif.) Rept.* **22,** (1958).
35. W. E. Scott, E. R. Stephens, P. L. Hanst and R. C. Doerr, *Proc. Am. Petrol. Inst. Sect. III* **37,** 171 (1957).
36. G. J. Doyle and N. A. Renzetti, *J. Air Pollution Control Assoc.* **8,** 23 (1958).
37. P. P. Mader, R. D. MacPhee, R. T. Lofberg, and G. P. Larson, *Ind. Eng. Chem.* **44,** 1352 (1952).
38. C. Ellis, "The Chemistry of Petroleum Derivatives," Vol. II. Reinhold, New York, 1937.
39. A. J. Haagen-Smit, *Ind. Eng. Chem.* **48,** 65A (1956).
40. A. J. Haagen-Smit and M. M. Fox, *J. Air Pollution Control Assoc.* **4,** 105 (1954).
41. A. J. Haagen-Smit and M. M. Fox, *Ind. Eng. Chem.* **48,** 1484 (1956).
42. E. E. Harton, Jr. and C. C. Bolze, *Air Pollution Foundation (San Marino, Calif.) Rept.* **23,** (1958).

CHAPTER 4

Air Ions

B. J. STEIGERWALD

Department of Civil Engineering and Engineering Mechanics, Case Institute of Technology, Cleveland, Ohio

I. Introduction

Since the first observations of atmospheric electrical phenomena late in the eighteenth century, air ions have been a challenging subject for investigators in many fields. In recent years there has been a revival of interest due not only to the development of more sensitive and reliable measuring equipment, but also to the recognition of the possible role of air ions in physics, meteorology, and medicine.

Interest in air ions by those in the field of air pollution will probably grow, since it appears that some types of air contaminants strongly affect and influence the concentration and size of ions found in the atmosphere. There is some evidence that air ions have a biological effect, at least in high concentrations, but the summation of present knowledge is certainly not conclusive. The public health significance of altering the characteristics of air ions as they are normally found in the atmosphere is seldom even considered. The effect of air contaminants on air ions has been used to measure air pollution, and these phenomena may prove of value for characterizing contaminated atmospheres and monitoring air pollution situations.

II. Nature of Air Ions

Air ions are small particles in the atmosphere (molecules, groups of molecules, condensation nuclei, or microscopic dust particles) which have an induced electrical charge acquired through the loss or gain of an electron, or through the adsorption of a molecule which has lost or gained an electron. Usually an ion pair is formed from a neutral gas molecule when an electron is driven off by ionizing radiation. The residual molecule is positively charged; the escaping electron attaches itself almost immediately to a nearby particle forming a negative ion. Some of these molecular ions become adsorbed onto condensation nuclei or join molecular aggregates giving a range in ion size, arbitrarily called small, intermediate, and large ions. Actually there are not distinct size classes of air ions but rather a continuous spectrum of sizes with the small (probably molecular aggregates) and the large or Langevin ions (probably condensation nuclei) predominating. The sizes of the various classes of ions have been estimated (*1*) by a number of theoretical and experimental methods with general agreement (Table I). These are in

TABLE I
TYPICAL SIZES AND MOBILITIES FOR ATMOSPHERIC IONS[a]

Type of ion	Approximate diameter (μ)	Typical mobility (cm./sec./volt/cm.)
Small	0.001–0.005	2.0 –0.5
Intermediate	0.005–0.015	0.5 –0.01
Large	0.015–0.10	0.01–0.0005

[a] V. A. Gordieyeff, *A.M.A. Arch. Ind. Health* **14,** 471 (1956).

reasonable agreement with calculations made using the Stokes-Millikan-Cunningham relationship (*2*) which shows that ions with mobilities of 0.7 and 0.0002 cm./sec./volt/cm. correspond to particle diameters of 0.0016 and 0.12 μ, respectively.

The assumption is usually made that an air ion carries only the charge of a single electron of either sign (4.8×10^{-10} e.s.u. or 1.6×10^{-19} coulombs). This assumption receives verification by Rich (*3*), who reports on the application of the Boltzmann law to the distribution of charges on small particles. Figure 1 summarizes the results of such calculations and indicates that multiple charges become a factor only with particles larger than about 0.1 μ in diameter.

Allowing this assumption of equal charge, the force on all ions in a constant electrostatic field is identical, and the net velocity of the ion becomes a function of its size, density, shape, and the nature of the

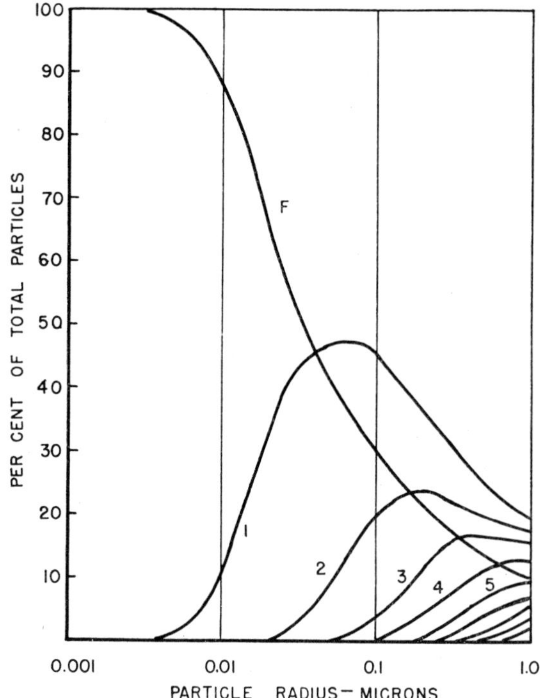

FIG. 1. Distribution of uncharged, charged, and multiply charged particles by particle size. F = number of uncharged particles, in per cent of total number of particles; 1 = number of singly charged particles in per cent of total number of particles; 2, 3, etc. = number of doubly charged, triply charged, etc. particles in per cent of total number of particles.

TABLE II
AVERAGE ION MOBILITIES [a]

Type of ions	Condition	Average mobility (cm./sec./volt/cm.)
Small +	In dry air	1.4
Small −	In dry air	1.9
Small +	In moist air	1.1
Small −	In moist air	1.2
Intermediate + and −	—	0.05
Large + and −	—	0.0004
Fog droplets	With single charge	0.5×10^{-6}
Fog droplets	With n charges	$0.5 \times 10^{-6} n$
Electron	In vacuum	100

[a] H. Neuberger, "Introduction to Physical Meteorology." Pennsylvania State Univ. Press, University Park, Pa., 1951.

surrounding media. These factors are grouped in a property of air ions called mobility which is expressed in centimeters per second per volt per centimeter. For example, an ion with a mobility of 1.0 would move with a net velocity of 1.0 cm. per second in an electrostatic field of 1 volt per centimeter strength.

Small negative ions appear to have higher average mobilities than small positive ions. The reasons for this phenomenon is not well understood. It may be due either to some selective process in the formation of the negative ion or to their powers of adsorption which in turn affect their size. Table II shows some average values of mobilities of several ion types under various conditions as given by Neuberger (*4*).

A. Ion Formation

The removal of an electron from a molecule to form an ion pair requires external energy (Table III; Wait and Parkinson, *5*). Solid radioactive substances, which are present in trace quantities nearly everywhere in the crust of the earth, are responsible for about ⅓ of the

TABLE III
Ionization of the Air near the Earth's Surface over Land[a]
(Per Cent of Total)

Source of ionization	Ionizing ray or particle α	β	γ	Cosmic rays	Total
Radium, in air	30	1	1	—	32
Thorium, in air	18	1	—	—	19
Radium and thorium, in soil	—	1	32	—	33
Cosmic rays	—	—	—	16	16
	48	3	33	16	100

[a] G. R. Wait and W. D. Parkinson, *in* "Compendium of Meteorology" (Thomas F. Malone, ed.), p. 120. Am. Meteorol. Soc., Boston, Mass., 1951.

ions in the air near the ground. This source is negligible over the oceans since sea water has about 1/1000 of the natural radioactivity of soil. Radioactive gases, which escape from the ground, account for about ½ the ionization in the lower layers of the atmosphere over land. This source is also negligible over the oceans. Cosmic rays, which are generally uniformly distributed over the earth's surface, account for about ⅙ of the total air ionization normally observed over land and essentially all the ionization over the oceans.

In addition to these normal, widely distributed sources of energy, ionization of the air may be produced in significant quantities by local phenomena such as electrical discharges (lightning), short-wave ultraviolet (mainly at high altitudes), X-rays, some combustion processes, hot wires, splashing water, and frictional electricity produced by drifting sand, dust, or snow. The concentration of ions present in any atmosphere is the result of a dynamic equilibrium established between these forces, which continually produce new ion pairs, and destructive forces which operate simultaneously. Destruction of an air ion occurs through neutralization of its charge either by coalition with an ion of the opposite sign (recombination) or by contact with a large surface such as a wall or the ground.

B. Small Ion Equilibrium

In clean, aerosol-free air, such as that found at high altitudes and over the oceans, there will be essentially no large ions, and the rate of change of small ion concentration with time may be expressed as the rate of formation minus the rate of destruction:

$$\frac{dn}{dt} = q - an_{+}n_{-} \tag{1}$$

where n is the number of positive or negative ions per cubic centimeter, q is the rate of ionization in numbers of ion pairs formed per cubic centimeter per second, and a is the recombination coefficient for small ions. At equilibrium the rate of change of small ion concentration is zero and we may write

$$q = an_{+}n_{-} \tag{2}$$

It is usually assumed that the concentration of small positive and negative ions is equal in clean air and Eq. 2 becomes

$$q = an^2 \tag{3}$$

The recombination coefficient a for small ions is usually taken as 1.6×10^{-6} cc./sec. although it has been found to vary slightly with temperature and pressure, and with the size of the specific small ions being studied.

C. Large Ion Equilibrium

In normal air over land which contains large numbers of particulate contaminants it is necessary to take into account the destruction of small ions not only by recombination with other small ions as indicated above but also by combination with large ions and by the alteration of small ions to large ions after collision with neutral uncharged particles present in the atmosphere. In a simplified situation which ignores intermediate size ions, the equilibrium conditions for small ions are:

$$q_+ = an_+n_- + bn_+N_- + cn_+N_0 \tag{4}$$
$$q_- = an_+n_- + dn_-N_+ + en_-N_0 \tag{5}$$

where q is the rate of formation of ions of specific sign per cubic centimeter (cc.) per second, n is the number of small ions of specific sign per cubic centimeter, N is the number of large ions of specific sign per cubic centimeter, N_0 is the number of neutral, uncharged particles or

TABLE IV

MEDIAN VALUES FOR COMBINATION AND RECOMBINATION COEFFICIENTS [a]

Relation	Symbol	Typical value (cc./sec.)
Small +, small −	a	1.6×10^{-6}
Small +, large −	b	2.4×10^{-6}
Small +, uncharged	c	0.6×10^{-6}
Small −, large +	d	4.5×10^{-6}
Small −, uncharged	e	1.1×10^{-6}
Large +, large −	f	1×10^{-9}

[a] G. R. Wait and W. D. Parkinson, *in* "Compendium of Meteorology" (Thomas F. Malone, ed.), p. 120. Am. Meteorol. Soc., Boston, Mass., 1951.

condensation nuclei per cubic centimeter, and a, b, c, d, e are constants of combination and recombination. Some median values for these constants are shown in Table IV, but these will vary considerably with the sizes of the ions and particles involved (*5*).

Large ions are formed through the combination of a small ion and an uncharged particle. Their rate of formation per cubic centimeter per second may be expressed:

$$Q_+ = cn_+N_0 \tag{6}$$
$$Q_- = en_-N_0 \tag{7}$$

A simplified equilibrium expression for large ions similar to that for small ions may be written:

$$Q_+ = dn_-N_+ + fN_-N_+ \tag{8}$$
$$Q_- = bn_+N_- + fN_-N_+ \tag{9}$$

Union of a large ion with an uncharged particle is not included in this equilibrium expression since it merely produces an ion of lower mobility which is still identified as a large ion.

D. Mean Life of Air Ions

The above equations predict that the equilibrium concentration of ions is a function of the ionization rate and the concentration of particulate matter in the air. The rate of ionization q averages 10 to 12 ions per cc. per sec. over land and is dependent generally upon the amount of radioactivity present in the soil of a locality, the rate of exhalation of radioactive gases from the soil, and the dispersion of these gases. The average life of the small ions formed depends upon the concentration and size of the particulate matter present in the atmosphere, which is in turn dependent upon the humidity and air quality. The mean life of a small ion varies considerably and may be 5 to 6 min. in clean air and only a few seconds where high concentrations of condensation nuclei are present. Because of air advection and the other variables just noted, the concentration of air ions varies greatly from locality to locality and for different times at the same site.

E. Observed Concentrations of Atmospheric Ions

Kornblueh (*6*) summarized the past work in air ion monitoring throughout the world and presented average ion densities for nearly thirty locations. Small positive ions ranged from approximately 200 per cc. to almost 2000 per cc.; small negative ions had a range in concentration from about 100 per cc. to almost 5000 per cc. Wait and Parkinson (*5*) reported an average concentration of small ions of 400 to 500 per cc. over the oceans and from about 100 ions per cc. of each sign over polluted land areas to 1000 per cc. for land areas with clean air. Correspondingly they found the large ion content of cities higher than rural areas, with values of about 1000 to 2000 per cc. in country air and 20,000 to 30,000 per cc. for atmospheres in some cities. The effect of weather on ion concentrations was noted by Yaglou (*7*), who measured ions with mobilities greater than 0.2 cm. per second in the Boston area. A minimum concentration of about 50 unipolar ions per cc. was observed on overcast days and a maximum of 700 per cc. on sunny days.

Generally, the concentration of small ions is higher in summer than in winter, higher on clear days than on rainy, foggy or overcast days, highest in the early morning, and lowest in the early afternoon. Also at lower altitudes the concentration of small positive ions generally exceeds that of small negative ions because of the earth's electrical field and because the higher mobility of small negative ions causes them to have higher combination coefficients. However, in the absence of particulate matter the concentrations of small positive and small negative ions are assumed nearly equal as in Eq. 3.

III. Measurement and Generation of Air Ions

Air ions are generally measured by collecting unipolar ions on a charged plate or cylinder and noting the magnitude of the ion current produced (*8, 9*). Control of the operating and structural variables such as the velocity of air drawn past the plates, and the voltage, polarity, and spacing of the plates allows determination of the sign and the mobility of the ions collected. The assumption of a unit electron charge

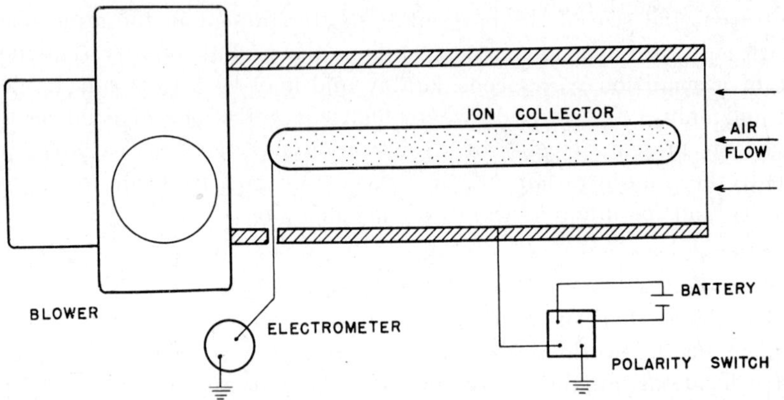

FIG. 2. Schematic drawing of a typical instrument to measure air ion concentrations.

for each ion (1.6×10^{-19} coulombs) allows calculation of the number of ions collected. The quantity of current made to flow by normal ion concentrations is very small, in the order of 10^{-14} amperes. Since reliable micro-micro ammeters have become generally available only recently the accuracy of much of the earlier reported data, particularly with regard to narrow ranges of ion mobilities and low ion concentrations, is questionable.

Figure 2 is a schematic diagram of a typical ion-measuring instrument utilizing concentric cylinders to provide the collecting surface and the electrostatic field. Air is pulled through the annular space at a known rate. Once inside the annulus, air ions are acted upon by an axial velocity vector, depending only upon the rate of air flow and a transverse velocity vector whose direction is determined by the polarity of the ion and the cylinders, and whose magnitude is a function of the strength of the electric field and the mobility of the ion. Setting the longitudinal travel time equal to the maximum radial travel time yields an expression for the ions of smallest mobility which will be collected with 100% efficiency.

$$M = \frac{h^2 \cdot Q/A}{v \cdot l} \tag{10}$$

where M = ion of smallest mobility which will be collected with 100% efficiency, centimeters per second per volt per centimeter
h = distance between cylinders, centimeters
Q = air flow rate, cubic centimeters per second
A = area of annulus, square centimeters
v = voltage differential between cylinders, volts
l = length of cylinders, centimeters

The length l, and distance between cylinders h are set in the initial design of the instrument. Ions of lower mobility (larger ions) can be collected with 100% efficiency by decreasing the air flow rate Q, or more practically by increasing the voltage v, impressed across the cylinders. In practice wide ranges of flow rates, from 1 to 50 cu. ft. per minute, and voltages, from 45 to 270 volts, are used to collect ions. An instrument designed and operated to collect all ions with a mobility of M or larger will also collect $p(M_1/M)$ of ions with a mobility of M_1, where p is the number of elementary charges the ion possesses.

A second method of air ion detection involves the measurement of the net space charge or the charge resulting from the excess in concentration and mobility of ions of one sign over ions of the opposite sign. The space charge alone measures neither total ion concentration nor ion mobility.

Air ions have been generated for laboratory study by many methods including the ionizing effects of radioactive materials, wires at high potential, heated wires, and ultraviolet radiation (*10*). Most of these produce ions of both polarities so that to achieve unipolar ionization it is necessary to remove ions of undesired polarity by passing the air stream through an appropriately charged tube or series of plates. Some of these methods also produce ozone and nitrogen oxides during the generation of air ions.

IV. Relationship of Air Pollution and Air Ion Characteristics

Knowledge concerning the relationship of air ions and air pollution is of a fragmentary nature and has come about generally as a result of more basic studies into the nature of air ions and atmospheric electricity. Very little quantitative data is available regarding specific effects of air contaminants on air ions, but many observations have been made of the existence of such effects. Some predictions can be made concerning the effects of an aerosol contaminant from a study of the equilibrium equations presented earlier. When particulate contaminants

(N_0) are introduced into an atmosphere, some of the small ions present attach to them and become intermediate or large ions of low mobility—depending on the size of the particulates introduced. Also, since small negative ions (n_-) have greater mobilities than small positive ions (n_+) (Table II), they make contact with the contaminant aerosol more frequently and are converted to intermediate or large ions at a preferential rate. Therefore, as an atmosphere becomes contaminated with small particulate matter the ratio of small positive to small negative ions, n_+/n_-, tends to increase, and the concentration of all small ions decreases. A corresponding rise would be expected in the concentration of intermediate and large ions. These effects also result in decreased atmospheric conductivity since such conductivity is dependent mainly on the concentration and mobility of the small ions present.

Physicists and meteorologists interested in atmospheric electricity have reported regular fluctuations in air ion mobilities and densities in response to high concentrations of condensation nuclei released to the atmosphere by periodic natural forces (*11*), and have noted the changes which occur in air ion characteristics near large cities (*12*).

A. Air Conductivity

A number of experiments have been conducted which bear out in a general way the predictions concerning the effect of air contaminants on air ions which may be made from the equilibrium equations. Phillips *et al.* (*13*) studied the effect of atmospheric particulate matter on air ion characteristics using a 3000-cu. m. cloud chamber. Normal atmospheric air was sealed in the chamber, and measurements of ion densities and air conductivities were taken while the air in the chamber was continuously cleaned with an electrostatic precipitator. Although no information was obtained on the nature or concentration of the particulate matter present, it was demonstrated that the magnitudes of the positive and negative conductivities, and therefore the densities of small ions, are greatly dependent on air quality. Figure 3 shows the observed change in negative and positive conductivity with increasing electrostatic cleanup. Initially both negative and positive conductivities were equal, a situation which is possible only when the concentration of small positive ions is greater than the concentration of small negative ions by about one-third. This is explained by the increased mobility of the small negative ions, which allows them to contribute more to air conductivity. As the particulate matter is removed by the electrostatic precipitators, both positive and negative conductivities increase, indicating an increased small ion concentration. It can also be noted that the negative conductivity has increased more rapidly and at the end of the 5-day period it is about one-third greater than the positive conductivity, a situation indicative of nearly equal positive and negative small ion densities.

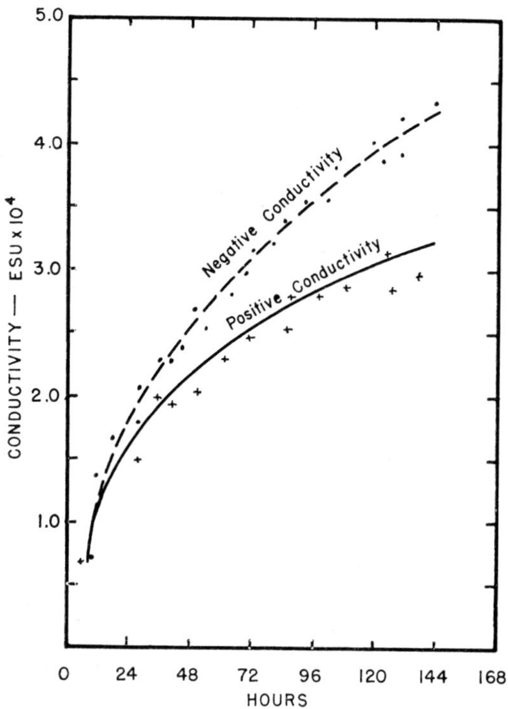

FIG. 3. The variation of positive and negative conductivities with electrostatic cleanup of the air.

B. Ion Life

The factors which affect the mean life of artificially produced small ions were studied by Stergis (*14*) at the Air Force Cambridge Research Center and a theoretical expression was obtained for the time variation of the concentration of small ions in a nonequilibrium system. It was found that the time required for the atmospheric ion concentration to return to normal after it had been disturbed by the introduction of high concentrations of small ions was a function of the normal ionization rate, temperature, pressure, and amount of air pollution. The author concludes that the most important factor by far is the amount of pollution present in the atmosphere. This is demonstrated in Fig. 4 which shows experimental data for tests runs conducted at Hanscom Field in Bedford, Massachusetts and at Sacramento Peak in New Mexico. At

Bedford, which was assumed to be an area of significant air pollution, the equilibrium small ion concentration of 310 per cc. was restored in about 1 min., while at Sacramento Peak, far from any source of air

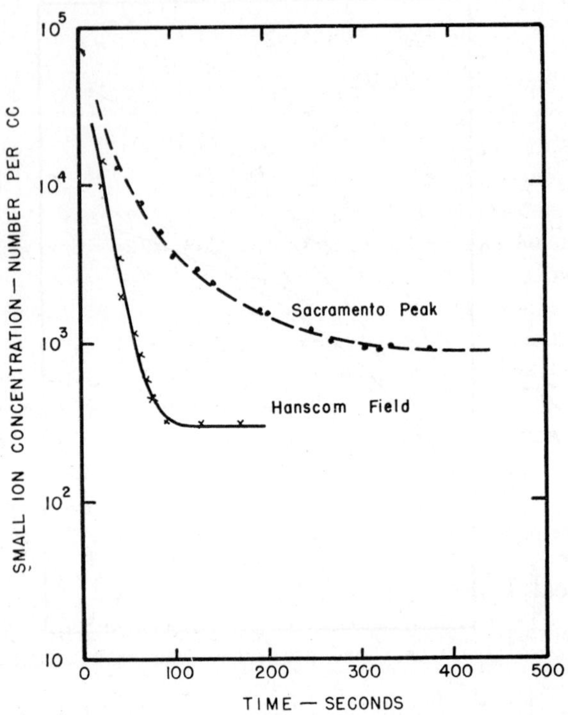

FIG. 4. Ion decay measurements at Hanscom Field, Massachusetts and Sacramento Peak, New Mexico.

pollution, the equilibrium concentration of 800 per cc. was not attained until 6 min. after disturbance. The lower equilibrium concentration of small ions at Bedford would also be expected from the previous discussion of the effect of air pollution on air ion characteristics.

C. Effect of Auto Exhausts on Air Ions

Auto exhausts are the only specific source of air contamination which have been linked with an effect on atmospheric ion characteristics. Beckett (*15*) measured small air ion concentration in a residential area a few miles from the industrial center of San Francisco and found typical small ion densities of 500 to 600 per cc. Near the San Francisco end of the Bay Bridge he found an average of less than 80 small ions per cc. However, intermediate ions reached peak levels of 400 per cc.

during morning and evening peak traffic flow on weekdays. There was a marked decrease in the concentration of intermediate ions on Saturday and Sunday. Mountain air showed densities of small ions between 200 and 2000 per cc., with essentially no intermediate ions present.

D. Use of Ions in Air Analysis

An instrument has recently been developed which utilizes the effect of aerosols on air ions and allows continuous measurement of certain gaseous contaminants (*16*). The contaminants are first changed into an aerosol by reaction with a suitable chemical agent, and the effect of this created aerosol on a standardized ion current is measured.

Small ion uptake on particulate contaminants also has been used in the development of an instrument which continuously measures and records the concentration of condensation nuclei and other very small particles in the atmosphere (*16a*). The results obtained in the city of Munich for a 3-month sampling period indicated aerosol concentrations from 0.8×10^4 to 1.2×10^5 per cubic centimeter, with automobile exhausts apparently exerting the major influence on the small particle concentration. The instrument was used also to measure larger dusts of industrial hygiene significance and successfully recorded concentrations as low as 20 particles per cubic centimeter.

V. Biological Effects of Air Ions

Since the early 1930's the scientific literature, particularly German, Russian, and American, has contained hundreds of references to the effects of ionized air on microorganisms, plants, animals, and man. The physiological parameters used as indicators in these studies have included ciliary motion, mucus production, electroencephalograms, pain intensity, convalescence time, blood pressure, blood pH, basal metabolic rate, endocrine gland production, respiration rate, pulse rate, growth, and body temperature.

Although a few workers have investigated the mechanism of the physiological effect which they have observed from air ions, most of the research has been devoted to demonstrating the effect itself and its possible clinical and therapeutic application. At present there is much controversy concerning the biological effect of air ions, with most investigators agreeing only that present knowledge is inconclusive. Many researchers report diverse and significant beneficial physiological effects caused by exposure to air ions after experiments with both animals and humans. Air ion therapy has been used with reported success in many European clinics since the 1930's (*17*). On the other hand, many of the investigations into the biological effects of air ions have not been reproducible in other laboratories or have given results which varied so widely from subject to subject as not to be significant under rigorous statistical analysis. Other investigators have not been able to find any biological effects of air ions (*18*).

Hicks (*19*), Nagy (*20*), and Hansell (*21*) have summarized much of the work on the biological effects of air ions. A few of the more interesting investigations are outlined below:

Silverman and Kornblueh (*22*) at the University of Pennsylvania Graduate Hospital studied the effect of negative air ions on electroencephalograms of various patients and showed that the alpha frequency was depressed. They suggested that negative ions have a transient tranquilizing effect. David *et al.* (*23*), in a study of seventy-five patients, reported that negative air ions reduced the pain generally associated with burns.

Worden (*24*), working with golden hamsters at Saint Bonaventure University, reported that the CO_2-combining power of plasma was significantly increased in negatively ionized atmospheres. He also found that the weight of selected body organs of the golden hamster such as the heart, liver, spleen, and kidney increased a statistically significant amount in animals exposed to negative air ions (*25*). No increase over control was noted in animals exposed to positive ions. Extensive recent work by Krueger and Smith (*26*) at the University of California has shown a marked effect of air ions on the respiratory tract of various animals. Using mice they demonstrated that negative air ions caused an increased mucus flow in the trachea and decreased the respiration rate by about 15%. In similar experiments using isolated rabbit trachea the effects of positive ions were observed only in atmospheres containing CO_2 and the effects of negative ions were observed only in oxygen.

Most of these investigations have involved high concentrations of unipolar ions of unreported mobilities, and the reports include very little experimental information such as control exerted over other environmental factors and the health of the subjects. The earlier investigations were also hampered by unreliable ion generating and measuring equipment. As a result, the experiments which have demonstrated a specific biological effect due to air ions generally do not remain definitive under critical review by other experimental physiologists. However, it is difficult to ignore the clinical success claimed for air ion therapy and the conviction of many experienced physiologists that air ions do have biological effects. More well-controlled biological experiments are necessary to resolve the debates.

Numerous suggestions have been made on the role atmospheric ions may play in various bioclimatological phenomena (*27, 28*). Changes in air ion characteristics would be expected in many situations where psychological reactions seem to be influenced by the natural environment. Since air pollution influences ionization, the possibility exists that there may be a relation between the extent of pollution and the extent of these reactions. This possibility has not been investigated in any detail.

References

1. V. A. Gordieyeff, *A.M.A. Arch. Ind. Health* **14,** 471 (1956).
2. R. C. Sagalyn and G. A. Faucher, *Quart. J. Roy. Meteorol. Soc.* **82,** 428 (1956).
3. T. A. Rich, *Intern. J. Air Poll.* **1,** 288 (1959).
4. H. Neuberger, "Introduction to Physical Meteorology." Pennsylvania State Univ. Press, University Park, Pa., 1951.
5. G. R. Wait and W. D. Parkinson, *in* "Compendium of Meteorology" (Thomas F. Malone, ed., supported by Air Force Cambridge Research Laboratories) p. 120. Am. Meteorol. Soc., Boston, Mass., 1951.
6. I. H. Kornblueh, *Bull. Am. Meteorol. Soc.* **41,** 361 (1960).
7. C. P. Yaglou, L. C. Benjamin, and S. P. Choate, *Heating, Piping, Air Conditioning* **3,** 865 (1931).
8. H. Israel, *in* "Compendium of Meteorology" (Thomas F. Malone, ed.) p. 144. Am. Meteorol. Soc., Boston, Mass., 1951.
9. W. W. Hicks and J. C. Beckett, *Trans. AIEE* (*I*)**30,** 108 (1957).
10. K. T. Whitby, "Generator for Producing High Concentrations of Small Ions," Univ. of Minnesota Tech. Report No. 12, 1960.
11. W. D. Parkinson, *Terrestrial Magnetism and Atmospheric Elec.* **53,** 305 (1948).
12. J. A. Chalmers, "Atmospheric Electricity." Pergamon Press, New York, 1957.
13. B. B. Phillips, P. A. Alee, J. C. Pales, and R. H. Woessner, *J. Geophys. Research* **60,** 289 (1955).
14. C. G. Stergis, Air Force Cambridge Research Center Tech. Report 54-13. Cambridge, Mass, 1954.
15. J. C. Beckett, *J. Am. Soc. Heating, Refrigerating, Air Conditioning* **1,** 47 (1959).
16. L. E. Maley, *Nucleonics* **18,** 126 (1960).
16a. D. Hasenclever and H. C. Siegmann, *Staub* **20,** 212 (1960).
17. H. Cauer, Special report to Intern. Soc. Bioclimatol. and Biometeorol., Paris, 1956; Westinghouse Electric Corp. Research Translation BL-T-8-0089-6G6-1, Bloomfield, New Jersey.
18. L. P. Herrington and K. L. Smith, *J. Ind. Hyg.* **17,** 283 (1935).
19. W. W. Hicks, *J. Franklin Inst.* **261,** 209 (1956).
20. R. Nagy, Westinghouse Electric Corp. Research Paper BL-R-8-0099-6G6-1 Bloomfield, New Jersey, 1959.
21. C. W. Hansell, "Atmospheric Ionization and Its Biological Effects." Radio Corp. of America, Princeton, New Jersey, 1960.
22. D. Silverman and I. H. Kornblueh, *EEG Clin. Neurophysiol.* **9,** 180 (1957).
23. T. A. David, J. R. Minehart, and I. H. Kornblueh, *Med. Sci.* **3,** 363 (1958).
24. J. L. Worden, Reprint of paper presented to Fed. Am. Soc. Exptl. Biol., Atlantic City, April 12, 1954 (available from author at St. Bonaventure Univ., New York).
25. J. L. Worden, *Sci. Studies (St. Bonaventure Univ.)* **15,** 71 (1953).
26. A. P. Krueger and R. F. Smith, *Roy. Soc. Health J.* **79,** 642 (1959).
27. H. C. Murphy, *Heating, Piping, Air Conditioning* **26,** 120 (1954).
28. J. C. Beckett, *Trans. AIEE (II)* **73,** 161 (1954).

CHAPTER 5

Diffusion and Stirring in the Lower Troposphere

R. C. WANTA

Allied Research Associates, Inc., Boston, Massachusetts

I. Introduction

Diffusion in meteorology is the exchange of fluid parcels, including their conservative contents and properties, between regions in the atmosphere, in apparently random motions, on a scale too small to be treated by the equations of motion (*1*). The basic assumption is that the net transport of a property in a given direction is proportional to the gradient in the same direction. Diffusion tends to make uniform the distribution of the property diffused, by reducing its gradient. The atmospheric motions diffusing such properties as momentum, heat, and water vapor have been studied extensively. These motions are in most cases of much larger scale than molecular. The exchanging parcels are called eddies, and the diffusion equation is extended by analogy to turbulent diffusion. Each application to turbulent diffusion requires observational verification. Nonrandom motions, called stirring, may lead to the increase of average gradient in a region, which is subsequently reduced by mixing or diffusion (*2, 3*).

In this chapter the details of the temperature and wind structure which form the background of atmospheric diffusion and stirring are emphasized. The concept of atmospheric stability is dwelt on because of its comparative unfamiliarity to nonmeteorologists. While quantitative employment of stability in atmospheric diffusion estimates is at present not feasible, it serves to explain qualitatively variations in the power of the atmosphere to dilute pollutants, and furthermore is an excellent parameter for categorizing meteorological statistics relating to air pollution.

II. Vertical Temperature Structure

The rate of decrease of temperature with increase in height is called the temperature lapse rate. If the rate of decrease refers to the air environment, it is called the environmental lapse rate; if to a parcel of air moving within the air environment, the process lapse rate (*1*). Since the air temperature below the stratosphere on the average decreases with height, the average environmental lapse rate in the troposphere is positive (Fig. 1).

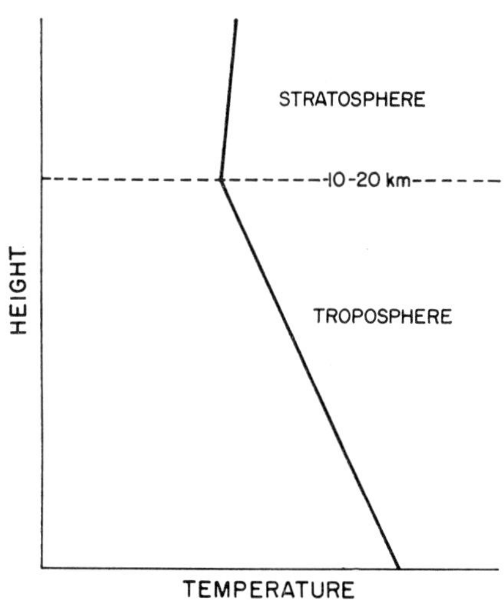

FIG. 1. Temperature change with height illustrating positive lapse in the troposphere.

Two significant lapse rates are:

(a) The adiabatic lapse rate for dry air—this is the process lapse rate of a parcel of dry air as it moves upward in a hydrostatically stable environment and expands slowly to lower environmental pressure without exchange of heat; it is also the rate of increase in temperature for a descending parcel. If the environmental lapse rate happens to be adiabatic, then such parcels at any height in that environment are in neutral equilibrium. As long as the air is unsaturated, the approximation of the adiabatic lapse rate by the dry-adiabatic lapse rate is satisfactory for most purposes. The dry-adiabatic lapse rate is 9.86°C./km. (*4*). The approximate values of 10°C./km. or 5.5°F./1000 ft. are in common use.

(b) The adiabatic lapse rate for saturated air (known as the saturation- or pseudo-adiabatic lapse rate)—this process lapse rate is smaller than the dry-adiabatic lapse rate because of the release of latent heat as the air parcel ascends and cools. The saturation-adiabatic lapse rate varies with temperature and height (*5*).

When the temperature decreases faster with height than the adiabatic rate, the lapse rate is superadiabatic. A rising air parcel, cooling at the adiabatic rate, becomes warmer and less dense than its environment and therefore buoyancy tends to accelerate it upward (Fig. 2). It is in

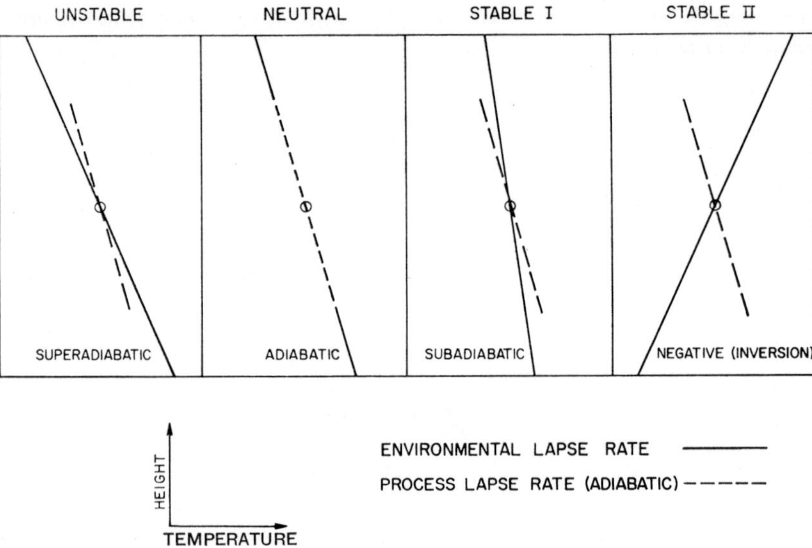

FIG. 2. Stability of an air parcel determined by environmental lapse rate.

unstable equilibrium. Vertical motions upward or downward are reinforced. When the environmental lapse rate is less than adiabatic—we might call it subadiabatic—or negative, a rising air parcel becomes cooler and more dense than its environment and tends to return to its starting point. It is in stable equilibrium. Vertical motions are resisted. Instability and stability are therefore defined with reference to a neutral equilibrium represented by the dry-adiabatic lapse rate for dry or unsaturated air, and by the saturation-adiabatic lapse rate for saturated air.

Environmental lapse rates in stable layers may have small positive (subadiabatic), zero, or negative values. The lapse rate in an isothermal layer is of course zero. If the temperature increases with height, the lapse rate is negative, and the condition is termed inversion (Fig. 2).

On a clear morning at sunrise, with light winds or calm near the surface, an inversion may extend upward from the ground to heights of 500 ft. or more, even attaining altitudes of 2500 ft. (*6*). An inversion is characterized by the heights of its base and its top, and the (negative) value of the lapse rate (Fig. 3). The inversion base may be either at the

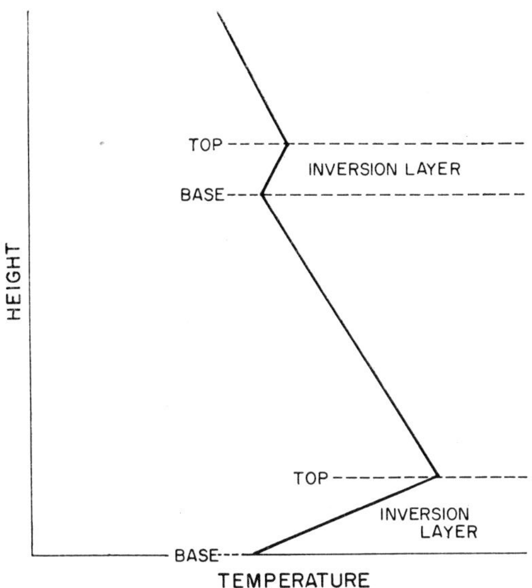

FIG. 3. Surface inversion and inversion aloft.

ground or aloft and more than one inversion can exist at the same time in the vertical structure, e.g., one between the ground and 500 ft. and another between 3000 and 3500 ft.

Temperature gradients are frequently grouped into two classes, lapse and inversion (*7*). Sometimes a third intermediate class is added (*8*). Lapse is defined to include superadiabatic and adiabatic lapse rates, and some or all subadiabatic lapse rates. Inversion is defined as treated above, although when an intermediate transitional class between lapse and inversion is added, it might include small inversions. It will be obvious therefore that lapse and inversion are not strictly synonomous with instability and stability. Standard definitions have not yet been proposed for the lapse-inversion or the lapse-transitional (neutral)-inversion classifications.

The temperature lapse rate often varies significantly with height. Above a surface inversion, the lapse rate may be zero or positive. This condition, commonly observed at night with clear skies and weak winds, is due to cooling of the ground by radiation and exchange of heat between ground and the lower air layers. Above a surface adiabatic or superadiabatic layer, the lapse rate may be zero or negative. This condition is frequently observed for an hour or two after sunrise, when solar heating of the ground and subsequent convective mixing of the layer nearest the surface have converted a deep surface inversion into a shallow layer of adiabatic or superadiabatic lapse rate with an isothermal layer or inversion above. In the coastal regions of southern California an inversion with base height, on the average, some hundreds of feet above the surface, is present as a semipermanent feature of the large-scale circulation (*9, 10*).

On a cloudless day a typical daily cycle of temperature lapse may start with an adiabatic, locally (i.e., near the surface) superadiabatic, lapse rate during the daytime due to strong solar heating, which is associated with well-developed thermal turbulence. An hour or two before sunset, the air near the ground begins to cool rapidly, the lapse rate there decreases, and finally a surface inversion develops. This inversion grows in intensity and depth during the night, reaching maximum depth near sunrise. After sunrise the ground is warmed by the sun; the inversion is gradually destroyed from the ground up in the succeeding 1–3 hr., and locally superadiabatic lapse rates again appear. This cycle may be interrupted or altered by the stirring due to strong winds aloft, or the presence of clouds or precipitation which not only weaken convection in the daytime but also prevent the formation of strong inversions during the night (*11*).

The typical cycle of temperature lapse rate described above is illustrated by the average temperature-time cross section of the lowest 5000 ft. at Oak Ridge, Tennessee during September–October, 1950 (Fig. 4). Within the dashed line the temperature lapse rate is negative. At midnight the temperature increases with height to about 800 ft., then decreases above, less rapidly below 1500 ft. The inversion grows slightly until a short time after sunrise. Beginning about 0700 hr. the inversion is destroyed from below. At 0900 hr. the temperature-height relation has three main segments, lapse below 500 ft., inversion from 500 to 900 ft., and lapse above. By 1000 hr. the breakup of the inversion is complete and the lapse rate becomes increasingly positive until early afternoon. The surface inversion forms again about 1700 hr., growing rapidly with height at first, and then more gradually for the remainder of the night.

Figure 4 represents the average of many temperature determinations over a 2-month period. Individual days will be expected to show departures. Superadiabatic lapse rates are increasingly common below 300 ft. (Fig. 5). Very near the ground, rates are observed which are higher than the adiabatic rate by a factor of 100 or more. The intense instability which might be implied by the foregoing is to a large extent compensated, e.g., by shearing circulations and other factors beyond the scope of the present discussion (*6, 12*). It should be noted that the range between extremes of positive and negative lapse rates is greatest near the ground and decreases with height. The interested reader may

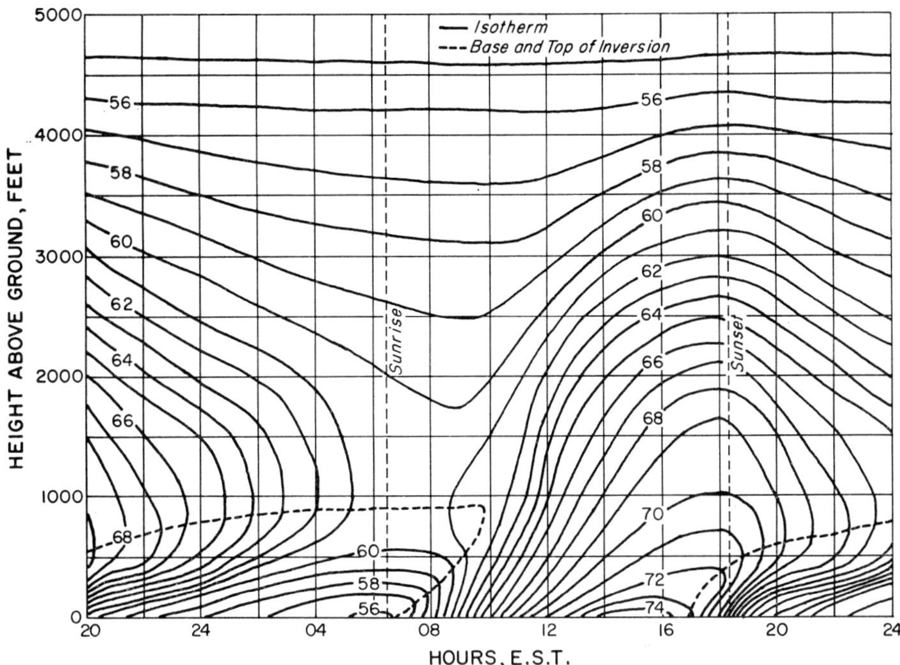

Fig. 4. Time cross section of average temperature (degrees F.) up to 5000 ft., September–October, 1950, Oak Ridge, Tennessee. [U. S. Weather Bureau, "Meteorological Survey of the Oak Ridge Area," Report ORO-99. U. S. Atomic Energy Commission, Oak Ridge, Tennessee, 1953.]

consult the following references for examples of temperature lapse rates as functions of hour, season, cloudiness, and wind speed (*6, 13–18a*).

The potential temperature, which remains constant for adiabatic processes, is defined as the temperature which a parcel of dry air would acquire when brought adiabatically from its initial pressure to a standard pressure of 1000 millibars (mb.) (*5*). Thus when the environmental lapse rate is adiabatic and passes through the 1000 mb. pressure surface, the air layer as a whole may be described as having a constant potential temperature. A parcel of air moving in such a layer would be in neutral equilibrium. If the change of potential temperature with height is negative, a parcel is in unstable equilibrium; if positive, it is in stable equilibrium. The vertical gradient of potential temperature appears as a parameter in certain formulas for effective stack height (Chapter 6).

An approximation, which is valid for many purposes, of the potential temperature θ at height z is $\theta = T + \gamma z$, where T is the absolute temperature at height z; z and dry-adiabatic lapse rate γ are in consistent

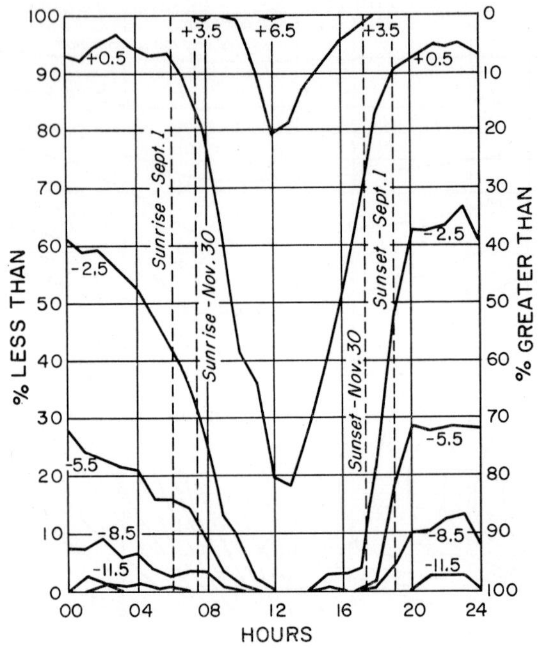

FIG. 5. Cumulative frequency of temperature lapse by hour across layer 5–183 ft., Fall, 1949–1950, Oak Ridge, Tennessee. Adiabatic lapse rate for layer is 1.0°F. [U. S Weather Bureau, "Meteorological Survey of the Oak Ridge Area," Report ORO-99. U. S. Atomic Energy Commission, Oak Ridge, Tennessee, 1953.]

units. The vertical gradient of potential temperature $d\theta/dz$ is given by $dT/dz + \gamma$. When the lapse rate is adiabatic, both dT/dz and γ have the same magnitude but opposite sign, and as already discussed the vertical gradient of potential temperature is zero. Time cross sections illustrating both temperature and potential temperature as functions of height for the same period facilitate comparison of their relative merits in portraying atmospheric stability (*13*).

For similar wind conditions, instability is more frequent and of greater degree in the daytime than at night, on clear days than on cloudy days, on cloudy nights than on clear nights, and on summer days than on winter days. Greater daily range of stability occurs in summer than in winter. A maximum in the fall occurs where the frequent presence of dry air masses enhances the daytime transmission of solar irradiation and the outgoing nocturnal radiation from the earth.

With nocturnal cooling and the formation of an inversion, fog forms in moist air cooled below its dew point. Fog within an inversion layer tends to make the layer of fog less stable (*18, 19*). A deep fog layer, however, will restrict the solar radiation reaching the ground, because of absorption in the fog layer and reflection and scattering from the fog droplets. Thereby the usual daytime increase in turbulence can be delayed or reduced; under these conditions convection does not assume its normal intensity for the time of day. During conditions of air stagnation, fog and pollutants similarly affect the receipt of solar radiation at the surface, and may cause the lowest air layers to remain stable for longer periods than otherwise—a feedback effect (*11, 20*).

During invasions of cold air masses, when on a large scale cold air is advected horizontally into new regions, an intense instability is observed because of a lag in cooling of the ground surface which leads to steepening of the lapse rate. Instability during the night is commonly due to cold advection. Strong warm advection has the opposite tendency and effect, i.e., stability. Similar conditions are observed on a smaller scale when air crosses boundaries between land and water surfaces which are at different temperatures.

The layer of vigorous mixing in the presence of cold air advection may be capped by a turbulence inversion with a base several thousand feet aloft. This inversion may be thought of as a consequence of overshooting by the rising air parcels (which are cooling at the adiabatic rate) into a more stable environment. Other inversions aloft are due to overriding of warm air masses as at frontal surfaces, subsidence (large-scale sinking) of air masses, and radiation from tops of cloud or fog (*21, 22, 23*).

The observational network of the weather services for upper air soundings is much less dense in space and time than the surface network for temperature and precipitation measurement. The details of the temperature structure of the lower troposphere and its temporal and geographic variation are subjects of considerable current interest (*6, 16, 18a, 24, 24a*).

III. Wind Structure

Air in motion very near the earth's surface is retarded by friction which varies with surface roughness. The effect of surface friction is transmitted upward, but diminishes with height. The air layer influenced by friction (called the planetary boundary layer) extends one-half to one mile above the earth's surface. In the presence of stable layers the degree of coupling between motions above and below is reduced, so that marked increases of wind speed are observed across stable layers (*21, 22*). The planetary boundary layer is deeper in unstable conditions, when the loss of momentum is more readily propagated upward, than in stable conditions. The average wind profile shows an increase of speed with height which is marked near the ground and in the planetary boundary layer. In the free atmosphere the wind continues to increase with height nearly to the tropopause. The increase of wind with height has led to the designation of a standard height for surface wind measurement (Chapter 16).

Laws to express the variation of wind speed with height near the ground are still the subject of vigorous investigation (*24, 25*). In the steady state such a law must allow for the effects of surface roughness, stability, and wind speed at the top of the layer of frictional influence. Additional complications enter if these parameters are changing in space or time. In this chapter discussion will be confined to the power law, which has been found valid for deep layers, i.e., up to several hundred or even one thousand feet, and over a wide range of temperature lapse rates. The other speed profile laws, e.g., Deacon's generalized power law, or Prandtl's logarithmic law, are mostly applicable for heights below 30 ft., except for the logarithmic law in strong winds (*12, 25*).

For a wind speed u at height z and wind speed u_1 at a reference height z_1, the power law is expressed by

$$u/u_1 = (z/z_1)^p$$

where the positive exponent p has a value between 0 and 1 (*12*). If the environmental lapse rate is adiabatic and the terrain is fairly level with low surface cover, the value of the exponent p is approximately 1/7. The exponent p increases with stability and is affected by surface roughness. Surface roughness is found to be a function of wind speed not only for water surfaces, but also for tall grass or crops (*12, 25*). An elevation of surface wind speed is noted during and following the loss of leaves from nearby deciduous trees in the autumn (*26*).

The diurnal variation of wind speed in the lowest few hundred feet exhibits a maximum speed in the early afternoon, when instability and the diffusion of momentum downward are maximum, and a minimum speed in the early morning hours (Fig. 6). Above this lowest several hundred feet there is a phase change, with a minimum speed near midday and a maximum during the night, when the coupling with the ground surface is a minimum because of stability and the consequent

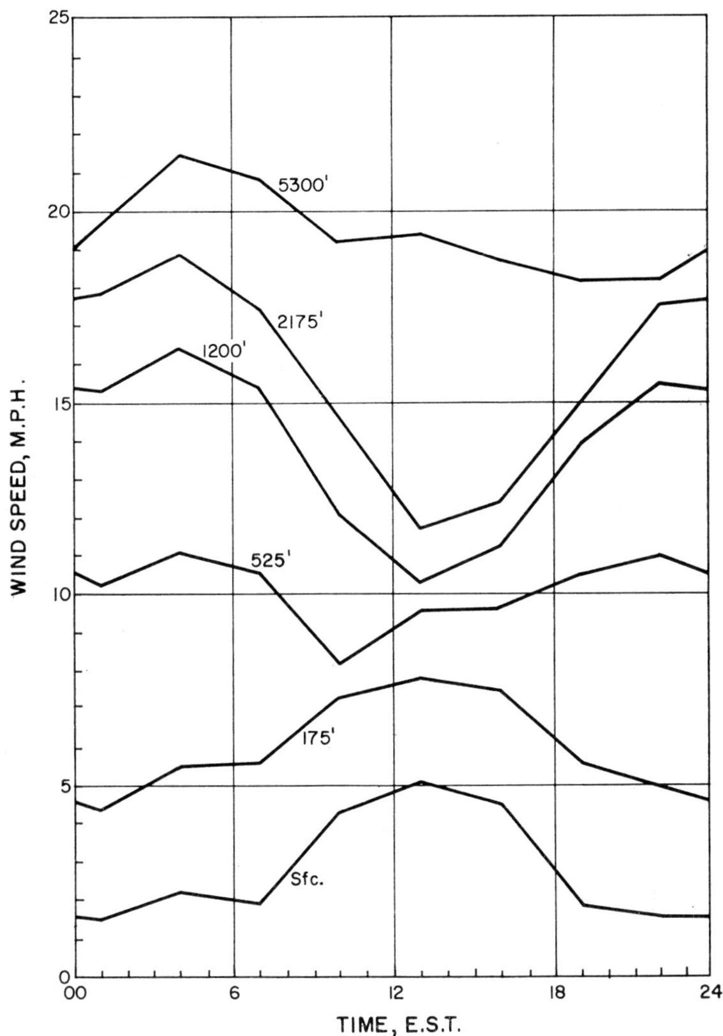

FIG. 6. Diurnal variation of average wind speed at various altitudes, Oak Ridge, Tennessee. [U. S. Weather Bureau, "Meteorological Survey of the Oak Ridge Area," Report ORO-99. U. S. Atomic Energy Commission, Oak Ridge, Tennessee, 1953.]

small vertical diffusion of momentum. In the presence of stability, energy lost by the surface air in friction is replaced slowly if at all, and a calm layer may develop even with moderate wind speeds aloft. In the daytime, with vertical coupling restored because of convection, wind speeds are higher, turbulence is greater, and convective motions enhance the vertical exchange of air properties (Fig. 7). The typical cycle of wind speed described above is further illustrated by the average speed-time cross section of the lowest 5000 ft. at Oak Ridge, Tennessee, during September–October, 1950 (Fig. 8). The corresponding temperature-time cross section appears in Fig. 4.

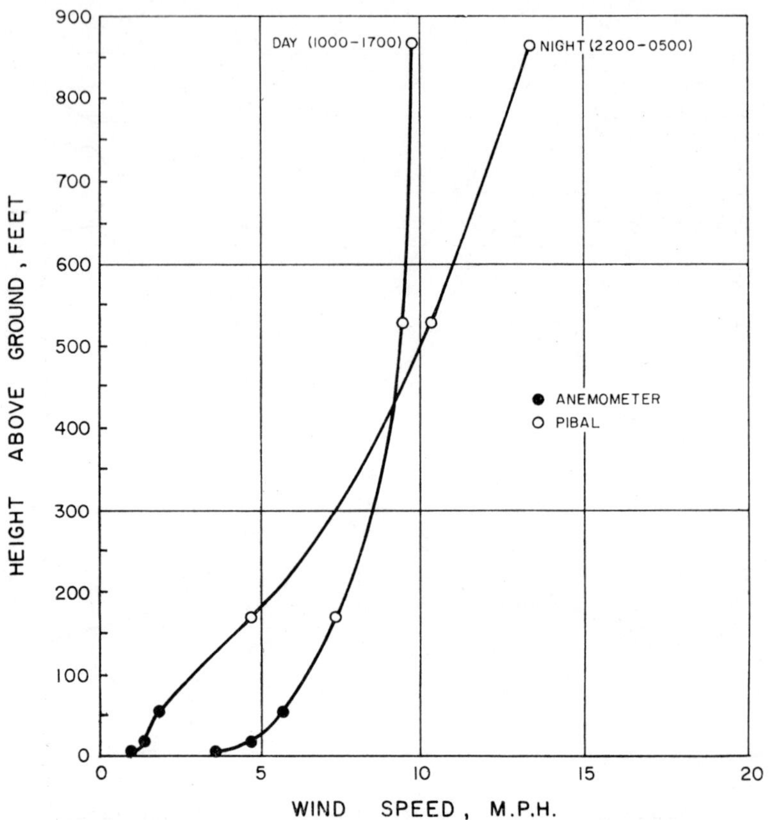

FIG. 7. Profiles of average wind speed, day and night, Oak Ridge, Tennessee. [U. S. Weather Bureau, "Meteorological Survey of the Oak Ridge Area," Report ORO-99. U. S. Atomic Energy Commission, Oak Ridge, Tennessee, 1953.]

The wind speed is generally higher in winter than in summer, but prolonged stagnation is possible in winter, especially in basins or bowls rimmed by high ground. There is a tendency toward maximum wind speeds in the spring.

The shearing stress due to friction at the surface and between layers of air, when added to the other (vector) forces which determine the wind, leads to a change of direction with height. The frictionless surface wind for straight, parallel isobars, i.e., the conceptual "geostrophic"

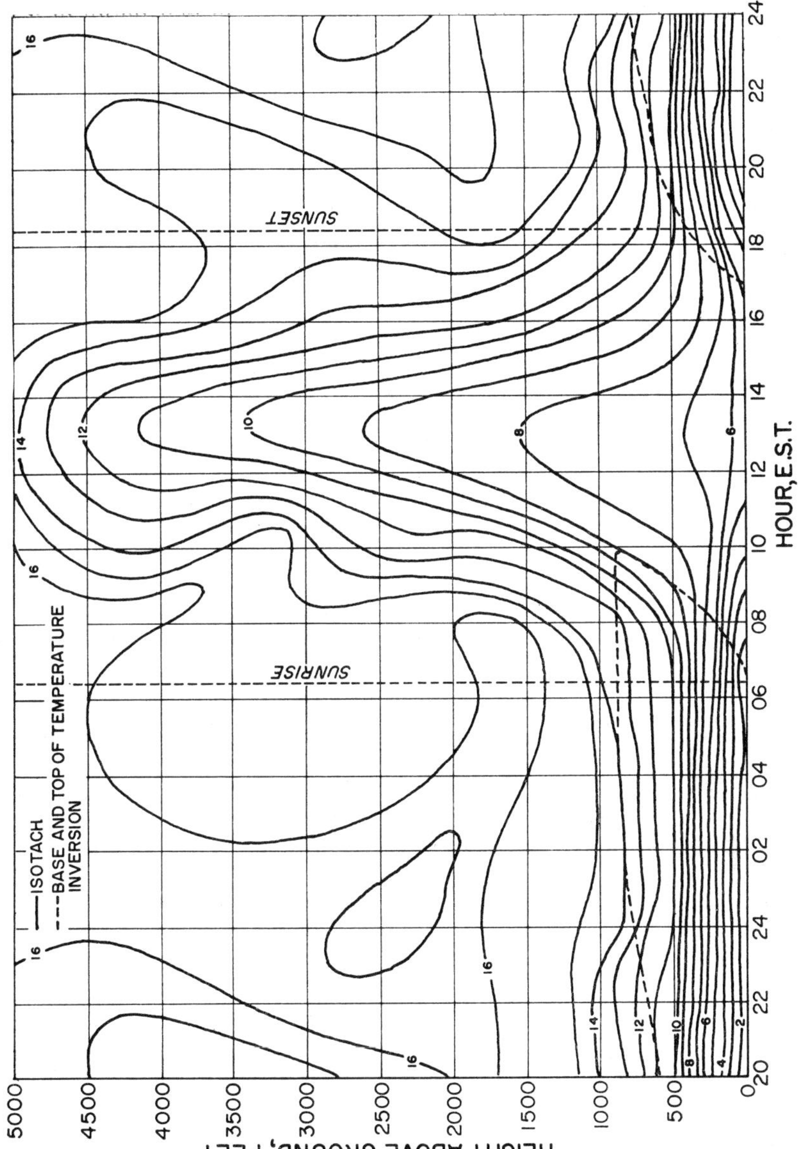

FIG. 8. Time cross section of average wind speed (m.p.h.) up to 5000 ft., September–October, 1950, Oak Ridge, Tennessee. [U. S. Weather Bureau, "Meteorological Survey of the Oak Ridge Area," Report ORO-99, U. S. Atomic Energy Commission, Oak Ridge, Tennessee, 1953.]

wind, is determined by the balance between the steady pressure gradient and the Coriolis force arising from the earth's rotation, and blows in a direction parallel to the isobars with a strength inversely proportional to the isobar spacing. Another conceptual wind, the gradient wind, takes account of curvature of isobars. The geostrophic or gradient wind is expected to be attained at the top of the friction layer (*4, 12, 21*). The influence of friction is to deflect the underlying surface current across the isobars toward low pressure (Fig. 9). The consequent clock-

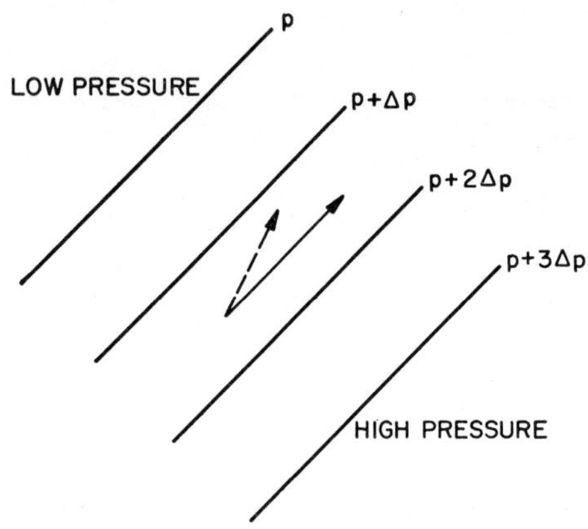

FIG. 9. Effect of surface friction on horizontal wind direction. Geostrophic wind, solid arrow; surface wind, broken arrow; isobars, solid line.

wise variation of wind direction with height in the layer of frictional influence is termed veering. In balance are the pressure gradient force, the Coriolis force, the frictional force from below, and the drag force from above (*4*).

The change of direction with height in the lowest 300 ft. is negligible in strong winds or in the absence of local topographical influences (*25*). However, in light to moderate winds, under about 13 m.p.h., changes due to surface friction, distortion of constant pressure surfaces by local temperature influences, etc. may affect wind direction appreciably. Moreover, the veering with height owing to friction is supplemented in the presence of warm air advection, and opposed in cold air advection. Typical values of the angle between surface and geostrophic wind because of friction are 5–15° over the ocean and 25–45° over land.

The effect of surface friction on the wind vector may be estimated, for light speeds over rough terrain, as reducing the speed to as low as 40% of the gradient speed, at an angle of 45° from the isobars, while over water the corresponding values would be 67% and 30° (*22*).

Mechanical turbulence is caused principally by surface friction. The greater the wind speed or the surface friction, the greater the mechanical turbulence and hence the turbulent exchange of air properties. This accounts for the tendency of strong winds to neutralize a pre-existing lapse rate. Moreover, the vertical growth of an inversion requires at least some wind near the ground, so that the cooling of the ground surface can be propagated upward by diffusion. Enhanced turbulent exchange of air properties implies enhanced diffusion of air pollution. The decrease of mechanical turbulence with altitude above the surface serves to explain the decrease in the value of diffusion coefficients with height (Chapter 6).

When coupling between air layers is reduced in a nocturnal inversion, the wind above may accelerate, and speeds approaching twice that expected from the geostrophic wind are observed (*27*). Under this low-level "jet," the wind shear may become high enough locally, for example, in the vicinity of surface obstacles such as low hills, to produce internal mechanical turbulence and mixing with the layers below (*28*).

The rate of change of wind in the vertical is generally more marked than in the horizontal, with the possible exception of transitory conditions associated with squall lines, thunderstorms, fronts, and sea or valley breezes. As in the case of the temperature structure, the details of the wind structure in the lower troposphere are under active investigation (*18a, 24, 25, 29*).

The most important mixing process in the atmosphere is called eddy diffusion and involves scales of length considerably larger than that of the molecular free path. The contribution of molecular diffusion is considered significant only under certain special conditions, such as extreme stability. Because of their vital role in mixing processes in the atmosphere, the spectral distribution of the energies of the many sizes of eddies which can occur concurrently is under intensive investigation (*24, 30, 31*). The presence of eddies is indicated by the fluctuations evident in continuous records of wind direction and speed, and on a larger scale by the changes of wind from day to day.

Eddy or turbulent diffusion is most efficient when the length scale of the eddy is similar to that of the body of polluted air being diluted. This is readily visualized by considering that much smaller eddies would be effective in diluting the parcel only on its margins, whereas much larger eddies would move the body of polluted air as a whole. Dilution by the atmosphere is thus a combination of diffusive mixing proportional to the gradient of the property being diluted, and of stirring which stretches and distorts the diluting body, thereby increasing its surface area and making diffusion by small eddies more effective. Eddy diffusion causes a parcel of polluted air to occupy larger and larger volume; i.e., the pollutant concentration decreases with time.

Atmospheric eddies are largely random. Those generated by air flow past a chimney or building, however, can be properly visualized as highly organized vortices. The presence of eddies implies turbulence and gustiness. Qualitatively the degree of turbulence may be estimated

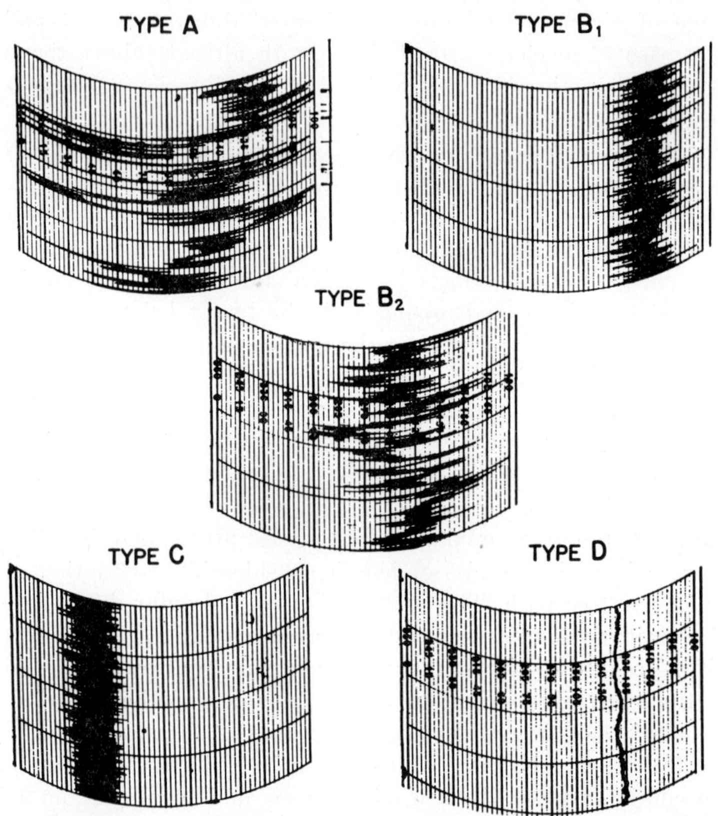

FIG. 10. Classification of gustiness types based upon the wind direction fluctuations at 355 ft. elevation. [M. E. Smith, *Meteorol. Monographs* **1,** 50 (1951); I. A. Singer and M. E. Smith, *J. Meteorol.* **10,** 121 (1953).]

from an examination of fluctuations evident in continuous measurements of wind, temperature, vapor pressure, etc., made with fast-responding sensors. Eddies or "gustiness types" have been classified on the basis of their effect on wind direction fluctuation (Fig. 10).

Atmospheric turbulence or eddies may be classified as mechanical or thermal as they are produced primarily by shearing stress or by convection. While both types are often present in combination, one or the other may dominate under particular meteorological conditions. Mechanical eddies, with typical wind fluctuation periods of the order of seconds, prevail on windy nights with neutral (i.e., neither warm nor cold) advection; whereas thermal eddies, with typical wind fluctuation periods of the order of minutes, prevail on sunny days with light winds.

Thermal eddies increase with uneven heating or with otherwise steepening lapse rate, for example, in cold advection. Thermal turbulence produced by solar heating will vary with that which varies heating, viz., latitude, season, altitude, cloud, fog or pollutant obscuration, and properties of the earth's surface such as absorptivity, conductivity, etc. It also varies with the stability condition of the atmosphere and the forces tending to maintain that stability. It is at a maximum on a clear sunny day in the early afternoon, and at a minimum on a clear winter day in the very early morning.

In summary, turbulence or turbulent energy, and hence the atmosphere's power to dilute pollutants, increases with increase of wind shear (and wind speed), surface roughness, and instability (*32*). Turbulent fluctuations in stable air are mainly of high frequency, with typical periods of the order of seconds (mechanical turbulence). In unstable air, lower frequency fluctuations, with periods of the order of minutes (thermal turbulence), also appear. It may be added that the horizontal component of turbulence exceeds the vertical component; this excess increases when averages are taken over greater times or larger areas. The typical periods or length scales of the vertical component of turbulence lengthen with increasing height above ground.

IV. Topographic Effects

Because of the diversity of most natural terrain, local flow patterns which deviate from the regional flow often appear, especially near shore lines or over uneven ground. The result may be remarkable changes of wind direction and speed with height or lateral distance. In such terrain, the air pollution investigator may find detailed study of the local flow pattern quite necessary.

Topography modifies the temperature and wind, and their profiles, because of the combined effects of surface friction, radiation, and drainage. The radiative and thermal properties of surface features influence the heating and cooling of the ground surface. Thermal effects due to outgoing radiation are enhanced at high altitudes where the absorbing mass of air overhead is reduced. Temperature lapse rates and wind profiles over built-up areas are observed to differ markedly from those in open country (*16, 33*). For example, instability may be observed to a height of three times the roof heights in otherwise stable air, i.e., away from the built-up area.

Even the heat exchange accompanying freezing, melting, condensation, and evaporation at the ground surface will affect the temperature profile in the lowest layers. Such processes are often not uniformly distributed over an area. For example, evaporation after a heavy rain will have a cooling effect that may significantly change the stability of the lowest layers locally in the area of heavy rainfall.

Sea-land breezes and mountain-valley winds are examples of local winds which deviate from the prevailing wind (*21, 22*). The sea breeze is caused by solar heating of the land near a coast at a faster rate than the water. It blows from the sea toward the land, generally beginning in the forenoon and persisting until about sunset. Above the landward moving air there is a return flow from land toward sea. At night a corresponding but often less developed circulation in the opposite direction, the land breeze, occurs. Because sea-land breezes are additive to the large-scale circulation, they are most evident on sunny days when the wind would otherwise be light. The depth of the sea breeze is usually less than 2000 ft. while the depth of the land breeze may be only a few hundred feet. Significantly, the boundary region of the sea breeze sometimes may remain nearly stationary or oscillate back and forth for periods up to several hours, and thus can be the site of nearly calm conditions or varying winds, and a slow net transport of air pollutants (*34*). In middle latitudes, sea breezes are most frequent in late spring, summer, and early fall; in the tropics they may occur year-round.

Differential heating also causes mountain-valley winds (*21, 22*). Upslope and up-valley winds develop in uneven terrain on sunny days when the general air movement is weak. At night, the radiative cooling of the elevated ground leads to downward moving currents owing to differences in air density, in the form of down-slope and down-valley winds. Pronounced stability may occur above such cold drainage currents. Changes in direction of the slope winds generally precede changes of the wind direction in the valley flanked by these slopes. The valley circulation tends to disappear near the top of the bordering ridges. Like the sea-land breezes, mountain-valley winds are also additive to the prevailing circulation, and show up best when the latter is weak. In a complex valley several valley circulations may add to each other. In windy seasons the valley circulation may be observed only occasionally, whereas with weak winds it appears consistently in irregular topography.

A current of air flowing in a direction other than parallel to a valley may suffer channeling, i.e., change of direction toward that of the valley axis (*17*). When a body of air is forced over a pass or ridge, constriction of the volume leads to increase of wind speed in the passes. Conversely, in crossing a valley a body of air diverges and the wind speed decreases. Troughs in pressure patterns appear on the lee side of mountain ranges, accompanied by shifts in wind direction which deviate from the prevailing current. The effect is most marked when the impinging air current is approximately normal to the ridge line. Deviations in wind may also arise from nonuniformity in the pressure-change field, as during the intensification of a storm.

The shielding effect of valley sides may prevent or limit the action of the prevailing regional wind, with resulting lower wind speeds at the surface inside the valley than outside. An exception is the strong down-valley (or canyon) wind which drains a large cool pool of air at higher surface elevations. Comparatively little exchange of air between a valley and the air outside may take place over long periods. An example of both processes is found in the occasional wintertime stagnation of air in the upper Snake and Columbia River valleys, while simultaneously strong destructive winds are observed in the narrow gorges through which the Columbia River drains miles downstream. Differential heating of one side of a valley with respect to the opposite side produces a cross-sectional circulation, with ascending flow on the heated slope. Such a circulation was identified in the Columbia River valley below the smelters at Trail, British Columbia (*35*).

V. Large-Scale Wind and Temperature

Most changes in wind, stability, precipitation, and other weather elements stem from the following circulations:

(1) Primary, represented by the semipermanent high and low pressure areas.

(2) Secondary, represented by the migratory high and low pressure areas seen on the daily weather map.

(3) Small-scale, represented by sea-land breezes, mountain-valley winds, thunderstorms, etc.

The semipermanent subsidence inversion on the lower California coast is an aspect of a primary circulation which has a direct and significant effect on air pollution. Because diffusion through an inversion is extremely slow, the California subsidence inversion acts as a lid on the air below. An example of secondary circulation is large-scale warm and cold air advection, which accompanies the rapid movement of tropical and polar air masses from source regions where they have acquired their characteristic thermodynamic properties. Large-scale convergence and instability is evidenced by the curvature of isobars or contours on upper air charts. Anticyclonic curvature (concave toward high pressure) is associated with greater divergence and stability than cyclonic curvature (concave toward low pressure). When a migratory anticyclone stagnates, i.e., a moving high pressure area ceases moving, a subsidence inversion will develop, usually at intermediate heights, owing to the slow sinking and divergence of the air mass. A layer of haze and smoke several thousand feet deep can develop under an inversion of this type. A nocturnal inversion may form below the subsidence inversion (*34*).

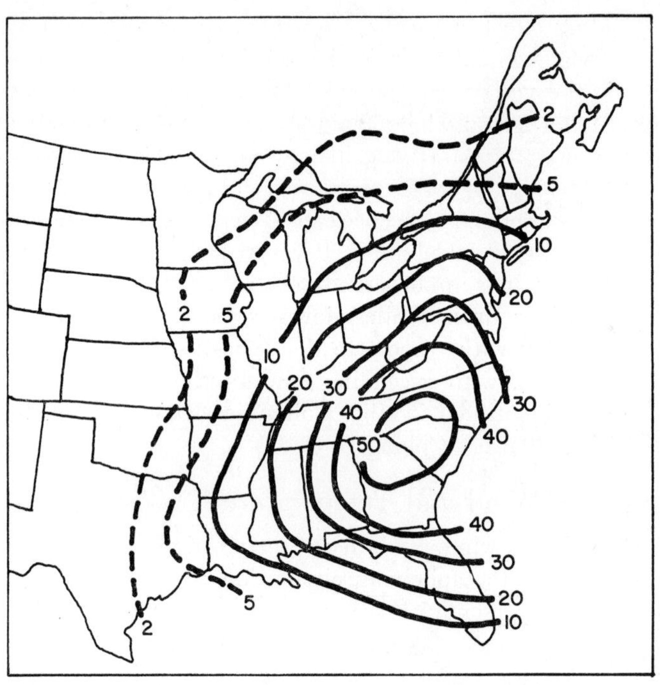

Fig. 11. Number of periods with low wind speed for 4 or more successive days, eastern United States, 1936–1956. [American Industrial Hygiene Association, "Air Pollution Manual. Part I: Evaluation." Am. Ind. Hyg. Assoc., Detroit, Michigan, 1960 (after J. Korshover, "Synoptic Climatology of Stagnating Anticyclones East of the Rocky Mountains in the United States for the Period 1939–1956," Report SEC TR-A60-7. Robert A. Taft Sanitary Engineering Center, Cincinnati, Ohio, 1960).]

The global wind field is interrelated with the global temperature field; likewise, smaller-scale perturbations of the global wind field are conditioned by temperature perturbations. Temperature gradients, both horizontal and vertical, increase during the winter and early spring, and so does the wind. This seasonal relation holds best in temperate and polar latitudes, but not as well in tropical latitudes where the annual variation is small. In the transitional seasons, fall and spring, and occasionally even in winter, prolonged periods of slight wind—lasting days at a time—occur. This phenomenon is observed over large land masses. (*11*). In the United States, east of the Rockies, the frequency of such periods is greatest during the fall, with a secondary maximum in the spring (*36, 37*). On an annual basis, maximum frequency of stagnation for 4 days or more is observed in the Southeast (Fig. 11). The prolonged period of stagnation represents an important departure from the wind condition (moderate to strong and reasonably steady in direction) for which working diffusion formulas are apt. In fact the usual idea of "downwind" may fail under these circumstances, especially in uneven topography with conflicting wind currents, when the same point source may cause simultaneous fumigations in all directions to several miles (*38*).

The build-up and persistence of high concentrations of pollutants near the ground in prolonged, near calm, stable conditions during periods of large-scale atmospheric stagnation is responsible for most of the well-known pollution cases (*11, 32*). The simultaneous occurrence of light and variable winds, great stability, and often fog in the surface layer is not unusual. However, persistence of such conditions over periods of several days is uncommon. During several decades preceding 1952 only one other fog in the London area was found comparable to that of December, 1952 (*39*). With respect to the Meuse Valley, it was found that during a 30-year period, fogs lasting more than 3 days occurred only five times in the district. A stagnation forecast service was developed for use in air pollution control in east Tennessee (*38*); a similar service for the whole eastern United States is now operational (*40, 40a*).

VI. Some Applications to Air Pollution Problems

Apart from the settling of sufficiently large particulate matter, a pollutant moves with its air environment. The basic importance of transport is signified by the attention that must be paid to the wind direction in treating discrete sources of air pollution. For a pollutant source emitting continuously, the pollutant will be more or less diluted along the direction of transport as the wind speed is high or low, simply because of "stretching" (dilatation), even with no changes in wind direction. The actual direction of transport is determined not only by the large-scale circulation, e.g., as represented on the surface weather chart, but also by such influences as the sea-land breezes, mountain-valley winds, local surface features including structures, surface covers of various types, heat sources and sinks, and also by parcels or masses of air of differing densities.

The locus of the successive positions of a parcel of air is called its trajectory. The direction of air flow shown by a synoptic weather chart for a particular time corresponds to streamlines. Unless a flow is steady a trajectory differs from a streamline. Care must be used in deducing information about trajectories from ordinary weather charts, just as care must be exercised in extrapolating the wind measurement at a point to another place and time, even nearby. The sinuous plume from a chimney is an example of neither a streamline nor a trajectory, but approximates a streak line, i.e., the locus of end points of the trajectories of particles which have passed through the same point fixed in space (*41*).

Trajectory analysis is useful when the wind changes with place and time due to changing pressure distributions or topography. Its accuracy is heavily dependent upon the accuracy and representativeness of local wind data. Sometimes a few wind observations may lead to valid and practical inferences. Trajectories have been computed for the Los Angeles basin from the measurements of a 58-station network (*42*). An example of the construction of trajectories is illustrated here (Fig. 12). The

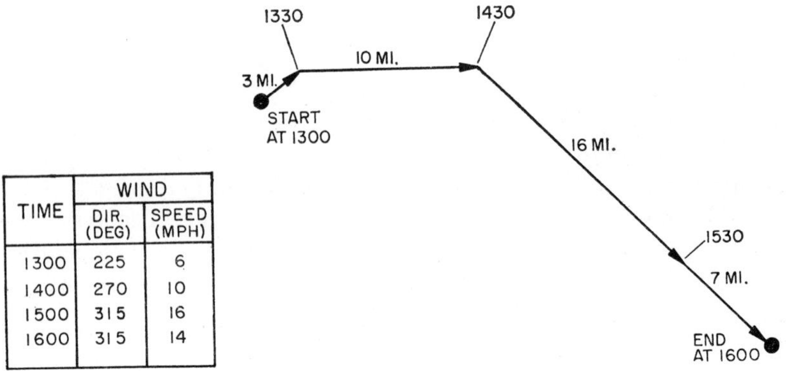

TIME	WIND DIR. (DEG)	WIND SPEED (MPH)
1300	225	6
1400	270	10
1500	315	16
1600	315	14

FIG. 12. Construction of air trajectory.

simplifying assumption of a wind unvarying with height in either direction or speed from its geostrophic value or from the value measured near ground level is a common feature of trajectory analysis.

The difference between trajectory and streak line shows up in the analysis of travel of pollutants within and away from large cities. We get information on the streak line by computing trajectories originating from the same point or sub-area at small intervals of time. Unfortunately, the details of the three-dimensional flow are often anything but simple, and even given a fairly dense network of, for example, surface wind stations, complete reliance cannot be placed on the resulting paths.

The analogy between diffusion of momentum and diffusion of a pollutant has useful application. Any of the situations previously described in which vertical flux of momentum varies may be interpreted in first approximation to apply similarly for the vertical flux of air pollutants. The greater the turbulence, the greater the diffusion. For example, cold air advection is associated with large positive lapse rates and rapid mixing upward of surface pollution; the opposites hold for warm advection. Also, for constant wind speed, the lapse rate is a good index of the capacity of the atmosphere to diffuse pollutants.

Measurements show that in continental areas the temperature profile in the lower layers of air is most frequently superadiabatic by day and isothermal or inverted by night. The diffusion of pollutants is so different in unstable and stable conditions that an average lapse rate for a period of as long as a day is generally not useful. Diffusion of pollutants is at a maximum on sunny, windy days and at a minimum on clear, calm nights.

In a ground-based stable layer, for example, in ground-based isothermal or inversion layers, diffusion of pollutants is relatively slow compared to that in an adiabiatic or unstable layer, other conditions being equal. Negative buoyancy leads to suppression or inhibition of vertical motions and pollutants diffuse slowly, and mainly horizontally. The spread of a pollutant, at a fixed distance from the source, is thus much smaller at night than in the daytime. Since, under these conditions, momentum lost in surface friction is not readily replaced by exchange with the faster moving air layers above, the wind speed decreases and the direction is more likely to be altered by density currents. Layers of pollutants aloft may briefly be mixed downward if the wind speed aloft increases and momentum and heat are mixed downward with consequent weakening of the inversion. The surface thermograph record is a useful indicator of this phenomenon (*34*). If the increase of speed aloft is only transient, then the former degree of stability tends to be re-established, and the pollutant brought down earlier will diffuse in the lower layer at the slow rate characteristic of stable air. The action suggests a flip-flop or multi-vibrator electronic circuit.

The appearance on stable mornings in and near cities, or even near small pollution sources, of lamina of smoke at many levels should be noted. Pollutants rise to an equilibrium level and then remain in lamina. The plume of pollutant from a stack or from a hot source at the surface in very stable air, reaching miles downwind, but remaining compact aloft during the night, will mix downward usually 1–3 hr. after sunrise, with the inversion breakup. The angular subtense of the fumigated area at a given distance may be less than a fraction of a degree (*34*).

It is a popular misconception that a valley or a bowl is a necessary adjunct to pollution build-up. Unfavorable topography is not a necessary condition for extreme pollutant concentrations provided the source strength is great enough compared with the diffusion rate. A city on a plain has a characteristic surface roughness greater than its immediate environment. The city is a relatively better sink for kinetic energy, and hence a favorable location for the formation of a stagnant pool of air.

Qualitative description of atmospheric processes affecting pollutant dilution is comparatively easy, but analytical expressions come hard. However, in relation to other uncertainties affecting any real air pollution problem, meteorological knowledge is often adequate. For example, consideration of only mean air flow jointly with stability may suffice in a particular problem of urban siting and zoning. The relative importance of the elements of weather, singly and in combinations, varies with the problem at hand. It should therefore be anticipated that the utility of measurements of given weather elements will change as the purpose for which they are used, the size of the area under consideration, or the period of interest, changes (*34*).

Some degree of practical success is realized in many air pollution problems by considering the continuously varying local weather as a succession of discrete stages, e.g., nocturnal inversion, morning inversion breakup, daytime lapse, and nocturnal inversion, etc., in which, from time to time, the sequence is interrupted by frontal passages, rapid pressure falls, etc. Each stage is defined by values of the weather elements for periods up to a few hours. Some understanding of typical diurnal variation of these elements, e.g., wind and temperature lapse rate, given approximately constant large-scale conditions, will serve to extend the valid time period for this point of view. (*18a*). Textbooks on physical climatology should be consulted (*43*).

VII. Nonturbulent Dispersal

A. Gravitational Fall of Particles; Fallout

Atmospheric diffusion does not remove pollutants but only dilutes them. If most of the pollutants were not eventually removed by other processes, the surface air would become intolerable. Discussion of chemical interactions among pollutants in the air, between pollutants and other constituents of the air, and adsorptive and contact removal of pollutants at the surface may be found elsewhere in this book.

Particulate pollutants are effectively removed from the atmosphere by gravitational settling if the particle size is sufficiently large (Fig. 13). For sizes less than a few tens of microns, the falling speed is negligible in comparison with atmospheric eddy velocities. The small particles are removed by impaction with surface cover and by aggregation to form larger particles which are removed by settling or washout. The growth of particles by coagulation or by attachment of water vapor molecules, which affects their falling speeds, is beyond the present scope, as is the effect of electrostatic forces (*43a, 43b, 43c*).

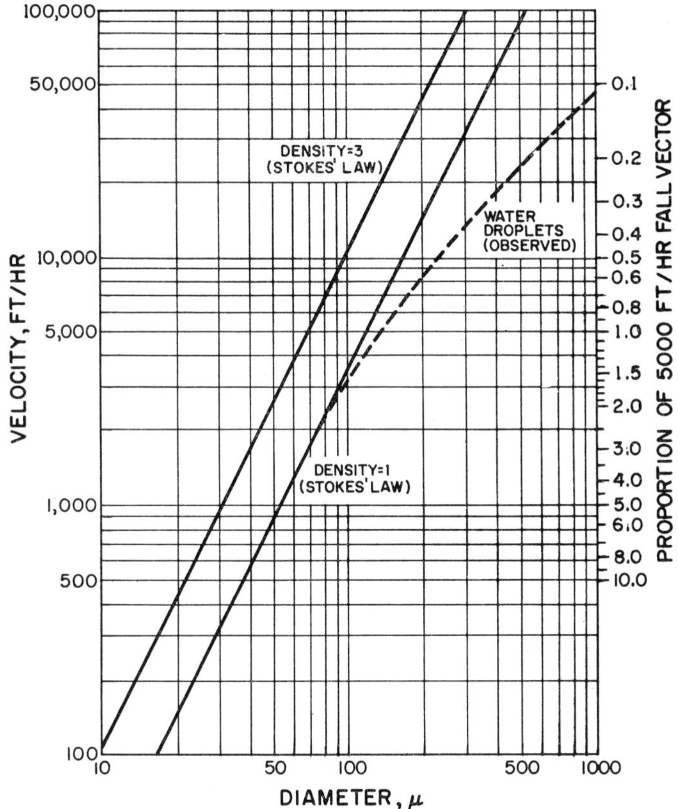

FIG. 13. Fall speed vs. size and density of spherical particles. [U. S. Weather Bureau, "Meteorology and Atomic Energy," Report AECU-3066. U. S. Atomic Energy Commission, Washington, D. C., 1955.]

The calculation of gravitational settlement of particulates is best illustrated by the case of "close-in" fallout from a nuclear burst. For simplicity, the fallout pattern on the ground is considered only a function of the height and horizontal dimensions of the particle cloud, the particle-size distribution within the cloud, and the wind structure between the cloud top and the ground (*17*). Given a representative wind structure, a graphical plot of the fallout area for two limiting sizes of spherical particles can be constructed, and the area can be arbitrarily enlarged to account for lateral growth by diffusion (Fig. 14). In practice, the wind may be averaged within 5000-ft. layers, and a vector diagram constructed first for a particle with falling speed 5000 ft./hr. ($OABC$). For this rate of fall, the falling speed and horizontal distance

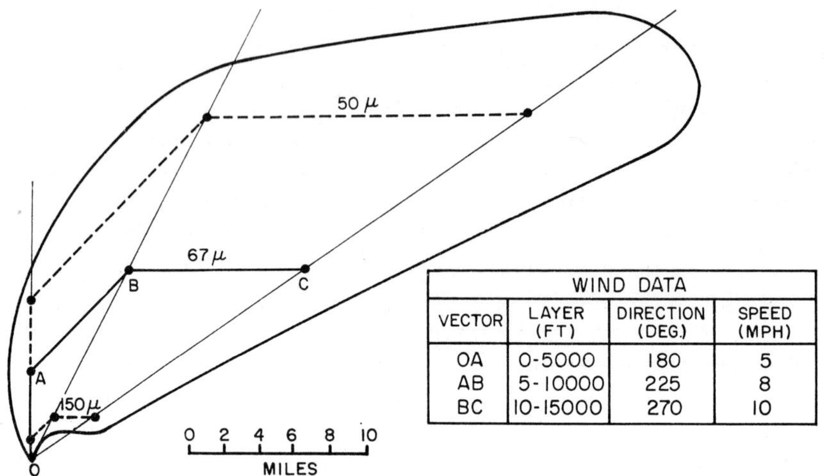

FIG. 14. Construction of fallout area.

scales are identical. Given the limiting particle sizes and their density, the ratios of the assumed fall rate and the limiting fall rates can be read from the previous figure (e.g., a density of 3 and limiting sizes of 50 and 150 μ), and the radius vectors OA, OB, . . . increased or decreased accordingly. The resulting area is increased on the sides and at the far end by 1 mi. for each 7 mi. distance from the point of particulate matter release (i.e., bomb burst), as a rough allowance for the spread due to wind uncertainties and to atmospheric diffusion.

While this example pertains to a cloud top of 15,000 ft., the procedure may be extended or abridged for other cloud top heights and modified for the case of plumes from stacks. If the surface elevation is above sea level, it is convenient to average the wind in the lowest layer from the surface to the first integral multiple of 5000 ft. above sea level, reduce the length of the first vector only, in proportion to the reduction in the thickness of this first layer, and proceed as above for the rest of the fallout diagram. While the order of effect of the winds on the falling particle is BC, AB, OA, construction of the equivalent vector diagram as shown allows specification of the cloud top height after the fallout pattern is drawn.

The preceding discussion of small-scale circulations and variations of wind makes it obvious that some sort of adjustment of the wind structure to correspond to conditions at the point and time of particulate matter release may prove necessary, especially for that portion of the cloud in the lower troposphere subject to the vagaries of surface influences.

B. Meteorological Precipitation

The most effective scavenger of the atmosphere is precipitation. Meteorological precipitation includes not only rain and drizzle, but snow and other forms of water vapor in the solid phase. While basic details of the precipitation process remain obscure, precipitation usually follows sufficient lifting of moist air. Lifting may take place when air flows over a ridge or mountain, when it is forced upward by a wedge of denser air, or in convection currents.

The larger particles in the air are readily removed by falling raindrops (*11*). The smaller particles may be accumulated in rain drops. This process is termed rainout rather than washout. The ocean is also effective in eliminating fine particulates. It has been reported that air pollutants may alter precipitation-forming processes (*44*). The infrequency of rain in southern California may be seen as contributory to the extended periods of high pollution levels which can occur.

While gravitational settling and impaction tap only the particles which are at the moment in the lowest air layers, precipitation scavenges from an air column which extends to the height from which it fell. Precipitation scavenges particulate material directly because of particle inertia, interception, electrostatic attraction, and random molecular (Brownian) motion, and indirectly because of prior incorporation of particles in cloud droplets (*17, 43a*). The efficiency of rain scavenging by particle inertia and interception has been treated theoretically as a function of the size of the rain drop, size of the particle, and their respective fall velocities and densities (*43a, 43b, 43c*). In application of this theory, an empirically determined distribution of rain drop sizes as a function of rainfall rate is used. A typical computation is that a uniform rain falling at the rate of 1 mm. per hour for 15 min. will scavenge 28% of the 10 μ particles from the air volume traversed by the rain (*43a*). Scavenging efficiency decreases with particle size and becomes negligible for particles 2 μ and smaller.

The drop size of drizzle ranges from about 50 up to 400 μ, while rain drops range in size up to several thousand microns (*17*). The fall rate diagram for density 1 (Fig. 13), as modified for the larger drops, can be used to construct the appropriate fallout diagram. Thus the fallout diagram in the example of the preceding section would be considerably smaller in the case of rain. A steady rain will increase the amount of particulate material brought to the ground near the source, and decrease the amount that would otherwise come down at greater distances from the source.

Experimental data on diffusion of pollutants during precipitation is scarce. The occurrence of ground fumigations from elevated sources has been observed during precipitation, and attributed either to the presence of an inversion aloft at a warm front surface or in showery precipitation to transport by descending currents of air (*35*).

VIII. On Mathematical Models of Diffusion

Air pollution in urban areas owes its complexity to the great number of sources and their variability as to type of pollutant, source strength, height, relative proximity, local geometry, conditions of emission, and the influence of topographic features including roughness and thermal properties of the surface. Moreover, the rate of emission of some pollutants, e.g., those attributable to space heating, is partly a function of meteorological conditions.

Theoretical reasoning and an admixture of empiricism have led to the development of several mathematical models of atmospheric diffusion, which have been adapted into formulas to apply to instantaneous or continuous emission of pollutants from idealized point, line, or area sources (*12, 17, 24, 32, 45, 46*). Point and line sources are discussed in Chapter 6. An entire city is an example of an area source. Preliminary attempts to adapt diffusion formulas to the city-wide area source have divided the city area into a number of sub-areas, each being assigned an appropriate source height and strength and then treated as a point source. A degree of success has been realized in comparing pollution levels computed by means of such models with observed pollution levels on hourly, daily, and monthly bases (*46a, 46b*).

The simplest model of area source diffusion consists of a box with base at the ground, top at an assumed upper limit of vertical mixing, and sides positioned to cover a city as an area source. Mixing is supposed to be complete throughout the box, and the wind passes through the sides. The predicted concentrations of pollutants are, for a given box size, a function only of the respective emission rates for individual pollutants and a suitable average wind speed. Admittedly crude, this model is defensible on the grounds of simplicity, flexibility, the magnitudes of errors in estimating source strengths, and the possibility of keying the model to pollutants for which both the emission rates and surface concentrations are measurable over the projected lower surface of the box.

If a city of source strength Q $[MT^{-1}L^{-2}]$ consists of a square with side S $[L]$, with the upper limit of mixing being h $[L]$, and the average wind speed being $\bar{u}$ $[LT^{-1}]$ parallel to a side, then it has been shown (*46c*) that the equilibrium concentration X_e $[ML^{-3}]$ is given by $QS/\bar{u}h$, which would be 90% attained in a time t $[T]$ given by 2.3 $S/\bar{u}$. Any consistent set of dimensional units may be used. In the case of particulate material with a settling speed V_g $[LT^{-1}]$, the equilibrium concentration X_e given by Q/V_g would be 90% attained in a time t given by 2.3 h/V_g. In the case of washout by rain when the fraction of pollutant removed per unit time is Λ $[T^{-1}]$, the equilibrium concentration given by $Q/\Lambda h$ would be 90% attained in a time t given by $2.3/\Lambda$. It should be noted that the size of the city affects the equilibrium concentration and the accumulation time only in the first case.

Another model which takes account of time variations of the wind utilizes trajectories computed for each of a number of sub-areas constituting the total source area. Each pollutant sub-cloud, initially the size of the sub-area source, grows by diffusion at some selected rate, and thus the average concentration within each sub-cloud decreases as the cloud moves away from the point of origin (*47*). For simplicity pollutant emission from each sub-area is sometimes considered to originate at a point or along a line inside the sub-area, and thus diffusion may be computed by the methods discussed in Chapter 6. The contribution of pollutant from each sub-area must be added to yield mean concentration of pollutant as a function of position and time over the whole area. Modern computing machines facilitate this kind of approach to area pollution problems.

Several outlines of the historical development of diffusion formulas have been published (*17, 32*). Deficiencies in the working formulas are generally recognized. For example, direct energy-supply concepts have not yet been incorporated, in spite of the intimate connection between turbulent energy and diffusion. There is no general agreement on the best theory among those now available. It seems that each formulation has optimum applicability for particular problems and sets of meteorological conditions, and much research remains to be done.

In applications of diffusion theory to practical problems it would be desirable to have a means of selecting diffusion rates solely on the basis of local measurements of weather elements such as wind, temperature, their vertical profiles, and a characterization of the terrain. But much empiricism and judgment enters today into the selection of diffusion rates in practical work. There are no fundamental diffusion constants which can be relied upon in the manner that a physicist or engineer employs a kinematic viscosity. *Ad hoc* field work is often required. The functional forms of various diffusion equations, however, have utility for interpolation and limited extrapolation of measurements and in planning field work. The recent diffusion studies of Pasquill and his collaborators (*48, 49, 50*) are regarded hopefully, but successful application would seem to require the development of a climatology of wind direction variance as a function of height, geographical location, wind speed, stability, and surface characteristics.

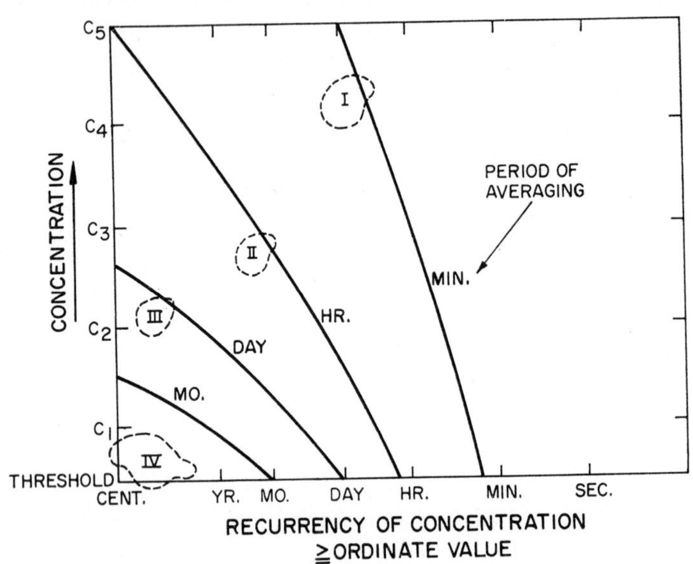

FIG. 15. Schematic concentration—averaging time—recurrency chart. Characteristic domains: I. Downwash in wake of stack or morning fumigation; II. Daytime pollution levels with dominant local flow patterns; III. Protracted periods of air stagnation; IV. Air pollution experienced over a lifetime. [R. C. Wanta and A. C. Stern, *Am. Ind. Hyg. Quart.* **18,** 156 (1957).]

The preferred hours for daytime diffusion measurements under approximately steady weather conditions extend from 2–3 hr. after sunrise to 3–4 hr. after noon. This assumes the absence of frontal passages, rapid local pressure changes, and local circulations such as sea-land breezes. Nighttime diffusion measurements with a similar aim should preferably be made when shear-stability interaction is also absent, i.e., both wind shear and stability are reasonably constant. However, complete reliance on these steady state situations introduces a bias into atmospheric diffusion measurements, since there is also need for knowledge of diffusion during transient states, precipitation, and at nonoptimal hours of the day. Personal visual experience with smoke plumes may be similarly biased, by lack of observations during the hours one is customarily indoors, or during the hours when plume contrast with the sky is poor. Visual observations on plumes may also be biased with respect to the frequency of fumigation of a fixed point at the ground within range of the plume, because the observer sees the diffusion process in two instead of three dimensions.

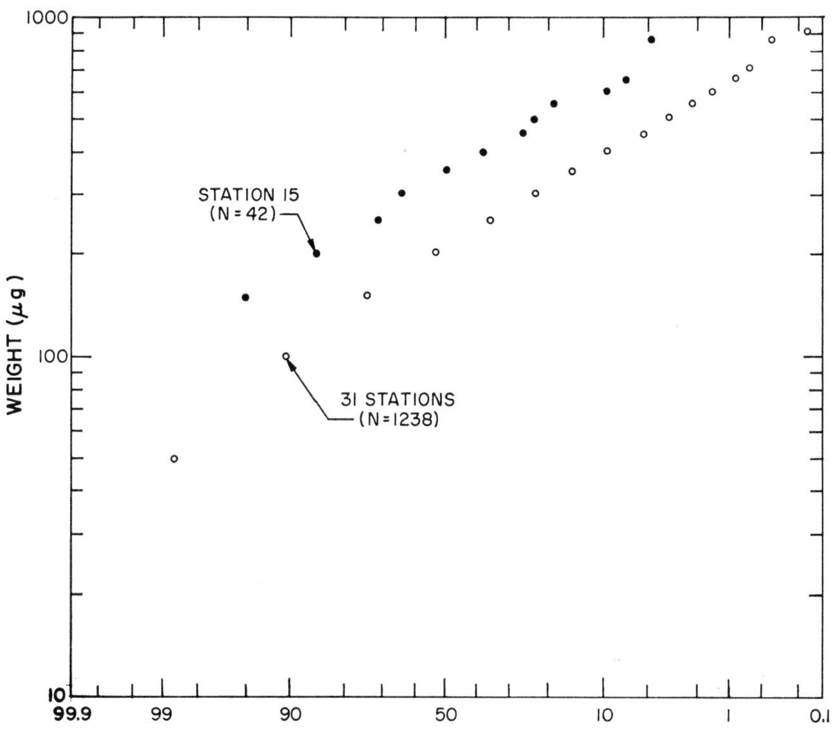

FIG. 16. Cumulative frequency distribution of suspended particulate matter, 24-hr. samples, May 7–June 17, 1951, Detroit, Michigan. [R. C. Wanta, *Bull. Am. Meteorol. Soc.* **37,** 186 (1956).]

The mathematical complexities involved in the description of changing wind and temperature fields (i.e., their structure) have not yet been overcome. It is not unlikely that the ultimate solution of the atmospheric diffusion problem will be a patchwork of solutions for each of several groups of weather and terrain conditions, comparable to the turbulent, laminar, and transition regimes over aerodynamically smooth and rough surfaces in ordinary fluid flow, with a final dependence upon selection from a group of suitable diffusion coefficients.

It may be argued that with respect to the scientific study of the diffusion and mixing of urban air pollution we are today still in a descriptive phase, and that we may expect a growing number of well-planned efforts at scientific description to precede a phase of genuinely reliable quantitative prediction.

A method of description of meteorological records that has promising application to air pollution work is the intensity—duration—frequency chart for precipitation. The corresponding triad, concentration—averaging time—recurrency, merits consideration in the description of air pollutant levels (Fig. 15). Many pollutant measurements are susceptible of this form of presentation. Also, the distribution of pollutant concentration for a given averaging time experienced at a point may in some cases be described by comparatively simple mathematical functions. The log-normal cumulative frequency distribution is commonly approximated in serial measurements of pollutant concentrations at points in cities, when the averaging time is 24 hr. (Fig. 16) (*51*). A start has been made in the explanation of this observation in terms of a fluctuating plume model of atmospheric diffusion (*52*).

Numerous examples of the use of these powerful descriptive tools, for other pollutants and averaging times, are included in recent reports of urban pollution surveys (*52a, 52b*). Analysis of such concentration distributions may throw further light on the "blind spot" in the neighborhood of a pollutant sampler, ascribed to the passage overhead of pollution from nearby sources, to explain the anomalies between parameters in models describing source strength and pollution effects (*52c*).

IX. Air Pollution Climatology

Air pollution in a community, apart from the background pollution level of incoming air, is a function of community activities and of weather conditions, both of which are functions of time. The temporal variations of weather are no less important in the study of air pollution than the temporal variations of community activities. Both community activities and weather conditions are also functions of location (*34*). Study of weather records made over a period of time with respect to temporal and space variation is therefore a prerequisite to understanding air pollution problems. The difficulties which stand in the way of strict quantitative analysis should not be permitted to obscure the fact that quantitative comparison of climatological features of actual or potential sites of pollutant sources is useful.

The basic climatological tool in air pollution work is the wind rose. A wind rose summarizes for a given height and location of wind instrument, and for a specified period of measurement, the occurrence of winds measured at intervals, usually hourly, by direction and speed, together with the occurrence of calms. The qualifications of height, location, and period of measurement are each important in applications, the first two because wind varies with height and location as has been discussed, and the third because length in period of record is necessary to obtain reliability for predictive use. That the weather over several years may differ significantly from that of the next several years is obvious if one recalls how droughts and rainy periods may alternate.

The annual wind rose should be broken down further by months or seasons of the year. Wind roses for unstable and stable conditions may differ markedly, especially in uneven terrain. In such cases the extra work of obtaining wind roses by stability condition is often justified (Fig. 17).

For certain air pollution problems, precipitation wind roses are useful in analysis. These are simply wind roses prepared only from wind data measured during precipitation. Periods of precipitation above some arbitrary intensity, or including only the hour of onset when the washout rate is high, may be used as bases for variants of the precipitation wind rose.

Because of the relative deficiency of measurements of stability compared with those of wind, indirect indices, such as the daily temperature range or a gustiness classification of a wind record, are usually used to document stability in the lowest layers of air. The rise in temperature from an early morning minimum to the afternoon maximum on clear or partly cloudy days is related to the strength of the inversion at sunrise. When the inversion is weak or absent, the daily range of temperature will be small. It will often be possible to identify the occurrence of warm or cold advection from weather maps (e.g., preceding warm fronts or following cold fronts). Analysis of the temperature record can become complicated, e.g., when sea breezes occur. Differences of temperature measured simultaneously at different surface elevations in a small area can provide similar information. The degree-day index, which is the deficit in degrees of the average temperature for the day with respect to a base of 65°F., is used to estimate domestic and other heating requirements; it can therefore serve for rough estimates of the air pollution attributable to space heating.

The climatological frequency of fog, low clouds, and low visibility is frequently useful in the assessment of air pollution potential. Qualitative comparison of air pollution potential between months or seasons of the year, or between different places, is thus made possible in the absence of wind fluctuation and temperature lapse data.

Besides frequency, the persistence of given weather conditions will

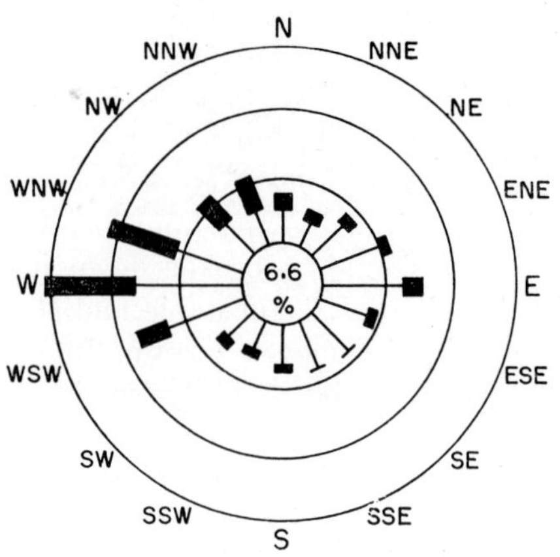

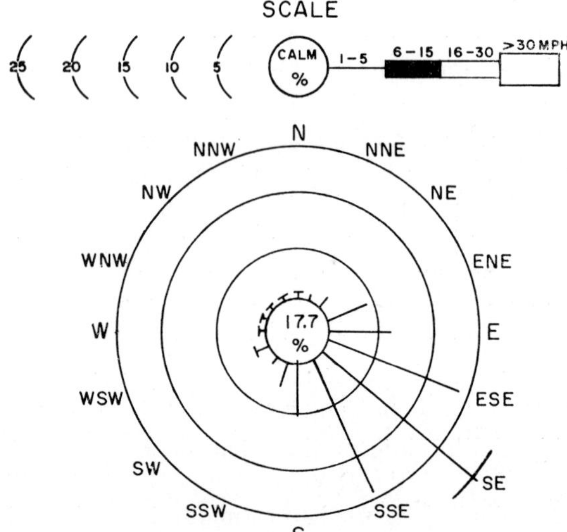

FIG. 17. Lapse and inversion wind roses, June 1955–May 1957, Shippingport, Pennsylvania. [D. H. Pack, C. R. Hosler, and T. B. Harris, "A Meteorological Survey of the PWR Site at Shippingport, Pennsylvania." U. S. Weather Bureau, Washington, D. C., 1957.]

often be found important in air pollution work. This is especially the case for the occurrence of protracted periods of light wind speeds, e.g., below some arbitrarily set level such as 8 mi./hr. for surface winds (*8*). Specialization in terms of smaller unit areas, or even individual valleys, and the persistence-duration curves for light winds with durations extending from a few hours to several days, are useful in certain applications. If done by wind direction, estimates are afforded of the frequency of exposure, i.e., occurrence and duration at a receptor for a given pollutant source upwind.

More advanced air pollution climatology would include the occurrence of sea-land breezes, mountain-valley winds, air masses of different types, cold and warm advection, various gustiness types, etc. Except for major investigations, it seems premature at present to obtain climatologies of vertical wind and turbulence intensities.

Familiarity with the types of climatological data that are available can save effort and expense. Sources of climatological data and some description of the kinds obtainable have been summarized (*17, 53*). Before undertaking one's own meteorological measurements in an air pollution study, the question of applicability of available summaries or the possibility of obtaining special summaries of available measurements should be answered, giving special attention to the location of these measurements relative to the point or area of interest. Sometimes it is desirable to make a check series of local measurements simultaneously with those at a nearby weather station to determine the applicability of the latter to the local site.

It is possible to draw reasonable inferences from conventional meteorological data of the frequency of meteorological conditions that would be conducive to relatively high levels of air pollution (*11*). The general topographical and meteorological conditions which are favorable for the occurrence of high levels of atmospheric pollution over industrial regions are quite well understood. The frequency distributions singly or jointly of wind, stability, and precipitation are more useful for estimation of the frequency of *relative* levels of pollution with time, day, or season than for absolute levels. In the absence of a reference standard, a well-defined air pollution climatology remains an ideal to be pursued.

A recent meteorological survey for an atomic energy plant serves to illustrate the types of climatic information which are of interest in advance of operations at a major potential source of atmospheric pollution (*8*). Apart from data needed for purely engineering and construction purposes, and other general climatological data, the following material was included:

(a) Description of local topography.

(b) Monthly wind roses at 200 ft. elevation.

(c) Annual wind roses at 15 and 200 ft. elevations.

(d) Annual precipitation wind rose.

(e) Monthly charts of diurnal wind speed range at 15 and 200 ft. elevations.

(f) Annual and seasonal per cent occurrence of three lapse rate categories measured between 5 and 200 ft.

(g) Diurnal curves of cumulative frequency of selected values of temperature lapse for four seasons, and height intervals of 5–50 and 5–200 ft.

(h) Monthly average and extreme times of inversion formation and termination.

(i) Cumulative frequency of duration of inversions by four wind quadrants for four seasons.

(j) Monthly average times for inversion to increase in depth from 50 to 200 ft.

(k) Seasonal duration-frequency charts of three categories of lapse rate.

(l) Seasonal duration probability charts of three categories of lapse rate, assuming a given lapse rate category is present.

(m) Seasonal cumulative frequency of inversion duration.

(n) Probability of no inversion for various weather conditions.

(o) Seasonal charts of wind roses at up to six locations in the area of the site, for unstable and stable lapse rate categories.

(p) Seasonal resultant wind hodographs by hour of day.

(q) Standard deviation of horizontal wind direction fluctuations at 200 ft. by four categories of lapse rate, three of wind speed, and four of direction.

(r) Summary of local diffusion measurements utilizing smoke pots.

The above climatological data were based on 2 years of local measurements. Other sources may be consulted for extended discussion of air pollution meteorology in relation to site surveys, accidents in nuclear plants, and city planning (*14, 17, 54–58*).

References

1. R. E. Huschke, ed., "Glossary of Meteorology." Am. Meteorol. Soc., Boston, Massachusetts, 1959.
2. C. Eckhart, *J. Marine Research* **7,** 265 (1948).
3. J. G. Edinger, *Bull. Am. Meteorol. Soc.* **36,** 211 (1955).
4. R. S. Scorer, "Natural Aerodynamics." Pergamon Press, New York, 1958.
5. R. J. List, ed., "Smithsonian Meteorological Tables." Smithsonian Inst., Washington, D. C., 1951.

6. H. H. Lettau and D. A. Haugen, *in* "Handbook of Geophysics" (C. F. Campen, Jr., *et al.*, eds.), p. 2-1. Macmillan, New York, 1960.
7. D. H. Pack, C. R. Hosler, and T. B. Harris, "A Meteorological Survey of the PWR Site at Shippingport, Pennsylvania." U. S. Weather Bureau, Washington, D. C., 1957.
8. N. E. Bowne and R. R. Soller, "A Meteorological Survey of the CANEL Site at Middletown, Connecticut." U. S. Weather Bureau, Washington, D. C., 1958.
9. M. Neiburger, *Science* **126,** 637 (1957).
10. J. G. Edinger, "The Meteorology of Los Angeles' Polluted Layer," Final Report. University of California, Los Angeles, California, 1958.
11. H. Wexler, *in* "Air Pollution," World Health Organization Monograph Series No. 46. Geneva, 1961.
12. O. G. Sutton, "Micrometeorology: A Study of Physical Processes in the Lowest Layers of the Earth's Atmosphere." McGraw-Hill, New York, 1953.
13. J. Z. Holland, *Bull. Am. Meteorol. Soc.* **33,** 1 (1952).
14. U. S. Weather Bureau, "Meteorological Survey of the Oak Ridge Area," Report ORO-99. U. S. Atomic Energy Commission, Oak Ridge, Tennessee, 1953.
15. J. B. Shaw, *Meteorol. Mag.* **84,** 233 (1955).
16. G. A. DeMarrais, *Bull. Am. Meteorol. Soc.* **42,** 548 (1961).
17. U. S. Weather Bureau, "Meteorology and Atomic Energy," Report AECU-3066. U. S. Atomic Energy Commission, Washington, D. C., 1955.
18. R. Geiger, "The Climate near the Ground." Harvard University Press, Cambridge, Massachusetts, 1950.
18a. I. A. Singer and G. S. Raynor, "Analysis of Meteorological Tower Data, April 1950–March 1952," Report BNL-461(T-120). Brookhaven National Laboratory, Upton, New York, 1957.
19. R. G. Fleagle, W. H. Parrott, and M. L. Barad, *J. Meteorol.* **9,** 53 (1952).
20. H. H. Schrenk, H. Heimann, G. D. Clayton, W. M. Gafafer, H. Wexler, "Air Pollution in Donora, Pennsylvania," Public Health Bulletin No. 306. U. S. Public Health Service, Washington, D. C., 1949.
21. H. R. Byers, "General Meteorology," 3rd ed. McGraw-Hill, New York, 1959.
22. H. S. Willett and F. Sanders, "Descriptive Meteorology," 2nd ed. Academic Press, New York, 1959.
23. S. Petterssen, "Introduction to Meteorology," 2nd ed. McGraw-Hill, New York, 1958.
24. F. N. Frenkiel and P. A. Sheppard, eds., "Atmospheric Diffusion and Air Pollution." Academic Press, New York, 1959.
24a. C. R. Hosler, *Monthly Weather Rev.* **89,** 319 (1961).
25. H. H. Lettau and D. A. Haugen, *in* "Handbook of Geophysics" (C. F. Campen, Jr., *et al.*, eds.), p. 5–1. Macmillan, New York, 1960.
26. R. H. Frederick, *Monthly Weather Rev.* **89,** 39 (1961).
27. A. K. Blackadar, *Bull. Am. Meteorol. Soc.* **38,** 283 (1957).
28. C. S. Durst, *Quart. J. Roy. Meteorol. Soc.* **59,** 131 (1933).
29. R. J. Taylor, *Quart. J. Roy. Meteorol. Soc.* **86,** 67 (1960).
30. H. A. Panofsky, *Bull. Am. Meteorol. Soc.* **36,** 163 (1955).
31. H. A. Panofsky and R. A. McCormick, *Quart. J. Roy. Meteorol. Soc.* **86,** 495 (1960).
32. C. H. B. Priestley, R. A. McCormick, and F. Pasquill, "Turbulent Diffusion in the Atmosphere," Tech. Note No. 24. World Meteorol. Organization, Geneva, 1958.

33. F. S. Duckworth and J. S. Sandberg, *Bull. Am. Meteorol. Soc.,* **35,** 198 (1954).
34. American Industrial Hygiene Association, "Air Pollution Manual. Part I: Evaluation." Am. Ind. Hyg. Assoc., Detroit, Michigan, 1960.
35. E. W. Hewson and G. C. Gill, see R. S. Dean and R. E. Swain, *U. S. Bur. Mines Bull.* **453,** 23 (1944).
36. J. Korshover, "Synoptic Climatology of Stagnating Anticyclones East of the Rocky Mountains in the United States for the Period 1936–1956," Report SEC TR-A60-7. Robert A. Taft Sanitary Engineering Center, Cincinnati, Ohio, 1960.
37. L. Machta, *Public Health Repts.* (*U. S.*) **75,** 307 (1960).
38. T. W. Kleinsasser and R. C. Wanta, *Proc. 49th Ann. Meeting Air Poll. Control Assoc., Buffalo* p. 7–1 (1956); *A.M.A. Arch. Ind. Health* **14,** 307 (1956).
39. C. K. M. Douglass and K. H. Stewart, *Meteorol. Mag.* **82,** 67 (1953).
40. L. E. Niemeyer, *Monthly Weather Rev.* **88,** 88 (1960).
40a. C. M. Boettger, *Bull. Am. Meteorol. Soc.* **42,** 615 (1961).
41. L. Prandtl and O. G. Tietjens, "Fundamentals of Hydro- and Aeromechanics." McGraw-Hill, New York, 1934; reprint, Dover Publications, New York, 1957.
42. M. Neiburger, N. A. Renzetti, and R. Tice, "Wind Trajectory Studies of the Movement of Polluted Air in the Los Angeles Basin," Air Poll. Foundation Report No. 13. Los Angeles, California, 1956.
43. H. Landsberg, "Physical Climatology," 2nd ed. Gray Printing Co., DuBois, Pennsylvania, 1958.
43a. S. M. Greenfield, *J. Meteorol.* **14,** 115 (1957).
43b. A. C. Chamberlain, "Aspects of Travel and Deposition of Aerosol and Vapour Clouds," A.E.R.E. Report HP/R 1261. Atomic Energy Research Establishment, Harwell, 1953.
43c. H. L. Green and W. R. Lane, "Particulate Clouds: Dusts, Smokes and Mists." Van Nostrand, Princeton, New Jersey, 1957.
44. R. Gunn and B. B. Phillips, *J. Meteorol.* **14,** 272 (1957).
45. W. L. Godson, *Arch. Meteorol. Geophys. u. Bioklimatol.* **10A,** 305 (1958).
46. F. Gifford, Jr., *J. Meteorol.* **12,** 245 (1955).
46a. D. B. Turner, "A Simple Diffusion Model for an Urban Area," AMS-AGU Meeting, Washington, D. C., 1959.
46b. F. Pooler, Jr., "A Prediction Model of Mean Urban Pollution for Use with Standard Wind Roses," AMS-AGU Meeting, Washington, D. C., 1959.
46c. M. E. Smith, Advance Papers, *Intern. Symposium on Chem. Reactions in the Lower and Upper Atmosphere, San Francisco, 1961* pp. 273–286.
47. F. N. Frenkiel, *in* "Smithsonian Report for 1956," p. 269. Smithsonian Inst., Washington, D. C., 1957.
48. J. S. Hay and F. Pasquill, *J. Fluid Mech.* **2,** 299 (1957).
49. J. S. Hay and F. Pasquill, *in* "Atmospheric Diffusion and Air Pollution" (F. N. Frenkiel and P. A. Sheppard, eds.), p. 345. Academic Press, New York, 1959.
50. F. B. Smith and J. S. Hay, *Quart. J. Roy. Meteorol. Soc.* **87,** 82 (1961).
51. R. C. Wanta, *Bull. Am. Meteorol. Soc.* **37,** 186 (1956).
52. F. Gifford, Jr., *in* "Atmospheric Diffusion and Air Pollution" (F. N. Frenkiel and P. A. Sheppard, eds.), p. 117. Academic Press, New York, 1959.
52a. D. M. Keagy, W. W. Stalker, C. E. Zimmer, and R. C. Dickerson, *J. Air Poll. Control Assoc.* **11,** 270 (1961).
52b. W. W. Stalker and R. C. Dickerson, *Proc. 54th Ann. Meeting Air Poll. Control Assoc., New York* June 11–15 (1961).

52c. R. I. Larsen, W. W. Stalker, and C. R. Claydon, *Proc. 54th Ann. Meeting Air Poll. Control Assoc., New York* June 11–15 (1961).
53. Stanford Research Institute, "The Uses of Meteorological Data in Large Scale Air Pollution Surveys." State of California Department of Public Health, Berkeley, California, 1958.
54. U. S. Atomic Energy Commission, "Theoretical Possibilities and Consequences of Major Accidents in Large Nuclear Power Plants," Report WASH-740. U. S. Atomic Energy Commission, Washington, D. C., 1957.
55. A. Brodsky and G. V. Beard, eds., "A Compendium of Information for Use in Controlling Radiation Emergencies," Report TID-8206 (Rev.). Office of Health & Safety, U. S. Atomic Energy Commission, Washington, D. C., 1960.
56. R. E. Munn, *Intern. J. Air Poll.* **1,** 276 (1959).
57. J. M. Leavitt, *J. Air Poll. Control Assoc.* **10,** 246 (1960).
58. P. J. Meade, "Meteorological Aspects of the Peaceful Uses of Atomic Energy. Part I. Safety and Location of Reactor Plants," Tech. Note No. 33. World Meteorol. Organization, Geneva, 1960.

CHAPTER 6

Atmospheric Dispersion of Stack Effluents

GORDON H. STROM

New York University College of Engineering, New York, New York

SYMBOLS

The following symbols are used in the equations of this chapter. In addition to this list, certain special symbols are defined where they appear.

A_p = cross-sectional area of particle
C_D = drag coefficient of particle, dimensionless
C_p = specific heat of air at constant pressure
C_{ps} = specific heat of stack gas at constant pressure
C_y = lateral diffusion coefficient, $(\text{length})^{n/2}$, (Eqs. 57, 63)
C_z = vertical diffusion coefficient, $(\text{length})^{n/2}$, (Eqs. 57, 64)
d = internal exit diameter of stack top
d_p = diameter of particle
d_s = external diameter of stack
e = base of natural logarithm

g = acceleration due to gravity
h = stack height
= elevation of stack top from ground level (see Fig. 7)
h_b = height of building
h_e = elevation of plume axis from ground level at given downwind location (see Fig. 7)
$= h + \Delta h$
Δh = plume rise
= height of plume axis above top of stack at given downwind location
l = reference length
N = macroviscosity of air (Eq. 66)
n = turbulence index, dimensionless
p = vertical diffusion coefficient, dimensionless (Eq. 54)
Q_h = heat emission rate of stack gas relative to ambient atmosphere
Q_m = mass emission rate of stack gas
Q_p = stack particulate emission rate, mass per time
Q_{vs} = volume emission rate of stack gas at temperature T_s
Q_{v1} = volume emission rate of stack gas at temperature T_1
q = lateral diffusion coefficient, dimensionless (Eq. 54)
R = radius of gas plume cross section at a given location
Re = Reynolds number of particle, dimensionless
$= \rho v_f d_p/\mu$
R_0 = radius of gas plume cross section at stack top
$= d/2$
S = Strouhal number, dimensionless (Eq. 91)
s = distance along plume axis from stack top
t = travel time of stack gas from stack top to given location
T = absolute temperature of ambient atmosphere
$\Delta T = T_s - T$
T_s = absolute temperature of stack gas (at stack top)
T_1 = absolute temperature at which density of stack gas would be equal to that of the ambient atmosphere
$\Delta T_1 = T_s - T_1$
u = wind speed at given location (time mean value)
V_p = volume of particle
V_s = stack gas ejection speed
v_f = free settling velocity of particle
$\overline{v'^2}$ = root mean square of velocity fluctuations in the y (lateral) direction
w_a = axial speed of stack gas at given location
$\overline{w'^2}$ = root mean square of velocity fluctuations in the z (vertical) direction
x = distance downwind of stack or source (see Fig. 7)

y = lateral distance from vertical plane through the stack or source and parallel to mean wind direction
z = height above ground except in Eq. 68
z_0 = roughness length (see Eq. 65)
Γ = atmospheric adiabatic temperature gradient
θ = potential temperature of ambient atmosphere
= T in a neutral (adiabatic) atmosphere
$\Delta\theta$ = difference between potential temperature of plume and ambient atmosphere
$d\theta/dz$ = potential temperature gradient of ambient atmosphere
μ = dynamic viscosity of air
ν = kinematic viscosity of air
ρ = mass density of ambient atmosphere
ρ_p = mass density of particle
ρ_s = mass density of stack gas
σ_y = standard deviation of lateral gas concentration distribution in plume
σ_z = standard deviation of vertical gas concentration distribution in plume
χ = gas concentration at given location (x,y,z) in plume, mass per volume
ψ = angle between plume axis and horizontal
ω = deposition of particulates at given location, mass per area-time

I. Introduction

Gaseous and particulate waste products are commonly discharged to the atmosphere through stacks of some form. These may range from short ventilation stacks on a small building to very tall ground-based stacks for a large power plant or smelter. Stack effluents vary widely in their physical and chemical characteristics as well as in their degree of undesirability. The environment into which a stack discharges its effluent is another factor of wide variability. Meteorological characteristics play an important role. The location of a stack in relation to obstructions to air motion, whether a building or a mountain range, may have an important effect. These various characteristics are significant to stack design.

Available analytical methods range in complexity from rule-of-thumb procedures to elaborate calculations. None account for all the above factors. Fortunately many cases occur in which some or most of these factors are negligible, and thus acceptable answers may be obtained. When analytical methods fail, model or field experiments may give the answer.

FIG. 1. Favorable gas plume dispersal characteristics are shown at the E. F. Barrett coal-burning power plant. (Courtesy of the Long Island Lighting Company.)

II. Characteristics of Stack Plumes

A. Concentration Distribution and Geometry of Plumes

A distinction must be made between an air pollution problem resulting from one or several closely grouped stacks and that of a large number of stacks over a wide area. Characteristics and methods of solution are generally quite different. In the area problem the pollution from any given stack may be low enough to be acceptable but the total from a large number of such stacks may be serious and will cover a wide area.

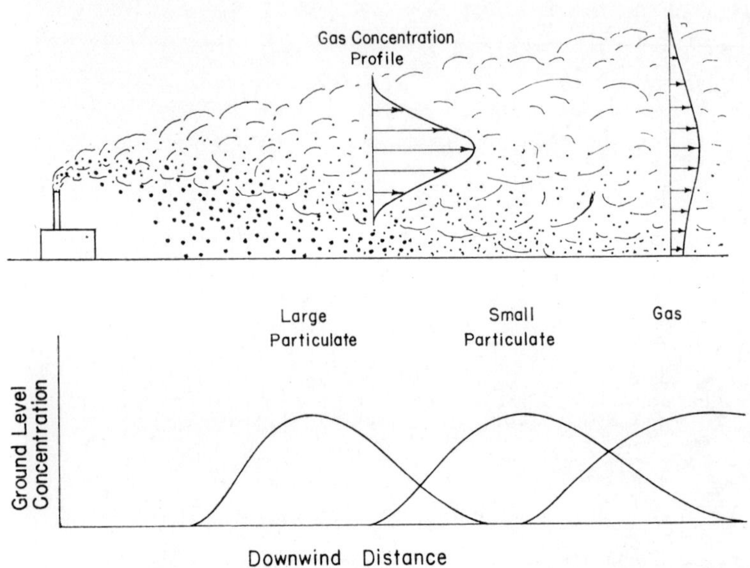

Fig. 2. Comparison of gaseous and particulate plumes at a given wind speed.

The pollution from a single stack will yield under neutral or unstable atmospheric conditions highest ground level concentrations relatively close to the stack, generally within a downwind distance equal to twenty stack heights. The effect of wind speed on the two cases may be diametrically opposed. While the area problem usually improves with wind speed, the single stack problem is often more serious at high speeds. Pollution characteristics of the single or small group of stacks is the subject of this chapter.

Stack effluents may be composed of gases alone or of gases and particulate matter. The nature of the effluent will to some extent, determine the information sought in an air pollution analysis. For particulates the accumulated deposition over a period of time may be of primary interest while short period exposure may be more important for gases. Techniques of analysis have been developed to a higher degree for gases.

Since particulates occur in a wide range of sizes, some particulate plumes may be composed of particles so small that they have concentration distributions similar to gas plumes. Particles on the order of 20-μ diameter or less have such low free fall or settling speeds that they move essentially the same as the gas in which they are immersed. Analyses for gases will, therefore, apply to very small size particulates. Large size particulates, owing to their significant free settling velocities, will form plumes which fall below gases and the higher ground level concentrations will occur closer to the stack as shown in Fig. 2.

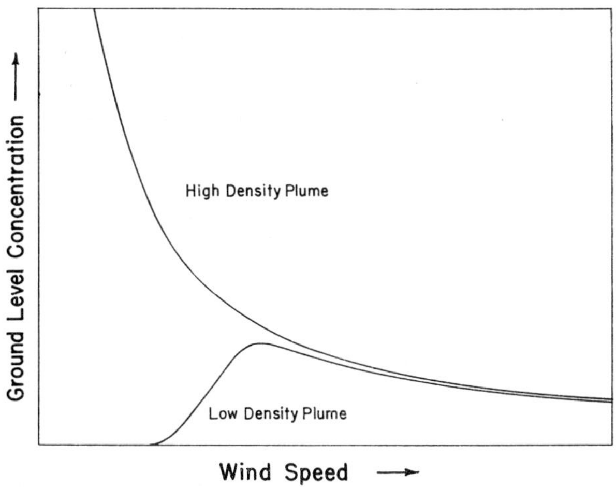

FIG. 3. Effect of wind speed on ground level concentration at a given downwind location.

As a stack effluent leaves a stack it immediately begins mixing with the surrounding atmosphere, and the degree of dilution increases as it moves downwind. This mixing is initially marked by relative motion of the plume and atmosphere and later by motions of the atmosphere unrelated to the stack. Concentration has a peak at the centerline or axis of the plume and decreases with radial distance as shown in Fig. 2. The path or centerline course is dependent on various factors among which are the characteristics of the effluent as it leaves the stack. The initial upward motion or ejection speed causes the plume to rise above stack top. An additional effect on path height results from the relative density of effluent and ambient atmosphere. Low density plumes rise above that elevation which results from ejection speed alone and, conversely, heavy plumes fall. Most effluents encountered in practice are less dense than the ambient atmosphere because of heat generated in so many processes which produce air pollution. Plume path equations presented in Section III show quantitatively the effect of stack effluent characteristics.

When there is little or no wind speed, low density gas plumes tend to rise to high elevations thus leaving the ground free of contamination in the neighborhood of the stack. High density gas plumes and particulate components of all plumes will fall to the ground in the vicinity of the stack. These two extremes in ground level concentration at low speeds are shown in Fig. 3. As wind speed increases, heavy plumes are carried downwind and the diluting action of the atmospheres reduces their concentration. Also as wind speed increases, low density plumes are deflected toward the ground and a speed is reached where the plumes make initial ground contact. Added wind speed causes further lowering of low density plumes and ground level concentration increases as shown in Fig. 3. Concentration reaches a maximum beyond which the diluting action of the atmosphere becomes dominant as high wind speeds are encountered.

B. Gas Plume Types and Effect of Meteorological Factors

The physical and chemical processes which may occur in gas plumes as they mix with the surrounding atmosphere produce a variety of effects. Precipitation will cause wash-out (see Chapter 5). Chemical changes may change the concentration of objectionable components (see Chapter 3). Evaporation of water droplets will cause reduction in temperature and increase in plume density. Motion and density of the ambient atmosphere have generally the most important environmental effects on diffusion of gas plumes.

Description of atmospheric motion must include a detailed specification of velocity, both temporal and spatial. For this purpose velocity is conveniently divided into its time mean direction and magnitude (the usual wind speed) and the fluctuating components termed turbulence (see Chapter 16). Velocity fluctuations have time periods which vary widely. Turbulence and mean values of velocity and direction will, therefore, depend on the time period over which the mean is taken. Means of consecutive periods of measurement will show changes in wind speed, direction, and turbulence. It is desirable to have time periods appropriate to each particular air pollution problem as discussed in Section II,C but data are often unavailable for all the desired time periods which are likely to arise.

The geometric features of a plume, as usually described, are the result of turbulence based on a relatively short time period, on the order of the length of time it takes the plume to travel the distance in view. Concentration data cover a wider range, up to an hour or more. When periods of interest to a particular problem are longer than the time period for which data are given, the analysis must include effects of both turbulence and changes in wind speed and direction. A method of analysis which accounts for these characteristics is discussed in Section III,A,3,*f*.

Atmospheric turbulence is divided into two types, convective and mechanical, depending on whether it is of thermal or mechanical origin. Mechanical turbulence arises from movement of air over the earth's surface and is influenced by nonthermal features of buildings and any objects which resist air motion. It increases with irregularity of the surface or "roughness" and its intensity increases with wind speed. While certain thermal conditions produce convective turbulence, there are others which do not produce turbulence but instead may suppress mechanical turbulence. Thermal and mechanical influences generally occur simultaneously in varying ratios. Convective turbulence tends to have longer period fluctuations, but the two types cannot be completely separated.

Convective turbulence is caused largely by differences in temperature between the surface and the overlying airstream (see Chapter 5). The vertical temperature gradient in the lowest layer of the atmosphere is directly related to this temperature difference and is an important indicator of convective turbulence. The range of temperature gradients is divided into unstable, neutral, and stable. The neutral case will show primarily mechanical turbulence, while the unstable adds convective turbulence, and the stable suppresses mechanical turbulence.

The geometrical form and concentration distribution of gas plumes is dependent on turbulence characteristics. Five types of plumes shown in Fig. 4 are due to distinctly different atmospheric conditions, although there may be a gradual transition from one type to another. The first three, looping, coning, and fanning, occur under differing but somewhat uniform turbulence conditions. A looping plume occurs with a high degree of turbulence, especially convective turbulence. This is typical of a daytime condition with intense solar heating of the earth's surface which causes unstable thermal conditions. Similar plume characteristics may also occur with large-scale mechanical turbulence such as is caused by large and sharp hills upwind of the stack. The coning plume occurs under more nearly neutral thermal conditions when mechanical turbulence of smaller scale is predominant. This is more likely to occur when there is cloud cover which reduces thermal effects whether due to incoming solar radiation in daytime or outgoing terrestrial radiation at night. The half-angle of the coning plume (angle between outline and centerline) is on the order of 10°. Fanning plumes occur under stable conditions when mechanical turbulence is suppressed. The vertical component is suppressed more than the horizontal, with the result that plume width is greater than its thickness. As viewed from above, the

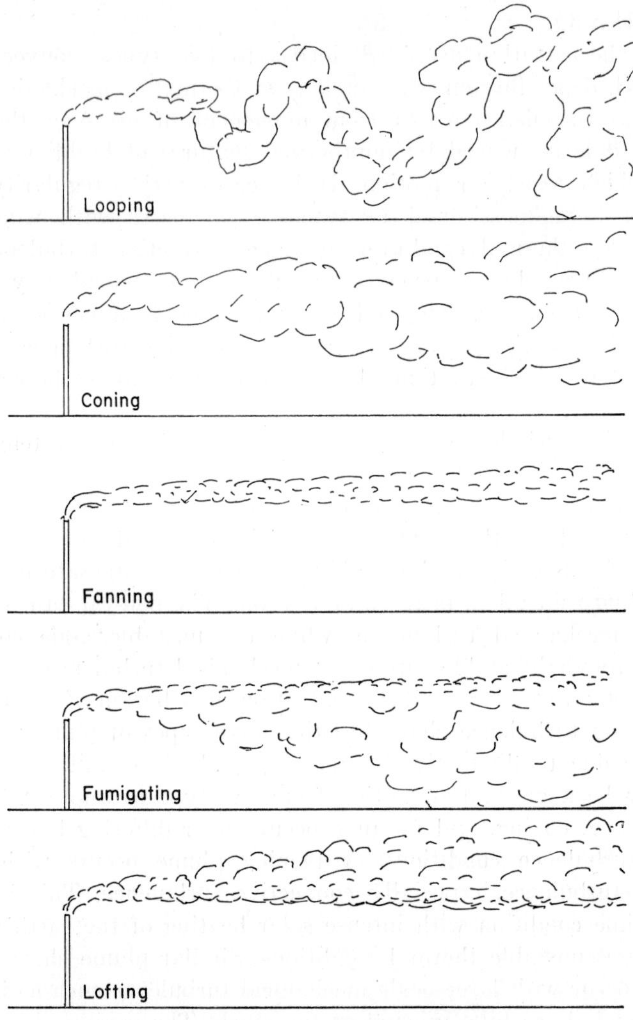

FIG. 4. Types of stack gas plumes.

plume may show lateral fluctuations of a sinuous nature. The fanning plume is most likely at night when the earth's surface is cooled by outgoing radiation.

It is apparent that stable conditions will keep a plume compact and prevent contact with the ground for considerable downwind distance if its density is not greater than that of the surrounding atmosphere. As conditions become less stable, nearest contact with the ground occurs closer to the stack as will also the location of maximum ground level concentration. This trend continues as conditions move into the unstable range. For extreme instability at low wind speeds, portions of a looping plume may reach the ground within a distance equal to one stack height. High wind speeds increase mechanical turbulence and reduce thermal effects. Plume features which arise from thermal effects are, therefore, more likely to occur at low wind speeds.

The remaining two plume types in Fig. 4 occur when there is marked difference in stability between the atmospheric layers above and below the plume. The fumigating plume which received early study by Hewson (*1*) is caused by unstable air below the plume and a stable layer above. This causes greater downward dispersion of gases, thus bringing more of the plume to the ground than would occur with unstable conditions above and below. The fumigating condition usually occurs in the morning when, following a night of marked stability, the rising sun heats the ground and causes an unstable layer to develop from the ground upward. When the unstable layer reaches plume level, the compact and highly concentrated plume quickly begins downward diffusion, and high ground level concentrations may occur for a period on the order of a half-hour.

The lofting plume is caused by stability conditions inverse to those for fumigation. The unstable layer is above the plume and the greater diffusion is upward. This is most favorable for maintaining low ground level concentrations. Late afternoon and early evening are favorable for this condition. A stable layer develops from below as solar radiation is reduced by setting of the sun.

When two or more stacks are closely grouped, they have mutual influences. The plumes tend to merge into one. There appears to be no data which evaluates this effect and it is not accounted for in available analytical methods. Limits on this effect are given in a paper by Bosanquet *et al.* (*2*) where it is stated that plumes from multiple stacks will rise higher than that from one of them but not as high as that of a plume from one stack replacing all of them. Presumably, the one stack would operate at the same ejection speed. In practice, multiple stacks are often in a line, and it is common experience to note that when the wind direction is in line with the stacks the plumes rise higher than for other directions. It can be reasoned that the mutual lifting effect is greater when in line with the wind since the multiple plumes merge into a more compact single plume. This feature is, however, complicated by the fact that a line of stacks is generally associated with a long building which will be in line with the wind at the same time as the stacks. This is the most favorable direction for minimizing adverse effects of the building. As more data of the type obtained by Gartrell *et al.* (*2a*) at TVA becomes available, the analysis of multiple-stack effects will be improved.

The ultimate height to which a low density plume will rise depends on atmospheric as well as on stack effluent characteristics. In an unstable atmosphere, it will tend to rise without limit since the buoyant forces continue to operate. Eventually the plume will be so diffused as to lose its identity. In a stable atmosphere the plume will reach an equilibrium level where its density becomes equal to the ambient atmosphere and there will be no tendency to rise further. Equations for evaluating this height are given in Section III,A,2,*b*. A rising plume may overshoot the equilibrium level and settle back to it. Scorer (*3*) illustrates this case with a photograph of a smoke plume.

C. Effect of Sampling Period

An instrument which can record the instantaneous value of gas concentration in a plume will show considerable variation in the time-dependent fluctuations as atmospheric stability changes. It is apparent that a looping plume will show high concentration when the instrument is in the dense part of the plume and low or zero values in between. A plume in a stable atmosphere will show much reduction in fluctuations. An instrument which reads the average concentration over a period of time will show lower maximum or peak concentrations than the instantaneous type since the periods of low concentration are averaged with those of high concentration. Thus the length of sampling period will affect the maximum concentration recorded. This was recognized by earlier investigators (*4*). Sensitivity to air pollution will vary depending on the effective time of exposure. Humans are aware of short-period high-intensity concentrations, but the corrosion of a structure is more dependent on the average concentration over a long period of time. Smith and Singer (*5*) made studies on the effect of sampling period on concentration. Experiments they conducted at the Brookhaven National Laboratory show that in one case the 5-sec. peak value of ground level concentration was thirteen times that of the mean of a 2-hr.-20-min. run. Other peak-mean ratios as high as thirty were obtained. Stewart *et al.* (*6*) show with experiments at the Harwell reactor that the dependence of peak-mean ratios for the plume axis under adiabatic conditions may be represented with a power-law relationship. A series of surveys showed the peak concentration to vary inversely with the fifth root of the sampling period. Sampling periods were 13 min. or less.

Gifford (*7*) presents a theoretical analysis of peak to average concentration ratio and analyzes experimental data from various sources. He shows the ratio to depend on sampling location as well as sampling period. He finds that the ratio increases with distance below plume axis and decreases with downwind distance. His graph shows that on the plume axis the concentration ratio varies approximately as the inverse 1/5 power of sampling period, while on the ground under the plume from an elevated source the inverse 3/4 power gives an approximate representation of the data. The dependence of concentration on sampling period makes difficult the comparison of various field results when sampling periods are not alike, as is often the case. Even under identical sampling periods peak-mean ratios will vary because of differences in local conditions. Length of sampling period which is important to a given problem will be determined by the nature of the item affected by air pollution (see Chapters 7A, 7B, 8, 9, and 10).

D. Effects of Buildings and Topography

Topography, buildings, and other obstructions to air motion affect gas plumes in two ways. They change the local wind speed and direction as well as turbulence. Thus the plume path and diffusion are affected. As in the case of turbulence over level surfaces, building and topographical effects may be mechanical or thermal in origin. The mechanical effects will first be discussed.

Results of a scale-model wind tunnel experiment conducted in the New York University air pollution wind tunnel (*8*) illustrate these effects for the case in which the building associated with the stack has significant influence. These are shown in Fig. 5. In comparing vertical concentration profiles through the center of the plume 1440 ft. downwind of the 160-ft. stack, it is noted that when the building is present, the plume is lower and diffusion is greater. Both of these factors contribute to the increase in ground level concentration. Another feature brought out by this experiment is the effect of change in wind direction when the building is present. Adverse effect is seen to be greater when the wind is normal to the long dimension. Ground concentration is in this case several times greater. For a building approximately square in plan, the least favorable direction is likely to be the diagonal, and this holds for rectangular plans where the length is not greatly different from the width. As the length-width ratio increases, the least favorable direction becomes that which is normal to the long dimension of the building.

The influence of an obstruction to air motion extends upwind a short distance, about that of the size of the obstruction, and its effect is primarily a local change in distribution of wind speed and direction.

There is no major change in turbulence. Downwind of the obstruction, turbulence as well as wind speed and direction are affected. For abrupt obstructions the generation of turbulence is the striking feature. It may completely overshadow all other features. A plume on the windward side

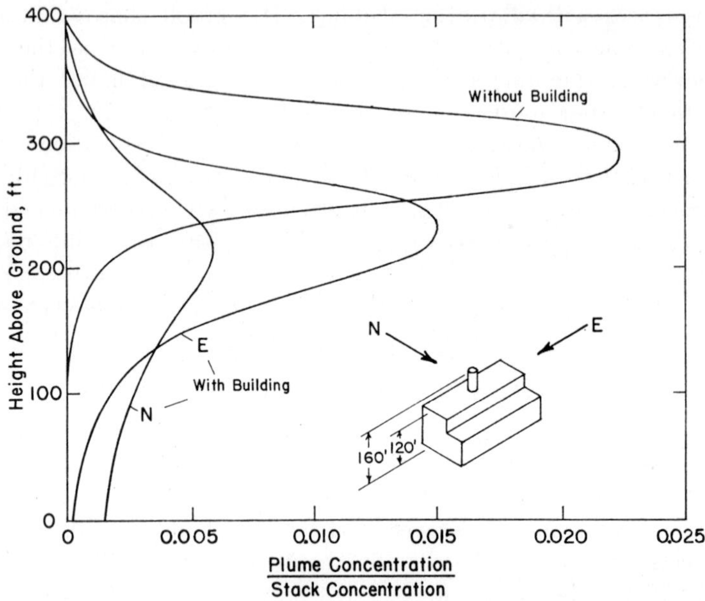

FIG. 5. Vertical concentration profiles through center of a gas plume found in a scale-model wind tunnel experiment. These were taken 1440 ft. downwind of the stack at a wind speed of 11.2 m./sec. The numerical values are prototype equivalents. (Redrawn from Fig. 2, Strom *et al.*, *J. Air Poll. Control Assoc.* **7**, 1957.)

of a hill follows the air stream up the side as shown in Fig. 6 with the usual diffusion about its now distorted axis. If, however, the hill is an isolated peak or has a three-dimensional shape which allows some of the air to move around rather than over, the layer which envelops the plume will move closer to the surface and may increase ground level concentration. On the leeward side it is quite different. In the turbulent region a plume may be brought quickly to the ground as shown, diffused over a wide area, or in extreme cases move up the hill because of a large standing eddy. The region of turbulence may extend to elevations well above hill top, depending on the abruptness of the windward side.

There are no accurate analytical procedures for predicting the influence of buildings and topography. Here the need for experimental procedures is most strongly indicated. Shapes of buildings and topographical elements vary so widely that results for one case have only limited application to another. As more experience is gained, rule-of-thumb procedures may be developed but at this stage only the crudest of estimates can be made.

If a stack discharges a considerable amount of polluting material, it is desirable that the plume remain clear of highly turbulent regions. This is one basis of stack selection, and experimental methods sometimes use this requirement as a basis for interpreting results. There are, however, many cases in which the quantity of polluting material is not sufficient to require the plume to remain completely clear of the turbulent region. Common examples are sources from residential buildings. Here the more serious pollution feature is often recirculation of effluent to windows and ventilation intakes of the building itself. This problem is even more difficult to handle.

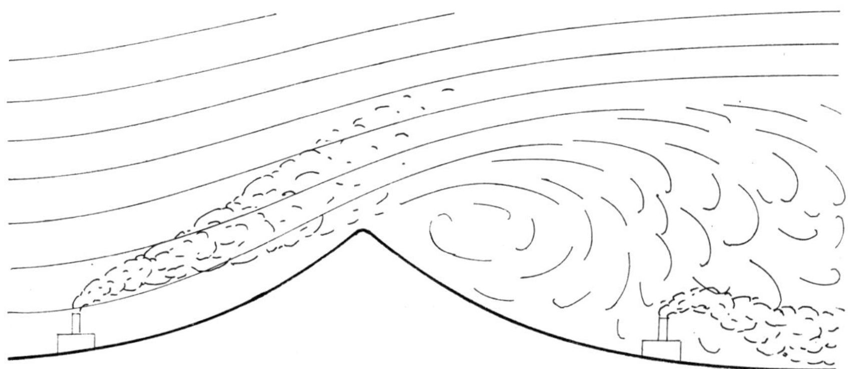

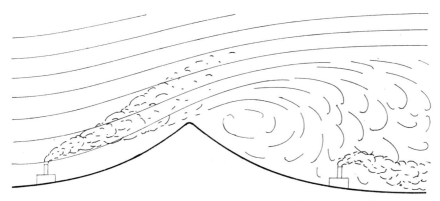

FIG. 6. Pattern of air motion over a hill showing effect on gas plumes.

The wide variation in turbulence and wind speed in the region downwind of an obstruction, whether topography or buildings, makes difficult the estimation of improvement obtainable with increased stack height. Gas diffusion theories discussed in Section III,A,3 show that ground level concentration decreases with the inverse of plume height squared. These theories assume that turbulence is essentially constant with elevation. In the case where an adjacent building causes an adverse effect, usually it is only the lower part of the plume which is caught in the turbulent region. As the plume is raised by higher stack or other means, it is expected that the improvement will be greater than shown by diffusion theory. In the author's experience with wind tunnel experiments in situations of this type, there is a considerable variation in height effect. Ground level concentrations vary between the inverse cube and seventh power of stack height (not necessarily plume height). On the other hand, the case of a plume completely immersed in the turbulent region downwind of a hill as in Fig. 6, the result may be much different. Mixing of the air may be so violent, and patterns of air motion so arranged, that increase of stack height gives disappointingly little improvement until the plume approaches the upper boundary of the turbulent region. Some very approximate methods of dealing with effects of building and topography are given in Section III,C.

Thermal characteristics of buildings and topography may have a marked influence on plume behavior. In rare cases, a building which houses a heat-producing process may emit sufficient heat to the atmosphere to produce a large plume of heated atmospheric air, especially at low wind speeds. This is favorable for a plume immersed in it. Off to the sides of this large air plume there may be down drafts which are locally unfavorable.

Thermal influences from topography vary widely in scale. The large-scale types may dwarf a gas plume and act as local changes in wind speed and direction. On a smaller scale, local air currents may have marked effect on plume diffusion. Hewson's studies (*1*) of the fumigating plume in a valley involved topographical thermal actions in which the rising sun heated one slope of the valley and caused overturning of the air mass. Differential heating or cooling between different surfaces of the topography is the cause of many thermal effects. Under some conditions oscillations of the valley air mass may occur. Uniform heating or cooling causes up-slope or down-slope winds, respectively. Sutton (*9*) reviews theories on mountain and valley winds.

E. Significance of Climatological Factors in the Application of Plume Diffusion Data

Meteorological characteristics taken over a period of time play an important part in analyzing an air pollution problem since time of exposure to air pollution is usually significant. For this purpose one must know the applicable quality standards, whether those of a regulating agency (see Chapter 37) or those adopted by a pollutant producer. Having such standards available, compliance may then be analyzed, using plume characteristics and climatological data. Unfortunately, all the climatological data desired are not likely to be available, and a special climatological survey may have to be conducted or estimates made on the basis of such information as is at hand.

A complete analysis of plume diffusion will supply data on ground level concentration under varying atmospheric conditions. This will enable one to determine for a given wind speed, direction, and atmospheric stability the magnitude of concentration. Having climatological data on duration of this condition, the time of exposure is then determined. A more refined analysis will include statistical properties of exposure periods and their frequency. The degree of refinement needed will depend on the standards to be met.

Time of exposure analysis is useful in evaluating stack designs. Having obtained annual hours of exposure at the various levels of concentration, direct comparisons of stack designs may be made. This procedure is very effective in the application of results obtained from scale model wind tunnel experiments.

III. Analytical Methods for Prediction of Plume Characteristics

A. Two-Step Plume-Path-Diffusion Method

1. *General Procedure*

Most analytical methods for obtaining concentrations of stack effluents at ground level or other locations generally perform the analysis in two steps. One step concerns the determination of the height of plume path or axis above the surface, termed effective stack height. The effective height may be needed at a series of locations downwind of the stack. The second step concerns the diffusion of gas about the plume axis and the deposition of particulates. Available gas diffusion equations do not account for those effluent characteristics which affect height of the plume. They treat only the case of a horizontal straight plume. Furthermore, diffusion equations assume that the plume starts as a point. Features of this model are shown in Fig. 7. An obvious assumption

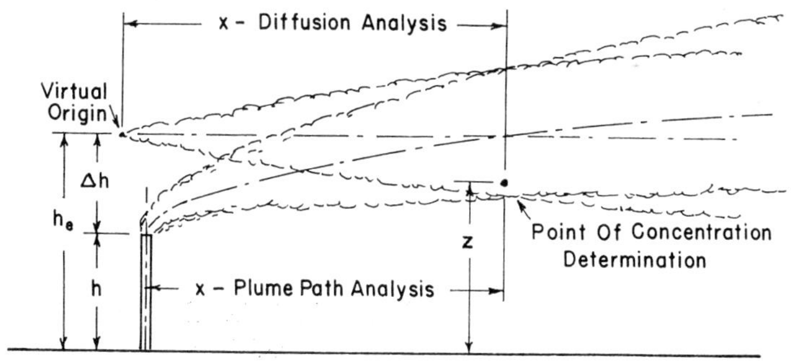

Fig. 7. Diffusion model used in the two-step gas plume analysis.

is that the fictitious horizontal model at effective stack height diffuses the same as the real plume. Near the source there is a marked difference between the two. The analysis should, therefore, not be used for small downwind distances. The model has a point source while the real stack has a finite area at its exit. To account for this difference, a virtual origin upwind of the real stack may be used. Also the diffusion process is initially different from that further downwind and may be unaccounted for by the diffusion equations. Adjustment of the virtual origin may partially correct for this difference. There is, however, little data on which to base the upwind location of a virtual origin. As the downwind distance to the point of concentration calculation is increased, the effect of virtual origin location becomes less significant and is often neglected, especially for nonstable atmospheric conditions.

2. *Plume Path*

a. Introduction. In the past decade or so there have been developed a number of procedures for estimating effective stack height of gas plumes. Some are entirely empirical in their development, being based on experiments in which plume path characteristics were measured. Others are based on theoretical analyses but generally require some fundamental experimental information. They all deal with a single isolated stack in an atmosphere uncomplicated by influence of obstructions to air motion, such as buildings and topographical features as well as local effects near stack top. Some procedures give only the ultimate total or maximum height of the plume, while others give height as a function of downwind distance.

b. Specific Procedures. The following procedures will be presented or commented on. They are in chronological order of their publication.

- i Bryant-Davidson
- ii Bosanquet, Carey, and Halton
- iii Oak Ridge
- iv Thomas
- v Sutton
- vi Bryant and Cowdry
- vii Priestley
- viii Bosanquet
- ix Scorer

This is not an exhaustive list but it includes those which have received attention in the literature. As discussed in Section III,A,2,*c,* the various procedures do not give the same result. Differences will depend on the conditions of a given case.

i. Bryant-Davidson formula. Davidson (*10,* see also *11*) developed the following empirical formula on the basis of Bryant's wind tunnel experiments.

$$\Delta h = d\left(\frac{V_s}{u}\right)^{1.4}\left(1 + \frac{\Delta T}{T_s}\right) \tag{1}$$

Consistent units must be used. The equation gives the rise to the height where the plume is almost horizontal. This is not the maximum height of plume rise.

ii. Bosanquet, Carey, and Halton procedure. Bosanquet *et al.* (*2*) published their procedure in a paper which presented a method for estimation of dust deposition. It has received wide use for gas plume analysis. It is based on a theoretical development and employs some fundamental experimental constants of diffusion. Momentum rise and buoyancy rise as functions of downwind distance are calculated separately and added to form total rise. These are for a neutral atmosphere.

Momentum rise is found as follows.

$$\Delta h_v = \Delta h_{vmax}\left(1 - 0.8\,\frac{\Delta h_{vmax}}{x}\right) \tag{2}$$

when $x >$ about $2\Delta h_{vmax}$ (x is measured downwind of stack).

$$\Delta h_{vmax} = \frac{4.77}{1 + 0.43u/V_s} \cdot \frac{\sqrt{Q_{v1}V_s}}{u} \tag{3}$$

Buoyancy rise is given by

$$\Delta h_b = \frac{6.37 g Q_{v1} \Delta T_1 Z}{u^3 T_1} \tag{4a}$$

$$X = \frac{ux}{3.57\sqrt{Q_{v1}V_s}} \tag{4b}$$

when $u^2 > (\Delta T_1 g/T_1) \cdot (Q_{v1}/V_s)^{1/2}$. X and Z are related by the graph of Fig. 8. The above equations are valid in any consistent units.

Total rise is

$$\Delta h = \Delta h_v + \Delta h_b \tag{5}$$

The following is an alternate form for the above equations in terms of other variables.

$$\frac{\Delta h_v}{d} = \frac{\Delta h_{vmax}}{d} \cdot \left(1 - 0.8\,\frac{\Delta h_{vmax}/d}{x/d}\right) \tag{6}$$

$$\frac{\Delta h_{vmax}}{d} = \frac{4.23}{1 + 0.43u/V_s} \cdot \frac{V_s}{u} \cdot \sqrt{\frac{\rho_s}{\rho}} \tag{7}$$

$$\frac{\Delta h_b}{d} = 5.00\,\frac{gd}{u^2} \cdot \frac{V_s}{u}\left(1 - \frac{\rho_s}{\rho}\right) Z \tag{8}$$

$$X = \frac{1}{3.16} \cdot \frac{x}{d} \cdot \frac{u}{V_s}\sqrt{\frac{\rho}{\rho_s}} \tag{9}$$

Bosanquet *et al.* state that the above equations for plume rise in a neutral atmosphere may be applied to other cases of stability for short downwind distances as used in dust deposition calculations.

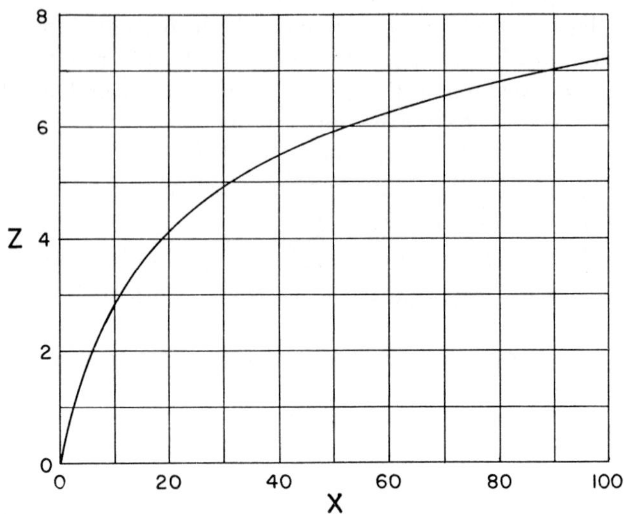

FIG. 8. Z as a function of X for use in buoyancy rise equations of Bosanquet *et al.* (Redrawn from Fig. 8, Bosanquet *et al.*, *Proc. Inst. Mech. Engrs.* **162,** 1950.)

Bosanquet *et al.* also give the following equation for maximum plume rise in a stable atmosphere. This gives a limit to the above equations for this atmospheric condition.

$$\Delta h_{\max} = \frac{4.77}{1 + 0.43u/V_s} \cdot \frac{\sqrt{Q_{v1}V_s}}{u} + 6.37g\,\frac{Q_{v1}\Delta T_1}{u^3 T_1}\left(\log_e J^2 + \frac{2}{J} - 2\right) \quad (10)$$

where

$$J = \frac{u^2}{\sqrt{Q_{v1}V_s}}\left(0.43\sqrt{\frac{T_1}{g(d\theta/dz)}} - 0.28\,\frac{V_s}{g}\,\frac{T_1}{\Delta T_1}\right) + 1 \quad (11)$$

Consistent units must be used.

iii. Oak Ridge formula. Holland (*12*) developed an empirical equation on the basis of observations of plumes from the X-10 pile and X-10 steam plant at Oak Ridge and the Watts Bar steam plant of the Tennessee Valley Authority. His development begins with an equation for momentum rise published by Rupp *et al.* (*13*). To this Holland adds a term for buoyancy rise based on the plume observations. The rise obtained from observations was apparently not the maximum rise but there is no statement on this point in (*12*). Hawkins and Nonhebel (*14*) describe the rise found with the Oak Ridge formula as occurring at a downwind distance equal to two or three stack heights. The Oak Ridge formula gives plume rise for neutral stability as follows.

$$\Delta h = (1.5V_s d + 1.34 \times 10^{-4} Q_h)/u \tag{12}$$

where V_s and u are in meters per second, Δh and d in feet, and Q_h in calories per second. Q_h may be evaluated in terms of other effluent variables with the following equation where consistent units must be used.

$$Q_h = Q_m C_{ps} \Delta T \tag{13}$$

Holland's field data cover a range of stability conditions. They show that plume height increases with instability. Holland suggests that stability be taken into account by adding 10 to 20% to plume rise found with Eq. 12 when unstable and subtracting the same amount when stable.

iv. Thomas formula. Thomas (*15*) developed his formula on the basis of plume observations at the Johnsonville power plant of TVA. He followed the procedure used by Holland and obtained the following equation.

$$\Delta h = (1.5V_s d + 2.68 \times 10^{-4} Q_h)/u \tag{14}$$

The units are the same as in the Oak ridge formula (Eq. 12). Thomas states that the observations give the maximum plume rise.

The equation is based on the average of observations obtained for a range of stability conditions. Thomas divides the observations into two groups termed light lapse and large lapse. He suggests that stability may be accounted for within the accuracy of his data by adding 10 to 25% to the rise obtained from the equation for large lapse and subtracting a like amount for light lapse. Information in the paper suggests that the terms "light lapse" and "large lapse" are equivalent to stable and unstable, respectively. In this event, it appears reasonable to assume that Eq. 14 applies to neutral conditions as does the Oak Ridge formula.

v. Sutton formula. Sutton (*9, 16*) presented a theoretical treatment of buoyancy rise in which the following equation gives the plume rise at the location where the plume axis forms the angle ψ with the horizontal. Momentum rise is not included.

$$\Delta h = 1.5(\nu_1/u)^3[\cot \psi \operatorname{cosec} \psi - \log_e (\cot \psi + \operatorname{cosec} \psi)] \tag{15}$$

where

$$\nu_1{}^3 = \frac{7Q_h g}{3\pi C_p \rho T C_1} \tag{16}$$

For evaluation of ν_1, C_p and ρ may be replaced with C_{ps} and ρ_s. C_1 is a diffusion coefficient which is essentially that used in the diffusion theory given in Section III,A,3,*c*. In the development of Eq. 15 Sutton makes a simplifying assumption which appears to require a value of zero for n in Eq. 57. The dimensions of the diffusion coefficient depends on n. It is not clear what effect this has on the numerical values which should be used for C_1. In his numerical examples Sutton makes a significant adjustment (not detailed in the reference) in the value of ν_1, to account for the simplifying assumption. The reference should be consulted before the application of Eqs. 15 and 16.

The following equation (Eq. 17) gives the distance s along the plume path to the location where Δh is found.

$$s = (\nu_1/u)^3 \cot^3 \psi \tag{17}$$

Sutton takes the plume to be virtually horizontal, therefore, near maximum rise when ψ is less than 10°. In cases where the rise is relatively small such as will occur with high winds, downwind distance x will be approximately equal to s.

vi. Bryant and Cowdry procedure. On the basis of wind tunnel experiments conducted at the National Physical Laboratory, Bryant and Cowdry (*17*) obtained basic characteristics of cold and hot gas plumes and used these in developing an approximate theory for plume path. In this theory the effect of atmospheric turbulence and stability is introduced by using plume-spreading characteristics obtained from Sutton's diffusion equation (*4*). Application of this theory to specific problems is made with the aid of five graphs presented in the paper. In these graphs plume rise vs. downwind distance is plotted for a stack of 10-ft. diameter and a series of ejection speed to wind speed ratios. Four different stability conditions ranging from "very turbulent" to "moderate inversion" are included. Also covered are cold plumes and hot plumes having a 200°C. increase in temperature. Specific problems having values other than the above are handled by relationships with which interpolation or extrapolation can be performed. One of the characteristics noted from inspection of the graphs is that plume rise decreases with increasing instability (greater atmospheric turbulence).

vii. Priestley procedure. Priestley's procedure (*18*) treats plume rise as occurring in two different phases to account for the change in nature of diffusing mechanism as the plume leaves the stack and becomes mixed with the surrounding atmosphere. It is based on an analysis of plume rise in still air given in an earlier paper where various conditions of atmospheric stability are covered. In the 1956 paper (*18*) only neutral stability is treated, but Priestley indicates that procedures for other conditions of stability could be developed along similar lines using the results of the earlier paper. All of the following apply to the neutral case except Eq. 34.

In the first phase of plume rise, turbulence induced by jet action of the effluent as it leaves the stack dominates diffusion. Plume axial speed w_a is given by

$$w_a{}^3 = \frac{3A_1 g}{2\theta c^2}\left(\frac{1}{\Delta h_v} - \frac{\Delta h_{vo}{}^2}{\Delta h_v{}^3}\right) + \frac{w_{ao}{}^3 \Delta h_{vo}{}^3}{\Delta h_v{}^3} \tag{18}$$

where the subscript "o" refers to stack top. The above and following equations are valid in consistent units.

$$A_1 = Q_h/\pi \rho_s C_{ps} \tag{19}$$

Δh_v is measured from a point located a distance Δh_{vo} below stack top where the lines forming plume outline meet, a form of virtual origin. Radius R of plume cross section is related to Δh_v.

$$R = c\Delta h_v \tag{20}$$

Determination of spreading coefficient c (dimensionless) is discussed below. Δh_{vo} is, therefore, related to R_o, the radius of stack top by

$$\Delta h_{vo} = R_o/c \tag{21}$$

Priestley states that the actual radius should be replaced with a fictitious radius based on effluent characteristics as follows.

$$R_o{}^2 = A_1/(w_{ao}\Delta\theta_o) \tag{22}$$

While w_a is defined as the axial speed in Eq. 18, an average w_{ao} at stack exit appears to be used in application of Eq. 22. In real cases ejection speed may be substantially constant (depending on stack configuration below the outlet) over the cross section and thus becomes the same as w_{ao}.

In order to relate plume rise to downwind distance, an expression for time to reach height Δh_v is needed. The following equation results from integration of Eq. 18 where w_a is equivalent to $d\Delta h_v/dt$.

$$t = \frac{\theta c^2}{2A_1 g}\left\{\left[\frac{3A_1 g}{2\theta c^2}(\Delta h_v{}^2 - \Delta h_{vo}{}^2) + w_{ao}{}^3\Delta h_{vo}{}^3\right]^{2/3} - [w_{ao}{}^3\Delta h_{vo}{}^3]^{2/3}\right\} \tag{23}$$

Here the limits of integration have been selected to measure t from stack top. For the case of no buoyancy rise Eq. 23 reduces to

$$t = \frac{\Delta h_v{}^2 - \Delta h_{vo}{}^2}{2w_{ao}\Delta h_{vo}} \tag{24}$$

Downwind distance x (from source) is given by

$$x = ut \tag{25}$$

where it is assumed that the plume acquires the speed of the ambient atmosphere as soon as it leaves the stack. Substitution of Eq. 23 or 24 into 25 yields x as a function of plume rise.

Potential temperature difference $\Delta\theta$ between plume and ambient atmosphere in the first phase is a function of plume rise and axial speed by the following equation.

$$\Delta\theta = \frac{A_1}{c^2 \Delta h_v{}^2 w_a} \tag{26}$$

Priestley shows the spreading coefficient c to be proportional to the square root of wind speed except at very low speeds where it approaches a value of 0.1 in a calm. On the basis of smoke plume photographs from wind tunnel experiments he gives a value of 0.75 at 2.44 m./sec. from which the following equation is formed.

$$c = 0.75(u/2.44)^{1/2} \tag{27}$$

where u is wind speed in meters per second.

In the second phase of plume rise, diffusion is due primarily to atmospheric turbulence. Axial velocity and potential temperature difference are governed by the following equations.

$$w_a = [w_{a1} + g\Delta\theta_1(t - t_1)/\theta]e^{-k(t-t_1)} \tag{28}$$

$$\Delta\theta = \Delta\theta_1 e^{-k(t-t_1)} \tag{29}$$

where the subscript "1" refers to conditions at transition and k is mixing rate. Priestley suggests that k be taken as proportional to wind speed until further experimental data show a better relationship. He gives numerical values which may be represented by the following equation for k in units of seconds^{-1}.

$$k = 0.0197u \tag{30}$$

where u is wind speed in meters per second.

Equation 28 is integrated to give plume rise relative to transition as follows.

$$\Delta h - \Delta h_1 = \frac{w_{a1}}{k}[1 - e^{-k(t-t_1)}] + \frac{g\Delta\theta_1}{\theta k^2}\{1 - [1 + k(t - t_1)]e^{-k(t-t_1)}\} \tag{31}$$

Δh_1 may be replaced with $\Delta h_{v1} - \Delta h_{vo}$. Downwind distance x is given by Eq. 25. w_{a1} and $\Delta\theta_1$ are found with Eqs. 18 and 26 using Eq. 32 below.

Location of transition between phases one and two occurs where the diffusive action of the two sources of turbulence are equal. This is expressed by equality of the derivatives $dw/d\Delta h$ for the two phases. Priestley describes a trial-and-error method of locating transition. Spurr (*19*) gives the following equation found with the above condition.

$$\Delta h_{v1}{}^6 - \frac{3A_1 g}{2\theta c^2 k^3}\Delta h_{v1}{}^2 - \frac{1}{k^3}\left(w_{ao}{}^3 \Delta h_{vo}{}^3 - \frac{3A_1 g \Delta h_{vo}{}^2}{2\theta c^2}\right) = 0 \qquad (32)$$

Having found Δh_{v1} from this equation, t_1 and $\Delta\theta_1$ may be calculated with Eqs. 23 and 26. Maximum plume rise Δh_c found when time increases without limit is given by the following.

$$\Delta h_c - \Delta h_1 = (w_{a1}/k) + (g\Delta\theta_1/k^2\theta) \qquad (33)$$

Priestley gives Δh_c for the case of non-neutral stability

$$\Delta h_c - \Delta h_1 = \frac{(kw_{a1}) + (g\Delta\theta_1/\theta)}{(g/\theta)/(d\theta/dz) + k^2} \qquad (34)$$

From this equation it is apparent that a maximum will exist not only for the stable case $(d\theta/dz > 0)$, but also for unstable cases when

$$|(g/\theta)/(d\theta/dz)| < k^2 \qquad (35)$$

viii. Bosanquet procedure. On the basis of certain fundamental principles of dilution of a gas plume in the atmosphere, Bosanquet (*20*) gives a theoretical development for plume rise which includes the effect of relative motion of plume and surrounding atmosphere as well as ambient atmospheric turbulence. These effects are introduced with dilution coefficients. As presented, the equations are based on the assumption of equal values for the dilution coefficients. Therefore only one coefficient appears in the equations below. Bosanquet shows that the plume rise is not sensitive to inequalities of the coefficients. All except Eq. 48 are developed for a neutral atmosphere.

Plume rise is given as follows.

$$\Delta h = A_2 u \left\{ f_{\mathrm{I}}(a) + f_{\mathrm{II}}(a_o) - \frac{0.615 a_o{}^{1/2}}{[(V_s/u)^2 + 0.57]^{1/2}} \right\} \qquad (36)$$

where

$$A_2 = \frac{gQ_{v1}\Delta T_1}{2\pi C_2{}^2 T_1 u^4} \qquad (37)$$

$$t_o = \frac{4V_s T_1}{3g\Delta T_1} \qquad (38)$$

$$a_o = t_o/A_2 \qquad (39)$$

$$a = (t + t_o)/A_2$$

$$= t/A_2 + a_o \qquad (40)$$

$$t = x/u \qquad (41)$$

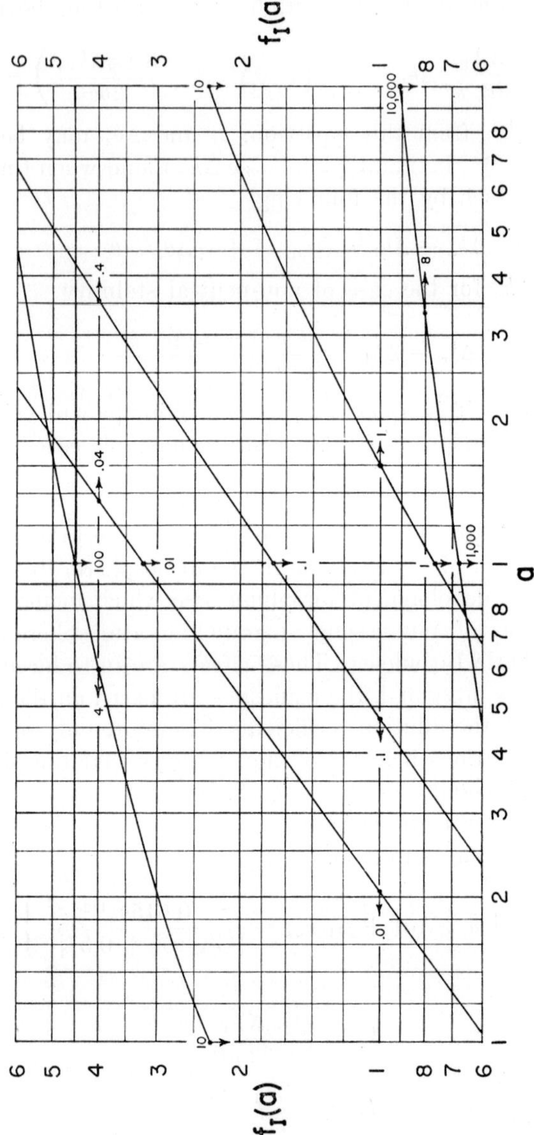

FIG. 9. $f_I(a)$ vs. a for use in Eq. 36. (Plotted from Table 1, Bosanquet, *J. Inst. Fuel* **30,** 1957.)

The above equations are valid with consistent units. $f_{I}(a)$ and $f_{II}(a_o)$ are obtained from the graphs in Figs. 9 and 10, respectively. For values of a and a_o outside the range of the graphs, the following apply. When a is very large

$$f_{I}(a) = \log_e a - 0.12 \tag{42}$$

and when a is very small

$$f_{I}(a) = 1.054a^{3/4} \tag{43}$$

When a_o is very large

$$f_{II}(a_o) = 1.311a_o^{1/2} - (\log_e a_o)/2 - 1 \tag{44}$$

and when a_o is very small

$$f_{II}(a_o) = -0.527a_o^{3/4} \tag{45}$$

Bosanquet recommends that the dilution coefficient C_2 be given the value 0.13. He also places a limit on plume rise by not exceeding the value of Δh for which $t + t_o$ is 200 sec.

For the case of no buoyancy (momentum rise only) maximum plume rise is given by

$$\Delta h_{\max} = \frac{(2Q_{v1}V_s/3)^{1/2}}{C_2\pi^{1/2}u}\left\{1.311 - \frac{0.615}{[(V_s/u)^2 + 0.57]^{1/2}}\right\} \tag{46}$$

when $V_s/u > 0.5$. For small values of V_s/u

$$\Delta h_{\max} = \frac{(2Q_{v1}V_s/3)^{1/2}}{C_2\pi^{1/2}u} \cdot 0.9(V_s/u)^{1/2} \tag{47}$$

The two equations give the same value at $V_s/u = 0.48$. They are approximate solutions of the differential equations for plume path and, according to Bosanquet, are within 1% of the exact solution found by numerical integration.

Maximum rise of a buoyant plume in a stable atmosphere is found from Eq. 36 using the following equation for $t + t_o$ or a value of 200 sec., whichever is smaller.

$$t + t_o = 1.527\left[\frac{2T}{g(d\theta/dz)}\right]^{1/2} \tag{48}$$

ix. Scorer formulas. Scorer (*3*) discusses in detail various characteristics of gas plumes in different phases of plume rise. He tabulates a number of expressions for these characteristics and uses them as a basis for developing equations for maximum plume rise. Maximum rise is defined by Scorer as occurring when vertical plume velocity is reduced to the magnitude of ambient turbulent velocities. Scorer's tabulation could

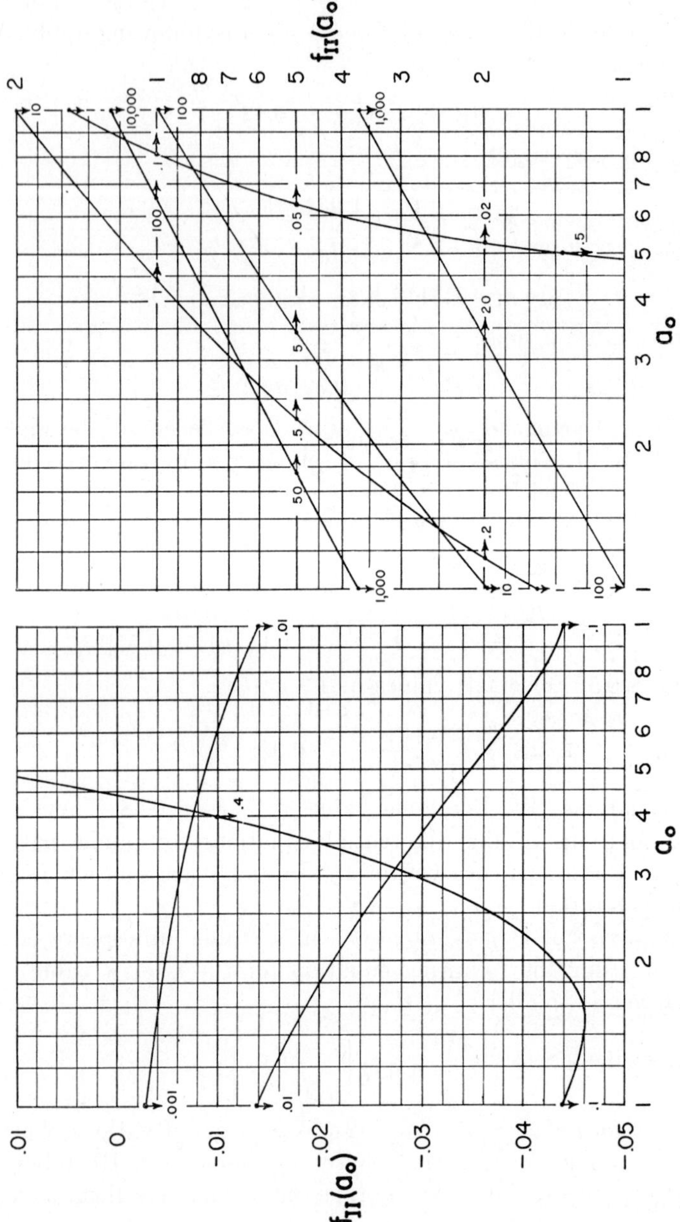

FIG. 10. $f_{II}(a_o)$ vs. a_o for use in Eq. 36. (Plotted from Table 2, Bosanquet, *J. Inst. Fuel* **30**, 1957.)

be used for developing equations for plume path, i.e., rise vs. downwind distance.

Plume rise is treated in two phases although one equation covers the total for the two. The first phase occurs when the plume is nearly vertical and the second when nearly horizontal. While in a real plume there is a gradual transition between the two, the analysis is carried out on the assumption that there is an instantaneous shift from one to the other. There is described a third phase in which the plume is "passive," but maximum rise occurs at the end of the second phase.

Maximum rise for a nonbuoyant plume is given by

$$\Delta h_{cmax} = 2.5R_o[(V_s/u)(\lambda^{-1/2} - \mu^{-1/2} + 2\mu^{-1}) - 2] \tag{49}$$

where $\Delta h_{c\ max}$ is plume rise measured from stack top to the "cap" of the plume. Location of the cap relative to plume axis is not given, nor does Scorer discuss this point. If the cap is taken as the top of a circular cross section plume, the difference between cap and axis elevation is plume radius. Scorer gives the following relation between plume rise and radius for the second phase.

$$\Delta h_v = 2.25R \tag{50}$$

From this, the difference between cap and axis would be on the order of half the plume rise which makes a considerable change in rise. Scorer's discussion on noncircular sections of real plumes shows the distance between cap and axis to be somewhat less than the radius of an equivalent circular sectioned plume. It would appear that, lacking additional information, Eq. 49 should be taken as an approximation for axial rise or at most be reduced by a fraction of plume radius. Additional information on details of plume structure is given in Scorer (*20a*).

The factor μ* determines the point where the first phase ends. This occurs when the vertical speed of plume equals μu. λ is the ratio of ambient turbulent velocities to wind velocity. Scorer gives μ an approximate value of 1.0 and λ an approximate value of 0.1 for neutral stability. Equation 49 is valid for consistent units.

Maximum rise of a buoyant plume is given by

$$\Delta h_{cmax} = (0.58F)/(\lambda^2 u^3) + 2.5R_o[(V_s/u)(-\mu^{-1/2} + 2\mu^{-1}) - 2] \tag{51}$$

when

$$g\frac{(\rho - \rho_s)}{\rho} > \frac{1.4\lambda^{3/2}u^2}{R_o}$$

Otherwise maximum rise will be less than that of the nonbuoyant plume in which case Eq. 49 should be used. $(\rho - \rho_s)/\rho$ is equivalent to $\Delta T_1/T_1$.

$$F = \pi g V_s R_o^2(\rho - \rho_s)/\rho \tag{52}$$

* The symbol μ as used on pp. 145 and 146 should not be confused with μ meaning dynamic viscosity as used elsewhere in the chapter.

For plumes of large buoyancy when

$$g\frac{(\rho - \rho_s)}{\rho} > \frac{0.7\mu^{3/2}u^2}{R_o}$$

plume rise is given by

$$\Delta h_{c\max} = \left[\frac{0.58}{\lambda^2} - \frac{2.25}{\mu^{5/2}} + \frac{3.8}{\mu^3}\right]\frac{F}{u^3} - 5R_o \tag{53}$$

c. Discussion. Comparison of the various plume rise procedures is difficult because of the variety of forms in which they appear. In some cases the equations are quite complicated and in others auxiliary graphs must be used which makes direct comparison impossible. In general, comparisons must be made on the basis of numerical examples. In view of the number of independent variables involved a rather large number of examples must be taken to give a significant coverage of the potential range of variables. No such study has been published.

Table I shows the type of plume rise results obtainable from the various procedures.

TABLE I

TYPES OF PLUME RISE RESULTS OBTAINABLE FROM THE VARIOUS PROCEDURES

		Plume rise as a function of distance		Maximum plume rise	
	Procedure	Neutral stability	Non-neutral stability	Neutral stability	Non-neutral stability
i	Bryant-Davidson	—	—	X	—
ii	Bosanquet *et al.*	X	—	X	X
iii	Oak Ridge	—	—	X	X[a]
iv	Thomas	—	—	X	X[a]
v	Sutton	X	—	X[b]	—
vi	Bryant and Cowdry	X	X	—	—
vii	Priestley	X	—	X	X
viii	Bosanquet	X	—	X[b]	X[b]
ix	Scorer	—	—	X	—

[a] Effect of stability accounted for by empirical change in neutral plume rise.

[b] Maximum rise obtained by placing limit on path equation.

While maximum plume rise is intended to give a practical ultimate height, it is defined in different ways by the various authors. Sutton places it at the point where the angle of plume axis with the horizontal is 10° or less, Bosanquet places a time limit, etc. Thus there may be differences, maybe small, due to the manner in which maximum rise is defined.

Since most plumes have a significant degree of buoyancy, numerical examples presented in the literature generally include buoyancy. The following comparisons will usually refer to buoyant plumes. Except when specified, they will also refer to maximum plume rise or, in the case of plume path equations, to rise obtained at considerable distances where near maximum will occur. Except where stated, neutral stability conditions will prevail. Of the procedures given above the Bryant-Davidson equation may be expected to give the lowest plume rise. Sutton's equation in a limited number of examples gives the highest rise, especially at low wind speeds. The Oak Ridge and Thomas equations seem to give values lower than most. The Oak Ridge equation will always give a lower value than Thomas since the buoyancy part of the Thomas equation is twice that of Oak Ridge and the momentum part is the same.

In his discussion of Bosanquet's paper, Nonhebel (*20*) mentions that the Bosanquet *et al.* (*2*) procedure gives excessive buoyancy rise for large plants. Numerical examples have shown that the Bosanquet procedure gives lower rise than Bosanquet *et al.* but both fall within the extremes given by the other procedures. A rather limited application of the Bryant and Cowdry procedure (neutral stability) shows it to fall in the vicinity of the Bosanquet procedure. Best (*21*) makes comparative calculations of maximum plume rise with the Sutton, Bosanquet *et al.*, and Oak Ridge procedures for conditions applicable to a range of power plant sizes. These show Oak Ridge to give the lowest rise, Bosanquet *et al.* the next, and Sutton the highest. There was a considerable range for the three. Two cases of stable conditions were used for the Bosanquet *et al.* maximum rise calculations.

Some applications of Scorer's equations (*3*) show values in the range of Bosanquet at high wind speeds but higher at low winds. Priestley (*18*) makes a comparative study of his procedure with those of Bosanquet *et al.* and Sutton as applied to the field experiments in the Bosanquet *et al.* paper. The Priestley procedure in all cases gave values lower than Sutton at the greater downwind distances and generally, but not always, greater than Bosanquet *et al.*

There is only a limited amount of field data for testing the various plume rise procedures. Several of the authors give field data with their presentations of plume rise analysis. In some cases these are used for comparison with results of their procedure while in others they are the basis for establishing an empirical equation. Those of Holland and Thomas fall in the latter category.

Bosanquet *et al.* compare results of their procedure with field data obtained for the purpose. The four plants from which the data were taken appear to have stacks of diameters under 10 ft. On the average there is good agreement for the smaller downwind distances while at greater distances the calculated values are lower. The authors point out that two of the plants had considerable water vapor in the plumes which on condensation released heat and caused the observed plumes to rise to higher elevations. The authors conclude that the agreement is good in view of the possible sources of error. Priestley compares his procedure with Bosanquet *et al.* field data and includes calculated rise vs. distance obtained with Sutton and Bosanquet *et al.* procedures. Priestley states that the average errors (compared with field data) of the Priestley, Bosanquet *et al.*, and Sutton procedures are —3%, —17%, and +38%, respectively, and the average errors regardless of sign are 13%, 21%, and 40%, respectively.

Stewart *et al.* (*6*) show field data on plume height obtained from the stack of the Harwell Reactor BEPO. Stack diameter was 11.5 ft. Gas ejection speed was 10 m./sec. and temperature was 50°C. above ambient. Comparison of field data for neutral conditions with calculated plume rise by Bosanquet *et al.* procedure shows that in the distance range of 1000 to 2000 ft. agreement is good at low wind speeds but at high speeds the calculated values are lower than observed. At shorter distances the calculated values tend to be higher or at least equal to the observed.

Effect of atmospheric stability is treated in some procedures but the results vary. Bosanquet *et al.* and Bosanquet show finite maximum plume rise only with stable atmospheres. Priestley shows finite maximum rise for a limited degree of instability as well as all degrees of positive stability. Holland and Thomas treat stability as a modification of plume rise obtained for neutral conditions. Comments of Stewart *et al.* on effect of instability show approximately the same effect as given by Holland and Thomas. The above authors show that increase in stability tends to reduce plume rise. Bryant and Cowdry show the opposite effect.

The Report of the Government Committee on Air Pollution (Beaver Report) (*22*) recommends that ground level concentration be calculated with a formula in which plume rise is obtained from the Oak Ridge formula. This is used in view of the ". . . present status of knowledge on the subject. . . ." A footnote refers to a then unpublished procedure by Bosanquet which seems to be the one published in 1957 (*20*). It states that there is substantial agreement with the results obtained with the Oak Ridge formula. Hawkins and Nonhebel (*14*) present their paper as an extension of Appendix 6 of the Government Report and comment on the Report's use of the Oak Ridge formula to the effect that it was preferred because of its simplicity. Hawkins and Nonhebel prefer the Bosanquet procedure and give graphs for its application to a range of conditions which cover most cases likely to occur. A graphical comparison of the Oak Ridge and Bosanquet procedures for one buoyancy condition shows the Oak Ridge rise to be approximately one-quarter less than that of Bosanquet.

Evaluation of the various procedures is complicated by the lack of agreement among field data. Direct comparison of field data is difficult for the same reasons as comparison of procedures. The Oak Ridge and Thomas formulas are empirically based on their own field data but they differ as must the field data. The Oak Ridge formula gives results considerably lower than Bosanquet *et al.* but the Bosanquet *et al.* field data show plume rises which are equal to or higher than calculated. Differences in field data are further increased when the Stewart *et al.* data for the Harwell Reactor BEPO are introduced. Undoubtedly some of these differences can be ascribed to factors not accounted for in the various procedures such as the effect of buildings and topography and differences in measurement of significant variables.

If conservative (high) values of ground level concentration are desired, the Oak Ridge or, less conservatively, the Thomas formulas may be used. Sutton results will be optimistic. In between are the Scorer, Priestley, Bosanquet, and Bosanquet *et al.* procedures. Hawkins and Nonhebel favor the Bosanquet procedure and this appears to be a reasonable choice if a mildly conservative result is desired. The Priestley procedure may be a little more cumbersome to handle than others. Scorer leaves doubt on the values to be used for some coefficients but his equations are relatively easy to use. It is to be noted that as wind speed increases, plume rise is reduced, ground level concentration is increased, and differences among the various procedures are reduced.

There has appeared a technique which with further application to new experimental data may obtain from existing procedures improved accuracy and range of application. This consists of comparing experimental data with results obtained from a given procedure and determining an empirical correction which gives the best agreement. This technique is used by Wippermann and Klug (*22a*) and Moses and Strom (*22b*).

In applying the various procedures, consideration should be given to the range of variables involved. Application of the more empirical type of formulae should not be extended much beyond the conditions under which field data were obtained. Some of the procedures include adjustable coefficients of diffusion properties for which the authors give suggested values. With the acquisition of more experimental data from which improved values for these coefficients may be obtained, improved accuracy of plume rise calculations may be expected.

The various plume rise procedures were developed to handle buoyant plumes primarily since they are the type usually encountered. Plumes which are heavier-than-air are encountered in the chemical industry. While some of the procedures may be modified to handle dense gases as is brought out in the discussion of Bosanquet's (*20*) paper, the accuracy is probably reduced. Bodurtha (*22c*) presents results of wind tunnel experiments in which heavier-than-air plumes were tested. His paper gives various data and procedures valuable to the investigation of dense plumes.

3. *Distribution of Gas Concentration*

a. Introduction. While diffusion of gases in the atmosphere has in recent decades been the subject of much theoretical and experimental analysis, there is no method which will in all cases give accurate prediction of concentration distribution in gas plumes. Predictions of acceptable accuracy can, however, be made in many cases where the less complicated topographical and meteorological characteristics occur.

Various theoretical studies on atmospheric diffusion have contributed much to the understanding of the physical processes involved, but the results of only two have found much application to specific problems of gas plume diffusion. Of these two, namely, Bosanquet and Pearson (*23*) and Sutton (*24*), the latter has seen the greatest use. Both will be covered in the following material, but that of Sutton will be given in greater detail.

There is a trend in the analysis of gas diffusion to use a more general basis than given by Sutton's equation and to relate the diffusion characteristics to meteorological variables which are more intimately related to the diffusion process. This is particularly evident in research programs. In these methods statistical properties of gas concentration distributions as represented by their standard deviations are used in place of the diffusion coefficients and turbulence index of Sutton's equation. This procedure is used in the Project Prairie Grass and Round Hill experiments described in Section III,A,3,*d*,*v*. Fundamental aspects of this subject are analyzed by Hay and Pasquill (*24a*) where they relate statistical characteristics of gas concentration to those of the wind fluctuations. These results are used by Pasquill (*24b*) to develop a procedure for estimating gas diffusion over a wide range of meteorological conditions and over distances up to 100 km.

In applying the results of diffusion theories to the calculation of concentration in gas plumes certain experimentally derived diffusion parameters must be evaluated. In their original presentations the authors give limited data on numerical values for these parameters.

Since then, much additional data has been found from the many field studies on gas diffusion, thus broadening the area of application of diffusion theories. In the material which follows, the results of several field studies are given. The coverage is still quite limited and available data are far removed from the conditions of many practical cases. Application of gas concentration equations may in such cases depend largely on guesswork.

b. Bosanquet and Pearson Formula. Bosanquet and Pearson (*23*) developed the following equation for determination of ground level gas concentration caused by a continuous elevated point source.

$$\chi = \frac{Q_m}{\sqrt{2\pi} pqux^2} \exp\left(-\frac{h_e}{px} - \frac{y^2}{2q^2x^2}\right) \tag{54}$$

where the variables must be expressed in consistent units.

Maximum ground level concentration is found at $y = 0$, $x = x_m$ where

$$x_m = h_e/2p \tag{55}$$

Concentration at this location, x_m, is given by

$$\chi_m = \frac{4Q_m p}{\sqrt{2\pi} e^2 u h_e^2 q} \tag{56}$$

Bosanquet and Pearson give the diffusion parameter p an average value of 0.05 with possible variations of at least a factor of 3 either way. They give an average value of 0.08 for q.

c. Sutton Formula. On the basis of statistical properties of turbulence Sutton (*24*) developed the following equation for gas concentration at any location downwind of a point source.

$$\chi = \frac{Q_m \exp(-y^2/C_y^2x^{2-n})}{\pi C_y C_z u x^{2-n}} \left\{\exp\left[-\frac{(z-h_e)^2}{C_z^2x^{2-n}}\right] + \exp\left[-\frac{(z+h_e)^2}{C_z^2x^{2-n}}\right]\right\} \tag{57}$$

where the variables are used with consistent units. In the development of Eq. 57 it is assumed that the ground is an inert surface which does not entrap or absorb the gas. The effect of the ground is introduced with the second term in the braces of the equation.

For negligible ground effect (valid for relatively large h_e) maximum gas concentration at a given x occurs on the axis of the plume, a horizontal line through the source at $z = h_e$, $y = 0$ in the direction of the mean wind.

$$\chi_{\text{axial}} = \frac{Q_m}{\pi C_y C_z u x^{2-n}} \tag{58}$$

Axial concentration is obviously greatest at the source, infinite for the point source assumed in above equations. Axial concentration varies inversely with wind speed as does concentration at other locations.

At ground level ($z = 0$) Eq. 57 reduces to

$$\chi_{z=0} = \frac{2Q_{\mathrm{m}}}{\pi C_y C_z u x^{2-n}} \exp\left[-\frac{1}{x^{2-n}}\left(\frac{y^2}{C_y^2} + \frac{h_{\mathrm{e}}^2}{C_z^2}\right)\right] \tag{59}$$

Maximum ground level concentration occurs at $y = 0$, $x = x_{\mathrm{m}}$ where

$$x_{\mathrm{m}} = (h_{\mathrm{e}}^2/C_z^2)^{\frac{1}{2-n}} \tag{60}$$

and the corresponding maximum concentration is

$$\chi_{\mathrm{m},\, z=0} = \frac{2Q_{\mathrm{m}} C_z}{\pi e u h_{\mathrm{e}}^2 C_y} \tag{61}$$

This equation shows maximum ground concentration to vary inversely with the square of plume height.

In the development of Eq. 57 it is assumed that the wind speed and diffusion coefficients are constant with elevation even though a gradient of wind speed is needed for generation of mechanical turbulence over flat ground. Since these characteristics usually vary with elevation in the real atmosphere, selection of specific values must be made. For axial concentration, values of u, C_y, and C_z at plume level are appropriate. For ground level concentration average values in the layer between the plume and ground may be used.

While the turbulence index n could in principle be determined from turbulence characteristics, such a procedure would be difficult to perform (*9*). Sutton (*24*) shows the relation of n to the mean wind velocity profile expressed in terms of the power law as follows:

$$u = u_1(z/z_1)^{\frac{n}{2-n}} \tag{62}$$

where u is the wind velocity at elevation z and u_1 is velocity at reference level z_1.

The diffusion coefficients are related to turbulence and other characteristics as follows.

$$C_y^2 = \frac{4\nu^n}{(1-n)(2-n)u^n}\left(\frac{\overline{v'^2}}{u^2}\right)^{1-n} \tag{63}$$

$$C_z^2 = \frac{4\nu^n}{(1-n)(2-n)u^n}\left(\frac{\overline{w'^2}}{u^2}\right)^{1-n} \tag{64}$$

Equations 63 and 64 apply to air flow over aerodynamically smooth surfaces, a condition not usually achieved in the atmosphere. For rough surfaces Sutton (*9*) replaces the kinematic viscosity ν with macroviscosity (eddy viscosity) N where the resistance to shear is dominated by the turbulent or eddy motions.

Macroviscosity is dependent on surface roughness and may be expressed in terms of characteristics determined from the velocity profile. The velocity profile over a rough surface for neutral thermal conditions may be represented with the following equation (*9*).

$$\frac{u}{u_*} = \frac{1}{k} \log_e \left(\frac{z}{z_o} \right) \tag{65}$$

where

u_* = friction velocity, a measure of surface shear stress
u = time mean velocity at elevation z
z_o = roughness length
k = von Karman constant

The von Karman constant is often given the value 0.4 (*9*). The value of 0.43 is quoted in the 1955 U. S. AEC Report (*11*). Velocity profile measurements may be used for finding u_* and z_o from Eq. 65.

In terms of the above characteristics

$$N = u_* z_o \tag{66}$$

Sutton (*9*, Table 23) gives representative values of z_o and u_* for various natural surfaces in the lower roughness range. Laboratory experiments with surfaces roughened with sand grains have shown that z_o is equal to 1/30 of the mean diameter of the grains.

Near the ground, C_y tends to be greater than C_z because of the suppression of the vertical component of turbulence. In his 1947 paper (*24*) Sutton gives $C_y = 0.21$ and $C_z = 0.10$ for zero temperature gradient at an elevation of 10 m. With increase in elevation, turbulence becomes more nearly isotropic and C_y and C_z become equal. Sutton gives equal values for C_y and C_z for elevations above 25 m. (Table II), which are

TABLE II
SUTTON'S DIFFUSION PARAMETERS

Stability condition	n	C_y, C_z (m.$^{n/2}$) Elevation (m.) 25	50	75	100
Large lapse rate	0.20	0.21	0.17	0.16	0.12
Zero or small temperature gradient	0.25	0.12	0.10	0.09	0.07
Moderate inversion	0.33	0.08	0.06	0.05	0.04
Large inversion	0.50	0.06	0.05	0.04	0.03

based on a tabulation of diffusion parameters in the U. S. AEC Report (*11*) derived from information in (*24*). The diffusion coefficients were determined for a 3-min. sampling period over the relatively smooth (but rolling) surfaces of downland at Porton, England.

d. Sutton Diffusion Parameters from Field Studies. i. Oak Ridge National Laboratory. J. Z. Holland (*12*) presents the results of meteorological observations at the Oak Ridge National Laboratory including data and computations of interest to gas plume diffusion. Wind profile measurements yield values of the turbulence index n and turbulence measurements are used to calculate diffusion coefficients with Eqs. 63 and 64. The coefficients are based on 15-min. observations.

The Oak Ridge area is located in a valley of the southern Appalachian mountain range in Tennessee. The surface conditions are described: "The ridges are completely wooded, while the valley is mainly overgrown farm land."

Table III is based on values taken from Holland's Table 50 (*12*).

TABLE III
DIFFUSION PARAMETERS FROM OAK RIDGE EXPERIMENTS

Stability condition	n	Parameter	Elevation (ft.)[a] 18	54	154	80
Daytime (superadiabatic	0.15	C_y[b]	0.34	0.28	0.22	0.21
lapse rate)	to	C_z[b]	0.23	—	—	—
	0.20	u[c]	1.5	1.8	2.4	2.7
Average (neutral stability)	0.25	C_y	0.20	0.17	0.15	0.13
		C_z	0.21	—	—	—
		u	0.9	1.2	1.8	2.7
Night-time (moderate	0.30	C_y	0.14	0.11	0.08	0.08
inversion)	to	C_z	0.14	—	—	—
	0.40	u	0.3	0.6	1.5	2.7

[a] Elevations 18 and 54 ft. are the same station. Elevations 154 and 80 are different stations and have heights above the valley of 230 and 420 ft., respectively.

[b] C_y and C_z have units of m.$^{n/2}$.

[c] u has units of m./sec.

ii. Brookhaven National Laboratory. As a part of their meteorological program, the meteorology group at the Brookhaven National Laboratory has conducted extensive diffusion experiments using oil-fog smoke emitted from a stack at an elevation of 355 ft. The Brookhaven group has developed a gustiness classification system for classifying conditions of atmospheric turbulence. Diffusion results are given in terms of these categories.

The five gustiness categories described by Singer and Smith (*25*) are based on the record of wind direction fluctuations measured with a standard Bendix-Friez Aerovane mounted 355 ft. above the ground. They are designated A, B_2, B_1, C, and D in decreasing order of amplitude of fluctuations. Each category is defined in terms of specific features of the wind direction record. In terms of increasing stability as measured by the average vertical temperature gradient, the categories take the order B_2, A, B_1, C, and D, but the D category has a wide range of values including some which are unstable. Type C appears to be closest to neutral stability and is associated with high winds with turbulence primarily mechanical in origin. Singer and Smith give statistical properties of various meteorological characteristics for each category. They reveal that the B_1 and D categories have the largest percentage of occurrence.

The Brookhaven topography is fairly flat. There are scrub oak and pine trees with heights of 25 to 30 ft. Several large areas of field grass are in the vicinity of the stack which is located at the meteorology tower.

Diffusion studies of Smith and Singer (*5*) are based on measurements of ground level concentration of oil-fog smoke. In contrast with Sutton's procedure for evaluating the turbulence index n, Smith and Singer do not use wind profile measurements. Sutton's gas concentration equation (Eq. 57) contains the three parameters n, C_y, and C_z. With sufficient concentration data these three may be evaluated without recourse to meteorological measurements. This is the basis for the values in Table IV (taken from Smith and Singer, *5*). Thus the values of n in Table IV

TABLE IV

DIFFUSION PARAMETERS FROM BROOKHAVEN EXPERIMENTS

Gustiness category	u[a] (m./sec.)	Temperature[a] gradient (°C./100 m.)	n	C_y (m.$^{n/2}$)	C_z (m.$^{n/2}$)
B_2	3.8	−1.4	0.17	0.31	0.36
B_1	7.0	−1.05	0.28	0.40	0.39
C	10.4	−0.55	0.48	0.54	0.34

[a] Taken from I. A. Singer and M. E. Smith, *J. Meteorol.* **10,** 121 (1953). Gradient is based on temperature difference between 410 ft. and 37 ft. elevations.

are not necessarily the same as those which would be found from the wind profile. The values of diffusion parameters shown are averages of a large number of experiments, and they are based on 1-hr. sampling periods.

iii. Round Hill Field Station. Diffusion parameters based on a set of observations of lateral wind direction fluctuations obtained at the Round

Hill Field Station are given by Friedman (*26*). The ground surface is described as aerodynamically rough and has a roughness length of 8.5 cm. The surface roughness elements are described by Cramer (*27*) as large. Three 24-min. runs taken in the afternoon, at sunset and in the evening are the basis for the values in Table V which are taken from Friedman (*26*). The diffusion coefficients are derived from an average of turbulence observations (in the form of gustiness factors) taken between elevations of 1.4 m. and the value given in the table. They are computed in accordance with Eqs. 63 and 64. Values of n are obtained from the wind profile.

TABLE V
DIFFUSION PARAMETERS FROM ROUND HILL EXPERIMENTS

Stability condition	N (m.^{2}/sec. $\times 10^4$)	u_* (m./sec.)	n	u (m./sec.)	C_y (m.$^{n/2}$) Elevation (m.) 2.7	5.5	11.0	22.0	44.0
Zero or small temperature gradient (afternoon)	388.5	0.48	0.28	6.4	0.36	0.32	0.29	0.28	0.26
Moderate inversion (sunset)	199.9	0.23	0.38	3.4	0.31	0.28	0.25	0.24	0.23
Large inversion (evening)	73.5	0.09	0.68	2.0	0.24	0.22	0.22	0.22	0.19

iv. Harwell Reactor BEPO. Stewart *et al.* (*6*) present results of diffusion experiments at the Harwell Reactor BEPO. Cooling air emitted from the reactor stack contains a steady source of radioactive argon which was used as a tracer to obtain gas concentration in the plume and at the ground. Vertical surveys were made with instruments attached to a cable suspended from a mobile barrage balloon.

The stack stands near one edge of the built-up area occupied by the Harwell Atomic Energy Research Establishment. The main buildings of the built-up area are between 8 and 16 m. high. The region surrounding the built-up area "consisted of fairly flat farmland with few striking features." The nearest and farthest edges of the built-up area are approximately 100 and 600 m. from the stack.

While Stewart *et al.* conducted wind speed measurements for determination of turbulence index n, they decided to use a constant value of 0.25 for all stability conditions and to evaluate the diffusion coefficients accordingly. This value of n is that which Sutton gives for neutral conditions.

TABLE VI
DIFFUSION PARAMETERS FROM VERTICAL SURVEYS IN HARWELL EXPERIMENTS[a]

Stability condition	n (assumed constant)	C_y (m.$^{1/8}$)	C_z (m.$^{1/8}$)
Unstable	0.25	0.15	0.25
Adiabatic	0.25	0.09	0.20
Stable	0.25	0.09	0.11

[a] Downwind distance = 150–1000 m.; sampling time = 15–20 min.

Table VI shows averages obtained from vertical surveys conducted for various wind directions. Average wind speed is 7 m./sec. Average plume height is 125 m. under adiabatic conditions.

Stewart *et al.* found a dependence of C_z on wind speed in accordance with the following equation.

$$C_z = 0.108 + 0.013u \tag{67}$$

where u has units of m./sec. and C_z, m.$^{1/8}$. They view the high value of C_z in relation to C_y as being caused by the interaction of the effluent with the atmosphere as it leaves the stack. See Section III,A,2,*c* for additional stack data.

TABLE VII
DIFFUSION PARAMETERS FROM GROUND SURVEYS IN HARWELL EXPERIMENTS[a]

Sampling time (min.)	Downwind distance (m.)	n (assumed constant)	C_y (m.$^{1/8}$)	C_z (m.$^{1/8}$)
40	590–620	0.25	0.46	—
40	1200	0.25	0.33	—
15	2400–2800	0.25	0.23	—
15	6000–9000	0.25	0.16	0.17

[a] Stability condition = adiabatic and unstable.

Table VII shows diffusion coefficients found from ground surveys for one wind direction. For this direction the built-up area is approximately 400 m. upwind and downwind of the stack.

The decrease in C_y with distance is attributed to the reduction of surface roughness when measurements are taken at locations downwind of the built-up area. For stable conditions no measurable ground level concentrations were found within a range of 10,000 m.

v. Project Prairie Grass and Round Hill experiments. Results of diffusion experiments conducted near O'Neill, Nebraska under Project Prairie Grass and at the Round Hill Field Station are analyzed by

Cramer (*27*). While these results are not presented in terms of Sutton's parameters, there is a similarity in form and comparisons may be made.

A continuous point source of sulfur dioxide gas near the ground was used in both the O'Neill and Round Hill experiments. Gas concentrations were measured for 10-min. sampling periods at a number of locations downwind of the source up to a distance of 800 m. Wind measurements were taken at an elevation of 2 m. near the source. The Round Hill site has a rough surface with a roughness length z_0 greater than 10 cm. and the O'Neill site is unusually smooth with z_0 less than 1 cm. A detailed presentation of Project Prairie Grass (a cooperative effort of scientists from several organizations) is given in Barad (*28*) and Haugen (*29*).

Cramer (*27*) shows that even though the two sites differ in roughness, gas concentration characteristics show excellent correlation with the standard deviation of azimuth wind direction fluctuations, better than with characteristics of thermal stratification. The standard deviations of gas concentration distributions which are a function of the azimuth wind direction fluctuations, as shown below, are used by Cramer in a diffusion model from which the following concentration equation is developed.

$$\chi = \frac{Q_{\text{m}}}{2\pi u \sigma_y \sigma_z} \exp\left[-\frac{1}{2}\left(\frac{y^2}{\sigma_y{}^2} + \frac{z^2}{\sigma_z{}^2}\right)\right] \tag{68}$$

where χ, Q_{m}, u, and y are defined as in Eq. 57 and z is measured vertically from a horizontal plane through the source. σ_y and σ_z are standard deviations of lateral and vertical gas concentration distributions, respectively, in units of length at the distance x. In Cramer's presentation the radial distance r from the source is used rather than x, a change which introduces a small error in Eq. 68. The equation is given for an elevated source with no ground influence. For calculation of ground level concentration with the source at an elevation equal to z, the value obtained from Eq. 68 should be doubled. Effect of the ground at other elevations may be introduced with terms similar to those in Eq. 57.

Graphs of σ_y and σ_z vs. downwind distance are given by Cramer in (*29*) and (*30*) and are replotted in Fig. 11. They are shown for five values of the standard deviation σ_{A} of azimuth wind direction fluctuations. σ_y was obtained directly from crosswind diffusion while σ_z was calculated on the basis of σ_y and axial concentration since vertical profiles of gas concentration were measured at only one distance.

Equation 68 is evidently similar in form to Sutton's equation although the intended source of diffusion data for the two is different. While there is greater flexibility in Cramer's equation, there are fewer data available for its application. The distance dependence of concentration need not be the same for lateral and vertical distributions. The nonlinear graphs of σ_z in Fig. 11 plotted on log-log coordinates show that σ_z does not follow a power law. If σ_y and σ_z are assumed to follow a power-law relationship if only for a limited downwind distance, they

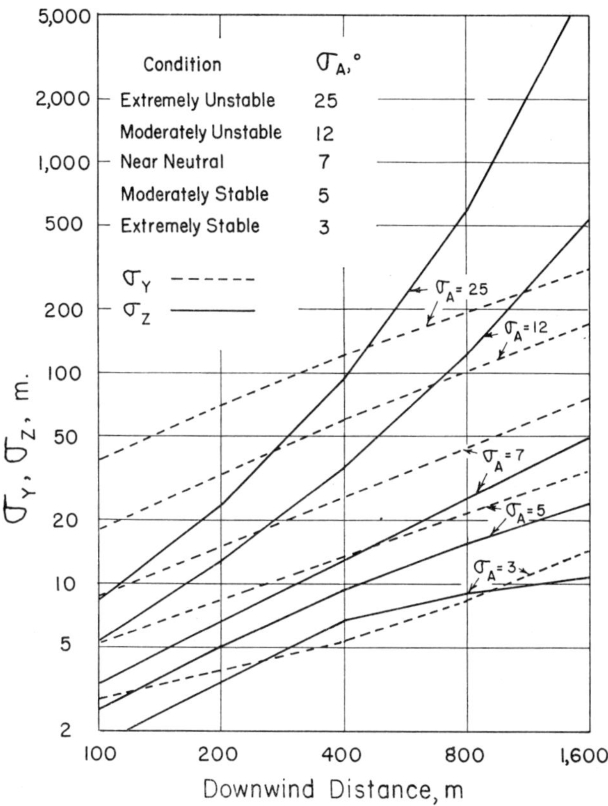

FIG. 11. Standard deviations σ_y and σ_z of gas concentration distribution for various degrees of stability. (Replotted from Figs. 3 and 4 in Cramer, *Bull. Am. Meteorol. Soc.* **40,** 1959.)

may be related to a modified form of Sutton's diffusion parameters. For this purpose Sutton's equation must be modified to have separate values for the turbulence index n in the lateral and vertical distribution as shown in the following revised form of Equation 57.

$$\chi = \frac{Q_m \exp\left[-y^2/C_y{}^2 x^{(2-n_y)}\right]}{\pi C_y C_z u x^{[2-(n_y/2)-(n_z/2)]}} \cdot \left\{ \exp\left[-\frac{(z-h_e)^2}{C_z{}^2 x^{(2-n_z)}}\right] + \exp\left[-\frac{(z+h_e)^2}{C_z{}^2 x^{(2-n_z)}}\right]\right\} \quad (69)$$

The various diffusion parameters in Eqs. 68 and 69 are related by

$$\sqrt{2}\sigma_y = C_y x^{1-(n_y/2)} \tag{70}$$

$$\sqrt{2}\sigma_z = C_z x^{1-(n_z/2)} \tag{71}$$

vi. Inversion studies at Hanford and Brookhaven. Two experimental investigations (*31, 32*) on plume characteristics for the markedly stable inversion condition show that diffusion parameters given in the preceding studies are not generally valid, especially when significant downwind distances are considered. Barad's (*33*) theoretical studies show the decrease in concentration with distance to be less rapid than that obtained with the usual range of n values given for stable conditions. Smith *et al.* (*31*) present a graph in which the rate of decrease in concentration obtained with Barad's analysis is close to that found with Sutton's equation using a value of 1.0 for n. Smith *et al.* measurements of axial concentration at the Brookhaven National Laboratory over a distance of approximately 5000 ft. show the variation with distance to be approximated with the above value of 1.0 for n.

On the basis of photographic and visual studies Smith *et al.* suggest values of C_y and C_z of 0.40 and 0.025 (m.$^{n/2}$), respectively. These together with a value of n equal to 1.0 give axial concentrations which are approximately 100 times as high as those measured. This is evidently caused by the fact that the real source is not the point source assumed in the diffusion equation, a difference which has a large effect for stable conditions. Barad (*33*) accounts for this characteristic by using an area source in his treatment. The use of the above values for n, C_y, and C_z together with a factor of 100 for reducing concentration calculated by Sutton's equation gives an acceptable representation of the Brookhaven data but a good deal of scatter is evident in the experimental values of axial concentration.

Hilst (*32*) presents results of experiments conducted at the Hanford Works under inversion conditions over a distance of 600 m. He analyzes the dependence on distance of standard deviations of concentration distributions. His results show that the standard deviation σ_z in the vertical direction (see Eq. 68) tends to follow a power-law relationship out to a distance of 300 m. from the source following which it tends to be constant, thus giving a plume approximately constant in depth beyond 300 m. The lateral standard deviations appear to follow the power law for greater distances. One of the features of Hilst's results is the wide variation in measured concentrations from one experiment to another which emphasizes the difficulty in assigning specific values to the diffusion parameters.

e. Fumigation Condition. One of the more important conditions of highly nonuniform spatial distribution of diffusion is the fumigation condition described in Section II,B. This cannot be handled even approximately with the usual diffusion equations. This condition was studied by Hewson (*1*) who found it played an important role in air pollution from a smelter.

Hewson (*34*) develops the following equation for estimating ground level concentration during fumigation. It is based on the assumption that the inversion plume before breakup has the form of a pie-shaped wedge of 5° included angle and constant thickness described by Smith (*35*). During fumigation the plume is treated as diffusing downward uniformly throughout a volume determined by the pre-breakup plume dimensions.

$$\chi = \frac{36Q_{\mathrm{m}}}{\pi u h_{\mathrm{e}}(x_2 + x_1)} \tag{72}$$

χ, Q_{m}, u, and h_{e} are defined as they were for Eq. 57, and x_1 and x_2 are the downwind distances to two locations between which the concentration is desired. For concentration at a location x, $(x_2 + x_1)$ is replaced with $2x$.

Holland (*12*) presents the following equation for concentration during fumigation obtained by integration of Eq. 57 with respect to z and distributing the result over the depth h_{e}.

$$\chi = \frac{Q_{\mathrm{m}}}{\sqrt{2\pi} C_y u h_{\mathrm{e}} x^{(2-n)/2}} \tag{73}$$

The values of C_y, u, and n should be those appropriate to the inversion prior to fumigation.

f. Long-Period Exposures. Exposure time may to a limited extent be handled in the preceding analysis by selection of diffusion parameters for appropriate sampling periods. Sampling periods for the available data are not generally longer than an hour. If data for the dependence of diffusion parameters on sampling period are available, extrapolation to longer periods could be made. For example, as described in Section II,C, Stewart *et al.* found in their experiments that axial concentration varied inversely with the fifth root of sampling period. In applying this relationship to the axial concentration given by Eq 58, it is found that C_yC_z is proportional to the fifth root of sampling period and extrapolation of this product may be made.

The above type of procedure for extrapolation can be used for only limited increases in exposure time. When much longer periods such as days, months, or years are of interest, other procedures must be used. Aside from lack of data, the above procedure could not be used, because the concentration equation assumes that the fluctuations in air motion have a normal distribution about a given direction.

An alternate method is to find an average concentration over a desired region based on the assumption that the wind direction fluctuations are uniform over the region. Holland (*12*) integrates with respect to the lateral coordinate y Sutton's equation for ground level concentration. He then averages the result over the desired region to obtain the following.

$$\bar{\chi}_{z=0} = \frac{2Q_{\mathrm{m}}f}{\alpha\sqrt{\pi}C_z u x^{2-(n/2)}} \exp\left(-\frac{h_{\mathrm{e}}^2}{C_z^2 x^{2-n}}\right) \tag{74}$$

where $\bar{\chi}_{z=0}$ is the average concentration at the distance x over the sector having an azimuth angle α in radians about the source; f is the wind direction frequency for the winds which blow toward the sector α, i.e., the fraction of time that the wind will carry the plume into the sector.

g. Discussion. Comparison and evaluation of Sutton's diffusion parameters obtained from the various field experiments is difficult because of the complicated form of the gas concentration equation, differences in the manner by which the parameters were determined, and differences in local surface roughness and meteorology of the various sites. The diffusion coefficients cannot directly be compared since concentration depends on turbulence index n as well. For example, axial concentration (Eq. 58) for a given source strength and wind speed varies inversely with $C_yC_zx^{2-n}$. Thus any number of combinations of diffusion parameters will for a given distance produce the same concentration. Taking a specific case, the Brookhaven diffusion coefficients for the C category (approximately neutral) are larger than most of those reported for other locations. The value of n is also larger. ($C_y = 0.54$, $C_z = 0.34$, $n = 0.48$). At $x = 1000$ m., $C_yC_zx^{2-n}$ for Brookhaven category C is approximately the same as obtained for $C_y = C_z = 0.2$, $n = 0.25$, representative of some others. Stewart *et al.* (*6*) introduce some simplification by choosing a fixed value of 0.25 for n regardless of the stability condition. This restricts the concentration vs. downwind relationship, but may be acceptable if only a limited range of distance is considered.

The following values for diffusion parameters supplement those given in the preceding tabulations. Hawkins and Nonhebel (*14*) base their concentration equations on a value of 0.17 m.$^{1/8}$ for C_y and C_z, and 0.25 for n, which they state are for average conditions. A concentration equation in the Report of the Committee on Air Pollution (*22*), though in different units, appears to be based on the same coefficient values.

Cramer's results (*30*) cannot in general be expressed in terms of

Sutton's diffusion parameters except for short ranges of downwind distance. The neutral case does, however, yield the form which fits the power-law relationship of concentration with distance. The following are found when Eqs. 70 and 71 are applied to the neutral case of Fig. 11.

$$C_y = 0.33 \text{ m.}^{0.21} \qquad n_y = 0.42$$
$$C_z = 0.06 \text{ m.}^{0.04} \qquad n_z = 0.08$$
$$\sqrt{C_y C_z} = 0.14 \text{ m.}^{0.125} \qquad n_{\text{av.}} = 0.25$$

The small value of C_z compared with C_y is undoubtedly due at least in part to the influence of the ground since these are derived from experiments with a ground level source.

The effect of diffusion parameters on maximum ground level concentration as given by Eq. 61 is dependent on the ratio C_z/C_y. At higher elevations C_y and C_z tend to become equal. Sutton (*24*) gives equal values for C_y and C_z at elevations above 20–25 m. for neutral conditions. Thus gas plumes of higher elevations tend to yield for a given elevation maximum ground level concentration independent of stability. The location of maximum concentration will vary as shown by Eq. 60 where it is evident that increased stability (decreased C_z) will move the location further away. For extremely stable conditions this may be well beyond the range of applicability of the concentration equation.

Equation 61 shows maximum ground level concentration to vary inversely with the square of plume height. This shows the effectiveness of increasing plume height whether by stack height or stack effluent variables. The same height variation is shown in the Bosanquet and Pearson equation (Eq. 56) although the actual value of concentration for a given height may differ depending on the diffusion coefficients.

Concentration equations of the preceding sections are in a form which requires all dimensional quantities be in consistent units. If, for example, in Eq. 57 plume concentration is to be obtained in units of micrograms per cubic meter, emission rate must likewise be in terms of micrograms. If the time unit is selected as the second, emission rate must be in micrograms per second. It then follows that velocity must be in meters per second and linear dimensions in meters. These units are consistent with those used for the numerical values of diffusion coefficients given in the preceding sections where the meter unit is employed. If it is desired to express emission rate in volume units of cubic meters per minute, the following conversion must be made.

$$Q_{\text{vs}} = 60Q_{\text{m}}/\rho_{\text{s}} \tag{75}$$

where Q_m has units of micrograms per second, Q_{vs} in units of cubic meters per minute and ρ_s in micrograms per cubic meter. Q_{vs} and ρ_s must be taken at the same temperature and barometric pressure.

Application of the diffusion equations to specific problems is facilitated through the use of charts and nomograms especially when a large number of calculations must be made. Gifford (*36, 37*) presents nomograms for solving Sutton's concentration equation. Similar nomograms are given in the U. S. AEC report (*11*), including maximum concentration and diffusion parameters. A contour chart in Hawkins and Nonhebel (*14*) gives ground level concentration at any location as a function of plume height, maximum ground level concentration, and location of maximum concentration.

The effectiveness of Sutton's equation and his method of evaluating diffusion parameters in giving correct formulation of concentration characteristics is the subject of much discussion. One of the features under scrutiny concerns the accuracy of representing the effect of distance on concentration by a power-law relationship. Cramer's graphs (*30*) of standard deviation of concentration distribution (Fig. 11), based on Project Prairie Grass data, show significant departure from the power-law relationship especially for vertical diffusion. It is to be noted that the field data terminate at 800 m. and the additional curves between 800 and 1600 m. are the author's extrapolation. If attention is confined to the results within the 800-m. range, departure from power law is much less, especially when the extremes of stability and instability are excluded. Hilst's data (*32*) show marked departure from the power law for vertical concentration distribution under strong inversion. Barad and Haugen (*38*) have analyzed Project Prairie Grass data with the view of examining Sutton's hypothesis. They conclude that for the 100- to 800-m. range and for stabilities ranging from slight lapse to strong inversion the departure from a power law is quite small. They determined their vertical diffusion characteristics in a different manner from that used by Cramer.

Sutton's procedure for evaluating the turbulence index n with the wind profile (based on Eq. 62) is examined by Barad and Haugen (*38*). They show that a single value of n for vertical and lateral concentration distribution cannot be used to represent the field data of Project Prairie Grass. Separate values must be used as shown in Eq. 69. This automatically eliminates use of the single value obtainable from wind profile. The field data show that n_y tends to be larger than n_z, which is in agreement with the above values obtained from Cramer's results. n_p obtained from axial concentrations is affected by lateral and vertical distribution and falls between n_y and n_z. From Barad and Haugen's graphs of n_y, n_z, and

n_p vs. n (from wind profile) it is evident that n cannot be used to represent n_y, n_z, or n_p. For a very limited range, n_p is approximately equal to n. The difference between n_y and n_z which was large in the Project Prairie Grass experiments is likely to be smaller for an elevated source where turbulence is more nearly isotropic.

The use of a point source in Sutton's equation, as well as in others, introduces inaccuracy because of the finite area of the usual real sources emanating from stacks. Another feature of real sources, while of a different nature, may be corrected for in a manner similar to that used for finite area, namely, the use of a virtual point source at a certain distance upwind of the real source (see Fig. 7). The second cause of inaccuracy is the rapid initial expansion of the plume not accounted for in the diffusion equation. Waskow and Moses (*39*) show with their data obtained with the Experimental Smoke Stack at the Argonne National Laboratory that the initial rate of expansion is many times that which occurs after the initial interaction of the plume with the atmosphere is terminated. There appears to be very little data for determining the virtual point source location. It depends on atmospheric stability and wind speed as well as stack effluent variables. For unstable conditions it may be only a few stack diameters upwind of the real source and will have little effect on the concentration characteristics of usual interest. For extremely stable conditions the virtual point source may be far upwind because of the small expansion angle of the plume.

In view of the uncertainties which exist in the application of diffusion theory, it is not advisable to extrapolate diffusion calculations to downwind distances much beyond the range for which data are available depending on the degree of accuracy desired. This will generally restrict the analysis to distances of less than a few miles. Extrapolation for neutral conditions will be more accurate than for non-neutral. This restriction on distance is in most cases not serious since it will usually include the region of maximum ground level concentration.

The rather limited amount of field data given in the preceding sections will only serve as a guide in selection of diffusion parameters. They may be termed accurate for their particular sites only. By choosing several sets of parameters for sites which approximate the conditions of a given problem, one may obtain the range of values within which the answer lies. It must be recognized that in many cases the result is inherently inaccurate because the necessary site information is not available. For example, atmospheric stability is an important characteristic in the selection of diffusion parameters. Lacking information on the distribution of stability conditions, it may appear valid to select an average stability for analysis of the problem. This average condition may, however, occur infrequently and be of lesser importance than other levels of stability. Thus in this case the distribution of stability must be estimated and this will naturally introduce inaccuracies. Precise calculation of pollution characteristics may, therefore, be useless. The need for accurate site information is evident.

Reference must be made to the discussion on the effects of buildings and topography in Section II,D. While surface roughness may be handled by proper selection of diffusion parameters, the effects of large discrete objects cannot be handled with the usual form of concentration equations.

4. *Deposition of Particulates*

a. Introduction. The nature of air pollution resulting from particulates is significantly different from that caused by gases. The distribution of concentration in the atmosphere as well as the deleterious effects on sensitive items is generally different, both of which affect the analysis.

When particulates have a very small diameter, generally less than 20 μ for materials of common density, they exhibit transport properties similar to gases. Their free settling velocities are so low that they have motions essentially the same as the surrounding gases and may be treated as such. An effect of small particulates generally neglected is the increase in density of the particulate-gas combination over that of gas alone.

Many particulates are chemically inert or react only slowly with affected items. Short period exposures of significance to gases are, therefore, not usually important for particulates. The accumulation of particulates on horizontal surfaces by gravitation settling is the characteristic of usual interest rather than concentration in the atmosphere.

Lack of field data on deposition of particulates is even greater than that for gas plume concentration. The development of formulas for prediction of particulate deposition is not as advanced as that for gas plume concentration. Most analyses start with gas plume characteristics and introduce in some manner the effect of free settling velocity of the particulates. They have, therefore, the limitations inherent in the gas plume equations.

The effect of topography and buildings is not included in the deposition equations. An obstruction in the path of particulates may show high local depositions in stagnant regions where gravitational settling becomes predominant. On the other hand, other regions near obstructions may show unusually low depositions. Deposition phenomena on a large scale occur in the formation of snow drifts. These may give a clue to the location of regions potentially high in particulate deposition.

The concept of a virtual point source for a gas plume is also applied to a particulate plume (see Fig. 7). The rise of the plume due to initial upward velocity and density is likewise applied to particulate analysis. The plume rise equations of Bosanquet, Carey, and Halton (*2*) were, in fact, developed for analysis of particulate deposition.

The effect of size, density, and shape of particulates is lumped into one characteristic, the free settling velocity v_f. This is the velocity a particle achieves in falling through still air and is the characteristic significant to its motion in the atmosphere. Bosanquet *et al.* (*2*), the U. S. AEC report (*11*), and Perry (*40*), as well as many handbooks on physical and chemical properties of materials, give free settling velocities of various particulates. The following equation from the AEC report (*11*) may be used to calculate free settling velocities of spherical particles.

$$v_f = \frac{2V_p g(\rho_p - \rho)d_p}{\mu A_p Re C_D} \tag{76}$$

where the variables are used in consistent units. Approximate values for C_D may be computed from the respective Re ranges, as shown in the tabulation.

Re range	C_D
10^{-4} to 2	$24/Re$
2 to 500	$0.4 + 40\,Re$
500 to 10^5	0.44

b. Bosanquet, Carey and Halton Procedure. Bosanquet *et al.* (*2*) have developed equations and graphs for the prediction of particulate deposition. The following gives the average deposition at the downwind distance x for average meteorological conditions.

$$\bar{\omega} = \frac{0.31aQ_p}{h_e^2} F\left(\frac{v_f}{u}, \frac{x}{h_e}\right) \tag{77}$$

where $\bar{\omega}$ = average deposition over a 45° sector at the downwind distance x, mg./cm.² month

a = wind direction frequency for winds which blow into the 45° sector

$F(v_f/u, x/h_e)$ = function given in Fig. 12

and velocities are in meters per second, distances in meters, and particulate emission rate in milligrams per second.

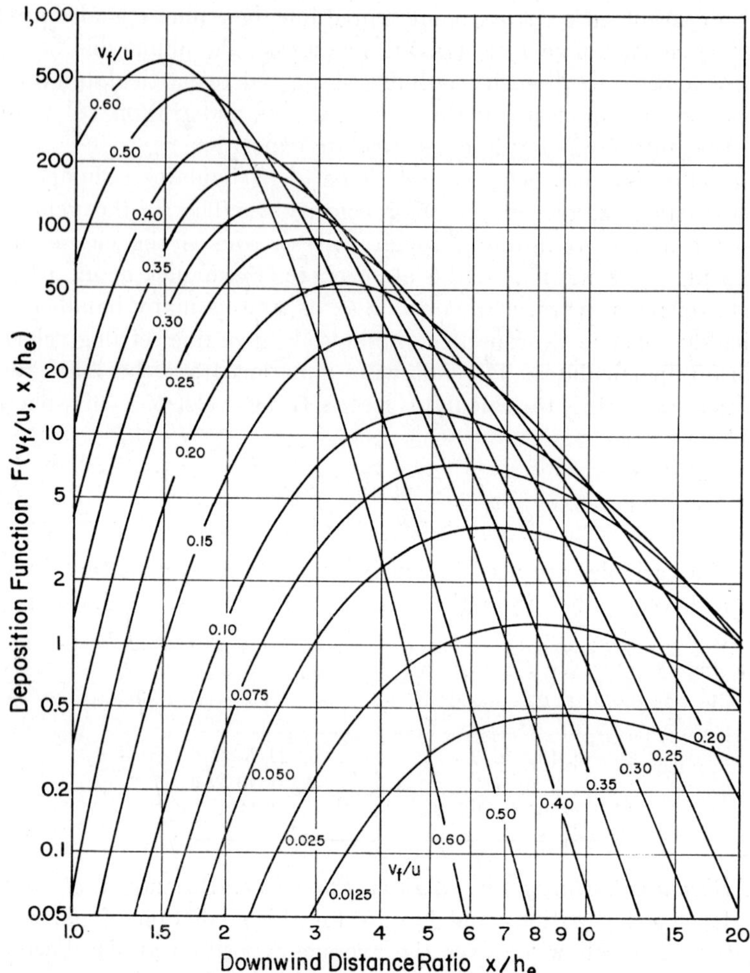

FIG. 12. Deposition function $F(v_f/u, x/h_e)$ for use in Eq. 77. (Plotted from Table 4, Bosanquet *et al.*, *Proc. Inst. Mech. Engrs.* **162,** 1950.)

Deposition rate ω under the axis of the plume is given by

$$\omega = 4.43\bar{\omega}/a \tag{78}$$

Equation 77 gives the average deposition for one wind speed and one free settling velocity. In application to specific problems a range of wind speed and particulate sizes will obviously occur. The range of wind speeds (determined from climatological data) and free settling velocities may be divided into a series of increments for each of which an average value is identified. Deposition may then be calculated for each increment and a total formed for a given downwind distance. Bosanquet *et al.* show sample calculations for this type of analysis.

Bosanquet *et al.* include field data on deposition rate for comparison with their theory. They estimate that their equations give results which are accurate within a factor of two. This they state is sufficiently accurate for design purposes.

c. Modified Sutton Equation. A modified Sutton equation such as presented in the AEC report (*11*) gives an elementary procedure for calculating deposition of particulates. This equation is obtained by superimposing on the characteristics of a gas plume the effect of free settling velocity of particulates. This is accomplished by reducing the distance between the ground and plume axis to account for the distance a particle will fall. To obtain the desired result, h_e in Eq. 59 is replaced with $h_e - x\,v_f/u$. The factor 2 is omitted on the assumption that there is no ground reflection, i.e., a particle which reaches ground level remains there. Deposition rate ω is found by multiplying the ground level concentration χ by free settling velocity v_f to give the following.

$$\omega = \frac{263Q_p v_f}{C_y C_z u x^{2-n}} \exp\left[-\frac{1}{x^{2-n}}\left(\frac{y^2}{C_y{}^2} + \frac{(h_e - xv_f/u)^2}{C_z{}^2}\right)\right] \tag{79}$$

where C_y and C_z are in units of m.$^{n/2}$, y in m., and other quantities have the same units as in Eq. 77; n and y are defined the same as in Eq. 57. Equation 79 gives the local deposition, not the average as obtained in Eq. 77. The average for a long period of time may be obtained using the technique discussed in Section III,A,3,*f*. Equation 74 may be modified to form the average of Eq. 79 by omitting the factor 2 and multiplying by v_f.

Equation 79, while an oversimplification of particulate plume characteristics, has the advantage of showing the effect of variables not included in Eq. 77. Numerical examples show that Eq. 79 gives for moderate size stacks results similar to those of Eq. 77 (with difference between local and average deposition accounted for) when C_y and C_z have values of approximately 0.2 m.$^{0.125}$ and $n = 0.25$.

d. Baron, Gerhard, and Johnstone Procedure. Baron *et al.* (*41*) present a procedure for deposition calculations based on Sutton's gas plume equation. They employ a modification similar to that used in Eq. 78 but include a modified source image in the development of their equations. Graphs of results for numerical examples show effects of stack height, particle size, and atmospheric stability. In contrast with maximum ground level concentration of gas plumes which remains substantially constant with change in atmospheric stability, maximum particulate concentration increases with increase in stability.

e. Csanady Procedure. Csanady's procedure (*42*) is an extension of Sutton's gas plume equation and includes effect of reflection of the particulate plume by the ground. Csanady summarizes results of his earlier papers and treats problems of application to real cases. He gives a procedure for analyzing deposition when the continuous distribution of particle free settling velocities is available, thus eliminating the need to divide the distribution into increments. He also presents a technique for obtaining a continuous distribution of wind direction frequency from the usual climatological data of averages over sectors by fitting a Fourier series.

B. Equations for Ground Level Gas Concentration

The analytical methods of the preceding section treat the computation of stack gas concentration in two steps. It may seem that a more accurate analysis would result from treating the whole process as a unit, but no such method appears available. This is undoubtedly due to the complex nature of the phenomena involved. Single equations which combine the operations of the two-step procedure are given by various authors (*12, 15, 22, 22a*). These give only the maximum ground level concentration and use a simple form of plume rise equation such as that of Holland (*12*). The more complex plume rise equations would yield unwieldy forms and little would be gained in forming a one-step procedure.

The use of the simpler equations gives a result which readily shows the existence of a maximum concentration with respect to wind speed. Following Holland's procedure (*12*) Eq. 12 for plume rise is added to stack height h to form effective plume height h_e; h_e is substituted into maximum ground level concentration Eq. 61. Following is the result when C_y and C_z are assumed equal.

$$\chi_{\mathrm{m},z=0} = \frac{2Q_\mathrm{m}u}{\pi e(uh + B)^2} \tag{80}$$

where $B = (1.5\ V_s d + 1.34 \times 10^{-4}\ Q_h)/u$. When Eq. 80 is maximized, maximum concentration is found at $u = B/h$ and the value of the maximum is

$$\chi_{\mathrm{mm},z=0} = \frac{Q_\mathrm{m}}{2\pi eBh} \tag{81}$$

It is to be noted that the above concentration is a maximum with respect to location as well as wind speed and is, therefore, a form of ultimate maximum. It may be of low practical significance as it may occur in the range of infrequent or nonexistent wind speeds.

Wippermann and Klug (*22a*) developed an equation for ground level concentration which gives a maximum with respect to location and wind speed. They perform an extensive analysis on gas diffusion and plume rise and give supporting experimental data.

C. Rule-of-Thumb Procedures

In air pollution control there are very few rules of thumb for stack design. Most of them concern the selection of stack height. It has for many years been common practice in the British electricity industry to make the height of power plant stacks 2.5 times that of the highest adjacent building. At this height the gas plume is likely to be free of adverse aerodynamic effects of the adjacent building and may be treated as if it were in the free atmospheric boundary layer. To take care of cases with low buildings an additional rule requiring stacks to be at least 120 ft. high is given in the Beaver Report (*22*). Small installations may be exceptions. In the AEC report (*11*) the 2.5-times-height rule is extended to include all buildings located within a distance equal to 20 stack heights.

A proposed code of good practice for Holland is cited by ter Linden (*43*), in which the stack should be 1.5 times the height of the highest building in the neighborhood of the plant when in flat country where high buildings are the exception. For large installations and for those in residential areas the rule should be more stringent. Pollution by dust deposition is the main concern of the code, and additional rules on dust emission rate are included.

An adverse effect on stack effluents occurs near the top of a stack when gas ejection speed is low. The lower edge of plume may be drawn into the low pressure region leeward of the stack. This causes an effective lowering of the plume and may form a diffused lower edge which reaches the ground much sooner than the main part. Sherlock and Stalker (*44*) show with wind tunnel experiments that the plume is largely clear of this downwash effect when the gas ejection speed is greater than wind speed.

Experience with scale model wind tunnel experiments shows wide variation in adverse effect of adjacent buildings on plume characteristics. Change in wind direction makes a large difference for buildings rectangular in plan. When wind direction is parallel to the length the adverse effect may be quite small, but for the least favorable direction the 2.5 rule is generally valid. Analysis of dependence of ground level concentration on wind speed (see Fig. 3), whether by experiments or analytical methods, shows there is a wind speed below which little or no concentration occurs. This initial contact speed may be quite significant for the high emission rates and less favorable wind directions since the concentration may increase rapidly with speed above initial contact. Results of wind tunnel experiments at New York University (*45*) summarized in Fig. 13 show a marked dependence of initial contact speed on the stack to building height ratio h/h_b. This figure is based on a number of experiments on models of

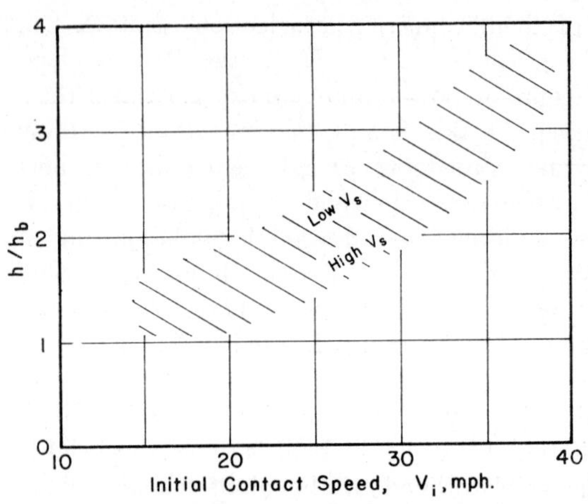

FIG. 13. Wind speed for initial contact of plume with ground for least favorable wind direction as affected by stack to building height ratio. (Reproduced from Fig. 3, Strom, *APCA News* **6**, No. 7, 1958.)

power plants of moderate to large size for which the stack gas temperature occurred between 250°F. and 350°F. and ejection speed between 25 to 125 ft./sec. Figure 14, based on the same experiments, shows dependence of location of maximum ground level concentration on stack to building height ratio.

The shape of a gas plume in near neutral atmospheric stability is roughly that of a cone as shown in Fig. 4. The half-angle of the cone is variously given between 5° and 15°. As atmospheric stability increases the angle becomes smaller and the cone is flattened. For very stable conditions the horizontal half-angle is a few degrees with very little vertical expansion after initial mixing.

Plumes from extremely short stacks on or near a building become completely dominated by the turbulence caused by the building when moderate or high winds occur. This is common with stacks for domestic heating and incineration and for ventilation exhausts. The effluent may be so violently dispersed that it envelops the entire building except for the windward side. The plume appears as if it originates from all over the surface of the building and has essentially the same geometry as the turbulent wake caused by the building. It extends to ground level. An approximate value for effluent concentration in the wake may be obtained by assuming the effluent to be uniformly distributed over the entire cross section of the wake. It is difficult to estimate the cross section without experimental data, but it will be at least as large as the maximum cross section of the building normal to the wind and may be twice as large or more especially when the windward side is normal to

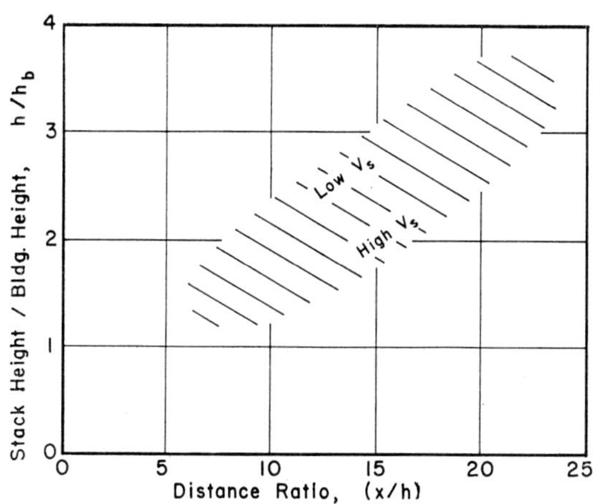

FIG. 14. Effect of stack to building height ratio on downwind distance of maximum ground level concentration for least favorable wind direction. (Reproduced from Fig. 2, Strom, *APCA News* **6**, No. 7, 1958.)

windstream. The uniform distribution of concentration starts shortly downwind of the building and continues for a limited distance following which mixing with the surrounding atmosphere will cause greater dilution near the edges of the wake. Diffusion around buildings is analyzed by Halitsky (*45a*). He presents methods for estimating concentrations which are based on results of wind tunnel experiments.

IV. Experimental Methods for the Prediction of Plume Characteristics

A. INTRODUCTION

In the analysis of specific air pollution problems experimental methods may provide an answer where analytical procedures fail. Two types of experimental methods have been extensively used, namely, full-scale field experiments and scale-model experiments.

Field experiments on plume dispersal have the advantage of being conducted under the actual conditions of atmosphere and stack operation and in the presence of buildings, topography, and all other details of the real situation. They will obviously not give an answer for a new installation in the design stage or an existing installation where modifications are being planned. Some information of value to the prediction of plume characteristics may be obtained where a series of identical items such as a number of stacks are to be modified. Tests on the modification of one of the series may give useful information but care must be used in its application since other units may be under other influences due to difference in location. Field experiments may, however, be indicated for a newly constructed installation to assess its air pollution characteristics.

Full-scale experiments may be costly in time since some of the desired atmospheric conditions may occur infrequently. A representative range of conditions for a given site can hardly be obtained in less than a year if the frequency of occurrence of meteorological variables is significant to the problem. Even one year is not likely to be an accurate representation of a period of several or more years.

Field experiments of limited scope may be of great value when supplemented with other methods of analysis. Determination of the climatology of a site is one of the most important types of field investigation. Climatological data is necessary for the application of analytical studies or scale model experiments. Weather Bureau stations usually take measurements for much of the kind of data needed in air pollution studies but the station may be too far away to give data representative of the site.

Scale-model experiments on stack gas plumes suffer from the same types of defects as model experiments in other fields. The prototype phenomena will probably not be completely scaled and may be only partially scaled in the model. Problems of extrapolation of model results to full scale must be dealt with. Model experiments have a time advantage since the conditions of the experiment may be changed at will. Alternate solutions may be tested and analyzed from an economic as well as air pollution viewpoint.

Any experimental program whether field or model must be carefully planned to avoid the cost of obtaining unnecessary data and, still worse, the omission of essential data. Too often an experimental program has been completed, instruments and equipment dismantled and personnel dispersed when it is found that essential measurements have been omitted. The intended application of results must be carefully reviewed to be sure essential data is obtained. A situation may arise in which an experimental program of limited objective is completed only to find that later the problem is enlarged and additional data is needed. The possibility of this occurrence should be studied in the beginning since the measurement of some additional data in the original program may be accomplished with relatively little increase in cost.

B. Field Experiments

Experiments for the measurement of various meteorological characteristics have been so widely performed that much literature is devoted to the techniques and instruments involved. The many publications of the U. S. Weather Bureau and the American Meteorological Society are major sources of information. A useful source of references is the *Meteorological and Geophysical Abstracts.*

A review of the analytical procedures in Section III reveals that the most important variables in plume dispersal are wind speed, wind direction, and one or more variables which characterize atmospheric turbulence. Variables which determine air density are also needed (temperature and barometric pressure are usually sufficient), but density at a given location does not show much variation compared with other variables. Barometric pressure may be unnecessary when only the ratio of stack effluent density to air density is required. In some cases measurement of humidity or precipitation may be needed when visibility or washout of pollutants are of interest. Many instruments for measurement of meteorological and other variables of interest to air pollution are described in Chapter 16 and in Yaffe *et al.* (*46*). In the measurement of turbulence a direct form of measurement is desirable but the instrument or its reading will be complex. Hewson (*47*) describes several turbulence-measuring instruments including some whose reading is a single number indicative of the degree of turbulence. Vertical temperature gradient is an indirect indicator of turbulence (especially the thermally induced form) which has proved very useful and should be included in any experiments related to gas plume diffusion. It requires the measurement of the difference in temperature between at least two elevations. If the depth of an inversion or stable atmospheric layer is to be determined, temperature measurements for a number of elevations are required.

The selection of stack height may be facilitated with an investigation of air flow patterns around structures near the stack to show regions of adverse air motion. Various devices such as smoke bombs described by Collins (*48*) are effective in making visible the movement of air. Characteristics of the stack plume itself is the subject of much experimentation. Geometric features obtained by observation of a visible plume are valuable but measurement of effluent concentration gives a more useful result. A given plume may have components which can be measured with available instruments or a tracer may be introduced. The use of fluorescent pigments as tracers is described by Falk *et al.* (*49*) and Haines *et al.* (*50*). These have proved effective.

Procedures for conducting field experiments are discussed in Chapter 16. Selection and characteristics of instruments are also covered.

C. Scale-Model Experiments

Scale-model experiments have proved effective in the solution of many air pollution problems. They have been conducted almost exclusively in wind tunnels. There is a brief mention (*51*) of the use of a water channel for smoke plume studies and Scorer (*20a*) employed water in the study of plumes and thermals. It has been suggested that the real atmosphere be used for scale-model experiments. The following discussion is oriented to the use of wind tunnels.

Early scale-model experiments on smoke plumes were conducted by Sherlock and Stalker (*44*) in a wind tunnel at the University of Michigan. They made an extensive investigation of local effects at the stack and showed the importance of the adverse effect of adjacent buildings. Bryant and his associates conducted scale-model wind tunnel experiments at the National Physical Laboratory (*17, 52*) and introduced the scale factor to be applied when stack gases are at elevated temperatures. Steam power plants are the subject of the above investigations and continue to be the more frequent application of scale-model experiments. Recently, in the development of wind tunnels for air pollution, increased emphasis has been placed on the simulation of atmospheric characteristics. Whether all the features of the atmosphere significant to plume dispersal can be simulated is open to question, but the possibilities have not been exhausted.

Once the significant variables of a physical phenomenon are established, the various scale factors and corresponding scaling equations for setting model variables in terms of their full scale counterparts can be readily developed by dimensionless analysis. Nearly all if not all past studies on scale-model air pollution experiments have proceeded on the basis that the geometric features of the rigid elements of the model must be the same as those of the prototype. Thus geometric similarity is preserved for stacks, buildings, topography, etc. In addition, geometric similarity of plume path is usually made a requirement or approximated. The following scaling equations or their equivalent have been found satisfactory (*53*).

$$u_M = u_P \sqrt{g_M l_M / g_P l_P} \tag{82}$$

$$\rho_{sM}/\rho_M = \rho_{sP}/\rho_P \tag{83}$$

$$V_{sM}/u_M = V_{sP}/u_P \tag{84}$$

$$\begin{aligned} Q_{vsM} &= Q_{vsP}(l_M/l_P)^2(u_M/u_P) \\ &= Q_{vsP}(l_M/l_P)^{5/2} \end{aligned} \tag{85}$$

where l is a reference length and the subscripts M and P refer to model and prototype, respectively. The other variables are defined under Symbols, pp. 118–120. The ratio l_M/l_P is the linear scale of the model. The second form of Eq. 85 is found by substitution of Eq. 82 and setting $g_M = g_P$. For cases in which stack gas density and atmospheric density are alike, Eq. 82 and 83 are eliminated and model test speed u_M is not restricted to a specific value.

Equation 82 is an application of Froude number, a fluid parameter which arises when there are gravitational forces. Wind tunnels to be used for testing in accordance with Froude number must be capable of operating at very low speeds especially when dealing with small model scales. There are serious wind tunnel design problems because at very low speeds unwanted convective air currents are produced in the test section and upstream sections when there is any difference in temperature between the airstream and exposed surfaces. A form of Froude number which includes fluid densities (*52*) has been used in scale-model fluid experiments in which gravity plays a role. It offers a possible alleviation of low-speed testing problems. In terms of the above scaling equations, Eq. 83 would be eliminated and Eq. 82 modified by including under the radical the term $\rho_P(\rho_M - \rho_{sM})/\rho_M(\rho_P - \rho_{sP})$. This form of scaling equation allows freedom in selection of wind speed but there appears to be no information on whether such freedom may be used in the modeling of gas plumes.

Equation 83 on density requirement does not show a restriction on the manner by which the density differences are produced whether by gas composition or temperature. A convenient method of achieving density control in the model without heating or cooling is to use a mixture of helium and air (*53*) or freon and air (*22c*) depending on whether low or high density gas is desired. Any inaccuracy introduced by substituting gases appears to be insignificant.

A geometric feature of the model flow field difficult to control by artificial means is the distribution of airstream velocity. The velocities of the atmosphere are characteristically nonuniform in space and time. Equation 82 should in principle be applied to every point in the flow field. This would logically apply to turbulence as well as mean motion. The following scaling equation is included for discussion purposes.

$$u_M/u_{oM} = u_P/u_{oP} \tag{86}$$

where u_M and u_P are wind velocities at geometrically similar locations in model and prototype, and the subscript "o" designates a reference location. The success of scale-model experiments has in large measure been due to the accuracy with which the velocity field is reproduced in the model for those cases of turbulent motion and flow pattern caused by buildings and topography. These are the cases which are so difficult to handle analytically. This is due to the dominating influence of these air motions on plume dispersion. Effectively Eq. 86 is satisfied. Figure 15 shows a typical scale model being tested. Smoke was used for photographic purposes, but sulfur dioxide was introduced as a tracer for concentration measurements.

The question arises as to whether Reynolds number, a scale factor which appears when fluid viscous forces are significant, is not also important to stack plume experiments. Experience has shown that patterns of air motion around objects with sharp edges and flat or irregular surfaces are practically independent of Reynolds number $(\rho lu/\mu)$ except at extremely low values. Scale effects may occur if the object has smooth curved surfaces, but this is not common in structures encountered in air pollution problems except possibly at the stack itself or for extremely smooth topographical surfaces. Scale effects at the stack do not seem large enough to have a noticeable effect on the results. Flow pattern over a model of smooth curving topography, fortunately a rare case, may be made more nearly like that of the prototype by roughening the surface. The control of flow pattern by modification of surface texture has been the subject of much study in the field of applied aerodynamics. This procedure is, however, not advisable except for small corrective action and then only when experimental evidence is available on the degree of roughness required. In seeming contradiction to the effect of surface roughness is the fact that small model elements such as hand rails, lattice work, and other small exposed parts will show exaggerated effects if geometrically scaled. Except when a number of such elements form a significant structure, their omission is favorable. Projecting solid surfaces such as parapets on a building must not be omitted.

Modeling of stack plumes in the absence of large obstructions to air motion is not sufficiently well developed to be applied to specific problems nor is it clear whether such modeling problems can be completely solved. Reynolds number may here be a significant fluid parameter. If there is no attempt at producing in the model air stream the equivalent

FIG. 15. A 1/240 scale model of the Astoria Generating Station is being tested in the New York University air pollution wind tunnel. An oil-fog type of smoke is used to make the gas plumes visible. (Courtesy of the Consolidated Edison Company of New York.)

of atmospheric turbulence, dispersal of the model plume will be deficient except near the stack where it is governed by the interaction of the plume and atmosphere. Once the initial mixing is completed, plume diffusion is governed by atmospheric turbulence. Bosanquet (*20*) shows in his development of plume rise equations that two-thirds of plume dilution is due to the motions in the atmosphere. Research on modeling of the atmospheric boundary layer through selection of surface roughness upstream of the model stack and the artificial introduction of turbulence and control of upstream velocity profile shows promise of at least a supplementary action in cases where local obstructions to air motion are not large enough to dominate the flow field around the plume.

Thermal influences may play an important part through their effect on air flow pattern and generation of convective turbulence. A large heat source in the vicinity of a stack may produce convective air currents which will have marked effect on the path of a stack plume. This can be simulated in the model by introducing a heat source by artificial means such as an electric heating element. The following scaling equation gives the strength of heat source needed to change local air temperature and thereby local air density in the same manner as in the prototype.

$$Q_{hM} = Q_{hP}(l_M/l_P)^{5/2} \tag{87}$$

where Q_h is heat emission rate to the local atmosphere. Wind speed must be in accordance with Eq. 82. g_M is assumed equal to g_P.

The simulation of convective turbulence introduces considerable modeling problems for which some success has been achieved. It is not difficult to produce some form of convective turbulence but whether properly scaled turbulence can be obtained is yet to be established. Experiments conducted at New York University (*54*) show promise. The widths of scale-model smoke plumes showed variation with temperature gradient similar to that of the prototype. The following scaling equation developed by dimensional analysis has been used with success in analyzing model results in terms of vertical temperature gradient.

$$[(dT/dz)_M + \Gamma]l_M/T_M = [(dT/dz)_P + \Gamma]l_P/T_P \tag{88}$$

where T is absolute temperature at the elevation z and Γ is the adiabatic temperature gradient expressed as a positive number. Equation 88 may be expressed in terms of potential temperature θ by replacing $(dT/dz) + \Gamma$ with $d\theta/dz$ and T with θ. Atmospheric turbulence studies have shown that Richardson number (*9*) is an important parameter and could conceivably be used to produce a scaling equation. One form of a Richardson number scaling equation may be formed by dividing Eq. 88 by the square of Eq. 82.

In most pollution problems involving individual stacks, convective turbulence, and other thermal effects are not generally major factors. Thermal influences are reduced as wind speed is increased. Holland (*12*) shows that diffusion coefficients based on turbulence characteristics obtained over a range of thermal conditions as indicated by temperature gradient tend to approach a common value at high speeds. Since the higher ground level concentrations generally occur at high wind speed, thermal influences play a lesser role. Thus model experiments in which the simulation of atmospheric thermal effects is omitted cover many practical problems.

Thermal influences in the form of density stratification by layers of differing degrees of stability such as cause the fumigating and lofting plumes of Fig. 4 do not appear to have been the subject of wind tunnel model experiments on plume dispersal. Stratification phenomena can be produced at model scale, but whether it can be so controlled as to simulate details of atmospheric motion and stability is for future investigation.

The selection of characteristics to be measured in a model plume involves considerations similar to those in field experiments on full-scale plumes. In most of the earlier scale model studies visual or photographic observations of smoke plumes were the basis for obtaining experimental data and this continues to be an effective technique. Two significant characteristics obtainable from such experiments are the location of plume edges and plume path. Experimental results presented by Sherlock and Lesher (*55*) are examples of the former. Location of lower edge of plume is given as a function of test variables. Hewson (*34*) describes a procedure in which the plume path location is used. Height of plume path determined in wind tunnel experiments is used with analytical procedures for calculation of diffusion to find ground level gas concentration. This procedure may be difficult to apply in cases where there is a dominating influence from turbulence caused by adjacent buildings since there is little data on diffusion coefficients under such conditions.

Measurements of gas plume concentration provide data very valuable in the selection of a stack. Analysis of results in terms of regulations on pollutant concentration and economic factors are facilitated. Rouse (*56*) describes the measurement of concentration in the plume of a ground source of sulfur dioxide in a wind tunnel model of an urban area. His graph of iso-concentration contour lines in a dimensionless form gives a quantitative picture of concentration distribution. Concentration measurements of sulfur dioxide in a stack plume are shown in a Strom *et al.* paper (*8*). The vertical concentration profiles through the plume give a more meaningful measure of plume characteristics than does a photograph. Location of plume axis can be accurately determined. Techniques for concentration measurements in the model plume are similar to those for the prototype. The same type of instruments may be employed. When the emission rate of the model stack is set in accordance with Eq. 85, concentration measurements are directly applicable to the prototype.

The modeling of plumes composed of particulates as well as gases has had very little development. Viscous fluid forces play a major role in the motion of small particles thus introducing Reynolds number as a significant parameter. The free settling velocity of particles is an important characteristic and provides a means of accounting for viscous effects. The ratio of settling velocity to wind speed appears to be a parameter which should have the same value in the model and prototype. The following scaling equation is suggested as a possible approach to the modeling of particulate plumes. There are other phenomena such as agglomeration which could have a significant influence on the model.

$$v_{fM}/u_M = v_{fP}/u_P \tag{89}$$

where v_f is free settling velocity as used in Section III,A,4. Since gravity plays a part, Eq. 82 must be applied. The equivalent of Eq. 84 is needed to insure proper initial conditions. Granville *et al.* (*57*) in their studies on modeling dust deposition in furnaces show two modeling parameters which are equivalent to Eq. 82 and 89.

The time scale in a model experiment, while not of prime importance in the study of plume characteristics, may be of some interest with reference to instrument response characteristics and is very important in studies of turbulence spectra. The following is developed from Eq. 82. g_M is assumed equal to g_P.

$$\Delta t_M = \sqrt{l_M/l_P}\Delta t_P \tag{90}$$

Δt is defined as the time for a fluid particle to move between geometrically similar locations in model and prototype. Thus the time for similar events to occur in the model is less than in the prototype.

The application of scale model results is most effective when analyzed in conjunction with climatological data. Most of the discussion in Section II,E on significance of climatological factors applies to the use of model results especially when concentrations are measured. Annual hours of ground concentration at various levels of concentration provide a basis for comparing design modifications. If data on tolerance levels for the pollutant are available, the analysis is more effective. When model data are in the form of visual observations of smoke plumes, one may obtain at least the annual hours for contact of plume with the ground. In the absence of climatological data, comparison of design modifications may be made in various ways. With visual data on smoke plumes, plume elevations at a given wind speed or wind speed at which the plume first contacts the ground may be compared. With concentration data comparison of concentration at a given wind speed or wind speeds at which certain concentration levels are reached may be compared.

If it is decided to conduct a scale model investigation, arrangements should be started early. The results of such an investigation could be used almost as soon as the decision is made to have it performed since they may affect the design of stack foundation or building structure. Before scale-model experiments can be performed, the model must be designed and constructed and a test program planned. These require the time-consuming task of gathering various data.

Scale-model investigations have a nontechnical value which must not be overlooked. The miniature form of the prototype obtained in a model gives the observer a grasp of the over-all situation difficult to obtain in any other way. Visualization of remedial measures is facilitated and the nontechnical observer obtains a better understanding of the problem.

V. Practical Problems of Stack Design

A. Design Features Which Reduce Ground Level Concentration

Aside from selection of site and control of source, reduction of pollution concentration at ground level is accomplished by raising the stack plume or reducing adverse atmospheric motions caused by the adjacent building. The latter is not a problem of stack design but it does affect pollution caused by stack effluents. Height of a building is a very important factor in causing adverse aerodynamic effects as implied by the rule-of-thumb procedures given in Section III,C. The shape factor plays a very important role and may in specific cases outweigh the height factor. A long narrow building with a large expanse of unbroken surface normal to the wind has much greater adverse effect than does one of the same height but more nearly square in plan. A stepped configuration which gives roughly a gradual rise to the top of the building on the upwind side is better than a single vertical surface. Wind direction may have a large effect as discussed in Section II,D. The question arises as to whether an existing building of adverse configuration may be improved by suitable additions which change the external shape. Scale model experiments have shown that such attempts are likely to be disappointing. Any significant modification of aerodynamic characteristics will usually require a major change in shape, one which will probably be costly and interfere with the functions of the building. Since this is to be accomplished by additions to the existing structure, the modified structure will be larger, an unfavorable factor in itself. Should a useful modification be found, it will probably be favorable for a limited range of wind directions and unfavorable or indifferent for others.

There are a number of design or operational characteristics of a stack which will increase plume elevation. Increase in stack height is obvious. Equation 61 for maximum ground level concentration shows a variation with the inverse square of plume elevation. Since at the higher wind speeds where adverse conditions often occur most of plume elevation is due to stack height, increase in stack height will reduce ground level concentration approximately as the inverse square. Equation 61 is, however, based on the assumption of uniform turbulence. As discussed in Section II,D, wind tunnel experiments show that, for a limited range, ground level concentration may reduce by as much as the inverse seventh power of stack height when close to a large building, while in other cases such as downwind of a large abrupt hill in Fig. 6 little improvement may be obtained until the plume touches the edge of the turbulent region. This applies also to other means of increasing plume elevation discussed below.

Plume elevation may be increased by increasing momentum or buoyancy rise. Obtainable increase in elevation by these means decreases as wind speed increases. If the critical pollution condition occurs at high speed, the improvement obtained may be very small. Plume rise can be increased in several ways. Momentum rise may be increased by reducing stack exit area if the effluent emission rate remains the same. This assumes there is adequate draft to overcome the added resistance to gas flow; otherwise momentum rise may decrease and the reduced flow rate may interfere with the process served by the stack. In the case of a new stack the problem is one of selecting stack diameter and forced draft equipment if needed. For structural reasons as well as for reduction of internal flow losses, the stack may be designed to have a greater diameter at the base, especially if it is quite tall. Reduction in diameter between the base and top can be accomplished with a gradual decrease over the entire height or a sudden decrease near the top accomplished with some form of nozzle. A nozzle is sometimes found to be an effective device for reducing the area of an existing stack. An example is the Avon Power Plant of the Cleveland Electric Illuminating Company shown in Fig. 16. On the basis of wind tunnel tests, it was decided to place nozzles on two of the stacks as shown. Experience with operation of the plant after installation of the nozzles confirmed the beneficial effects predicted in the model experiments. This case is discussed in a conference paper (*58*). The addition of a nozzle to the top of a stack gives a slight increase in stack height which is also beneficial. The nozzle must not be too short or the plume may experience the unfavorable action of the wake formed by the wider part of the stack below the nozzle.

Processes in which stack effluent emission rate varies from time to time will show varying ground level concentration for otherwise constant

FIG. 16. The addition of nozzles to two stacks of the Avon Plant solved an air pollution problem. (Courtesy of the Cleveland Electric Illuminating Company.)

meteorological conditions. If the effluent has considerable momentum and buoyancy rise, reduction in emission rate is likely to cause sufficient lowering of the plume to give higher ground level concentration, this in spite of the fact that emission rate is less. This characteristic is common to large power plants where full load will give lower ground level concentration than partial load. If the emission rate is reduced to sufficiently low values, a reversal point is reached where reduction in ground level concentration will result from further decrease in emission rate. To solve the part-load problem when a stack gives satisfactory characteristics for full-load or rated emission, special devices for the top of the stack have been used. They have the purpose of decreasing the exit area at will, thereby providing the means for producing full-load ejection speed at partial load. The result will not be as good as that with a plain stack having the reduced area because the stack top is larger and, therefore, causes local interference with air motion. Generally any structure added near the top of an otherwise plain circular stack will be detrimental. A square stack is inferior to one of circular shape.

Modification of the physical characteristics of gaseous effluents offer possibilities for pollution reduction. Addition of air to an effluent for the purpose of dilution before it leaves the stack will have little effect at distances where pollution problems occur. Dilution due to mixing with the surrounding atmosphere is much greater than that which can be accomplished by dilution within the stack. On the other hand, introduction of excess air is sometimes considered for the purpose of increasing the effluent ejection speed and, thereby, plume rise. If this is done by using air at ambient temperature, little or no reduction in ground level concentration may result because of the resulting reduction in temperature or density of the effluent mixture as compared with the unmodified effluent. It is even possible to experience an increase in ground level concentration. The addition of air at the temperature or density of the effluent will bring about an improvement. The addition of heat to a gaseous effluent will markedly improve pollution characteristics. For a given emission rate heat addition will reduce gas density and increase gas ejection speed through thermal expansion. While heat addition is costly, it offers a potential solution in that its use may be limited to critical meteorological conditions. The analytical procedures given in Section III,A will serve as a guide for evaluation of these types of remedial measures.

Modification of effluent by removal of objectionable components should be examined for its potential adverse effect on plume characteristics. A removal process aimed at removing only a small component may have an important effect on the remainder. An example is the removal of sulfur dioxide from combustion gases by wet scrubbing. Experience with scrubbing of stack gases in two power plants located in London show adverse effects on plume characteristics. Scrubbing reduces effluent temperature to near-ambient values. Water droplets may be drawn with the gaseous effluent and as the plume mixes with the atmosphere the droplets evaporate and reduce effluent temperature. The net result may be the creation of a plume having greater density than that of the ambient atmosphere. It will fall to the ground and if any polluting component remains after scrubbing, its full effect will be felt on the ground. The effect of scrubbing is discussed by Scorer (*3*), Hawkins and Nonhebel (*14*), and Bryant and Cowdrey (*17*).

When two or more stacks operating simultaneously produce objectionable ground level pollution, a possible solution lies in combining their outputs into one stack. A new and larger diameter stack with the same ejection speed as the old stacks will be an improvement since the new plume will be larger and have proportionately greater rise. If the output of two or more stacks is ducted into one of them, there will be an improvement due to higher ejection speed, but this needs greater draft to overcome increased flow resistance.

Various nonuniform conditions of the atmosphere present cases difficult to handle analytically at the present state of knowledge. They may be the cause of serious pollution situations. Plumes having high momentum and buoyancy rise tend to remain clear of the ground at low wind speeds as discussed previously. More moderate amounts of plume rise may show high short-period ground level concentration when there is intense convective turbulence. This is most likely to occur at low wind speeds. Cases of this type may best be handled on the basis of effect of sampling period discussed in Section II,C but little data is available.

Atmospheric layers of varying degree of stability cause some of the serious area-wide pollution problems. An inversion (stable) layer of low elevation suppresses the desirable upward diffusion and reduces plume rise. If this is accompanied with low wind speed, as is often the case, stack effluents accumulate below the stable layer. This condition is more likely to occur in a persistent manner for regions of large variations in topography such as valleys, which restrict air movement. It may occur in more nearly level regions if the larger-scale meteorological characteristics are such as to restrict air movement. At locations where inversion layers persist, selection of stack height to carry the plume above the layer will do much to the alleviation of area-wide pollution. This requires climatological data on local characteristics. Estimate of plume rise within a uniform stable layer may be made with equations such as Eq. 10.

Nonhebel (*58a*) discusses many practical aspects of stack selection with particular reference to the Clean Air Act, 1956 (Great Britain). He presents various data and procedures for analysis of gas concentration and dust deposition.

B. Limitations on Stack Height

There are various limitations which prevent stacks from being constructed as high as may be desired from a pollution viewpoint. Most obvious is the economic factor but there are others. Limitation due to interference with air traffic near an airport is not unusual. This limitation is usually given in the form of an inclined limit line starting from the end of the nearest runway and having an angle of magnitude with the horizon which depends on the type of air traffic. Stack height may be limited by the designer for esthetic reasons or the stack may be given a configuration intended to conceal its real purpose. The results are sometimes ludicrous if not tragic.

Cost of stack construction varies with location due to variations in labor and material costs. Variations in environmental factors affect design, construction, and maintenance. Steel, brick, and reinforced concrete are three common materials of construction. A stack lining is generally required depending on the properties of stack effluent. The lining may be an independent structure such as a brick lining within a brick or concrete stack, or it may be an integral part of the stack such as a gunite lining within a steel stack. The foundation is a sizable item whether it is a separate foundation for a ground-based stack or added structure and foundation for a roof-based stack. Increasingly stringent air pollution requirements and increased size of industrial installations have forced taller and taller stacks. Some are reaching the 700-ft. level. An example is the Clifty Creek Power Plant of the Ohio Valley Electric Corp. at Madison, Indiana, which has three 680-ft. stacks. High stacks are found in the metallurgical industry. Clark (*59*) discusses various factors which affect stack design and expresses the opinion that stacks will reach the 1000-ft. level in the foreseeable future.

Wind pressure is an environmental factor important to stack design. It varies directly with air density and wind speed squared. Local maximum wind speeds should be used but accurate data may be unavailable. Many stacks have been built for a lateral wind pressure of 30 lb./sq. ft. (based on projected area) which is approximately that found at a wind speed of 120 m.p.h. (*60*). Such a simple design criterion should be closely examined when applied to high stacks in view of the increase of wind speed with elevation. The most recent wind data should be consulted. Excellent data is being obtained at several meteorological towers such as that of the Brookhaven National Laboratory.

Steel stacks may experience a destructive dynamic phenomenon which is not necessarily dependent on maximum wind pressure. It is caused by the lateral (crosswind) periodic aerodynamic force which results from the alternate shedding of vortices from the sides of the stack. If the natural vibration frequency of the stack coincides with that of the force, resonant vibration is induced. If structural damping is not sufficient, as may be the case with steel stacks, the amplitude of vibration may reach critically high values. Two or more closely spaced stacks in line with the wind appear to amplify vibration of the down-wind stack. Dynamic characteristics and structural damping of brick and concrete stacks are such that the phenomenon does not occur.

There is some disagreement in data on the exact frequency of the periodic aerodynamic force caused by the shedding vortices. For a wide range of Reynolds number the frequency may be expressed in terms of wind speed, size, and a dimensionless quantity known as Strouhal number S.

$$S = fd_s/u \tag{91}$$

where f is frequency in cycles per unit time, d_s is diameter, and u is wind speed in consistent units. For example, f may be in cycles per second, d in feet and u in feet per second. For a long cylinder normal to an air stream experiments show S to have a value between 0.18 and 0.20 (*60*). For a given value of S, frequency will, therefore, increase directly with wind speed in accordance with Eq. 91. Laboratory experiments show disappearance of periodicity at high Reynolds numbers (*61*) which seems to disagree with field experience on stack vibration. Ozker and Smith (*62*) found in their experiments on large stacks that frequency, not Strouhal number, remains at a constant value which they found to be 0.86 cycles/sec.

Stacks may vibrate in two different modes, one of which is a lateral swaying where the stack vibrates as a cantilever beam. In the other mode, termed ovaling, the circular cross section deforms into an oval shape. Design of stack for resonant vibration is based on the use of an equivalent lateral pressure. Ozker and Smith (*62*) and Stankiewicz (*60*) give formulas and data for estimating lateral pressure. Stankiewicz considers various structural aspects.

Stankiewicz (*60*) and von Hohenleiten and Kent (*63*) analyze comparative costs of steel, brick, and concrete construction for heights above 100 ft. In both papers it is shown that for the lower range of heights steel is less costly and for the higher range concrete is less costly. Brick is more costly than one or the other of steel and concrete over the entire range. The concrete stack becomes less costly above 275 ft. in von Hohenleiten and Kent (*63*) and above approximately 175 ft. in Stankiewitz (*60*). The latter gives a number of graphs for estimating stack cost for various types of construction in terms of local unit costs.

VI. Meteorological Control

Meteorological control is the reduction or suspension of stack effluent or an objectionable component during unfavorable atmospheric conditions. Complexity of control method ranges from the simple action of reducing a process when there is visible evidence of unfavorable diffusion to complex procedures which require lengthy preparatory operations and special forecasting services for predicting unfavorable meteorological conditions.

Use of meteorological control presupposes the process which produces the pollutant can be controlled at will either in immediate response to a control action or within a certain period following a control command. Meteorological control can generally not be applied to processes such as the generation of heat or electricity, which must immediately respond to the user's demand or which cannot be subjected to rapid change of operation without danger of damaging valuable equipment or creating a hazardous condition. In some cases a delayed control can be accomplished by substituting raw materials which produce less pollution. Meteorological control in any form is likely to increase costs. It does not appear advisable to design and locate a new plant where meteorological control will be needed unless the economic aspects are clearly favorable.

The type of meteorological data and diffusion analysis required depends to some degree on the time-dependent characteristics of the pollution-producing process and its effects. For processes which have rapid response to control action current meteorological data may be sufficient. When there is a significant delay in response to control action, a forecast of the necessary meteorological characteristics is needed. When items affected by the pollutant respond to accumulated exposure over a period of time, a history of conditions may be needed along with a time integration of their effect.

A different type of meteorological control is the use of favorable atmospheric conditions to discharge pollutants which have been accumulated during unfavorable periods. If the pollutant can be stored for limited periods, this procedure allows the pollution-producing process to continue under unfavorable atmospheric conditions. This and other aspects of meteorological control are discussed by White and Pack (*64*) and additional information is given in the 1955 U. S. AEC report (*11*).

The work of Hewson (*1, 65*) at the Trail Smelter is an example of meteorological control of an industrial process based in part on turbulence properties of the atmosphere measured with a special instrument. Permissible emission rate was given in terms of the readings of a gust accelerometer (*47, 66*), on time of day and on season as to growing or nongrowing. The gust accelerometer integrates changes in wind speed and displays a single number which is a measure of turbulence. Turbulence is too complex a phenomenon to be completely measured in terms of a single variable, but a simple reading is necessary for routine air pollution evaluations. To retain this simplicity the design of the instrument must be based on an arbitrary selection of characteristics to be a measure of turbulence. Another example of a turbulence-measuring instrument is one developed at the Brookhaven National Laboratory (*67*) which reads gustiness categories. These categories (discussed briefly in Section III,A,3,*d*,*ii*) classify atmospheric turbulence. They had previously been found by visual inspection of wind direction charts.

The meteorological control program developed at the Brookhaven National Laboratory (*68*) is a case in which the history of pollution level is important. It concerns the cumulative exposure to a radioactive component in the reactor-cooling air which was discharged through a stack. Each day the average exposure for a certain number of preceding days and the day following were calculated and used as a basis for determining whether reactor operation should be limited during the following day. This involved the use of meteorological measurements obtained during the preceding days and a forecast of values for the following day. This program was developed before the reactor was constructed and did not receive extensive use once the reactor was placed in operation, because later information on the potential hazard of exposure showed the levels to be quite low.

A special forecasting service for meteorological control of a large power plant is described by Kleinsasser and Wanta (*69*). The purpose was to provide a forecast of adverse meteorological conditions sufficiently far in advance to give the time needed to set into operation the necessary control action. The forecasted elements include wind speed, wind direction, turbulence, temperature gradient, and humidity. In developing the procedure, field measurements of gas concentration and meteorological variables were analyzed to find those atmospheric conditions which caused undesirable pollution situations. Data on the general circulation of the atmosphere were analyzed to find large-scale weather patterns which were likely to cause adverse local conditions. Stagnation conditions for extended periods were found to be potentially serious because of local accumulation of pollutants.

Determination of ground level concentration for given meteorological conditions, whether measured or forecasted, presents problems similar to those involved in the development of analytical procedures such as discussed in Section III. Some of the data in Section III were in fact obtained from field experiments conducted for meteorological control purposes. These analytical procedures could be used for meteorological control purposes but greater accuracy would usually be desired. Having a specific plant and location, the effect of local conditions should be included.

For an existing plant a good procedure is the correlation of local measurements of ground level concentration with meteorological variables. If the stack effluent does not have a component suitable for concentration measurement one may be introduced as described by Haines, Hemeon, and Cember (*50*). When a sufficiently wide range of conditions has been measured, an empirical relation between concentration and meteorological variables can be established. This automatically includes the effect of such local influences as buildings and topography, but there will be some degree of inaccuracy because at this stage of knowledge on atmospheric diffusion it is not possible to find a unique relationship between concentration and a limited number of meteorological variables. If in an existing plant only current information on pollution characteristics is needed, the entire process of predicting ground level concentration could be bypassed with local sampling of stack effluent. This is feasible if the region of potentially serious pollution is limited; otherwise a prohibitively large number of samplers may be needed. Thus a procedure for predicting concentration may be desirable even though the plume is available for measurement.

In cases where the plant is yet to be built various methods have been used to predict local pollution characteristics. A source of tracer material emitted at the future location or height of the plume has been used with success. The Brookhaven field experiments mentioned earlier used an oil-fog smoke whose concentration was measured at various downwind locations. Falk *et al.* (*49*) used a source of fluorescent particles. They also describe the application of their field data to the development of a system for prediction of concentrations. The method developed by Davidson and Halitsky (*70*) is especially interesting because it does not require concentration measurements. Photographs of a smoke plume together with bivane measurement of wind fluctuations are used in the development of equations for finding instantaneous as well as long-period ground level concentrations. Prediction of concentration may be made in the absence of a tracer plume on the basis of turbulence measurements and a diffusion theory such as Sutton's (see Section III,A,3,*c*) in which diffusion parameters are expressible in terms of turbulence characteristics. An example is the Oak Ridge program described by Holland (*12*). In any procedure where the experiments are made before the installation is built one must not overlook the possible effects that the presence of the installation may have on diffusion characteristics.

The Air Pollution Potential Forecasting Service was initiated in 1960 by the U. S. Weather Bureau and Public Health Service for areas of the United States east of the Rocky Mountains. This service is available to air pollution control and research units. It originates with the Weather Bureau Research Station at the Robert A. Taft Sanitary Engineering Center of the Public Health Service in Cincinnati, Ohio. The users of this service are notified of the beginning and ending of periods of high pollution potential.

References

1. E. W. Hewson, *Quart. J. Roy. Meteorol. Soc.* **71,** 266 (1945).
2. C. H. Bosanquet, W. F. Carey, and E. M. Halton, *Proc. Inst. Mech. Engrs.* **162,** 355 (1950) (incl. unpublished appendices).
2a. F. E. Gartrell, F. W. Thomas, and S. B. Carpenter, *J. Air Poll. Control Assoc.* **11,** 60 (1961).
3. R. S. Scorer, *Intern. J. Air Poll.* **1,** 198 (1959).
4. O. G. Sutton, *Quart. J. Roy. Meteorol. Soc.* **73,** 257 (1947).
5. M. E. Smith and I. A. Singer, *Proc. 3rd Natl. Air Poll. Symposium, Pasadena, California* p. 80 (1955).
6. N. G. Stewart, H. J. Gale, and R. N. Crooks, *Intern. J. Air Poll.* **1,** 87 (1958).
7. F. Gifford, Jr., *Intern. J. Air Poll.* **3,** 253 (1960).
8. G. H. Strom, M. Hackman, and E. J. Kaplin, *J. Air Poll. Control Assoc.* **7,** 198 (1957).
9. O. G. Sutton, "Micrometeorology." McGraw-Hill, New York, 1953.
10. W. F. Davidson, Trans. Conf. Ind. Wastes, *14th Ann. Meeting, Ind. Hyg. Foundation Am.* p. 38 (1949).
11. "Meteorology and Atomic Energy," U. S. Atomic Energy Commission Rept. AECU-3066 (1955).
12. J. Z. Holland, "A Meteorological Survey of the Oak Ridge Area," U. S. Atomic Energy Commission Rept. ORO-99 (1953).
13. A. F. Rupp, S. E. Beall, L. P. Bornwasser, and D. F. Johnson, "Dilution of Stack Gases in Cross Winds," U. S. Atomic Energy Commission Rept. AECD-1811 (1944).
14. J. E. Hawkins and G. Nonhebel, *J. Inst. Fuel* **28,** 530 (1955).
15. F. W. Thomas, *J. Air Poll. Control Assoc.* **4,** 7 (1954).
16. O. G. Sutton, *J. Meteorol.* **7,** 307 (1950).
17. L. W. Bryant and C. F. Cowdrey, *Proc. Inst. Mech. Engrs.* (*London*) **169,** 371 (1955).
18. C. H. B. Priestley, *Quart. J. Roy. Meteorol. Soc.* **82,** 165 (1956).
19. G. Spurr, *Quart. J. Roy. Meteorol. Soc.* **83,** 269 (1957).
20. C. H. Bosanquet, *J. Inst. Fuel* **30,** 322 (1957).
20a. R. S. Scorer, "Natural Aerodynamics." Pergamon Press, New York, 1958.
21. A. C. Best, *J. Inst. Fuel* **30,** 329 (1957).
22. H. Beaver (Chairman), "Report of the Committee on Air Pollution," Cmd-9322. Her Majesty's Stationery Office, London, 1954.
22a. F. Wippermann and W. Klug, "Schornsteinmindesthoehen. Ihre Bestimmung aus Gesetzmässigkeiten der turbulenten Diffusion in der Atmosphäre." Entwurf einer VDI-Richtlinie, Darmstadt, 1960.
22b. H. Moses and G. H. Strom, *J. Air Poll. Control Assoc.* **11,** 455 (1961).

22c. F. T. Bodurtha, Jr., *J. Air Poll. Control Assoc.* **11,** 431 (1961).
23. C. H. Bosanquet and J. L. Pearson, *Trans. Faraday Soc.* **32,** 1249 (1936).
24. O. G. Sutton, *Quart. J. Roy. Meteorol. Soc.* **73,** 426 (1947).
24a. J. S. Hay and F. Pasquill, *Advances in Geophys.* **6,** 345 (1959).
24b. F. Pasquill, *Meteorol. Mag.* **90,** 33 (1961).
25. I. A. Singer and M. E. Smith, *J. Meteorol.* **10,** 121 (1953).
26. D. G. Friedman, *J. Meteorol.* **10,** 372 (1953).
27. H. E. Cramer, *Proc. 1st Natl. Conf. on Appl. Meteorol., Hartford, Conn.* p. c-33 (1957).
28. M. L. Barad (ed.), *Geophys. Research Papers* No. 59, Vols. I and II (1958).
29. D. A. Haugen (ed.), *Geophys. Research Papers* No. 59, Vol. III (1959).
30. H. E. Cramer, *Bull. Am. Meteorol. Soc.* **40,** 165 (1959).
31. M. E. Smith, I. A. Singer, F. E. Bartlett, and L. Marcus, *J. Air Poll. Control Assoc.* **7,** 194 (1957).
32. G. R. Hilst, *J. Air Poll. Control Assoc.* **7,** 205 (1957).
33. M. L. Barad, *Meteorol. Monographs* **I,** No. 4, 9 (1951).
34. E. W. Hewson, *Trans. ASME* **77,** 1163 (1955).
35. M. E. Smith, *J. Air Poll. Control Assoc.* **6,** 11 (1956).
36. F. J. Gifford, Jr., *Bull. Am. Meteorol. Soc.* **34,** 101 (1953).
37. F. J. Gifford, Jr., *Bull. Am. Meteorol. Soc.* **34,** 216 (1953).
38. M. L. Barad and D. A. Haugen, *J. Meteorol.* **16,** 12 (1959).
39. P. E. Waskow and H. Moses, Argonne National Laboratory (Radiol. Phys. Div.) Semi-Annual Rept. ANL-6049, p. 85 (1959).
40. J. H. Perry (ed.), "Chemical Engineers' Handbook." McGraw-Hill, New York, 1950.
41. T. Baron, E. R. Gerhard, and H. F. Johnstone, *Ind. Eng. Chem.* **41,** 2403 (1949).
42. G. T. Csanady, *Australian J. Appl. Sci.* **9,** 1 (1958).
43. A. J. ter Linden, *in* "Problems and Control of Air Pollution" (F. S. Mallette, ed.), p. 236. Reinhold, New York, 1955.
44. R. H. Sherlock and E. A. Stalker, *Univ. Mich. Eng. Research Bull.* No. 29, (1941).
45. G. H. Strom, *APCA News* **6,** No. 7, 4 (1958).
45a. J. Halitsky, Paper No. 61-35. Air Poll. Control Assoc., Pittsburgh, Pa., 1961.
46. "Encyclopedia of Instrumentation for Industrial Hygiene" (C. D. Yaffe, D. H. Byers, and A. D. Hosey, eds.). Univ. of Michigan, Ann Arbor, 1956.
47. E. W. Hewson, *J. Air Poll. Control Assoc.* **5,** 235 (1956).
48. G. F. Collins, *Ind. Wastes* **2,** 109 (1957).
49. L. I. Falk, W. R. Chalker, J. A. Greene, C. B. Cave, and C. W. Thorngate, *J. Air Poll. Control Assoc.* **4,** No. 2, 35 (1954).
50. G. F. Haines, Jr., W. C. L. Hemeon, and H. Cember, *J. Air Poll. Control Assoc.* **7,** 262 (1958).
51. G. H. Strom, Proc. 7th Hydr. Conf., *State Univ. Iowa Studies in Eng. Bull.* **39,** 91 (1959).
52. Anonymous, "The Industrial Application of Aerodynamic Techniques," Notes on Appl. Sci. No. 2, Natl. Physical Lab. Her Majesty's Stationery Office, London, 1952.
53. G. H. Strom and J. Halitsky, *Trans. ASME* **77,** 789 (1955).
54. G. H. Strom and E. J. Kaplin, Argonne National Laboratory (Radiol. Phys. Div.) Semi-Annual Rept. ANL-6199, p. 119 (1960).

55. R. H. Sherlock and E. J. Lesher, *Trans. ASME* **77,** 1 (1955).
56. H. Rouse, *Meteorol. Monographs* **I,** No. 4, 39 (1951).
57. R. A. Granville, A. Sigalla, and H. Lubanska, *J. Iron. Steel Inst.* (*London*) **187,** 121 (1957).
58. G. H. Strom, *Proc. 1st Natl. Conf. on Appl. Meteorol., Hartford, Conn.* p. c-24 (1957).
58a. G. Nonhebel, *J. Inst. Fuel* **33,** 479 (1960).
59. A. M. Clark, *Eng. News-Record* **154,** 47 (May 12, 1955).
60. E. J. Stankiewicz, Paper No. 54-A-260. Am. Soc. Mech. Engrs., New York, 1954.
61. S. Goldstein (ed.), "Modern Developments in Fluid Dynamics," Vol. II, p. 421. Oxford Univ. Press, London and New York, 1938.
62. M. S. Ozker and J. O. Smith, *Trans. ASME* **78,** 1381 (1956).
63. H. L. von Hohenleiten and R. H. Kent, *Air Repair* **3,** 195 (1954).
64. F. D. White and D. H. Pack, *J. Air Poll. Control Assoc.* **6,** 151 (1956).
65. E. W. Hewson, *in* "Compendium of Meteorology" (T. F. Malone, ed.), p. 1139. Am. Meteorol. Soc., Boston, Mass., 1951.
66. E. W. Hewson and G. C. Gill, *U. S. Bur. Mines Bull.* **435,** 23 (1944).
67. G. S. Raynor and M. E. Smith, Paper No. 57-6. Air Poll. Control Assoc., Pittsburgh, Pa., 1957.
68. M. E. Smith, *Meteorol. Monographs* **1,** No. 4, 50 (1951).
69. T. W. Kleinsasser and R. C. Wanta, *J. Air Poll. Control Assoc.* **6,** 228 (1957).
70. B. Davidson and J. Halitsky, *J. Air Poll. Control Assoc.* **7,** 316 (1958).

PART II

The Effects of Air Pollution

CHAPTER 7A

Effects of Air Pollution on Materials

JOHN E. YOCOM*

Bay Area Air Pollution Control District, San Francisco, California

Air pollution damage to nonliving materials has long been a significant source of economic loss in urban areas. Some of this loss results directly from damage by pollutants such as the corrosion of metal objects, or the weakening and eventual loss of textile or leather articles by direct action of pollutants. The other portion of this loss is indirect and includes, for example, the increased cost of clothing replacement because of excessive cleaning required by a polluted environment, or the loss in property values in highly polluted areas.

Considerable effort has been made in England to determine the costs of the effects of air pollution. The Beaver Report (*1*) states that the total economic loss from air pollution is of the order of 250 million pounds per year. Of this about 150 million are direct costs, and the remaining 100 million result from loss in efficiency, for example, losses in efficiency in the operation of transportation facilities. The distribution of direct costs as listed in the report is shown on page 200.

Most of the deterioration of materials by air pollution goes unnoticed because it cannot be distinguished from what might be called normal or natural deterioration. However, one source for the Beaver Report estimated that one-third of the cost of replacing steel railroad rails in England was attributable to corrosion induced by air pollution. The

* Present address: Arthur D. Little, Inc., Research and Development Group, Western Laboratories, San Francisco, California.

report further states that as a direct result of the 1952 London smog the owner of one chain store had to reduce prices of damaged goods by 90,000 pounds in order to sell them.

In the United States no recent detailed studies have yet been made of the economic loss from air pollution. In 1949 Gibson (*2*) reported that direct economic loss from air pollution could easily be 1½ billion dollars per year. This would be equivalent to about 10 dollars per capita per year. The estimates for some cities (for example, Chicago) showed per capita losses up to 20 dollars per year. For England, by comparison the Beaver report (*1*), prepared about 5 years later than Gibson's report, sets the average yearly per capita economic loss from air pollution at 5 pounds. Losses in the heavily industrialized areas were twice this value. It must be remembered that the British figures include a "loss in efficiency" factor which presumably the United States figures do not.

Cost item	Millions of pounds sterling per year
Laundry	25
Painting and decorating	30
Cleaning and depreciation of buildings other than houses	20
Corrosion of metals	25
Damage to textiles and other goods	52 5
	152.5

I. Mechanisms of Deterioration in Polluted Atmospheres

There are a host of ways in which air pollutants damage materials.

(1) *Abrasion.* Solid particles of sufficient size and traveling at high velocities are capable of causing destructive abrasion.

(2) *Deposition and removal.* Solid and liquid particles can deposit on a surface and may not damage or change the material itself except perhaps to spoil its appearance. The removal of these particles may cause some deterioration. A single washing or cleaning of a fabric to remove embedded particles may not cause noticeable deterioration, but frequent cleaning ultimately can. It is the increased frequency of cleanings that determines the deterioration related to air pollution.

(3) *Direct chemical attack.* Some air pollutants react irreversibly and directly with materials and cause deterioration. Examples of this are the tarnishing of silver by H_2S and the etching of a metallic surface by an acid mist.

(4) *Indirect chemical attack.* Certain materials absorb pollutants, but their deterioration results not from the absorbed pollutant, but from

products of its chemical conversion. An example of this would be the absorption of SO_2 by leather and its conversion to sulfuric acid.

(5) *Electrochemical corrosion.* Much of the atmospheric deterioration of ferrous metals is by an electrochemical process (*3, 4*). Numerous small electrochemical cells tend to form on ferrous metal surfaces exposed to the atmosphere. Anodes and cathodes are set up as a result of local chemical or physical differences on the metal surfaces. The distance between the anodes and cathodes is usually small. The potential difference between the anode and cathode is the driving force for the corrosive action. If the metal is clean and dry no current will flow because the external resistance between anode and cathode is infinite; as a result no corrosion will occur. If an electrolyte, such as water, is present on the surface, even as a molecular layer on a surface that appears to be dry, current will tend to flow. If the water is contaminated with air pollutants it is likely to have more electrical conductivity and corrosion will tend to proceed faster. Larrabee (*4*) reports that when iron remains in dry air for an appreciable length of time it develops a protective film of oxygen. This film insulates the iron from atmospheric moisture, but when SO_2 is present the protective oxygen layer is broken down.

II. Factors Which Influence Atmospheric Deterioration

Among the more important factors that influence the attack rate of damaging pollutants are:

(1) *Moisture.* Without moisture in the atmosphere there would be little if any atmospheric corrosion even in the most severely polluted environments. Visible wetting of surfaces is not required for corrosion to take place. For several metals there seems to be a critical atmospheric humidity which, when exceeded, produces a sharp rise in the rate of corrosion. Sanyal and Bhadwar (*5*) report that for atmospheres containing SO_2 aluminum has a critical humidity of 80% and mild steel has two at 60 and 75%. Aziz and Godard (*6*) state the critical humidities for nickel and copper in the presence of SO_2 as 70 and 63%, respectively, while zinc and magnesium showed critical humidities in unpolluted air of 70 and 90%, respectively.

Moisture in the form of rain often appears to reduce corrosion rates of metals in polluted atmospheres. The effect is probably that of dilution and washing away of corrosive materials, although under some conditions the corrosives can accumulate at the lower edge of a metallic object and cause accelerated corrosion.

(2) *Temperature.* The most obvious influence is that on the rate of the chemical reaction responsible for deterioration. Objects exposed

during a radiation temperature inversion lose heat rapidly and usually cool to temperatures below that of the ambient air. If their surface temperature falls below the dew point condensed moisture forms on them. The resulting moist surface, in the presence of corrosive pollutants whose concentrations are increasing under the stable influence of the temperature inversion, provides an ideal environment for the promotion of certain types of damage to materials.

(3) *Sunlight* can cause direct deterioration of certain materials, in addition to producing damaging agents such as ozone through a series of complex photochemical reactions in the atmosphere (Chapter 3). In cases of rubber cracking, or the fading of certain dyes it is not always possible to distinguish direct sunlight damage from that caused by ozone.

(4) *Air movement.* Wind speed is significant in the case of solid and liquid agents since it may determine whether they impact on vertical surfaces or settle on horizontal surfaces. In cases of deterioration caused by pollutants released nearby from a point source wind direction is a most important variable. Air movement in libraries, where leather bound books are stored, is a critical factor when the air is contaminated by SO_2.

(5) *Other factors.* Position in space is an important variable in the atmospheric corrosion testing of metals. Corrosion samples are usually mounted 45° from the horizontal. The under surfaces often are corroded more rapidly than the upper surfaces because corrosive agents are not as well washed off them by the rain.

The order in which substances contact a surface can also be highly significant. Aziz and Godard (*6*) state that when copper is exposed first to unpolluted air a thin oxide film develops which protects it against attack by hydrogen sulfide.

III. Measurement of Atmospheric Deterioration

Deterioration of materials manifests itself and is measured in a variety of ways, as shown in the tabulation on page 203.

There exists a great deal of literature on the subject of deterioration of materials, and significant amounts of it deal directly with that caused by atmospheric pollution (*7*). Much data on corrosion of various kinds of metals are related not to individual or classes of air pollutants, but instead to generalized environments such as "rural," "marine," and "industrial" (*8*). The "marine" and "rural" categories may adequately describe two specific types of environments, but "industrial" is a vague term presumed to mean that corrosion test samples, during their long exposure, were acted upon by air pollutants emitted from industrial

Materials	Typical manifestation	Measurement
Metals	Spoilage of surface; gross loss of metal	Weight gain of corrosion products; weight loss after removal of corrosive products
Building stone	Discoloration; leaching	Not usually measured quantitatively
Fabrics and dyes	Discoloration; fading; weakening	Decrease in light reflectance; loss of tensile strength
Leather	Weakening; embrittlement	Loss of tensile strength
Paper	Embrittlement	Decrease in folding resistance
Paint	Discoloration	Not usually measured quantitatively
Rubber	Cracking; weakening	Loss in elasticity; increase in depth of cracks when under tension

operations. In all too few instances is there any mention of the specific pollutants and the mechanism of attack on the exposed samples. Table I gives data on the relative corrosiveness of several types of atmospheres on various nonferrous metals and alloys (*8*).

An important exception to this pattern is the excellent work of W. H. J. Vernon and co-workers in England, extending from 1923 to the present, which is reviewed by Aziz and Godard (*6*).

A refreshing approach to research on the corrosion of metals in polluted atmospheres is embodied in the work of Lodge and Havlik (*9*) in which metal films placed on glass slides by vacuum deposition serve as indicators of the relative corrosiveness of atmospheres. By using different metals some specificity for individual pollutants is obtained. Light transmission, electrical conductivity, microchemical analysis, X-ray and electron diffraction patterns offer possible means of reporting significant changes to the surfaces.

In an air pollution survey in the Tulsa area (*10*) wrought-iron discs were exposed and their change in weight was used as a measure of air-pollution-induced corrosion. The results showed a fairly clear-cut area of high corrosion rates adjacent to a group of industrial plants which included oil refinery, fertilizer, and sulfuric acid manufacturing operations.

Figure 1 is a photograph of a typical sampling site for this survey which shows corrosion discs and a dustfall jar.

The book by Greathouse and Wessel (*11*) is excellent with respect to the deterioration of materials other than metals since it brings together much of this diverse information.

TABLE I

WEIGHT LOSS OF 9 × 12 × 0.035-INCH SPECIMENS AFTER 20 YEARS' EXPOSURE IN VARIOUS ATMOSPHERES (About 1930–1954)[a]

City	Exposure classification	Average loss in weight (%)					
		Commercial copper 99.9%+ Cu	Commercial aluminum 99%+ Al	Brass 85% Cu 15% Zn	Nickel 99%+ Ni	Commercial lead 99.92% Pb 0.06% Cu	Commercial zinc 99% Zn 0.85% Pb
Altoona, Pa.	Industrial	6.1	—	8.5	25.2	1.8	30.7
New York, N. Y.	Industrial	6.4	3.4	8.7	16.6	—	25.1
La Jolla, Calif.	Seacoast	5.4	2.6	1.3	0.6	2.1	6.9
Key West, Fla.	Seacoast	2.4	—	2.5	0.5	—	2.9
State College, Pa.	Rural	1.9	0.4	2.0	1.0	1.4	5.0
Phoenix, Ariz.	Rural	0.6	0.3	0.5	0.2	0.4	0.8

[a] H. R. Copson Report of ASTM Subcommittee VI, of Committee B-3 on Atmospheric Corrosion, *ASTM Spec. Tech. Publ.* No. 175 (1955). Used by permission of American Society for Testing Materials.

FIG. 1. Test site showing corrosion discs used in Tulsa survey (*10*). (Courtesy of Tulsa, Oklahoma City-County Health Department.)

IV. Atmospheric Pollutants and Their Effects on Materials

A. CARBON DIOXIDE

CO_2 concentrations over heavily industralized areas, where large amounts of fossil fuels are being consumed, can reach several times the so-called normal value of 0.03%. The principal undesirable effect of atmospheric CO_2 is deterioration of building stones—in particular, carbonate rock such as limestone (*12*). In the presence of moisture, CO_2 produces carbonic acid, which attacks calcium carbonate, converting it to the water-soluble bicarbonate which is then leached away. It is doubtful whether this type of deterioration can occur in the absence of moisture. Carbon dioxide is also responsible in part for the atmospheric corrosion of magnesium.

B. Sulfur Oxides

Sulfur dioxide has its principal sources in combustion or roasting operations in which some SO_3 is created along with the SO_2. Both compounds are usually implicated together in deterioration of materials. In 1939 Burdick and Barkley (*13*) surveyed the available literature covering the deterioration of many materials in atmospheres containing SO_2. Much work on the effect of SO_2 on materials has been carried out in laboratories using SO_2 concentrations (usually in excess of 200 p.p.m.) which would not normally exist in the free atmosphere; nevertheless, a wide variety of materials has been shown to be affected.

1. *Effects on Metals*

a. Ferrous Metals. It was pointed out earlier that moisture must be present for sulfur oxides to attack iron and steel and that there appears to be a critical humidity above which the corrosiveness of SO_2 is ac-

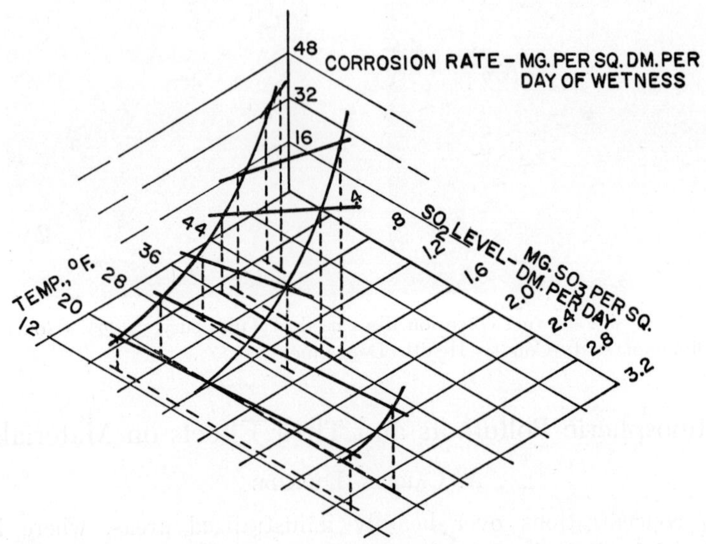

FIG. 2. Corrosion rate of steel versus temperature and SO_2 level, based on a day of wetness (*14*). (Courtesy of *Industrial and Engineering Chemistry*.)

celerated. Figure 2 summarizes the recent work of Sereda (*14*) and relates corrosion of steel to outdoor concentrations of SO_2. Samples of steel were exposed over an 8-month period and the "time of wetness" was determined for the exposure period by measuring surface moisture on both sides of the samples. The temperature of the exposed surfaces was recorded continuously and SO_2 concentrations determined by the lead peroxide method. The author stated that a concentration of approximately 0.025 p.p.m. SO_2 would result in deposition in lead peroxide of 1 mg. SO_3 per square decimeter per day. Using the method of least squares the best equation for the plane in Fig. 2 was found to be:

$$Y = 0.131X + 0.018Z + 787$$

where Y = log corrosion rate, MDD_W (milligrams per square decimeter per day of wetness)

X = sulfur dioxide pollution rate, MDD (milligrams SO_3 per square decimeter per day)

Z = temperature, degrees Fahrenheit (monthly average during the time of wetness)

b. Aluminum. Aluminum appears to be fairly resistant to attack by concentrations of sulfur oxides normally found in polluted atmospheres (*15*). Aziz and Godard (*6*) have studied the corrosion of aluminum under laboratory conditions at various humidities and at high concentrations of SO_2 (280 p.p.m.). Despite this high concentration the authors feel that these experiences give insight into the mechanism of atmospheric corrosion of aluminum by SO_2.

Figures 3 and 4 show the weight gain of samples of aluminum exposed to 280 p.p.m. SO_2 at various humidities. At 52% humidity (Fig. 3) the two types of aluminum show the same weight increase—time relationship and reach a limiting value. This curve is essentially the same as that from the direct oxidation of aluminum in the absence of SO_2. Thus, at relatively low humidities SO_2 does not influence the atmospheric corrosion of aluminum. Under these conditions there is no apparent visual change to the metal surface.

From Fig. 4 it can be seen that at the higher humidities (72 and 85%) both kinds of aluminum samples corroded much faster than at the lower humidity. At high humidities SO_2 plays an essential role in the corrosion of aluminum. The white powdery deposit on the surface of the samples under these conditions was found to be $Al_2(SO_4)_3 \cdot 18H_2O$. Some H_2S was detected at the end of each run. It was probably produced by the reduction of SO_2 according to the following reaction:

$$2Al + SO_2 + H_2O \rightarrow Al_2O_3 + H_2S$$

c. Copper. Sulfur oxides enter into the formation of the well known greenish coating on copper and copper alloys in many urban and industrial areas. This consists of basic copper sulfate (*16*) which is extremely

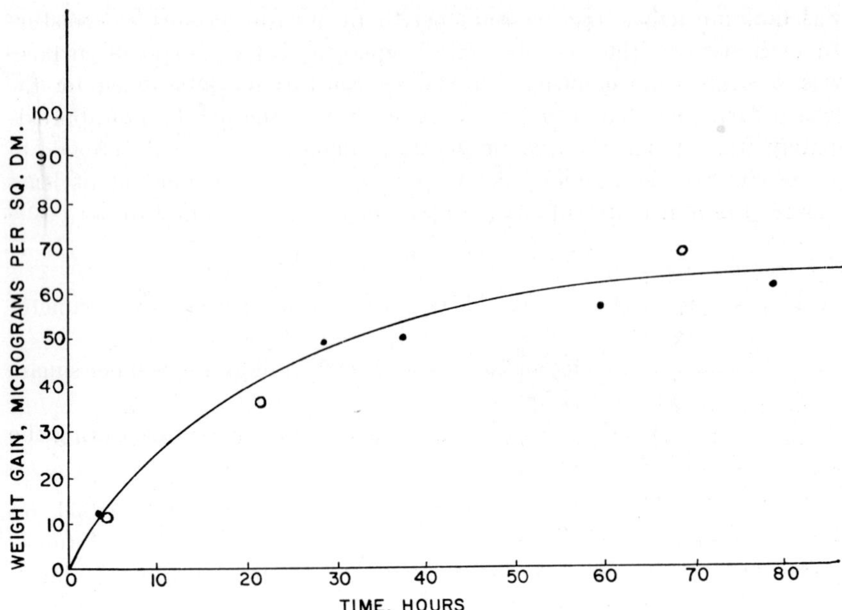

Fig. 3. Atmospheric corrosion of aluminum at a relative humidity of 52% SO_2 concentration, 280 p.p.m. (*6*). Key: ○ = super purity aluminum; ● = 3003 aluminum. (Courtesy of *Corrosion*.)

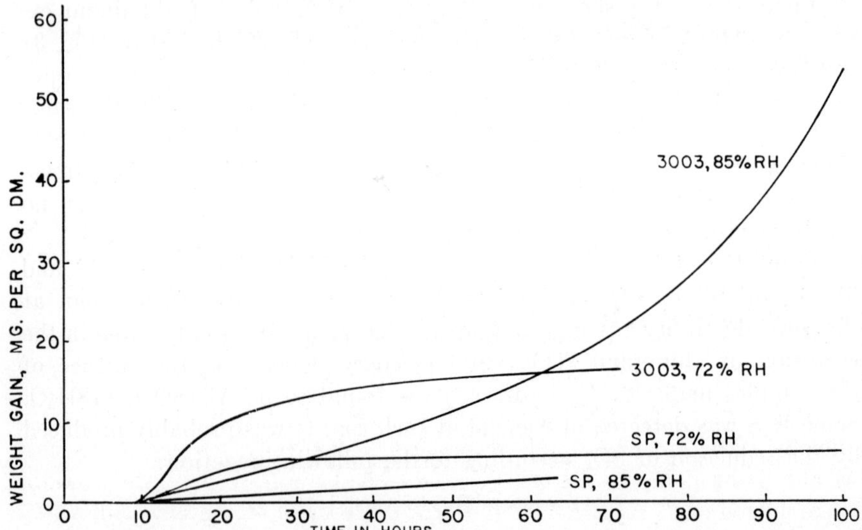

Fig. 4. Atmospheric corrosion of super-purity and 3003 aluminum at relative humidities of 72 and 85%. SO_2 concentration = 280 p.p.m. (*6*). (Courtesy of *Corrosion*.)

resistant to further atmospheric attack and therefore acts as a protective film. However desirable this effect may be from the standpoint of esthetics and further attack, these same reaction products are unwanted when they form on electrical contacts made of copper and thereby change the electrical resistance of the contacts.

d. Nickel. The fogging of nickel surfaces is due to the simultaneous presence of sulfur dioxide and water vapor (*17*). The surface film that is formed is basic nickel sulfate. It has further been shown that SO_2 in the presence of water vapor is catalytically oxidized by the nickel surface to sulfuric acid.

2. *Building Materials*

Sulfur oxides are capable of attacking building materials, including limestone, marble, roofing slate, and mortar. Any carbonate-containing stone is damaged by having carbonates converted to relatively soluble sulfates, which can be leached away by rainwater. Stones, such as granite and certain sandstones, in which the grains are cemented together with materials containing no carbonate, are relatively unaffected by SO_2 in the atmosphere (*18*).

3. *Leather*

SO_2 has strong affinity for leather causing it to lose much of its strength and ultimately to disintegrate. As early as 1843 Faraday came to the conclusion that the rotting of leather upholstery on chairs in a London club was the direct result of sulfur compounds in the air (*19*).

The storage of leather-bound books in libraries can pose a serious problem. The bindings of books stored in rooms with a free exchange of polluted air were found to deteriorate much more rapidly than those in confined spaces or inside of glass cases.

Leather safety belts exposed to polluted atmospheres containing SO_2 can be dangerously weakened in a few years' exposure. The analysis of leather which had rotted under these conditions showed it to contain 6 to 7% sulfuric acid.

4. *Paper*

Paper made prior to about 1750 is not seriously damaged by sulfur dioxide (*20*), but that made since then is seriously affected. This date is about the point in history when chemical methods for paper making were introduced. Apparently the small amounts of metallic impurities in "modern" paper accelerates the conversion in the presence of moisture of absorbed SO_2 to sulfuric acid. The sulfuric acid content of some papers has been found to be as high as 1%, which makes the paper extremely brittle. Kimberly (*21*) found that exposure of books and writing paper to SO_2 in concentrations of 2 to 9 p.p.m. for 10 days caused embrittlement and decreased their folding resistance.

5. *Textiles*

Sulfur oxides are capable of causing deterioration of a variety of natural as well as synthetic fibers used in textiles. Cotton is a cellulosic fiber and, like paper, is weakened by SO_2. The work of Race (*22*) in England showed that the breaking strength of cotton fabrics in winter was considerably less than that found in summer. Without atmospheric pollutants one would expect the reverse to be the case because of the higher sunlight intensity in summer which in itself can cause deterioration of the fabric. Wool, being a proteinaceous material, behaves like leather and is capable of absorbing and being weakened by SO_2.

Damage to women's nylon hose by air pollution (presumably SO_2 or SO_3) has made newspaper headlines in many areas. The exact mechanism of attack has not yet been determined, but it has been shown that even dilute solutions of sulfuric acid are capable of reducing significantly the strength of nylon (a polymeric amide). It has been postulated that extremely small atmospheric particles containing adsorbed SO_2 (*23*), or tiny droplets of sulfuric acid which have formed around particles (*24*), become attached to the very thin nylon fibers and these, being under some tension, fail. Other materials of nylon, such as the fabric in shirts and dresses, are made from fibers of much larger diameter than those of nylon hose and are not under the same tension, hence are not as easily damaged by sulfur oxides.

C. Hydrogen Sulfide

Hydrogen sulfide can be oxidized in the atmosphere to SO_2 and SO_3, particularly under conditions of high humidity. However, there are several forms of deterioration which are related directly to hydrogen sulfide gas.

1. *Metals*

In the presence of H_2S such metals as silver and copper tarnish rapidly. Copper which has first been exposed to unpolluted air for a significant period resists the effects of H_2S. In the case of silver, both moisture and oxygen must be present for H_2S to cause tarnishing (*25*). The sulfide coating formed on open copper and silver electrical contacts can increase greatly the resistance across these contacts when they are closed. This also may result in welding the contacts together in the closed position.

2. *Paint*

House paint containing lead compounds is rapidly darkened in the presence of even low concentrations of H_2S by the formation of black lead sulfide. Figure 5 is a photograph of a building at the southern end of San Francisco Bay. The paint on this building has been discolored

FIG. 5. Paint damage from hydrogen sulfide emitted from polluted bay waters. (Photo by J. E. Yocom.)

by H_2S emitted from polluted bay waters. The work of Hess (*26*) points out, however, that the dark lead sulfide is in turn oxidized to lead sulfate, thus eventually turning the paint film white once again if the atmosphere remains free of H_2S.

Since highly polluted atmospheres often contain appreciable quantities of dark particulate matter, there is the chance that the dirtying of a painted surface by this kind of material can be mistaken for lead sulfide darkening. Another type of paint surface darkening which has been confused with hydrogen sulfide damage is caused by certain types of fungus (*27*). This kind of damage occurs most frequently where the humidity remains above 60%. It is most likely to occur with paints containing a high percentage of raw linseed oil and some of the newer latex-emulsion-based exterior paints.

D. Hydrogen Fluoride

Being a corrosive gas, and at the same time extremely hygroscopic, hydrogen fluoride can attack a wide variety of metals, glass, and enamel-coated materials. Hydrogen fluoride can attack window glass to the extent that the glass is rendered opaque (*28*). It should be pointed out, however, that the concentrations required to produce visible damage to glass and other materials are in excess of those required to kill many types of vegetation. Therefore, other than in causing occasional localized damage, hydrogen fluoride does not appear to be an important contributor to the deterioration of materials.

E. Ozone and Photochemical Smog

The earth's atmosphere normally contains a small amount of ozone (0 to 0.05 p.p.m.) which is largely formed by sunlight. In atmospheres polluted with nitrogen oxides and certain types of hydrocarbons, sunlight promotes a complex series of chemical reactions (Chapter 3) which produce a number of undesirable effects such as eye irritation, vegetation damage, and reduced visibility. One of the by-products of these reactions is ozone, which is characteristic of smog problems of the larger urban areas of coastal California where ozone concentrations can reach ten times the normal background level. It is this high ozone content or oxidizing capacity of the atmosphere which is largely responsible for the observed deterioration to materials associated with this type of air pollution.

1. *Rubber and Elastomers*

One of the early indications of the smog problem in Los Angeles was the excessive cracking of rubber products. It had been known that atmospheric oxidants, especially ozone could cause rubber-cracking. Crabtree and Kemp (*29, 30*) carried out extensive studies as early as 1946 on the attack of natural rubber by light-energized oxygen and ozone. The cracking of rubber in an ozone atmosphere of even high concentration (1 to 5%) does not appear to proceed until the rubber is stretched. Even the slightest stretching under these conditions brings about rapid deterioration.

The Los Angeles County Air Pollution Control District has used as one of its measurements of ozone concentration in the atmosphere a method developed by Bradley and Haagen-Smit (*31*) in which bent strips of rubber of precise formulation are exposed to the air to be sampled. By determining the depths of cracks at the end of definite exposures it is possible to estimate the ozone content of the atmosphere.

According to present theory, elastomers of the unsaturated type are attacked by ozone at the double bond in the carbon-to-carbon chain (*32*). If the chain is under stress it breaks, which leaves its neighbor under additional strain. Synthetic rubbers, such as butadiene-styrene or butadiene-acrylonitrile, being unsaturated, are affected in this same

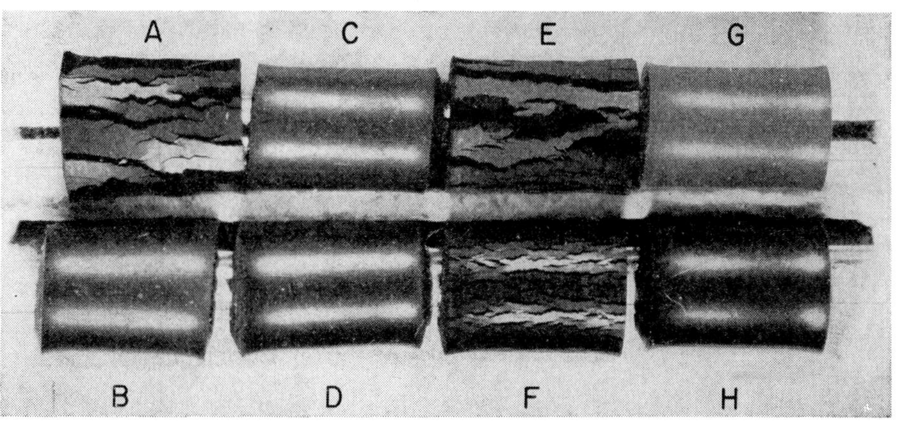

FIG. 6. Effect of ozone exposure on samples of various rubber compounds. Key: $A =$ GR-S; $B =$ Butyl; C, $D =$ Neoprene; $E =$ Buna N; $F =$ natural rubber; $G =$ silicone; $H =$ Hypalon. (Photo courtesy of F. H. Winslow, Bell Telephone Laboratories.)

manner. Neoprene, although unsaturated, resists ozone attack, presumably because of the presence of the chlorine atom adjacent to the double bond. Butyl, thiokol, and silicone polymers, being saturated, are highly resistant to attack by ozone. This effect is especially important to tires and rubber-insulated electrical wires. Figure 6 shows the effects of ozone on various types of synthetic rubber and natural rubber.

2. *Textiles and Dyes*

Ozone has long been known to affect the strength of fabrics and the color-fastness of dyes. Only recently, however, have any experiments been carried out to determine the quantitative effects of ozone in community air pollution on fabrics and dyes. A committee of the American Association of Textile Chemists and Colorists (*33*) has presented preliminary results on the exposure of a group of different fabrics and dyes to Los Angeles smog. The samples were exposed in chambers which provided free passage of contaminated air inside the chamber but permitted no direct sunlight to strike any of the samples. Although this was

TABLE II

Effect of Smog on Dyes—Visual Color Evaluation [a,b,c]

Fabric description	Dyestuff	Exposure conditions: Smog-forecast days (hr.)			No-smog-forecast days (hr.)		
		72	112	152	72	112	152
Acetate, light blue knit	Acetate	30D	15D	20D	NC	5D	10D
Viscose, dark blue	Direct	NC	NC	10RD	NC	NC	NC
Viscose, aqua	Vat	NC/D	NC/D	NC/D	NC	NC	NC
Nylon, light blue knit	Acetate	20D	20D	20D	NC	NC	NC
Nylon, red, knit	Acid	10BR	10BR	15BD	NC	NC	NC
Cotton, aqua	Direct	5D	5B	5BD	NC	NC	NC
Cotton, dark green	Vat	NC	5NC	NC	NC	NC	NC
Orlon, red	Basic	5NC	NC	NC	NC	NC	NC
Orlon, aqua	Acetate	NC	NC	NC	NC	NC	NC
Acetate/viscose (50/50—blue)	Acetate	5R	10R	10R	NC	NC	NC
Wool, rose	Metalized	5Y	10Y	10Y	NC	NC	5D
Wool, red	Acid	NC	NC	NC	NC	NC	NC
Wool, green	Premetalized	10B	10BD	10BD	NC	5D	10D
Rubberized, blue	Acetate	15B	20BD	30B	5B	10B	20B
Rubberized, green	Acetate	15D	20D	30D	5D	10D	20D
Rubberized, white	Acetate	NC	NC	NC	NC	NC	NC
AATCC Gas Fading Standards	Acetate	15RD	15RD	20R	10R	10RD	20R

[a] Data are based on average visual observations of three experienced color matchers.

[b] Results are expressed in terms of shade loss and shade change: B = blue, O = orange, Y = yellow, R = red, V = violet, D = duller, NC = no change. Example: 10BR = 10%, shade loss; BR, shade change, bluish-red.

[c] Adapted from T. P. Lee, S. Burner, R. Landry, P. Noonan, and F. Wiggelsworth, *Am. Dyestuff Reptr.* **45,** 919 (1956). (Courtesy of Am. Dyestuff Reptr.)

a preliminary investigation it was concluded that exposure to smog conditions caused definite deterioration of a number of fabrics and dyes. Table II summarizes the data obtained on the effects of smog on dyes. It is certain that this type of smog is detrimental to a number of natural and synthetic materials, but the awareness and understanding of the many factors are so new that active research projects on several of the factors are just now getting under way.

Salvin (*34*) showed that nitrogen oxides are also responsible for some fading of fabrics. Ozone appears to cause fading of cotton materials. The combined effect of acid gases, ozone, and nitrogen oxides probably contributes to the lack of reproducibility in sunlight testing of fabrics between various geographic locations.

F. Solid Particulates

The role of solid air pollutants in causing deterioration is normally to produce soiling. This can be either the soiling of light surfaces such as a tablecloth or a white marble column on a building by dark-colored particulate matter such as soot; or the soiling of a dark surface such as a polished mahogany table by light-colored solids such as cement dust. The soiling does not necessarily cause deterioration directly, but its removal does.

1. *Metals*

Particulate matter appears to be an important factor in the corrosion of metals, particularly in the presence of pollutant gases of an acidic nature. In work carried on at the Chemical Research Laboratory in Teddington, England (*35*) it was shown that the rusting of iron in a moist atmosphere containing SO_2 is greatly accelerated by the presence of particulate matter. In an experiment one sample was exposed to a moist atmosphere containing traces of SO_2. Another sample was exposed to the same atmosphere, but protected from particulate matter by means of a muslin cage which permitted only the gaseous constituents to contact the sample. The rusting of the protected sample was negligible compared with the sample which was unprotected. It was not known, however, how much of the moisture and SO_2 were adsorbed by the fabric making up the cage, or whether equilibrium was established.

The same effect was confirmed by Preston and Sanyal (*36*), but in a laboratory environment. They "inoculated" various metallic surfaces (coated and uncoated) with fine powders or "nuclei" using such materials as sodium chloride, ammonium sulfate, ammonium chloride, sodium nitrate, and flue dust. The samples were then exposed to atmospheres held at various humidities and the resulting corrosion was measured. The corrosion observed was of the filiform type so named because of its filamental configuration. In most of the cases corrosion increased with humidity, the exception being ammonium chloride. The addition of traces of SO_2 to the test atmosphere greatly increased the corrosion at high humidities.

Barton (*37*) carried out experiments to determine the corrosive effects of a variety of artificial dusts on metals. He came to the conclusion that the quantity of water-soluble components in the dust, the pH of the resulting solution, and the concentration of chloride and sulfate ions were important factors in this type of corrosion. He stated that, contrary to previously expressed opinions, corrosive action was not affected by dusts with high adsorptive capacities for water and SO_2.

Deposits of dust on electrical relays can cause serious problems in telephone exchanges. Bell Telephone Laboratories (*38*) has developed unique methods for studying such deposits by making plastic replicas of the contact surfaces.

2. *Building Materials*

The tarry components of carbonaceous material resulting from poor combustion of coal or oil which accumulate on buildings are likely to be sticky and also acidic in nature (*24*). Their corrosiveness persists over extended periods of time since they cannot be flushed off by rain. Large expenditures are made to sandblast off these sooty layers.

This same type of particle can produce holes in canvas used in awnings and other outdoor articles. On board ships the deterioration of canvas from this type of "acidic" soot is such a serious problem that special acid-resistant canvas has been developed for such uses.

Dust collecting on electrical insulators on high tension power lines can cause short circuits when damp. This is a particularly serious problem in California where the summers are rainless and dust can collect over a 3- to 4-month period. With the coming of the first fall rains the utility companies are invariably faced with a rash of damaged equipment because of short circuits. Special equipment has been developed for hosing off such insulators without endangering the operator.

Droplets of cooking oils and greases settling on the asphalt roofs of restaurants can cause serious damage to such roofs.

3. *Painted Surfaces*

One of the principal reasons for repainting houses in urban areas is the accumulation of discoloring particulate matter on the surfaces. These particles are placed there by thermal, electrostatic, and mechanical forces. Newly painted houses are especially susceptible since the surface is sticky and even large particles can attach themselves easily and permanently.

The automobile with its glistening painted finish is an excellent indicator of corrosive or damaging particulate matter. A specific occurrence of damage to automobile finishes from atmospheric solids resulted from the deposit of iron particles from a grinding operation (*39*). It was noted that brown particles were attaching themselves tenaciously to the paint of automobiles in a parking lot. A brown stain surrounded each particle and many cars had to be repainted. The particles at the center of each stain were iron grindings or cuttings identified microscopically by their peculiar shape. The mechanism of the staining was felt to be more complex than simple rusting. The investigators postulated that it resulted from the formation of ferrous hydroxide in the presence of moisture which, being in colloidal form, diffused into the paint film, and upon drying and oxidizing left the brown stain of ferric oxide.

A similar type of damage was experienced in Detroit (*40*). However, it was theorized there that some of the oxygen for the formation of iron oxide came from the paint itself. The result was a pit, filled and covered over with a bump of iron oxide.

The electrical resistance and the anticorrosive properties of varnish and paint films are seriously impaired by the presence of included dust particles (*41*). The particles can act as wicks in a moist environment and transfer corrosive agents to the underlying metal surface.

4. *Textiles*

The dirtying of fabrics by particulate matter is not in itself damaging unless the dust is highly abrasive and the fabric is frequently flexed. The deterioration arises mainly from repeated attempts to clean the fabric.

Rees (*42*) discusses the mechanical, thermal, and electrostatic mechanisms by which cloth is soiled. Using a light reflectance method of assessing dirtiness it was found that in exposing cloth samples to moving air containing finely divided carbon, the cloth with the tightest weave was most resistant to soiling. Soiling by thermal precipitation, as one might expect, was found to be directly related to the degree the surface temperature was cooled below the air temperature. Thicker samples of cloth had higher surface temperatures and therefore collected less dust.

The soiling of certain types of cloth, like acetate rayon, by electrostatic attraction of particulate matter has been a problem in their manufacture. The cloth becomes electrostatically charged by friction with the metallic parts of the loom. Cotton and viscose rayon are relatively conducting and their charges do not build up.

In the experiments described by Rees (*42*) samples of cotton fabric were exposed to laboratory air at both plus and minus electrical potentials. As one would expect, the relative soiling of the samples rose with increased potential. The samples exposed at positive potentials showed greater soiling than those exposed at equivalent negative potentials because, perhaps, of the preponderance of negatively charged particles in the atmosphere.

G. Liquid Droplets

Much of the particulate matter which is responsible for soiling is in the form of minute liquid or semiliquid droplets, yet it is not possible to distinguish the soiling caused by droplets from that caused by solid particles. The same holds true for minute droplets of corrosive liquids such as sulfuric acid. Certainly some of the resulting corrosion is caused directly by these droplets, but the relative amount cannot be determined. The larger the liquid droplets responsible for deterioration the easier it is to assess their unique damaging effect on materials. Relatively large droplets of dirty water from a scrubber without adequate entrainment separation can cause serious soiling problems to the immediate surroundings.

There are a host of corrosive solutions used in various processes which, if emitted to the air in the form of mist, can cause serious corrosion and other forms of deterioration in the surrounding neighborhood. A good example of this is chromic acid mist which was found in Detroit (*40*) to cause serious damage to auto finishes. It produced permanent brown stains on light-colored cars and a "blush" stain on darker shades of paint.

References

1. H. Beaver (Chairman), "Committee on Air Pollution Report." Her Majesty's Stationery Office, London, 1954.
2. W. Gibson, *Proc. 1st Natl. Air Poll. Symposium, Stanford Research Inst., Pasadena* p. 109 (1949).
3. U. R. Evans, *in* "Corrosion Handbook" (H. H. Uhlig, ed.), Sec. 1, p. 3. Wiley, New York, 1948.
4. C. P. Larrabee, *Corrosion* **15,** 36 (1959).
5. B. Sanyal and D. V. Bhadwar, *J. Sci. Ind. Research (India)* **18A,** 69 (1959).
6. P. M. Aziz and H. P. Godard, *Corrosion* **15,** 39 (1959).
7. J. E. Yocom, *Corrosion* **15,** 51 (1959).
8. Am. Soc. Testing Materials, *ASTM Spec. Tech. Publ.* No. 175 (1955).
9. J. P. Lodge, Jr. and B. R. Havlik, *Intern. J. Air Poll.* **3** (1960).
10. W. C. Galegar and R. O. McCaldin, *Am. Ind. Hyg. Assoc. J.* **22,** 187 (1961).
11. G. A. Greathouse and C. J. Wessel, eds., "Deterioration of Materials, Causes and Preventive Techniques." Reinhold, New York, 1954.
12. L. Whitby, *Trans. Faraday Soc.* **29,** 844 (1933).

13. L. R. Burdick and J. F. Barkley, *U. S. Bur. Mines Inform. Circ.* No. 7064 (1939).
14. P. J. Sereda, *Ind. Eng. Chem.* **52,** 157 (1960).
15. W. W. Binger, R. H. Wagner, and R. H. Brown, *Corrosion* **9,** 440 (1953).
16. W. H. J. Vernon and L. Whitby, *J. Inst. Metals* **42,** No. 2 (1929).
17. W. H. J. Vernon, *J. Inst. Metals* **47,** No. 1 (1932).
18. H. B. Meller, *Trans. Am. Soc. Heating Ventilating Engrs.* **37,** 217 (1931).
19. A. Parker, "The Destructive Effects of Air Pollution on Materials." Natl. Smoke Abatement Soc., London, 1955.
20. W. H. Langwell, *Proc. Roy. Inst. Gt. Brit.* **37** (Pt. II, No. 166), 210 (1958).
21. A. E. Kimberly, *J. Research Natl. Bur. Standards* **8,** 159 (1932).
22. E. J. Race, *J. Soc. Dyers and Colourists* **65,** 56 (1949).
23. H. A. Belyea, Personal communication (1958).
24. L. Greenburg and M. Jacobs, *Am. Paint J.* **39,** 64 (1955).
25. R. H. Leach, *in* "Corrosion Handbook" (H. H. Uhlig, ed.), Sec. II, p. 319. Wiley, New York, 1948.
26. M. Hess, "Paint Film Defects; Their Causes and Cure." Reinhold, New York, 1951.
27. P. F. Klens and C. F. Koda, *J. Air Poll. Control Assoc.* **5,** 203 (1956).
28. P. Sadtler, "Smoke in the Cuyahoga Valley of Cleveland," S. P. Sadtler and Son, Philadelphia, Pa.
29. J. Crabtree and A. R. Kemp, *Ind. Eng. Chem.* **38,** 278 (1946).
30. J. Crabtree and A. R. Kemp, *Anal. Chem.* **18,** 769 (1946).
31. C. E. Bradley and A. J. Haagen-Smit, *Rubber Chem. and Technol.* **24,** 750 (1951).
32. J. E. Gaughan, *Rubber World* **133,** 803 (1956).
33. T. P. Lee, S. Burner, R. Landry, P. Noonan, and F. Wiggelsworth, *Am. Dyestuff Reptr.* **45,** 919 (1956).
34. V. S. Salvin, *Am. Dyestuff Reptr.* **47,** 450 (1958).
35. A. R. Meetham, "Atmospheric Pollution, Its Origin and Prevention," 2nd ed. Pergamon Press, New York, 1956.
36. R. St. J. Preston and B. Sanyal, *J. Appl. Chem. (London)* **6,** 26 (1956).
37. K. Barton, *Werkstoffe u. Korrosion (Weinheim)* **9,** 547 (1958).
38. H. W. Hermance and T. F. Egan, *Bell Labs. Record* **34,** 289 (1956).
39. E. G. Fochtman and G. Langer, *J. Air Poll. Control Assoc.* **6,** 243 (1957).
40. B. Linsky, Personal communication (1958).
41. C. Graff-Baker, *J. Appl. Chem. (London)* **8,** 590 (1958).
42. W. H. Rees, *Brit. J. Appl. Phys.* **9,** 301 (1958).

CHAPTER 7B

Effects of Air Pollution on Visibility

ELMER ROBINSON

Stanford Research Institute, Menlo Park, California

I. Introduction

The deterioration of visibility is probably the first indication of air pollution of which a citizen becomes aware (Fig. 1). While the theoretical aspects of visibility are well understood, they have not yet been widely applied to air pollution problems. The way to progress is, there-

FIG. 1. Air pollution in the form of visibility restricting particulate materials engulfs San Francisco, California on June 2, 1960. (*San Francisco News-Call Bulletin* photo.)

fore, through increased incorporation of basic visibility theory into air pollution technology.

II. Visibility

A. Definition

The definition of visibility as given in the Glossary of Meteorology (*1*) is:

> Visibility: In United States weather observing practice, the greatest distance in a given direction at which it is just possible to see and identify with the unaided eye (a) in the daytime, a prominent dark object against the sky at the horizon, and (b) at night, a known, preferably unfocused, moderately intense light source. After visibilities have been determined around the entire horizon circle, they are resolved into a single value of *prevailing visibility* for reporting purposes.

In this definition it is important to note that the visibility reading reported in a station weather record is a composite value for the whole horizon and is not the visibility in just a single direction. Whenever a transmissometer measurement is reported in a station weather record it does not replace the regular visual observation but is listed under "Remarks and Supplemental Coded Data." It is also important to remember that meteorological visibility data are taken primarily for aircraft operations.

Instructions for determining prevailing visibility are given in the Manual of Surface Observations used by the U. S. Weather Bureau and the Military Services (*2*). Prevailing visibility is defined as the greatest visibility which is attained or surpassed around at least half of the horizon circle, but not necessarily in continuous sectors. To determine prevailing visibility under nonuniform conditions, the horizon is divided into several sectors of equal size in which the visibility is substantially uniform. The value reported as the prevailing visibility is the highest sector visibility which is equal to or less than the visibility of sectors that account for at least half of the horizon. In other words, the visibility around at least half the horizon is equal to or better than the prevailing visibility reported. For example, if the horizon were divided into four sectors and the respective visibilities were 3, 4, 5, and 8 mi., the prevailing visibility would be 5 mi. This follows from the definition since this is the maximum visibility which is equaled or exceeded by the visibility around at least half the horizon. Thus the station record would report a visibility of 5 mi. at this time and unless it were particularly important for aircraft safety there would probably be no record made of the fact that the visibility around the horizon varied from a low of 3 mi. to a maximum of 8 mi. Visibility can vary markedly even in a homogeneous atmosphere owing to variations in scattered light intensity with illumination angle. This factor could lead to the postulation of differences in pollution levels when no real difference existed. The weather record will carry additional data on especially low or variable visibility situations under the notation of "Remarks."

The reporting of prevailing visibility has been the standard procedure in the weather services since January 1, 1939 (*3*). Prior to that date the reported visibility for a station was the maximum visibility which could be observed around the horizon from the station (*4*). This change in definition is important in the evaluation of long-term visibility records and trends.

B. Observation

As the definition indicates, visibility is determined by an observer looking around the horizon and noting whether he can identify known landmarks or lights. As a guide each weather station will have a chart or photograph showing prominent objects and lights in various directions along with distances from the station. When there are no suitable markers at a particular distance in a given direction, the observer must estimate the value of the visibility from the sharpness with which the available objects stand out. For the best determinations, during daylight hours, the markers should be black, or nearly black, objects standing against the horizon sky.

Figure 2 is a copy of the Visibility Check-Point Diagram for the U. S. Weather Bureau Office at the Oakland, California airport. This figure shows the more distant check-points. A separate diagram is used at this station for distances out to 1½ mi. Because San Francisco Bay is west and southwest of this station visibility targets are not available in these sectors except on days when the far side of the bay can be seen. Hills about 6 mi. east of the station limit visibility in this sector. Mountain peaks provide additional check-points beyond the chart limits. It is quite apparent that the estimation of the visibility from a chart such as Fig. 2 depends to a large degree on the training and good judgment of the observer.

This description of the observation of visibility shows the manner in which subjective factors can influence the visibility record. However, considering the problem involved in reducing such a variable as the visibility around the horizon to a usable and reportable observation, the accepted system must be considered a satisfactory compromise.

A large number of the reporting weather stations observe and record the visibility at hourly intervals. The visibility is reported in statute miles at land stations. There is no fixed upper limit for reportable visibility. A number of stations do not have suitable markers at distances beyond 15 mi., and under such conditions the visibility over 15 mi. is recorded as 15+. Such a procedure could cause confusion in preparing summaries if data were carelessly lumped together.

The fact that most visibility observations are taken at airports and thus not in congested downtown areas must be clearly remembered in

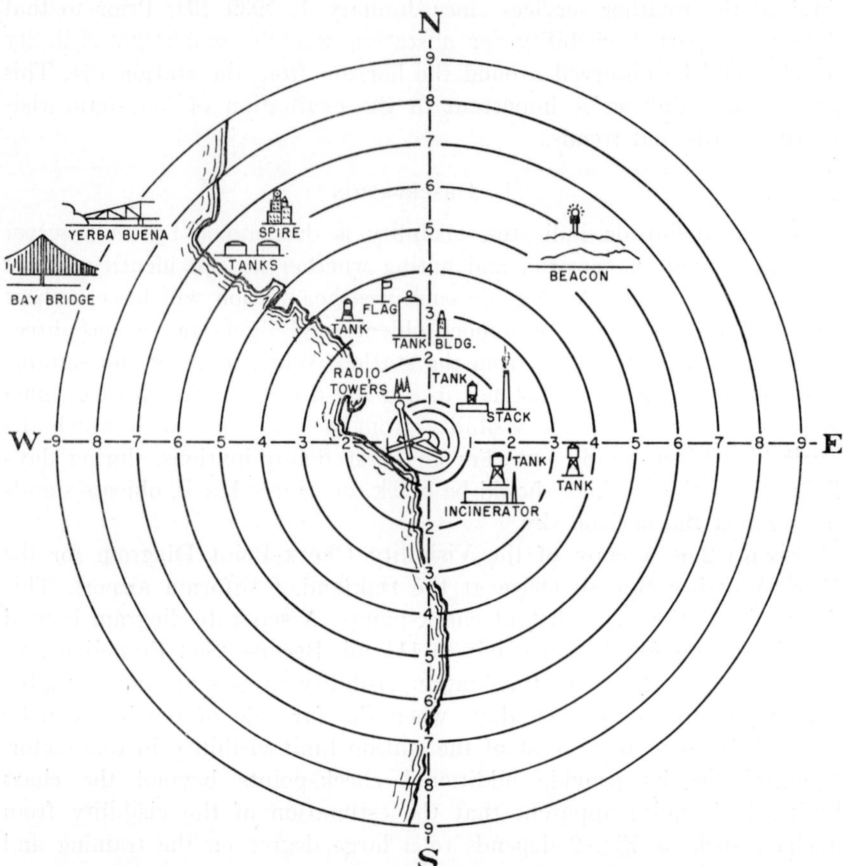

Fig. 2. Visibility check-point diagram, 1–10 mi., Oakland Airport, California.

the use of these data for urban air pollution studies. Since most airports seem to be located on the fringe of the city, it is entirely possible for the value of the prevailing visibility to be obtained without any consideration being given to the visibility over the more congested areas. When there are important differences between the reported visibility and the visibility in specific directions, such as toward the city, the visibility for specific directions is often entered in the "Remarks" column. Such notations do not find their way into any climatological records and can be obtained only by studying a copy of the actual station record.

C. Related Weather Elements

In addition to the prevailing visibility, a station weather record will contain information on the cause of reduced visibility, i.e., visibility less than 7 mi. Whenever this occurs the observer must report the reason. This reason can be either precipitation—rain, snow, etc.—or an obstruction to vision—haze, smoke, fog, etc. These notations can often be used as a valuable source of data for air pollution studies. It should be noted, however, that such explanations are required only when the visibility is less than 7 mi.

In air pollution studies as well as in weather reporting it is usually necessary to discriminate between fog, haze, and smoke. Circular N (*2*) gives the weather observer the following definitions to aid him in his choice.

Fog: Minute water droplets suspended in the atmosphere. These droplets have no visible downward motion. Fog differs from clouds in that the base of fog is at the surface and the base of clouds is above the surface. It is easily distinguished from haze by its dampness and grey color. Although fog seldom forms when the difference between the air temperature and the temperature of the dew point is greater than 4.0°F., it should be reported when observed regardless of the temperature-dew point difference.

Haze: Suspended dust or salt particles so small that they cannot be felt, or individually seen by the unaided eye; however, they reduce visibility and lend a characteristic opalescent appearance to the air. Haze resembles a uniform veil over the landscape that subdues its colors. This veil has a bluish tinge when viewed against a dark background, such as a mountain; but it has a dirty yellow or orange tinge against a bright background, such as the sun, clouds at the horizon, or snow-capped mountain peaks. When the sun is well up, its light may have a peculiar silvery tinge owing to haze. These color effects distinguish haze from light fog, whose thickness it may sometimes attain.

Smoke: Fine ash particles suspended in the atmosphere. When smoke is present the disk of the sun at sunrise and sunset appears very red and during the daytime has a reddish tinge. Smoke at a distance, such as from forest fires, usually has a light greyish or bluish color and is evenly distributed in the upper air.

There are obvious difficulties in separating haze and smoke in urban areas and it is usual to find haze and smoke listed together as an obstruction to vision. Sometimes fog and smoke are listed together. Normally the experienced weather observer does not find it particularly difficult to discriminate between fog and haze.

D. Visual Range

In some meteorological literature the term "visual range" is used in the same manner as "visibility" is used above. It is argued that visual range is a more logical term to signify a distance that something can be seen, while visibility, outside of meteorological circles, expresses the clarity with which objects stand out from their surroundings. The switch to the term "visual range" has made little headway and there is every indication that "visibility" will continue to be the commonly used term to denote how far one can see.

III. Weather and Visibility

A. Air Mass Considerations

The air pollution investigator usually considers visibility to be an indication of the particulate pollution load of the atmosphere, while the meteorologist uses visibility as an indicator of air mass history and of the wind and turbulent mixing which are characteristic of the atmosphere. When an air mass has low wind speed and a stable lapse rate near the ground, poor visibility can be expected. On the other hand, an air mass with gusty winds and well-developed convective turbulence will be accompanied by good visibility.

B. Inversion Height and Wind Speed

The observed visibility is dependent both upon the nature of the particulate material in the atmosphere and upon the volume of air into which the material may be mixed. One measure of this available air volume is the height of the base of a low level temperature inversion. Figure 3 shows the relation between the daily average visibility, as measured instrumentally at Pasadena, and the height of the inversion over the Los Angeles area (*5*). The relation between visibility and the inversion height at 7:00 A.M. clearly shows better visibility with a higher inversion, as would be expected. In the morning, conditions over the area are fairly uniform and the 7:00 A.M. relationship is probably a useful one; however this is not the case for the 1:00 P.M. data. The reasons for the markedly different 1:00 P.M. relation are not discussed by Wiggins (*5*) but can probably be attributed to the fact that the inversion was measured at Long Beach, a coastal location, and related to the visibility measured 30 mi. inland at Pasadena. Marked differences in the midday surface heating regimes coupled with differences in sea breeze exposures would be expected to alter significantly the midday inversion conditions. Thus a poor direct relation between these 1:00 P.M. observations is not unexpected. If both inversion and visibility data were available for Pasadena, a more consistent daily pattern would be expected. Meteorological data should always be studied carefully to guarantee that the observations used are all applicable to the same set of conditions.

Wind speed is another measure of the dilution potential of the atmosphere and it would be logical to expect better visibilities when stronger winds provided better dilution. Figure 4 shows the frequency

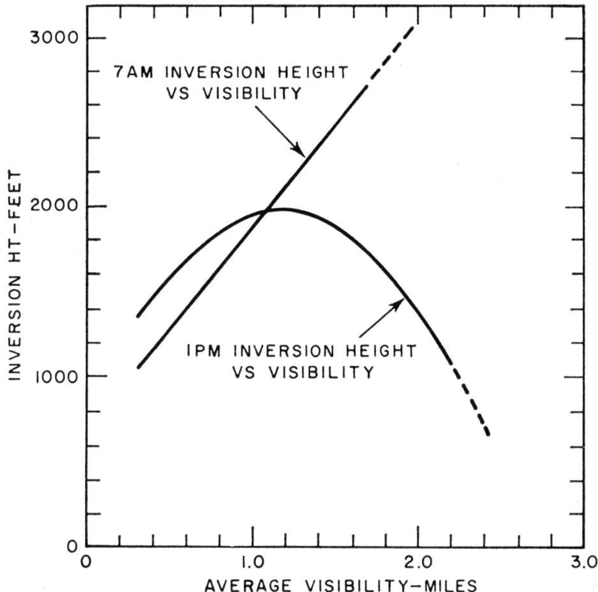

FIG. 3. Regression curves relating inversion height at Long Beach and visibility at Pasadena, California at 7:00 A.M. and 1:00 P.M., August–November 1954 [E. J. Wiggins, *in* "An Aerometric Survey of the Los Angeles Basin August–November, 1954" (N. A. Renzetti, ed.), Sec. IX, Rept. No. 9. Air Poll. Foundation, Los Angeles, 1955].

of poor visibility, i.e., less than 10 mi., for various ranges of wind speed for Bakersfield, California (*6*). The data show a steady decrease in frequency of less than 10-mi. visibility as the wind increases to 15 m.p.h., as would be expected. The increase in the frequency of low visibility when the wind exceeded 15 m.p.h. is doubtless the result of dust being raised by the stronger wind in the extensive agricultural areas around the airport observation point.

C. Hygroscopic Particles and Relative Humidity

In addition to those factors which affect visibility through changes in the dispersion of particulate materials, there are those which alter visibility by affecting the size of hygroscopic particulate materials in the atmosphere (*7*). Under high, but still not saturated, humidity con-

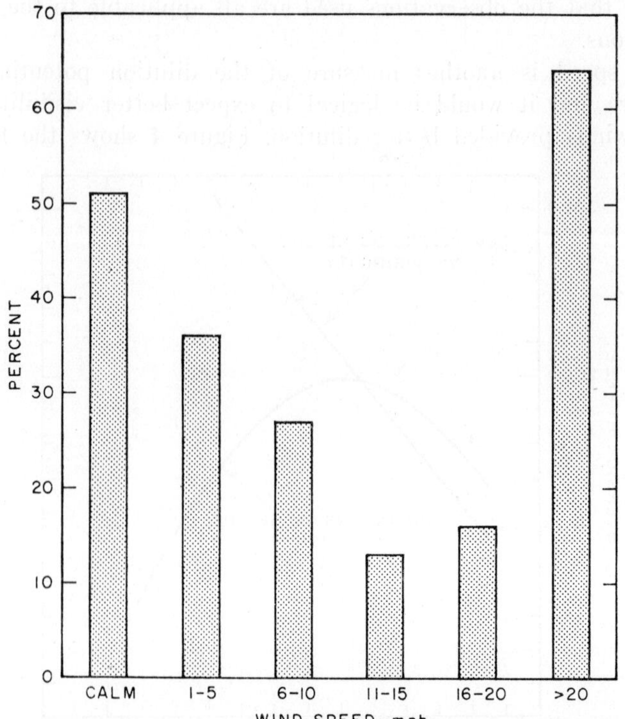

Fig. 4. Per cent frequencies of 0–10 mi. visibilities by wind speed classes, Bakersfield, Calif., 7:30 A.M.–5:30 P.M., May, July, September, November, 1948–1957 [G. C. Holzworth and J. A. Maga, *J. Air. Poll. Control Assoc.* **10**(6), 430 (1960)].

ditions, hygroscopic particles pick up water and increase in size. As they increase in size they become more effective in reducing visibility.

Two commonly encountered hygroscopic particulate materials are sea salt and sulfuric acid droplets. Tests of these materials have been carried out in several ways, some using an adaptation of the Wilson cloud chamber (*8*). In this apparatus a rapid expansion lowered the temperature and raised the humidity. If hygroscopic activity was marked the aerosol particles increased in size and reduced the amount of light transmitted through the aerosol.

Numerous tests were run with sulfuric acid mist formed by the initial generation of sulfur trioxide followed by hygroscopic sulfuric acid droplet formation. These tests showed that hygroscopic sulfur trioxide was effective as a cloud-forming agent at all humidities tested down to 34%, but that it became most effective when the humidity was increased from 75 to 80%.

Similar cloud chamber tests showed that sodium chloride produced by an aspirator-type aerosol generator as an approximation for sea salt was inactive as a fog-forming substance below a relative humidity of 66% but that it was quite active at higher humidities.

Direct determinations of sea salt nuclei have been made by Twomey by viewing the transition of particles under a microscope (*9*). He found the transition of sea salt from a crystal to a droplet to occur at 75% relative humidity. Table I shows the predicted humidities for the transition from a crystal to a droplet for a number of other materials.

TABLE I
PREDICTED CRYSTAL-TO-DROPLET TRANSITION HUMIDITIES FOR A NUMBER OF SALTS[a]

Compound	Relative humidity (%)
K_2CO_3	43–45
NaBr	58
$CoCl_2$	67
$(NH_4)_2SO_4$	80–82
KCl	84–86
K_2SO_4	97

[a] S. Twomey, *in* "Atmospheric Chemistry of Chlorine and Sulfur Compounds," Geophys. Monograph No.3. Am. Geophys. Union, Washington, D.C., 1959.

An example of a relation found between visibility and relative humidity at the Los Angeles International Airport is shown in Fig. 5 (*10*). The sharp steady decrease in visibility above 67% relative humidity is obvious in these data. In view of the location of the airport within about 2 mi. of the Pacific Ocean, a source of sea salt particles, this close agreement was not unexpected.

A more detailed analysis of visibility and relative humidity has been made by Buma (*11*) for the city of Leeuwarden on the North Sea coast of the Netherlands. Daytime data were used and classified according to whether the wind was from continental or maritime directions. Table II shows some of the results of this study. Low visibilities at Leeuwarden were more frequent at all relative humidities for continental air than for maritime air. For continental air the frequency of low visibility changed at a more gradual rate with decreasing humidity than was the case for maritime air. In the relative humidity range from 69 to 76% low visibilities were ten times more probable in the continental air than with maritime air. The maritime air data fit the previous discussion of the hygroscopic effects of sea salt. The continental air data probably show the influence of air pollutants from various continental sources. The persistence of visibility effects at low relative

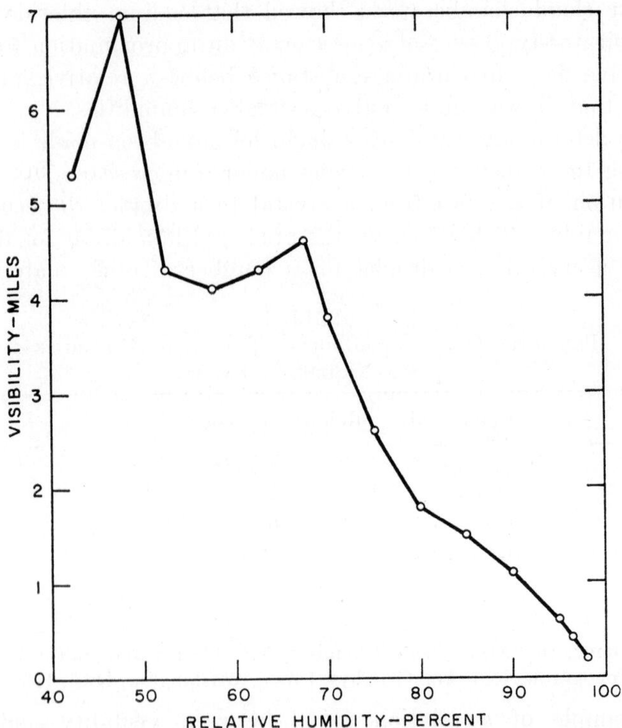

FIG. 5. Average visibility for various values of relative humidity, Los Angeles International Airport [M. Neiburger and M. G. Wurtele, *Chem. Revs.* **44,** 321 (1949)].

TABLE II

FREQUENCY OF VISIBILITY LESS THAN 7 KM. (4 MI.) AS A FUNCTION OF RELATIVE HUMIDITY, LEEUWARDEN, THE NETHERLANDS[a]

Relative humidity	Continental air (% < 7 km.)	Maritime air (% < 7 km.)
100–99	100	95
98–97	97	89
96–93	88	62
92–89	72	32
88–83	57	19
82–77	47	11
76–69	45	4
68–61	35	1
60–50	20	0

[a] T. J. Buma, *Bull. Am. Meteorol. Soc.* **41** (7), 357 (1960).

humidities is one of the properties of sulfuric acid aerosols, as mentioned previously (*8*). There are no confirmatory sampling data, however.

D. Air Quality Standards

The response of common air pollutants to relative humidity was considered by the California State Department of Public Health when standards were established for ambient air quality in 1959 (*12, 13*). In the standard for particulates, an "adverse" level is considered to have been reached when the particulate concentration is sufficient to reduce visibility to less than 3 mi. when relative humidity is less than 70% (cf. Fig. 5).

The introduction of the humidity qualification in the visibility limit in these standards was an attempt to restrict the influence of naturally occurring hygroscopic pollutants and in this manner to obtain a truer measure of the man-made air pollutants. The limit of 70% relative humidity is a stricter discriminant than is the 4°F. temperature-dew point difference which is used by the Weather Bureau to differentiate between haze and fog.

IV. Mathematical Considerations of Visibility

A. Alteration of Contrast

The mathematical basis for meteorological visibility has been presented in detail by a number of authors, and only some of the more pertinent features will be presented in this discussion. In general, the notation and development of Middleton (*14*) will be used.

Visibility is dependent upon the transmission of light through the atmosphere and the ability of the eye to distinguish an object because it contrasts with the background. Contrast C may be expressed in terms of a suitable isolated target of luminance B surrounded by a uniform and extensive background of luminance B'.

$$C = \frac{B - B'}{B'} \tag{1}$$

If the background is brighter than the object, as is the usual case for dark visibility targets, then C is negative and is equal to -1 for a black target. The value of C is positive when the target is brighter than the background but contrasts greater than 10 seldom occur (*14*).

A change in contrast with viewing distance occurs for both dark and bright objects. With dark objects the atmosphere introduces light, called "air-light," into the sight path and the dark object appears brighter at increasing distances. In the case of bright objects light is lost from the line of sight until there is no apparent contrast between the bright object and the background. In both cases the result is the same. The contrast between the object and the background approaches zero since the light coming from the direction of the target approaches the intensity of the light from the background.

B. Scattering and Absorption of Light

This alteration of contrast or light intensity is due to the absorption and scattering of light by the atmosphere, which may be described by considering a length dx of the light path from the object to the observer illuminated by a light beam of intensity I. This light in passing through a distance dx is reduced by absorption and scattering by an amount dI proportional to the intensity I. This may be written as the following expression

$$dI = -\sigma I dx \tag{2}$$

where σ is the extinction or attenuation coefficient and the minus sign indicates that intensity is being reduced by the effect of the atmosphere. By integration Eq. 2 becomes

$$I = I_0 e^{-\sigma x} \tag{3}$$

where I is the intensity reaching the viewer, I_0 is the original intensity, and x is the length of the light path.

It can also be shown that apparent contrast can be expressed in a similar manner.

$$C = C_0 e^{-\sigma x} \tag{4}$$

where C is the apparent contrast at distance x from an object with actual contrast C_0 relative to its background.

The extinction coefficient σ includes both the results of scattering and of absorption. It is sometimes useful to consider these two processes separately in which case Eq. 3 becomes

$$I = I_0 e^{-(b+k)x} \tag{5}$$

where b is the scattering coefficient and k is the absorption coefficient. In some cases a third coefficient might be added to b and k to account for extinction due to the reflection of light by particulate materials.

It should be remembered that the value of the extinction coefficient will be dependent upon the wavelength of the incident light. In all of these expressions monochromatic light is assumed.

1. *Rayleigh Scattering*

The extinction coefficient is generally determined by the particulate materials in the atmosphere even though the air molecules are responsible for some scattering of incident light. This molecular scattering is the familiar Rayleigh scattering. The extinction coefficient for Rayleigh scattering is given by

$$b_R = \frac{32\pi^2}{3n\lambda^4}(m - 1)^2 \tag{6}$$

where n is the number of molecules per cubic centimeter and m is the index of refraction of the atmosphere (*15*). If Rayleigh scattering were the only contributor to the extinction of light, a visibility of more than 150 mi. can be calculated. Thus even without particulate materials in the atmosphere, the visibility would not be infinite. Rayleigh scattering is predominant when the particles in the atmosphere are much smaller in size than the wavelength of the incident light.

2. *Mie Scattering*

The scattering due to atmospheric particulate material is of prime importance in air pollution work and is usually due to particles of a size comparable to the wavelength of the incident light. The theory of scattering under these conditions was developed by Mie and is usually called Mie scattering. The expression for the scattering coefficient for Mie scattering is given by

$$b = NK\pi r^2 \tag{7}$$

where N is the number of particles of radius r and K is the scattering area ratio for a particle of radius r (*14*). This scattering area ratio K is the ratio of the area of the wave-front acted on by the particle to the area of the particle. The value of K is dependent upon the radius of the particle, the wavelength of the incident light, and the refractive index m of the particulate material.

When the particulate material is not homogeneous, the value of b is the sum of the individual values and is expressed as

$$b = \sum_{i=1}^{n} N_i K_i \pi r_i^2 \tag{8}$$

Values of K are shown in Fig. 6 for aerosols of sulfur, water, and oil. These data were given by Sinclair (*16*) and are for light of wavelength $\lambda = 5240$ Å which approximates daylight. Values of K will frequently be found as a function of $2\pi r/\lambda$ for which α is the usual symbol.

A very complete discussion of light scattering, absorption, and reflection can be found in the book by van de Hulst (*17*).

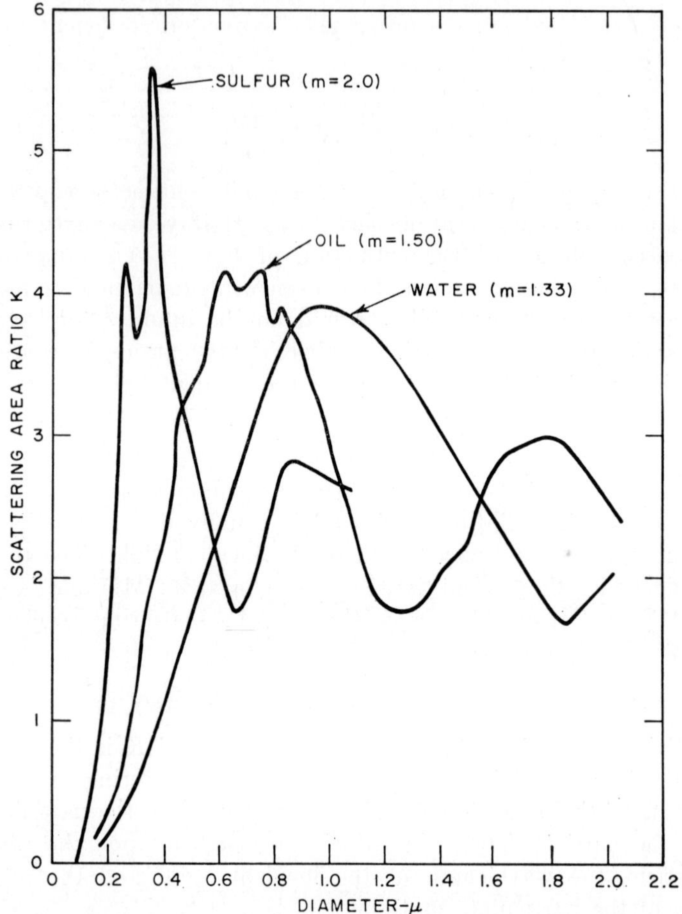

FIG. 6. Scattering area ratio K as a function of diameter for spherical particles, $\lambda = 5240$ Å [D. Sinclair, *in* "Handbook on Aerosols," Chapter 7. U. S. Atomic Energy Commission, Washington, D. C., 1950].

Values of K are not widely available for all of the possible aerosol materials. Van de Hulst shows that for spheres which do not absorb but only scatter the incident radiation, K can be adequately approximated by the curve of Fig. 7. The abscissa is in terms of $4\pi r(m - 1)/\lambda$ where m is the refractive index of the particulate material, r is its radius, and λ is the wavelength of the light.

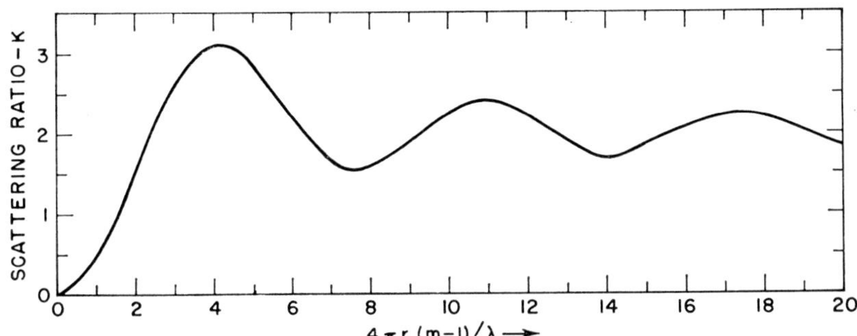

FIG. 7. Approximate values of the scattering area ratio K for nonabsorbing spheres as a function of $4\pi r\,(m\text{–}1)/\lambda$ [H. C. van de Hulst, "Light Scattering by Small Particles." Wiley, New York, 1957].

These data are of more than theoretical interest to the air pollution investigator since K values for most condensed smokes can be approximated by this figure (*17, 18*).

3. *Absorption*

In Eq. 5 the extinction coefficient was separated into scattering and absorption factors. Work by Foster on wood smoke (*18*) has shown that attenuation by these particles when in the submicron range is almost entirely due to scattering and that only a negligible amount is due to absorption. These results could probably be extended to a wide variety of common air pollutants including oil mist and incineration smoke.

However, for smokes of obvious color such as open hearth emissions, absorption cannot be ruled out. Middleton summarizes a number of measurements of industrial "haze" in England which show that the absorption coefficient was more or less equivalent to the scattering coefficient. The absorption factor was particularly important close to the ground, as would be expected from the dark color of the industrial smokes, and then decreased in magnitude with height. Layers with strong absorption were sometimes observed aloft (*14*).

Some calculated data on extinction, scattering, and absorption area ratios, or K values, as given by van de Hulst, are shown in Fig. 8 (*17*). These data are for iron spheres with a refractive index of $m = 1.27 - 1.37i$ where i signifies $\sqrt{-1}$. Note that the abscissa is in units of $2\pi r/\lambda$. The left side of the figure shows the values of K from $2\pi r/\lambda = 0$ to 3, while on the right side the range is from 1 to ∞. The significant feature of these calculations is the fact that the coefficients for absorption and scattering are comparable for a wide range of particle sizes.

Limited information on the scattering and absorption characteristics of carbon for α less than 1.57 can be obtained from some of the calculations of Stull and Plass (*18*a). Their calculations of scattering and extinction cross sections for 0.2-μ diameter carbon particles at $\lambda =$ 4000 Å, $\alpha = 1.57$, give $K_e = 3$, $K_s = 1.3$, and $K_a = 1.7$. These are very close to the values shown for iron in Fig. 8. With decreasing values of α, K_s for carbon seems to follow closely the curve shown for iron while K_e and K_a for carbon appear to decrease more rapidly than is the case

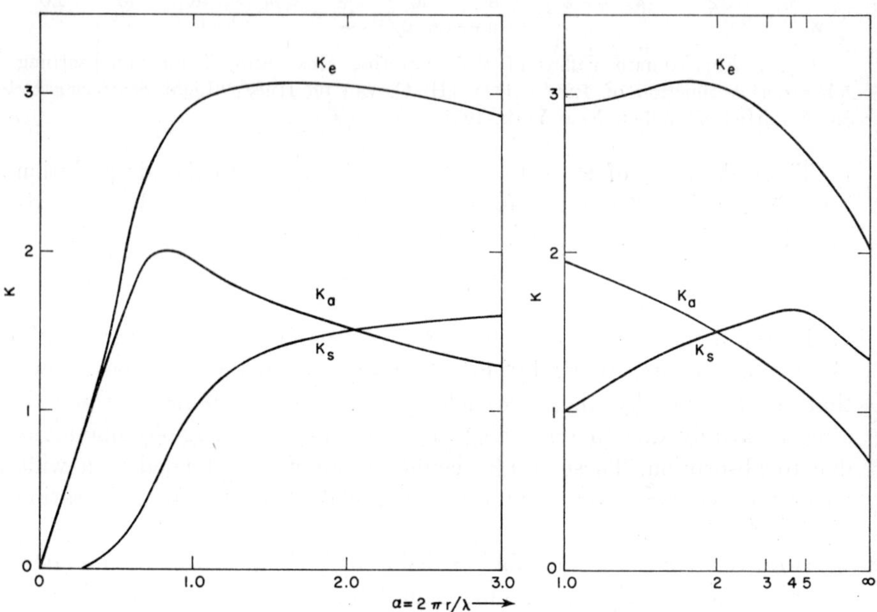

FIG. 8. Area ratio values for extinction, K_e, absorption, K_a, and scattering, K_s, for iron spheres [H. C. van de Hulst, "Light Scattering by Small Particles." Wiley, New York, 1957].

for iron. The data given by Stull and Plass (*18*a) do not indicate the maximum values for the carbon cross section ratios. More complete data on carbon would be of considerable assistance to the air pollution investigator if they were available.

In the absence of better data it would seem that the absorption coefficient could be assumed to be equal to the scattering coefficient in situations where there were heavy carbonaceous or metallic emissions. In areas such as Los Angeles where hydrocarbon aerosols predominate or where smoke is comparable to that from wood, the extinction coefficient could probably be adequately approximated by the scattering coefficient alone. This is a research topic which should be given more attention.

C. Attenuation Concepts in Air Pollution Situations

Since the extinction coefficient is a function of the wavelength of light used in its measurement as well as of the average particle size of

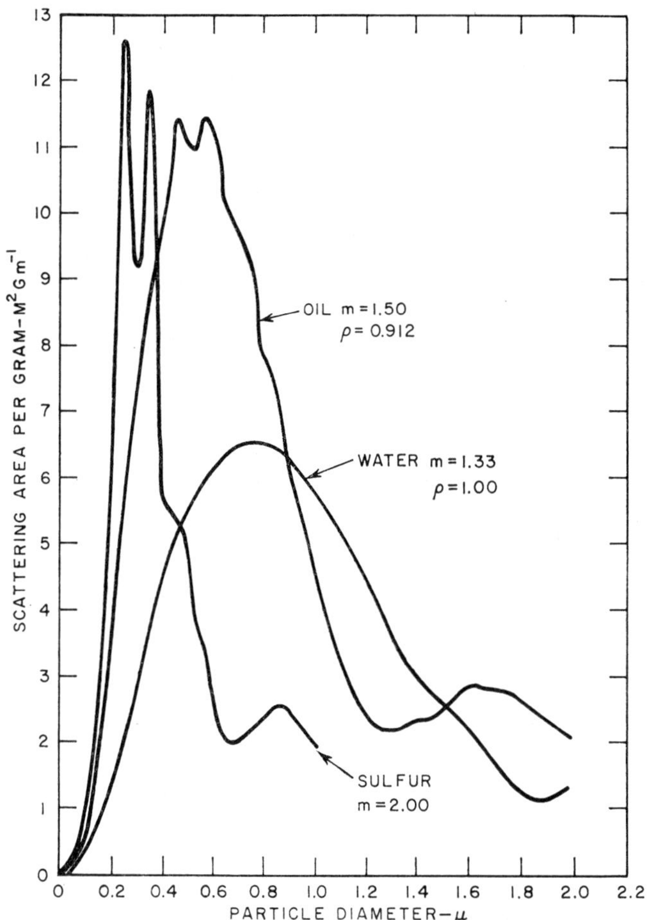

Fig. 9. Total light scattered per gram of particles as a function of diameter for spherical particles, $\lambda = 5240$ Å [D. Sinclair, *in* "Handbook on Aerosols," Chapter 7. U. S. Atomic Energy Commission, Washington, D. C., 1950].

the scattering material, it is possible to obtain data on the size of the scattering particles from extinction coefficient measurements using light of two wavelengths (*19*).

Submicron particles are more effective, per unit mass, in reducing visibility than are larger particles. Sinclair (*16*) has calculated the scattering area per gram of material as a function of particle size for sulfur, water, and oil ($m = 1.50$) when illumination is at 5240 Å (Fig. 9) which clearly shows that the most effective particles are those below 1 μ. For water droplets the most effective size is about 0.8 μ, where the scattering effectiveness per gram is about four times greater than for 2-μ particles. An oil aerosol is most effective when the particles are about 0.6-μ diameter where the scattering effectiveness is about four times greater than that for 1.5-μ particles. Sulfur has a more strongly peaked distribution with a most effective size of about 0.3 μ, which has more than five times the effectiveness of 0.6-μ diameter particles.

The practicability of this result should be readily apparent to the air pollution investigator who is concerned with the alleviation of visibility restrictions. If he is to bring about significant improvement in visibility he must solve the problem of controlling the emission or atmospheric generation of submicron particles. His problem is compounded by the fact that emission control for small particles is generally much more expensive than is the control of large-sized particles.

D. Calculation of Visibility

Visibility can be calculated from the extinction coefficient. This follows from the expression for the alteration of contrast, Eq. 4. Since for visibility determinations the target can be assumed to be black, it follows from Eq. 1 that $C_0 = -1$ and thus Eq. 4 becomes

$$-C = e^{-\sigma x} \tag{9}$$

In this expression x is in units of length while σ is in the same units but to the -1 power. The minus sign occurs in Eq. 9 because the target is darker than the background. In order to obtain an expression for the visibility in terms of the extinction coefficient from Eq. 9, it is necessary to determine what lower limit of contrast can be distinguished by the eye since the eye is the sensor specified for the determination of visibility. It is generally assumed that the limiting contrast for daytime visual determinations is 0.02 although experimental data show that the average observer has a contrast detection threshold close to 0.05 (*14*). The symbol ϵ is generally used to indicate the visual contrast limit. When the limiting visual contrast value, 0.02, is substituted in Eq. 9 the distance x becomes identical with the definition of visibility V. Thus Eq. 9 can be written

$$|0.02| = e^{-\sigma V} \tag{10}$$

and when natural logarithms are taken Eq. 10 becomes

$$V = \frac{3.9}{\sigma} \tag{11}$$

Here both V and σ must be in compatible units, i.e., miles and $(\text{miles})^{-1}$. In this expression V is sometimes written as V_2 to denote that a contrast limit of 0.02 was used in the derivation. When a value of 0.05 is used in the derivation the symbol V_5 is often used. Calculated values of V_2 are often referred to as the "meteorological range" with the specific definition of V_2 being "that distance for which the contrast transmission of the atmosphere is 2%."

These derivations depend on several assumptions which fortunately are reasonably applicable to the atmosphere. A homogeneous atmosphere is required with uniform illumination between the observer and the horizon. Thus the extinction coefficient σ is constant along the path of sight. Nonuniformity in the atmosphere is a more significant factor

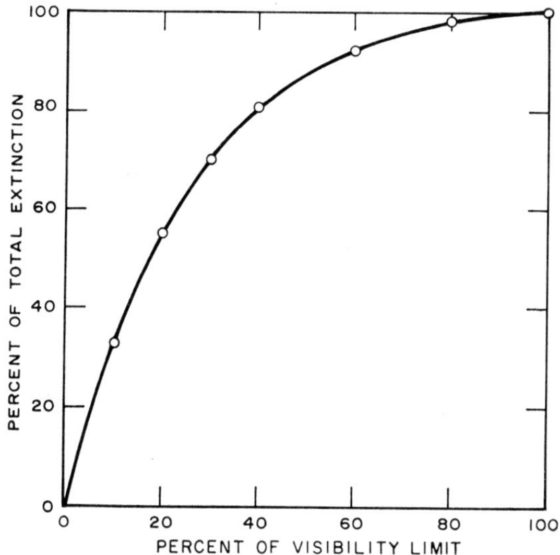

FIG. 10. Net contributions to final extinction value due to various portions of the sight path.

if it occurs close to the observer than if it is at the far end of the line of sight. Figure 10 shows the per cent of extinction which is derived from various sectors between the observer and the limit of visibility in the case of a homogeneous atmosphere. It is important to note that 33% of the finally observed extinction occurs in the closest 10% of the path and 90% in the closest 50%. This feature of the extinction is due to the fact that air-light introduced into the line of sight is also attenuated by the atmosphere closer to the observer. This attenuation of the air-light reduces the final effect of the more remote portions of the sight path.

E. Applications of Visibility Calculations

Measurements of visibility can be used to obtain information on the particulate material in the atmosphere. Although the following arguments require several assumptions and are obvious simplifications, the results can still serve useful purposes when more detailed sampling data are not available.

If the assumption is made that the particulate material in the atmosphere is of uniform size and that scattering alone accounts for the extinction, then the concentration of particulate material coinciding with a given visibility can be determined. This derivation uses Eq. 11 for visibility, and Eq. 7 for the extinction coefficient. After substitution for σ and the introduction of the volume of a particle it follows that visibility in meters can be expressed as a function of the concentration M (gm./m.^{3}) of the material contained in uniform spherical particles of radius $r(\mu)$ and density ρ(gm./cm.^{3}). This expression is

$$V = \frac{5.2\rho r}{KM} \tag{12}$$

Values of K as a function of r can be obtained from Fig. 6 for an average illumination of $\lambda = 5240$ Å. For oil droplets of 0.6-μ diameter where $\rho = 0.9$ and $K = 4.1$, the concentration M for a visibility of 1 mi. is 2.1×10^{-4} gm./m.^{3}. Figure 11 shows the relation between concentration and visibility for several different particle sizes of oil aerosol. Note that the mass concentration for any particular visibility increases markedly with an increase in particle size above 0.6-μ diameter.

If Eq. 12 is rewritten as

$$VM = \frac{5.2\rho r}{K} \tag{13}$$

it is apparent that, for example, a doubling of the concentration M of a given particulate material of radius r will reduce the visibility to half its former value. The units of VM are mass per unit area with the specific units of gm./m.^{2} being those used in the present discussion. Thus the product of the visibility and the mass concentration is an indication of the total mass which is between the observer and the limit of visibility, per unit of cross-sectional area. The product VM for the oil aerosol example just given is 0.34 gm./m.^{2}. This means that the visibility is determined by the length of a column of 1 square meter cross section which contains 0.34 gm. of oil aerosol of 0.6-μ diameter. For a water aerosol of 1.0-μ diameter particles where $K = 3.9$, the visibility limit is determined by 0.67 gm./m.^{2}.

These calculations substantiate a rule of thumb which is often useful. This is that half a gram of material of the optimum particle size per square meter will determine the limit of visibility.

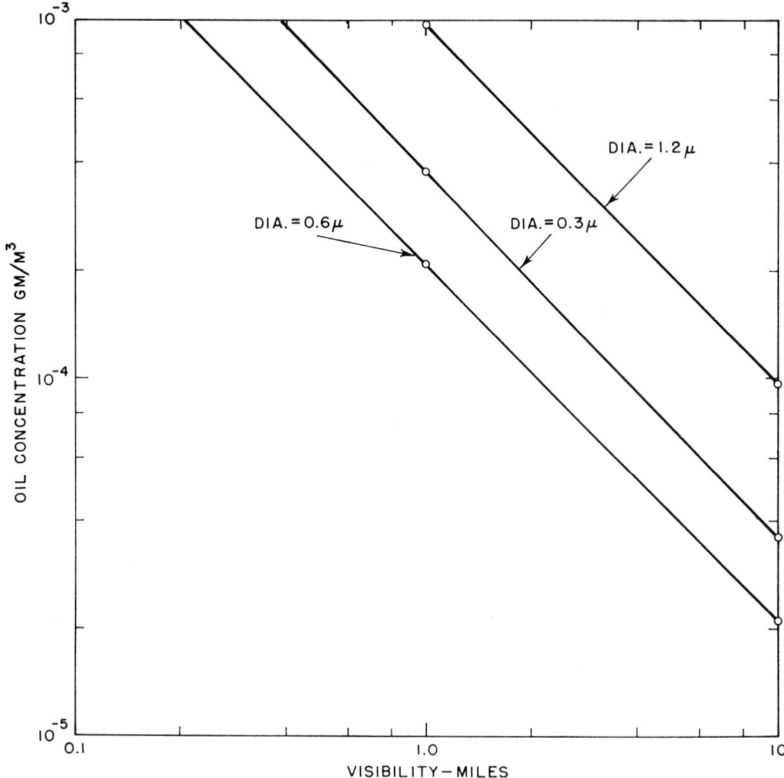

FIG. 11. Relation between visibility and concentration for three sizes of oil aerosol.

Equation 13 can also be used to obtain a rough estimate of atmospheric particulate concentrations from estimates of the other parameters. For example, if visibility is reduced to 5 mi. (8×10^5 cm.) by small dust particles, $\rho = 2.5$ gm./cm.^{3}, $K = 2$, estimated to be 1-μ diameter, the particulate concentration M can then be estimated to be

$$M = \frac{5.2 \times 2.5 \times 0.5 \times 10^{-4}}{2 \times 8 \times 10^5} = 0.41 \times 10^{-9} \text{ gm./cm.}^3$$

or 0.41 mg./m.^{3}. While precise results cannot be obtained in this manner, there are many situations where estimates such as this will be useful.

F. Angular Distribution of Scattered Light

Visibility observations in polluted areas frequently show strong directional variation which is dependent upon the angle of the sun. Lower visibilities will normally be observed in the direction of the sun than away from it, even in a uniformly mixed atmosphere. This is due to another aspect of light scattering by small particles in the polluted air. Small particles scatter more light in the forward direction—toward an observer looking toward the sun—than they scatter in the back direction (*14, 16*). It has already been shown that the greater the amount of scattered light, the larger is the extinction coefficient and the poorer is the visibility.

In situations where visibility variations are dependent upon the direction of illumination, it would obviously be impossible to relate the observed variations to different concentrations of particulate materials in the atmosphere.

V. Application of Visibility Observations

A. General Considerations

Analyses of visibility records have been used in different ways in various air pollution programs. The results from several of these will be described briefly because they illustrate how these data can be handled. In general, visibility observations reflect the local environment so strongly that the results of visibility correlations with air pollution parameters should not be expected to hold in another area.

B. Assessment of Local Sources

Table III illustrates a frequently used technique for the determination of the severity of a local air pollution situation through the comparison of visibility statistics in the suspected air pollution area with statistics from a similar but less polluted area (*20*). These tabulated data relate the difference in the frequency of a 2-mi. or lower visibility at Los Angeles Airport and at San Diego. The positive frequencies indicate for these tabulated months and hours that the Los Angeles visibility was more likely to be low than was the San Diego visibility. In the mid-morning hours during the fall months the differences were most marked. The conclusion which was originally drawn from this Los Angeles-San Diego study was that these differences in visibility were due to the increased air pollution in Los Angeles as compared to San Diego.

If such a conclusion were based solely upon a tabulation such as Table III it would be very suspect. In order to make a valid comparison between affected and control stations it is necessary to establish that air pollution is the only significant factor involved in visibility observations which affects the two locations differently. It has been pointed out in Section III that the visibility reflects humidity, wind, and inversion conditions in a complex way. Even the manner of observation can bring about apparent differences. Each of these factors should be evaluated in some detail to determine the significance to be attached to the result. In many cases it is only necessary to be satisfied that likely differences are such as to cause differences opposite to those caused by air pollution. However, this makes it more difficult to determine the effects of air pollution sources.

TABLE III
COMPARISON OF LOS ANGELES AND SAN DIEGO VISIBILITY[a]
(August 1937–December 1946)

	Visibility comparison (%)[a]			
Month	4:00 A.M.	10:00 A.M.	4:00 P.M.	10:00 P.M.
Jan.	24	24	5	13
March	2	9	1	0
May	11	9	2	3
July.	16	29	4	9
Sept.	11	13	2	5
Nov.	19	25	2	12

[a] Per cent of time Los Angeles Airport visibility is 2 mi. or less, minus the per cent of time San Diego visibility is 2 mi. or less.

Two-station comparisons may also be made for a group of selected days, normally the most serious air pollution days or periods. In a study of this nature, since it is concerned with fewer situations, more details of the weather conditions can be investigated. Such a study was carried out for Los Angeles for July, August, September, 1949 (*21*). In this particular study two control stations were used: Goleta, 100 mi. north near Santa Barbara, and El Toro Marine Air Station, 45 mi. south. Humidity data were studied to rule out fog situations. It was concluded that 90% of the visibility reduction in downtown Los Angeles on smog days was due to man-made pollution and only 10% to natural haze. This was a more definitive and satisfactory result than that obtained from the comparison of Los Angeles and San Diego average data.

C. Assessment of Long-Term Visibility Trends

Sometimes in an air pollution control program someone asks whether conditions are really any different than they had been over the years. An answer to such a question has often been sought from visibility observations available in the Weather Bureau records. Visibility data are used with the assumption that only pollution sources will exhibit long-term trends and that the visibility will properly reflect changes in air pollution. Neither assumption can be guaranteed.

In California three areas have been studied to determine possible visibility trends. These areas are Los Angeles, San Francisco, and the Central Valley.

1. *Visibility Trends in Los Angeles*

The most complete study of the Los Angeles situation has been done by Neiburger (*22*) using punch-card machine techniques on the downtown Los Angeles visibility and weather observations. A 23-year period of data was available. In order to eliminate as much as possible the effects of various weather conditions, the visibility data were sorted according to various wind direction and relative humidity classes. The data, both when grouped and separated according to humidity and wind, show lower visibilities in the 1940's than in the 1930's. The lowest values occurred around 1944–1947 followed by some possible improvement in the period 1948–1954.

Neiburger analyzed the trend in the frequency of occurrence of visibilities in various classes rather than the trend of some "average" visibility. The use of frequencies will enable changes to be observed more easily. Upon analysis these visibility data showed the most marked changes in the higher visibility ranges. The frequency of observations of visibility greater than 12 mi. at noon in the period from 1932–37 was 30% while in 1944–49 it was only 18%. Although this study was able to show some downward trend in Los Angeles visibility it also showed that visibility in Los Angeles even in the 1930's, that period old-timers call the smog-free years, was not especially good even though the population was only half that in 1950. In the summer and early fall months visibility exceeded 12 mi. very infrequently even in the 1930's.

2. *Visibility Trends in San Francisco*

A trend study, similar to Neiburger's Los Angeles study, has been carried out for San Francisco (*23*), using observations at noon for the period from 1933 through 1956. These data were classified according to humidity and to wind speed (rather than direction) in order to segregate periods when air pollution effects would be emphasized.

Figure 12 shows the annual frequencies of San Francisco visibility for four ranges of visibility when the humidity was less than 70% and the wind speed was less than 10 m.p.h. It would appear from this figure that the visibility in the 1933–39 period was generally better than in later years. However, an analysis of observational techniques showed that the reporting of "prevailing visibility" began in 1939 (*3, 4*), and it was reasoned that this change could account for lower reported frequencies for the higher ranges of visibility. With this change in 1939

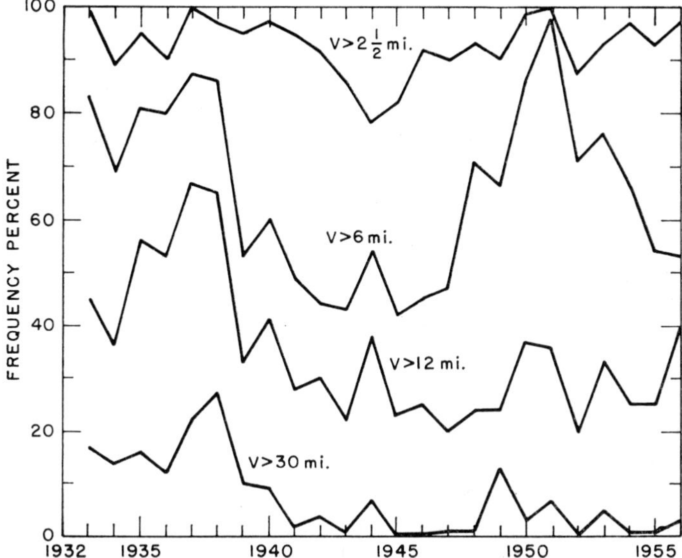

FIG. 12. Annual visibility frequencies, U. S. Weather Bureau Office, San Francisco, noon weekday observations, relative humidity less than 70%, wind less than 10 m.p.h. [E. Robinson, H. Currie, and H. A. James, Paper presented at *187th Natl. Meeting Am. Meteorol. Soc., Eugene, Oregon, 1960*].

ruled out as far as air pollution effects are concerned, it was not possible to establish any consistent trend in these data. Thus it must be concluded that any changes in the air pollution pattern in San Francisco have not caused significant changes in visibility. However, it could not be concluded that there were no changes in air pollution patterns.

3. *Visibility Trends in the California Central Valley*

An analysis of long-term data was carried out to determine whether air pollution, in the form of reduced visibility, was making inroads into the primarily agricultural Central Valley of California (*6*). Data from Sacramento back to 1935 and Bakersfield back to 1948 were used for the months of May, July, September, and November and limited to daytime hours, 7:30 A.M. to 5:30 P.M. Consideration was given to both humidity and wind effects.

In the analysis of these visibility records the authors introduced the argument that since the total of visibility frequencies for any given sample period must total 100%, any frequency change in any one of the given ranges of visibility must be compensated for by changes in the frequencies of the other ranges. Thus, with a trend of deteriorating visibility the resultant frequency changes with time in given visibility ranges are shifted toward each next lower range. This general scheme of analysis seems to offer a method of appraising the data which will shed some light on the over-all changes in visibility patterns.

This study showed that there apparently has been a worsening of visibility in this area over the years. Further, there was a stronger correlation of lower visibility to periods when the wind was from nearby urban areas than when it came from rural areas. Both of these conclusions pointed toward growing air pollution in the study area.

D. Correlations of Visibility with Particulate Concentrations

Correlations between visibility and particulate concentrations have been sought in a number of studies with the idea that this would enable past observations of visibility to be translated into some sort of pollution index applicable to both current and past data. The usual scheme has been to attempt to relate particulate samples to visibility either through mass loading or soiling index and to add in correction factors for humidity and wind. Statistical techniques are usually used for the derivation of regression equations relating the several variables.

In the Detroit-Windsor study carried out by the International Joint Commission correlations were determined between instrumental visibility observations, the density of the soiling on a filter surface, and the total mass of particulate material in the air (*24*). The conclusions drawn from this study were that transmissometer measurements of visibility cannot be used to determine either the soiling index or the weight of atmospheric aerosol. Neither can a soiling measurement on a filter be used to obtain the total weight of aerosol or visibility.

Other studies along these lines have been carried out by the Public Health Service in St. Louis, Cincinnati, and at other sites where air pollution surveys were run (*25*). These data showed considerable variation about any mean value and correlations which were not especially high.

It seems apparent from the results available in the literature that any relation which is found between visibility and particulate concentration measurements would be limited in application to the specific sampling location and probably to the time period when the sampling was done. General applicability of results is not indicated. This should not really be a surprise when the multitude of different factors affecting both visibility and particulate concentration measurements are considered. Like most atmospheric phenomena these are very complex measurements in spite of their apparent simplicity.

E. Short-Term Studies of Visibility

The fact that the visibility is representative of both the prevailing weather conditions and the previous history of the air mass makes it very difficult to use visibility as a measure of short-term changes in air pollution emissions. Short-term comparisons are apt to be attempted if, for example, a major air pollution source in a community ceases to operate for a period of time. In such situations there is often a strong tendency to try and show the degree to which the source pollutes the local atmosphere by displaying visibility records before and after shutdown. Depending upon the prevailing weather patterns which occurred during the periods used one could expect to show that the shutdown either reduced pollution, made no change, or perhaps in some way increased the pollution. Unless there is a careful analysis of all of the weather factors affecting the visibility, a short-term before-and-after type of visibility study is very unreliable.

VI. Air Pollution Effects on Solar Radiation

A. Calculated Solar Extinction

The same rules of extinction due to scattering and absorption that have been discussed for visibility hold for solar radiation received at the earth's surface. Concern over the loss of sunlight in polluted areas is twofold—loss of illumination and loss of the biologically important ultraviolet component of sunlight.

The fact that most polluted atmospheres are shallow layers is a factor which keeps the extinction of sunlight from being a more serious problem than it is. Some calculations of extinction can show what might be expected in a typical situation. If it is assumed that an incident light path through a uniformly polluted atmosphere is 0.2 mi. long with a visibility of 2 mi. ($\sigma = 1.96$), the intensity of sunlight transmitted would be:

$$I = I_0 e^{-1.96 \times 0.2} = I_0 e^{-0.39} = 0.68 I_0 \qquad (14)$$

an extinction of 32%. If this 32% were all absorbed the total sunlight lost would be 32%. However, if the extinction were caused by scattering, only the back-scattered light would be lost. If, as indicated by the iron sphere data, it were assumed that scattering and absorption were equal, and that each accounted for a 16% loss of direct sunlight, then the net energy loss at the earth's surface would be 16% (absorbed) plus an estimated 9% (back-scattered) for a probable net loss of approximately 25%.

B. Observations of Radiation Losses

During the 4 years from 1944 to 1948 comparative measurements were made of total solar and sky radiation at the Post Office Building in downtown Boston and at the Blue Hill Observatory, 10 mi. south-southwest (*26*). Figure 13 shows the mean daily radiation values for

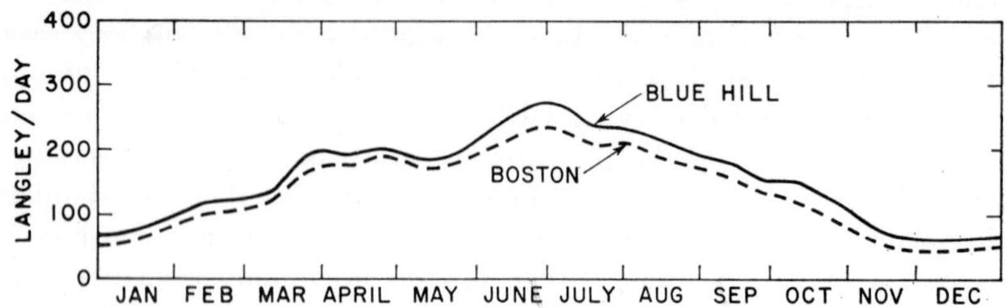

Fig. 13. Total solar and sky radiation, 4-year mean values, 1944–1948, Boston and Blue Hill Observatory [I. F. Hand, *Bull. Am. Meteorol. Soc.* **30**(7), 242 (1949)].

Boston and Blue Hill for these 4 years. In the winter months these curves indicate that the total radiation in Boston was 17% less than at Blue Hill. The Boston instrument location was between the two largest railway yards at a time when soft coal was the common engine fuel. Other smoke sources were also located in the surrounding business district. However, it was on a 23-story building which doubtless caused it to show a better picture than would a surface-located instrument. On a diurnal basis more radiation was lost in the early morning and late afternoon than near mid-day. The maximum loss measured was at 9:00 A.M. on January 18, 1944 when a depletion of more than 90% occurred (*26*), "owing almost exclusively to a dense smoke pall."

Similar radiation studies in Seattle in 1950–51 (*27*) and in Los Angeles in 1954 (*28*) show similar differences. In Seattle the 2-year study showed the radiation at the urban station at University of Washington to be 83.3% in 1950 and 87.7% in 1951 of that at the rural station at the Seattle-Tacoma Airport. Nine months of data from an industrial area showed radiation of only 79.5% of the rural value.

The 4-month Los Angeles survey by the Air Pollution Foundation (*28*) resulted in the conclusion that the radiation received in downtown Los Angeles was some 10% less than it would be without pollution.

This relatively low value for Los Angeles reflects the strong influence of scattering due to the small effective particle size found in the Los Angeles polluted atmosphere.

C. Diminution of Ultraviolet Radiation

One of the effects of air pollution which was an early concern of investigators was the excessive loss of ultraviolet radiation from sunlight when it had penetrated an urban smoke pall. Solar ultraviolet radiation is a major factor in the body's generation of natural vitamin D.

The excessive loss of the shorter wavelength ultraviolet compared to losses of visible light is readily explained by the inverse relationship between the wavelength of the light and extinction caused by small particles. In the case of very small particles, Rayleigh scattering is applicable, and, as shown by Eq. 6, the extinction is dependent upon λ^{-4}.

Measurements of losses of ultraviolet and visible solar radiation due to Los Angeles smog clouds have been reported by Stair (*29*). He worked in Pasadena in the fall of 1954. Measurements of conditions during the morning prior to the midday arrival of heavy smog clouds permitted the effects of the smog to be evaluated. He reported that while there were large drops in solar intensities at all wavelengths when the smog reached the observation location, the greater percentage-wise reductions occurred with the shorter wavelengths. In some cases for the shorter wavelengths the smog reduced the intensities to immeasurable levels.

Stair was able under smog conditions to detect losses in transmittance both from general scattering and from absorption (*29*). The scattering was attributed to the small particles in the smog while the absorption was attributed to gaseous pollutants. The absorption occurred in two general parts of the short-wave spectrum with increased absorption occurring at wavelengths shorter than 3200 Å and in a broad band centered around 3600 to 4000 Å. The absorption in the region below 3200 Å was attributed primarily to ozone although calculations seemed to indicate that the expected ozone concentrations could not account for all of the absorption which was observed in this region. The broad band around 3600 to 4000 Å was attributed to nitrogen dioxide absorption.

VII. Stack Plume Opacity Measurements

A. Calculation of Plume Opacity

To calculate the opacity of a typical metallurgical fume from light-scattering data, it is necessary to calculate the number of particles in each size interval per unit of gas volume (Table IV). Certain assumptions are necessary in order to permit these calculations to be made.

TABLE IV

MASS AND NUMBER OF PARTICLES OF TYPICAL FUME[a]

Size range (μ)	Relative weight emitted (mass/volume)	Representative diameter (μ)	Proportionate mass per particle	Proportionate number of particles[b]	Proportionate number of particles per unit volume[c]
2.5–3.0	3.0	2.77	11.25	1.00	3.0
2.0–2.5	7.0	2.28	6.25	1.80	12.6
1.5–2.0	20.0	1.79	3.06	3.68	73.6
1.0–1.5	45.0	1.30	1.15	9.78	441.0
0.9–1.0	8.0	0.95	0.465	24.2	193.6
0.8–0.9	7.0	0.85	0.335	33.6	235.2
0.7–0.8	5.0	0.75	0.230	48.9	244.5
0.6–0.7	3.0	0.65	0.151	74.6	223.8
0.5–0.6	0.5	0.56	0.092	122.	61.
<0.5	1.5	0.30	0.013	865.	1298.

[a] Fume from open hearth furnace [G. L. Allen, F. H. Viets, and L. C. McCabe, *U.S. Bur. Mines Inform. Circ.* No. 7627 (1952)]. Emission rate: 120 lb./hr.; stack volume: 16,000 s.c.f.m.

[b] Determined by dividing weight of 2.77-μ particle by weight of smaller particle.

[c] The product of the Relative weight emitted and Proportionate number of particles.

The principal ones are:

(1) The fume can be considered an aerosol composed of iron spheres.

(2) Illumination is by light of 5500 Å wavelength—a reasonable approximation of daylight.

(3) The extinction of light by the aerosol is such that a cloud containing N particles will have an effect equal to N times the effect of a single particle.

These assumptions are reasonable and probably introduce no more uncertainty than is associated with the determination of the size distribution of the aerosol.

Table V shows some of the calculation steps necessary for determining the relative extinction under these conditions. The last column of Table V which tabulates cumulative extinction as a function of particle size permits a rough estimate to be made of the change in extinction resulting from the change in weight distribution that would occur from the use of fume removal equipment. For example, the removal of all particles larger than 0.8 μ would remove 90% of weight of the aerosol, but would only remove 76.3% of the light extinction potential of the effluent. If the 90% reduction in weight were obtained by collecting 90% of each particle size group, rather than collecting only the largest 90% of the weight, the extinction would also be reduced by 90%.

In practice, the efficiency of collection of a fume of this type de-

TABLE V
EXTINCTION CALCULATIONS FOR THE TYPICAL FUME OF TABLE IV

Particle diameter (μ)	Area ratio K	Extinction $NK\pi r^2$	Relative extinction (%)	Cumulative weight (%)	Cumulative extinction (%)
2.77	2.2	40.2	1.1	3.0	1.1
2.28	2.3	118.4	3.3	10.0	4.4
1.79	2.3	434.2	12.2	30.0	16.6
1.30	2.4	1411.2	39.8	75.0	56.4
0.95	2.5	350.4	9.9	83.0	66.3
0.85	2.6	355.2	10.0	90.0	76.3
0.75	2.7	298.3	8.4	95.0	84.7
0.65	2.8	214.8	6.0	98.0	90.7
0.56	2.9	43.9	1.2	98.5	91.9
0.30	3.1	285.6	8.1	100.0	100.0

creases with particle size (*30*). The per cent total extinction for each particle size class as shown in the fourth column of Table V can be used to compare the changes in opacity which would result from the use of a fume collector of variable size-efficiency (Table VI). The calculations

TABLE VI
ESTIMATED EFFECT OF ELECTROSTATIC PRECIPITATOR ON OPEN HEARTH FUME

Particle diameter (μ)	Relative weight (%)	Relative extinction (%)	Precip. efficiency (%)	Final weight[a]	Final extinction[b]
2.77	3.0	1.1	96.5	0.105	0.039
2.28	7.0	3.3	96.0	0.280	0.132
1.79	20.0	12.2	95.3	0.940	0.573
1.30	45.0	39.8	94.5	2.475	2.189
0.95	8.0	9.9	93.6	0.512	0.634
0.85	7.0	10.0	93.3	0.469	0.670
0.75	5.0	8.4	93.0	0.350	0.588
0.65	3.0	6.0	92.6	0.222	0.444
0.56	0.5	1.2	92.2	0.039	0.094
0.30	1.5	8.1	90.5	0.143	0.769
	100.0	100.0		5.535	6.132

[a] Determined from Wt. × (100 − Efficiency)/100.
[b] Determined from Extinction × (100 − Efficiency)/100.

in Table VI show that the postulated precipitator would have a collection efficiency of 94.5% (i.e., 100 — 5.5) by weight, and that 93.9% (i.e., 100 — 6.1) of the extinction due to light scattering would also be eliminated. If it is assumed that the extinction due to absorption is reduced a like amount, this means a 16-fold decrease in opacity at any point in the plume relative to the uncontrolled condition.

B. Calculation of Plume Opacity Control Limits

Plume opacity in either Ringelmann numbers or equivalent opacity can be expressed mathematically in terms of the particulate concentration and other parameters. This follows from a restatement of Eq. 3:

$$\frac{I}{I_0} = e^{-\sigma x} \tag{15}$$

In this situation I_0 would be the intensity of the light entering the plume, I the intensity seen by the observer, σ the extinction coefficient, and x the distance through the plume. From Eq. 7 it can be shown that since

$$M = N\rho \frac{4}{3}\pi r^3 \tag{16}$$

and thus

$$N\pi r^2 = \frac{3M}{4\rho r} \tag{17}$$

that

$$\sigma = \frac{3KM}{4\rho r} \tag{18}$$

where K, M, ρ, and r have the same meaning as in Eq. 12. Thus it follows from Eqs. 18 and 8, through substitution and taking logarithms, that

$$\log_e \frac{I}{I_0} = -\frac{3x}{4\rho} \sum_{i=1}^{n} \frac{K_i M_i}{r_i} \tag{19}$$

In making such a calculation, I/I_0 should equal 80% for Ringelmann No. 1, 60% for No. 2, etc.

The Bay Area Air Pollution Control District adopted a provision in their control regulation for visible plumes which is based upon this equation (*31*). The regulation states that an effluent would not be subject to visual opacity rules if it can be shown that the stack concentration of particulate materials is less than that given by

$$n = \frac{0.12}{L} \tag{20}$$

where n = source emission, grains/ft.^{3}
L = square root of the area of the emission point (for a circular stack, $L = 0.89 \times$ diameter).

The constant, 0.12, in this formula was chosen so that an oil aerosol with the size distribution of Table VII would approximate No. 2 Ringelmann (60% transmission). This aerosol will show slightly more than 60% transmission according to calculations for daylight conditions.

TABLE VII
ASSUMED OIL AEROSOL SIZE DISTRIBUTION FOR SECTION 3113 REGULATION 2, BAY AREA APCD

Diameter (μ)	Relative mass	Relative no. particles
0.16	1	6400
0.32	1	800
0.64	1	100
1.27	1	12.5
2.54	1	1.6

This Bay Area regulation is the first attempt to augment a Ringelmann opacity regulation with calculated opacity limits. Its usefulness in a community air pollution program remains to be determined.

REFERENCES

1. R. E. Huschke, ed., "Glossary of Meteorology." Am. Meteorol. Soc., Boston, 1959.
2. "Manual of Surface Observations" (WBAN), Circular N, 7th ed. USGPO, Washington, D. C., 1955.
3. U. S. Weather Bureau, "Instructions for Airway Meteorological Service," Circular N, 4th ed., pp. 31–32. USGPO, Washington, D. C., 1939.
4. U. S. Weather Bureau, "Instructions for Airway Meteorological Service," Circular N, 3rd ed., p. 6. USGPO, Washington, D. C., 1935.
5. E. J. Wiggins, *in* "An Aerometric Survey of the Los Angeles Basin August–November, 1954" (N. A. Renzetti, ed.), Sec. IX, Rept. No. 9. Air Poll. Foundation, Los Angeles, 1955.
6. G. C. Holzworth and J. A. Maga, *J. Air Poll. Control Assoc.* **10**(6), 430 (1960).
7. C. Junge, *in* "Compendium of Meteorology" (T. F. Malone, ed.), pp. 182–191. Am. Meteorol. Soc., Boston, 1951.
8. Stanford Research Institute, "The Smog Problem in Los Angeles County," 2nd Interim Report. Western Oil and Gas Assoc., Los Angeles, 1949.
9. S. Twomey, *in* "Atmospheric Chemistry of Chlorine and Sulfur Compounds," Geophysical Monograph No. 3. Am. Geophys. Union, Washington, D. C., 1959.
10. M. Neiburger and M. G. Wurtele, *Chem. Revs.* **44,** 321 (1949).
11. T. J. Buma, *Bull. Am. Meteorol. Soc.* **41**(7), 357 (1960).
12. State of California, Department of Public Health, "California Standards for Ambient Air and Motor Vehicle Exhaust." The Department, Berkeley, California, 1959.
13. J. A. Maga, *Am. Ind. Hyg. Assoc. J.* **21**(5), 430 (1960).
14. W. E. K. Middleton, "Vision Through the Atmosphere." Univ. of Toronto Press, Toronto, Ontario, 1952.
15. J. C. Johnson, "Physical Meteorology." Mass. Inst. Technol. Press. Cambridge, Mass., 1954.

16. D. Sinclair, *in* "Handbook on Aerosols," Chapter 7. U. S. Atomic Energy Commission, Washington, D. C., 1950.
17. H. C. van de Hulst, "Light Scattering By Small Particles." Wiley, New York, 1957.
18. W. W. Foster, *Brit. J. Appl. Phys.* **10,** 416 (1959).
18a. V. R. Stull and G. N. Plass, *J. Opt. Soc. Am.* **50**(2), 121 (1960).
19. C. Steffens and S. Rubin, *Proc. 1st Natl. Air Poll. Symposium, Pasadena, Calif., 1949,* pp. 103–108.
20. Stanford Research Institute, "The Smog Problem in Los Angeles County," 1st Interim Report. Western Oil and Gas Assoc., Los Angeles, 1948.
21. Stanford Research Institute, "The Smog Problem in Los Angeles County," 3rd Interim Report. Western Oil and Gas Assoc., Los Angeles, 1950.
22. M. Neiburger, "Visibility Trend in Los Angeles," Report No. 11. Air Poll. Foundation, Los Angeles, 1955.
23. E. Robinson, H. Currie, and H. A. James, Paper presented at *187th Natl. Meeting Am. Meteorol. Soc., Eugene, Oregon, 1960.*
24. G. D. Clayton and P. M. Giever, *Anal. Chem.* **27**(5), 708 (1955).
25. E. W. Burt, *Am. Ind. Hyg. Assoc. J.* **22,** 102 (1961).
26. I. F. Hand, *Bull. Am. Meteorol. Soc.* **30**(7), 242 (1949).
27. R. G. Tyler, "Report on an Air Pollution Study for the City of Seattle." Environmental Research Lab., Univ. of Washington, Seattle, Washington, 1952.
28. N. A. Renzetti, "An Aerometric Survey of the Los Angeles Basin August–November, 1954," Report No. 9, pp. 193–200. Air Poll. Foundation, Los Angeles, 1955.
29. R. Stair, *Proc. 3rd Natl. Air Poll. Symposium, Pasadena, Calif., 1955,* pp. 48–55.
30. A. J. Grindle, Paper presented to *Air Poll. Control Assoc. (East Coast Section) Semi-Ann. Meeting, Harrisburg, Pa., 1953.*
31. Bay Area Air Pollution Control District, Regulation 2, Section 3113. San Francisco, California, 1960.

CHAPTER 8

Effects of Air Pollution on Plants

C. STAFFORD BRANDT

Agricultural Research Service Liaison, United States Public Health Service, Cincinnati, Ohio

I. Introduction

The significant and sometimes devastating effects of air pollutants on vegetation have long been recognized and, in fact, much of our concern with air pollution has revolved around these effects on vegetation. While urban smoke was sufficiently unpleasant to be classed as a nuisance in early ordinances, the failure of crops and the death of trees gave dramatic proof of the adverse effects of air pollution (*1*). The most dramatic effects were those from sulfur dioxide emitted from smelters.

By the time Haselhoff and Lindau issued their handbook (*2*) on sulfur dioxide and other pollutant effects on vegetation, they had had several decades of prior experience and observations to draw upon.

Even with the striking evidence found in this publication, the effects were often ignored. The scars of the "little desert," near Ducktown, Tennessee, remain after more than half a century (*3, 4*) as a vivid reminder of the destructive effect of sulfur dioxide.

While the effects of fluorides on plants have been known for some time, these compounds have become a serious toxicant to vegetation only with the industrial expansion of the last 25 years (*5*). Because of the wide distribution of fluorine in nature, its air pollution aspect has been complicated. From the agricultural standpoint the problem has been doubly important because vegetation appearing perfectly normal can have a serious deleterious effect on the grazing animal. Our present thinking about the atmospheric concentration which is required to injure vegetation has also necessitated a change in concept with respect to fluorides as compared with sulfur dioxide. Even the most sensitive plants can tolerate almost continual exposure to 0.3 p.p.m. sulfur dioxide, while a level of hydrogen fluoride one-thousandfold less will severely injure some sensitive plants (*6*).

Injury to vegetation by air pollutants results not only from industrial sources, but also from sources associated with the complexities of urban living. This has been well illustrated during recent years by the smog problem of southern California (*7*). This general type of pollution is of growing concern to all. The effects of this smog-type pollutant on vegetation are important, not only from the standpoint of economic loss, but also because of the use of vegetation damage as a means of monitoring and defining the extent of the pollution complex (*8, 9*).

The complete destruction of vegetation associated with the early history of air pollution is no longer a problem, though it could possibly arise again. The problem now is more widespread, with many sources of sulfur dioxide occasionally exceeding the toxic limit of plants, many sources of fluorides ever a threat, and "photochemical" smog on the increase. Typical smog and ozone injury to plants has been found in most of the major metropolitan areas of the United States (*10*). Because of the nature of the problem, it is impossible to make a firm assessment of the cost of air pollution damage. The best estimates of the yearly loss in agricultural crops in California range from 6 to 10 million dollars mainly in the Los Angeles region (*11*). This represents only the visible injury affecting yield or marketability. The estimate does not include the possible growth effects, the value of produce in back yard gardens, the loss in ornamentals, or other marginal effects. If we are to estimate the total cost of air pollution on vegetation, we should take into account the fumigation which severely marks or kills a back yard apple tree, the continued cost of erosion from the Ducktown desert, as well as many other items. If we could do this, the total annual cost would undoubtedly be in the hundreds of millions.

In the past decade there have been several reviews (*6, 12–15*) covering in varying detail the effects of air pollution on vegetation. These give some idea of the growing interest in the problem. The most recent review was prepared by Thomas (*15a*) for the World Health Organization. This has an excellent bibliography of 129 entries and several color plates showing typical injury symptoms on vegetation. A brief review by Garber (*15b*) has a bibliography of 331 entries with a very complete coverage of the German literature.

No attempt will be made in this review to make a comprehensive analysis of the symptomatology of air pollution effects on vegetation. The general patterns will be described and the characteristic symptoms of the major pollutants will be outlined. An effort will be made to evaluate the possible physiological upsets which do not develop into characteristic visible symptoms.

II. General Injury Symptoms

The visible injury symptoms on the leaves of plants attributable to air pollution can be considered in three general categories, not necessarily mutually exclusive: (1) leaf tissue collapse, (2) chlorosis or other color changes, and (3) growth alterations. In many of the cases the injury pattern developed is highly characteristic of the toxic agent, but while characteristic, the pattern is by no means specific for the agent. Disease, insects, nutrition, and other factors can produce leaf patterns very similar to those produced by air pollutants.

In order to define a base terminology for the discussion to follow, consider briefly the structure of the leaf. If you hold it up to the light, you will see a network of denser structures, the veins, all tracing back to the base or stem of the leaf, the petiole: these are the transport systems of the leaf. Between these veins, the interveinal areas, are the functional cells of the leaf. On cross section of an interveinal area you will see three main specialized layers. On the upper and lower surface there will be a single layer of heavy walled cells, seemingly empty; these layers are the epidermis or skin. Directly under the upper epidermis will be a row of rather uniform, elongated cells standing on end and packed closely together; this is the palisade layer. Between the lower edge of the palisade layer and the lower epidermis, you will find a loosely packed area of cells of somewhat irregular shape, the spongy parenchyma. Large air spaces are common. On more careful examination of the epidermis you will find pairs of specialized cells edging an opening, or stoma, through the epidermis into one of these interior air spaces.

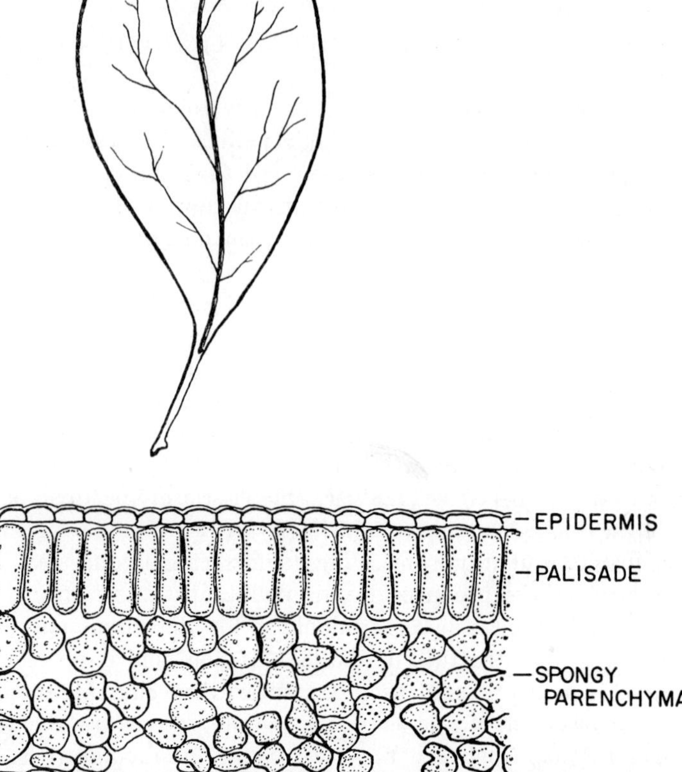

Fig. 1. Normal dicotyledon leaf and cross section.

These stomatal cells are capable of movement, of opening or closing the stomata. A generalized diagram of the structure of a normal leaf is given in Fig. 1.

A. Tissue Collapse

One of the most common effects of air pollutants is the plasmolysis of the cells and final collapse of the tissue. The initial plasmolysis, a loss firstly of water, and finally of structural integrity, may occur in the parenchyma cells, as in the case of most "smog" injury; in the palisade cells, as in the case of ozone; or through the entire leaf, as in the case of fluorides, and often of sulfur dioxide. Following the initial plasmolysis and loss of structure, the other adjacent segments of the leaf may be affected, depending on the nature of the toxicant, its concentration, the species of plant, and many other factors. In most cases the first symptom visible on the intact leaf is a slightly water-soaked or bruised looking area. These areas then generally dry out, leaving the necrotic pattern characteristic of the toxicant.

B. Sulfur Dioxide

In sulfur dioxide injury the initial disruption of cellular integrity usually appears in the spongy parenchymal cells. Subsequently, the palisade layer immediately above is often affected. These areas then become dry and papery, usually bleached to a light ivory or tan color. The final effect is a pattern of light-colored blotches, mainly interveinal. The veins may remain green and intact, tracing a green pattern across the blotches which seem to have run together. With time and/or severe injury the veins may also become affected and bleach out. The general characteristics of sulfur dioxide injury to leaves are shown in the diagrams of Fig. 2.

Grasses have veins which run in parallel rows without branching. However, the basic blotching pattern of collapse with sulfur dioxide still holds true. The final bleached pattern gives a streaked effect. Often, only the principal central vein remains intact. The grasses have no palisade layer, so the collapse is generally uniform through the thickness of the blade.

Conifer leaves, or needles, in internal structure bear little resemblance to the leaf structure of either grasses or other plants. On being subjected to a toxicant such as sulfur dioxide, the cells are killed and lose some structural properties, but collapse hardly describes the process. The cells undoubtedly lose water on death due to sulfur dioxide, and the green chlorophyll is destroyed. The effect is similar to that of old age in that the needles become brown and somewhat brittle. Either the entire needle or only the tip portion may be affected. Sometimes a banding of darker color develops which may be symptomatic of a series of fumigations, each killing a little more of the needle.

Sulfur dioxide is thought to enter the leaf as a gas and to act directly on the functional cells near the stomata. There is a definite atmospheric concentration response threshold that depends upon the variety of plant and on the age of the leaf. The plant can tolerate exposure to sulfur dioxide below this concentration practically indefinitely. It is assumed that the cell has the capacity to detoxify the sulfur dioxide or sulfite, the solution product of the gas, by conversion to sulfate at a certain rate. If this rate is exceeded, the sulfite builds up, the water relations

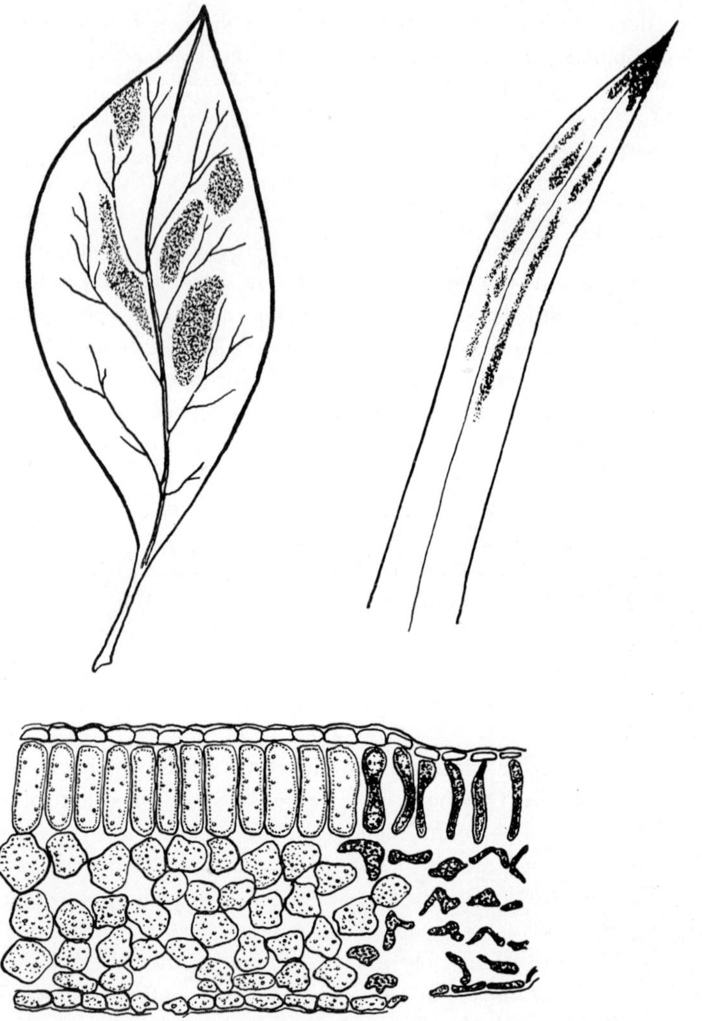

FIG. 2. Sulfur dioxide injury. Note blotchy interveinal areas on dicotyledon leaf and streaked areas on monocotyledon leaf (grass type).

of the cell are disrupted, and plasmolysis and collapse ensue. O'Gara first expressed this threshold-effects relation as a time-concentration equation. Thomas (*16*) has modified these relations and published the limiting parameters for a large group of plants (*6, 13, 14*).

In the last couple of years some interesting and excellent work with SO_2 from Germany has appeared. The July 1960 issue (Heft *13*) of *Der Forst- und Holtzwirt* was devoted to "smoke" problems on forest plantations. An extensive study is under way at Biersdorf (*16a*) exposing a wide variety of plants around an industrial source. A very preliminary report of the concentrations found at the six stations ranging from 325 to 6000 meters from the source has appeared (*16b*). A report by Zahn (*16c*) describes some preliminary intermittent fumigations with varying recovery periods under semi-field conditions and a report by Van Haut on some controlled laboratory fumigations includes some excellent color plates (*16d*).

C. Fluorides

Fluorides appear to act as cumulative poisons to the plant. Presumably, a plant grown in an atmosphere containing any gaseous fluoride, of no matter how low a concentration, will, in time, provided the leaf lives long enough, accumulate enough fluoride to injure the leaf tissue. The commonest effect of fluoride when it reaches toxic concentration is the plasmolysis and collapse of the internal cells of the leaf. The effect usually starts on the margin and tips of the leaf, progressing inward with time and continued exposure. It appears that fluoride enters the leaf through the stomata, without injury at the site of entry, and is translocated toward the margin and tip with the normal flow of water. Fluoride does not seem to move in the opposite direction (*17*), though we know that other ions do move out of the leaf.

On collapse the cells dry out and generally turn deep brown to tan. The result is a rather striking and characteristic tip and marginal burned appearance. Usually the line of demarcation between healthy and necrotic tissue is sharp and made more distinct by a narrow dark reddish-brown line of dead tissue adjacent to the healthy tissue. In the case of the broad leaf plants, the effect may occur at any place on the margin, though more frequently it takes place toward the tip. With some leaves, such as peach, the necrotic tissue is quite fragile and drops off, leaving a chewed appearance to the leaf. While the veins have a somewhat greater resistance, this resistance is not as striking in the broad leaf plants as in the grasses. Figure 3 shows in diagram form the characteristics of fluoride injury.

In grasses the characteristic necrosis occurs at the tip, progressing down the blade. The front usually has irregular streaking down the margin or between veins. The line of demarcation is, however, quite sharp, with the accentuating dark line usually present. In the conifers, tip burn is characteristic, with again a sharp well-marked line between dead and healthy tissue.

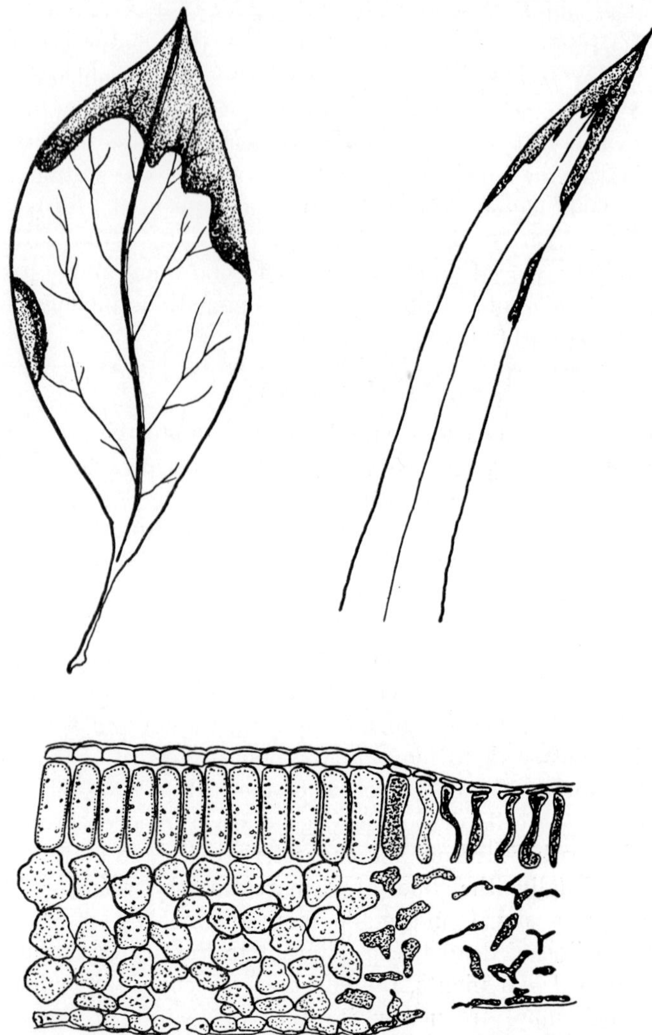

FIG. 3. Fluorine injury. Note the tip and edge necrosis on both the dicotyledon leaf and the monocotyledon (grass type) leaf with sharp line of demarcation. Section shows severe collapse and shrinking of internal structure.

D. OZONE

While our knowledge of the effects of ozone is more fragmentary than is that of sulfur dioxide and fluorides, there does appear to be a rather characteristic type of collapse associated with exposure to ozone. These characteristic symptoms are generalized in Fig. 4. The initial effect seems to be in the palisade layer. The association of the site of injury with stomatal entry is not clear. Seemingly, under certain conditions only a few palisade cells at scattered points over the leaf are involved. The cells collapse somewhat and, in the case of grape and some other

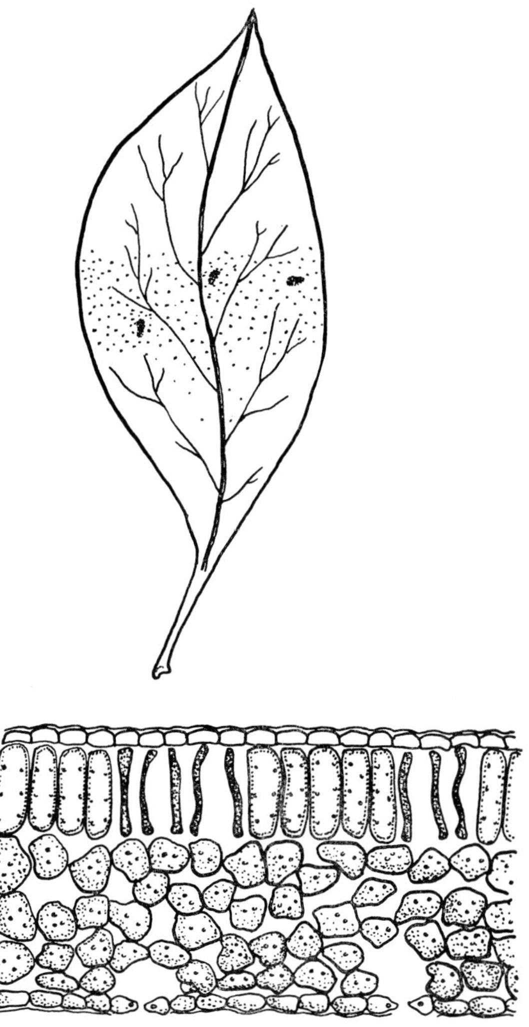

FIG. 4. Ozone injury. Note flecking or stippled effect on leaf. On sectioning only the palisade layer is affected.

plants, develop a dark pigment. This gives a brown, stippled appearance to the leaf, often limited to the upper surface (*18*). In severe cases the spongy cells will be affected and the stipple will go through the leaf. In ozone attack on tobacco, the same upper surface stipple appears, but the collapsed areas are often bleached white or tan rather than pigmented (*19*). While the injury symptoms on a variety of plants, produced by ozone fumigations in control chambers, have recently been published (*20*), our field knowledge is limited mainly to the stipple-type injury on broad leaf plants. Since this toxicant may be of growing importance in the highly urbanized areas of the east, it deserves considerably more attention from plant pathologists.

E. Oxidant Smog

The phytotoxicants which produce the oxidant or smog type of injury on plants, initially described by Middleton (*21*), are not fully known. One of the effects, a tissue collapse, has been well described (*22*). In this

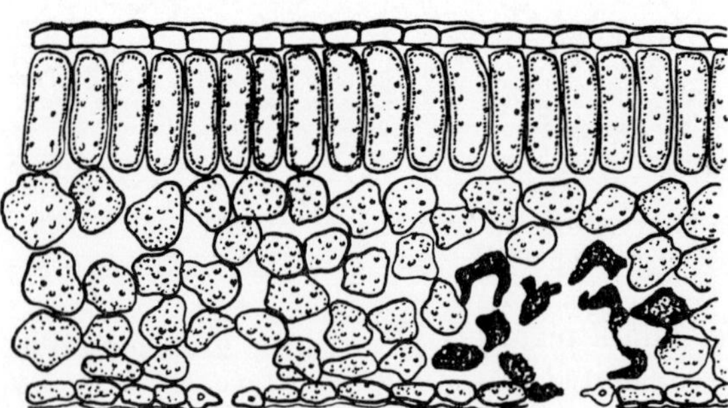

Fig. 5. Smog type injury. Note position effect with age of leaf. On sectioning, initial collapse is in the region of a stomata.

case the initial collapse is in the spongy parenchyma cells surrounding the air space into which a stoma opens. In some cases the effect is limited more or less to the cells nearest the lower epidermis. This produces the characteristic underside silvering or bronzing. In other cases, such as those of petunia and some tobaccos, the collapse is through the entire thickness of the leaf. Since the cells of these leaves are sensitive for only a short period during their development, a cross leaf banding, associated with sequential cell maturation along the leaf blade from tip to base, develops. In grasses this effect is quite common and characteristic. Since grasses do not have the palisade layer, the effect is usually clear through the leaf. Some of the characteristics of oxidant smog injury are diagrammed in Fig. 5.

While smog injury may affect the entire thickness of the leaf and cause the collapsed area to lose its green color, this type of injury is not easily confused with sulfur dioxide damage. Collapse due to smog usually does not cause as marked a difference in leaf thickness as that due to sulfur dioxide. The general smog damage pattern is more of a cross-leaf banding rather than of the blotching or streaking associated with sulfur dioxide. The actual response pattern created by smog probably varies more with species than does that caused by any other toxicant (*23*).

F. Other Pollutants

Some of the other pollutants, nitrogen oxides, chlorine, and hydrogen sulfide, which generally occur in concentrations sufficient to affect plants only as accidental spills, also produce a dramatic tissue collapse of the leaf. Sulfuric acid mist may be the cause of a pock-marked type of injury occasionally found on leaves in regions where escape of sulfur trioxide or the corresponding acid might be expected. In these cases the injury appears on the upper or exposed surface of the leaf as small collapsed areas. Sometimes the area is almost black, with the edges slightly raised. Thomas (*6*) indicates that a sulfuric acid aerosol associated with some smog-type conditions may be responsible for a similar injury found on chard and table beets.

Ethylene was once a troublesome pollutant in greenhouses, coming as it did from the manufactured gas used in heating. With a better understanding of the hazard and with the shift to oil and natural gas, this problem is no longer as serious. However, ethylene as an atmospheric pollutant is a problem for certain crops in certain areas. The injury occurring on orchids (*24*) is a collapse type of injury called "dry sepal," and causes considerable loss in the orchid industry of California. The effect on cotton (*25*) is also sometimes a collapsed type of injury but, more important, there is a growth alteration which will be noted later.

G. Color Changes

Chlorosis, the loss or reduction of the green plant pigment, chlorophyll, is a very common and nonspecific symptom in plants. Its appearance generally indicates a deficiency of some nutrient required by the plant. In many respects, it is analogous to anemia in the animal. The loss of chlorophyll results usually in a pale green or yellow pattern. Sometimes other colors develop from pigments already present but normally masked by the green of the chlorophyll, or from pigments which develop as a result of the upset which reduced the chlorophyll. Over the years we have learned to recognize certain patterns of chlorotic development in the leaf as being characteristic of certain deficiencies. There are other color changes in the leaf, often with general chlorosis, which we associate with maturity or senescence, as with the color change in the fall.

As noted above, the collapsed tissue resulting from air pollutants often has a characteristic color. We associate bleaching with sulfur dioxide, and a brown coloration with fluoride. The dark band of color marking the edge of necrotic tissue is often helpful in diagnosing fluoride injury. The pigmentation of small areas of the palisade cells seems to be characteristic of ozone injury in some plants. A silvering or bronzing of the under surface of some leaves is associated with oxidant-type-smog injury.

Chlorosis often appears in association with the more dramatic, collapsed-tissue effects of air pollution on plants. In the case of fluoride burn, a narrow, slightly chlorotic area is often found adjacent to the margin of the necrosis. With sulfur dioxide there may sometimes be a blotchy diffuse pattern of chlorosis in addition to the blotchy, bleached, collapsed areas. When a plant has been exposed for a long time to subthreshold levels of sulfur dioxide, a diffuse chlorosis of the older leaves may be the only symptom of exposure. This may be a saltlike toxicity resulting from excessive sulfate accumulation and often resembles the chlorosis associated with senescence.

In at least two species, corn and citrus, fluorides produce a characteristic chlorosis before the typical edge and tip burn occur. In corn a faint chlorotic streaking occurs on either side of the midrib, about midway along the length of the blade. In some respects the pattern is similar to that developed under conditions of zinc deficiency. The color change is fainter, tending more to pale yellow-green than to the light yellow found with zinc. It is usually best seen by transmitted light. Whether or not there are structural changes in the leaf, as this might indicate, has not been reported. In citrus, the fluoride chlorosis (*26*) is somewhat similar to manganese deficiency, with a spotty yellow interveinal development. The fluoride pattern usually develops more toward the tip than does that caused by a manganese deficiency, though this pattern formation alone is not a sufficient basis for diagnosis. Seen together, however, the fluoride and manganese symptoms are usually distinguishable.

In some cases the oxidant type of smog also produces a chlorosis. The pattern, however, is not distinctive, appearing as an early senescence. The leaves simply turn the usual yellow or brown color of old age, and fall off the plant. The effect has for some time been noted on citrus, especially lemon (*27*), and more recently on elm and other trees (*28*).

H. Growth Effects

There are few distinctive alterations of growth which can be attributed to air pollutants, although generally poor growth is a very real effect in some cases. Weed control sprays on roadsides, as well as in grain fields, on occasion constitute air pollution to surrounding areas. These materials, when they drift out of the desired spray pattern produce very marked abnormalities in growth since most have a hormone action. These abnormalities are usually twisting and/or elongation patterns on both leaves and stems.

Ethylene has long been known to induce epinasty, or drooping of the leaves, as well as to induce abscission. Hall *et al.* (*25*) have reported a damaging abscission of the young bolls in the cotton plant as well as an apparent loss of apical dominance. This results in a spreading, almost prostrate plant rather than the desired compact upright cotton plant. While this effect has been demonstrated in other plants, its economic importance in the field has not been established.

A stunting of growth, or lack of normal vigorous growth attributable to air pollution, has been observed in the United States as well as in England (*6, 8, 27*). A serious decline in citrus is being experienced in the area surrounding Los Angeles. The manifestations of the decline are early loss of leaves, changes in water relationships, smaller fruit, and generally poor growth. Somewhat similar effects are detected in the vegetable and horticultural crops of the area. The early senescence mentioned above is a part of the syndrome. Smog—urban air pollution—is a very probable agent for this decline. Some of the effects such as early leaf drop, changes in water relations, increased respiration, and subnormal growth of vegetables, have been experimentally alleviated by filtering the air which is supplied to enclosed plants through activated carbon. Whether these nonspecific growth effects are of importance in other areas is not known.

It should also be noted that air pollution injury to the leaves of plants can have an effect on growth. A plant, unlike an animal, does not take in prebuilt organic compounds necessary for its cell structure and function, but rather builds these complex compounds itself from simple inorganic compounds, water taken from the soil, and from carbon dioxide taken from the air. The leaf is the site of manufacture of these materials. If the function of the leaf is destroyed, the entire organism is put on a limited diet. Thus, a significant effect of fluoride which destroys part of the leaves of a tree, such as prune or one of the sensitive varieties of apricot, is an excessive dieback of bearing branches. We have no evidence, however, that this effect is due to anything more basic than simple leaf destruction which limits the food necessary for the tree to maintain itself and grow in a normal manner.

I. Problems of Diagnosis

A plant is a product of its environment, responding in many ways to the stresses of, as well as to the support afforded by, that environment. Air pollution must be considered simply another vector of the environment along with climate, soil, insects, diseases, and genetic history, as well as care or abuse by man. The patterns of injury created by an air pollutant may not only be modified or obscured by other environmental factors, but from these other factors the plant may develop patterns of injury which are difficult or impossible to distinguish from air pollution effects.

The modifying effect of prior climate—rainfall, temperature, and wind—are often difficult to assess. In alfalfa a water-stress phenomenon produces the disease of white spot which is often distinguishable from sulfur dioxide damage only with great difficulty. High temperatures can produce a scorch on maple and some other trees which will appear quite similar to sulfur dioxide injury. Temperature and wind, under certain conditions of soil moisture, can cause an edge burn on the leaves of many plants which is very similar to fluoride injury. In any of these cases, the climate stress may be of short duration, and the very existence of the stress difficult to establish after the symptoms have developed. The modifying effect of genetic make-up must also be considered. The fact that different species respond differently to air pollution, as well as to other environmental factors, is generally expected. However, the differences within the species—varietal differences—are often equally great. Some varieties of gladiolus may have 50% of the leaf destroyed by fluoride, whereas another variety growing next to it may have only the tip of the blade injured. In the case of tobacco, susceptibility to ozone-induced fleck is markedly affected by genetic make-up. In fact, an active breeding program is under way, whose goal is to breed ozone resistance into new tobacco strains along with certain other desirable characteristics.

Closely related to the factors of climate are the environmental factors of soil, nutrition, and management. All of the chlorotic patterns, early senescence, and poor growth effects of air pollution noted above can be duplicated by the proper combination of poor soil, nutrition, or management. It would be very foolish to diagnose a chlorotic pattern on citrus as an atmospheric fluoride effect without having first carefully considered the fertilizer used and the management practices of the grove. Dieback on apricot could be the result of nutritional deficiency, winter injury, defoliation by fluoride, a combination of any of these, or a host of other factors. The poor growth of an ornamental in an urban area could be due to air pollution or to poor soil or care. Most of our ornamentals and many of our crops must be considered foreign to the area in which we desire them to grow. To get such material to thrive man must modify the natural environment of the area through management practices. Before attributing poor growth to air pollution, one must examine all these factors of management. Even in areas such as Los Angeles, where there is evidence that early senescence and limited growth may be an air pollution factor, management practices must be considered.

When faced with the list of bacteria, fungi, viruses, and insects that can wreak destruction on plants, one is inclined to adopt the concept of a vengeful nature set upon destroying the plant world. Many of these agents can produce injury symptoms in plants which are quite similar to the symptoms produced by air pollutants. Leafhoppers can produce on alfalfa a blotchy pattern of white interveinal necrosis very similar to that caused by sulfur dioxide. Rose chafer can produce an injury quite similar to one wrought by sulfur dioxide, while *Botrytis* infection of gladiolus is difficult to distinguish from fluoride injury. Many of the bacterial and fungal blights of the grasses can produce the banding, tip burn, and striping similar to the effects created by smog, fluoride, or sulfur dioxide. In the summaries of air pollution symptoms given below, only a few of the possible confusing disease and insect effects are noted. To properly diagnose air pollution effects on vegetation, the problem must, therefore be seen in the field, and should preferably be supported by measurements of the concentration in the ambient air of the suspected pollutant; furthermore, the observer must have a thorough knowledge of local cultural conditions.

III. Summaries of Air Pollution Symptoms

In the following outlines an attempt has been made to summarize the significant points in the symptomatology of air pollution on vegetation in the case of the five most important pollutants: sulfur dioxide, ethylene, ozone, oxidant smog, and fluorides.

A. Sulfur Dioxide

1. *Leaf Markings*

a. Broad leaf: Irregular marginal and interveinal necrotic blotches bleached white to straw (sometimes brown). Often some chlorosis of surrounding tissues. At low concentrations limited cellular injury occurs without complete collapse of the tissue. This is often a blotchy to stippled effect, with the color ranging from white to reddish-brown. Sometimes, with long exposures at very low concentrations a general chlorosis of the older leaves develops.

b. Grasses: Irregular necrotic streaking on either side of the midvein bleached light tan to white. The tips may be affected. Chlorosis is generally not pronounced.

c. Conifers: Brown necrotic tips of the needles often with a banded appearance. Generally, there is chlorosis of adjacent tissue.

2. *Similar Markings*

a. Broad leaf: White spot of alfalfa, leafhopper injury, rose chafer injury, various virus mosaics, cherry leaf spot, and other fungal diseases, producing blotchy markings. High-temperature scorch on maple and horse chestnut.

b. Grasses: Victoria blight on oats, bacterial blight of barley and other grains. Terminal bleach in cereals.

c. Conifers: Winter and drought injury. Red spider and mite injury.

3. *Levels*

The degree of injury follows a time (t)-concentration (c) relation with a definite threshold and can be expressed as

$$t(c - a) = b$$

where a and b are constants depending on the species and the degree of injury. Thus for alfalfa the relations are:

$$t(c - 0.24) = 0.94 \text{ for incipient injury}$$
$$t(c - 1.4) = 2.1 \text{ for 50\% leaf destruction}$$
$$t(c - 2.6) = 3.2 \text{ for 100\% leaf destruction}$$

with t in hours and c in parts per million SO_2. Parameters for other species will be found in (*14*).

4. *Sensitivity of Indicators*

These are listed in general order of increasing resistance.

a. Sensitive: Alfalfa, barley, cotton, wheat, apple.

b. Resistant: Potato, onion, corn, maple.

B. Ethylene

1. *Leaf Markings*

a. Broad leaf: Epinasty and/or abscission without markings. On some plants a tissue distortion similar to 2,4-D injury has been reported with high concentration fumigations; loss of apical dominance also reported.

b. Grasses: Not well defined, some loss of upright form, possibly chlorotic bleached areas.

c. Conifers: Not well defined, abscission of needles.

d. Blossom: Dry sepal in orchid, sleepiness in carnation, blasted buds in rose.

2. *Similar Markings*

a. Broad leaf: Water stress (wilting), bacterial wilts, root upsets, nematode, aphids, 2,4-D sprays.

b. Grasses: See above.

c. Conifers: See above.

d. Blossom: Water relations.

3. *Levels*

Dry sepal reported at 5 p.p.b. or less, epinasty in tomato at approximately 0.1 p.p.m.

4. *Sensitivity of Indicators*

a. Sensitive: Tomato, orchid blossom, carnation blossom, cotton.

b. Resistant: Grasses, lettuce.

C. Ozone

1. *Leaf Markings*

a. Broad leaf: Upper surface stipple or flecking with small irregular, collapsed areas, pigmented red-brown (stipple), or bleached straw to white (fleck), depending on species. Depending on plant and/or severity, small areas coalesce to form irregular blotches frequently through the leaf.

b. Grasses: Not well established.
c. Conifers: Not well established.

2. *Similar Markings*

a. Broad leaf: Blotchy areas somewhat similar to those caused by SO_2; various insect injuries give upper surface pustule with which they could be confused. Some rusts and leaf spots give similar patterns.
b. Grasses: See above.
c. Conifers: See above.

3. *Levels*

Time concentration relations not fully established; sensitive varieties in the field respond to peak levels (1–2 hr.) above 0.15 p.p.m.

4. *Sensitivity of Indicators*

Varietal differences are very great. Order of sensitivity within general class is not established.
a. Sensitive: Tomato, tobacco, bean, spinach, potato.
b. Resistant: Mint, geranium, gladiolus, pepper, bean.

D. Oxidant Smog

1. *Leaf Markings*

a. Broad leaf: On leafy-type vegetables and some other plants a collapse of the tissue on the underside of the leaf, giving a silvered or bronzed appearance. Sometimes cells proliferate with a corklike formation. On tobacco, petunia, and similar leaves, collapse is through the thickness of leaf, usually in a banded pattern, on some, a blotchy pattern slightly resembling SO_2 injury, but usually without the typical bleach. An early maturity or senescence is also associated with smog conditions.
b. Grasses: Irregular collapsed banding bleached yellow to tan, sometimes appearing more as a chlorotic or bleached band than necrotic.
c. Conifers: Not highly specific needle blight with some chlorosis or bleaching.

2. *Similar Markings*

a. Broad leaf: "Sun scald"; various virus and fungus diseases which produce blotchy pattern. Typical silvering is seldom duplicated by other agents.
b. Grasses: Various fungal and bacterial blights produce streaked and banded markings.

c. Conifers: Red spider and mite injury, drought injury, excessive soil salts.

3. *Levels*

Since the phytotoxicants are not known, only the indirect measurement of total oxidant is available. A time-concentration relation probably holds, but is not well established. Oxidant levels above 0.2 p.p.m. will often result in plant damage.

4. *Sensitivity of Indicators*

Order of resistance is difficult to establish and varietal differences are marked.

a. Sensitive: Petunia, romaine lettuce, pinto bean, annual bluegrass.

b. Resistant: Cabbage, corn, wheat, pansy.

E. Fluorides

1. *Leaf Markings*

a. Broad leaf: Necrotic or "burned" tip and/or edge of the leaf, occasionally interveinal blotches. The edge between dead and living tissue is sharp, usually accentuated by a narrow darker brown-red band. A narrow, slightly chlorotic band is sometimes found adjacent to the necrotic area. On some species the necrotic edge is fragile and drops away, leaving a seemingly healthy leaf except for a "chewed" edge. Citrus shows a chlorosis before the levels in the leaf are sufficient to cause necrosis.

b. Grasses: Tip "burn"—brown necrotic tips with the necrosis extending down leaf in irregular streaks. Same sharp accentuated line between dead and healthy tissue as with broad leaf plants. Corn develops a chlorosis before the more typical necrotic pattern appears.

c. Conifers: Brown to red-brown necrotic tips of the needle. As with all plants, the necrosis may affect the entire leaf.

2. *Similar Markings*

a. Broad leaf: Various fungal diseases cause leaf spots which sometimes are confused with fluoride. These generally do not show the characteristic edge and tip injury. Wind, high temperatures, and drought can often cause an edge and tip necrosis similar to fluorides.

b. Grasses: Many of the fungal- and bacterial-produced "scalds," "blotches," and "streaks" of the grasses could be confused with fluorides. *Botrytis* blight and *Verticillium* on gladiolus can easily be confused.

c. Conifers: Winter and drought injury. Sulfur dioxide injury.

3. *Levels*

Fluoride must be considered an accumulative poison in the leaf tissue. Time-concentration factors have not been worked out. Generally, leaf concentrations in the range of 50 to 200 p.p.m. will result in necrosis on susceptible plants. On resistant species levels can go above 500 p.p.m. without producing injury. Air levels can be extremely low and still injure the sensitive plants. Gladiolus fumigated at 0.1 p.p.b. for 5 weeks developed necrosis over one inch of the leaf blade and had a leaf concentration of some 150 p.p.m.

4. *Sensitivity of Indicators*

These are listed in general order of increasing resistance.

a. Sensitive: Gladiolus (light colors generally more sensitive than dark colors), Chinese apricot, Italian prune, pine.

b. Resistant: Alfalfa, rose, tobacco, cotton, tomato.

IV. Evaluation of Injury

While the markings on the leaves of a plant may be identified with an air pollutant, it is often quite difficult to evaluate these markings in terms of the response of the intact plant. The question which must be answered is: Have the essential processes of the plant been so altered by the air pollutant as to significantly affect the growth, survival, yield, or use of the plant? For example, 2,4-D may markedly and adversely alter the growth habit of grape. A sufficiently severe fumigation with sulfur dioxide at the proper time could so weaken a pine tree that it would not survive the winter. If ethylene caused the young bolls of cotton to drop off, the yield would certainly be affected. A smog which bronzed the leaves of lettuce just before harvest would not greatly affect the yield but would affect its use; the housewife would not use it. Often in this question of use we are more concerned with the superficial appearance than with the physiology of the plant.

In evaluating some of the leaf injury effects, the problem is relatively straightforward. This is especially true in the cases where the appearance of the plant is paramount, or where there is a loss of the desired product or a failure of the product to develop. Many of the cases, however, require some assumption as to how the leaf injury has affected the essential processes of the plant. Always associated with this is the old question of hidden injury. As originally proposed, the term hidden injury referred to adverse effects of air pollutants on the growth, development, survival, or use of a plant, without the development of injury symptoms on the leaves. However, whether the air pollutants upset the basic plant processes directly, as postulated in hidden injury, or indirectly through injury to the leaf, is really immaterial to the question of injury evaluation.

A. Direct Leaf Injury

Romaine lettuce, like many truck crops, sells on the market on the basis of appearance. If the leaves have been marked by smog or any other agent, the crop may not be marketable. The labor of stripping the outer leaves, as well as the ultimate loss of shape, may not be justified. The yield in crates per acre may be unaffected, but the crop may still be a total loss.

Gladioli, as flowers, are sold with a price differential on grades based upon bloom size, and spike length. Even though fluorides may not have altered the grade distribution of a cut, if the foliage has been marked, the net income will be reduced. While the buyer pays for flower grade, he expects clean foliage along with the spike. The fluoride-injured foliage must be trimmed by the grower, thereby increasing his labor cost.

Where a crop, such as alfalfa, is marked by sulfur dioxide, the case is somewhat more complicated. Hill and Thomas (*29*) showed that the yield of such crops was reduced in proportion to the area of leaf destroyed, whether the reduction in effective leaf area was caused by sulfur dioxide or by clipping. This offers a method of evaluating the injury sustained by such crops. Because the effect varies somewhat with the stage of growth at the time of injury, the evaluation requires a degree of familiarity with the area. Since heavy damage may have an effect on subsequent cuttings—similar to that of cutting at too early a stage—the need for competent and experienced evaluation is increased. This type of injury can, however, be evaluated within reasonable limits.

The effect of leaf damage on a fruit tree becomes far more difficult to evaluate. Data are not available comparable to the data on alfalfa and similar crops. We do not know the effect a given percentage of leaf destruction will have on total yield or on the distribution of grades in the crop. We know that in severe cases the growth of the tree will be affected; yet it is very difficult to assess this effect in terms of value of subsequent crops. In forest trees the problem is similar. There is evidence of reduced growth rings attributed to leaf injury. To properly evaluate this effect on a crop which is to be harvested 10 to 20 years from now requires more knowledge than we now have.

The problem of leaf injury to ornamentals is equally difficult. In the nursery, if the injury is severe, the stock may not be salable. If it is less severe, pruning may make the stock salable, but at a reduced price. The economic loss in these cases is usually estimable. However, the problem of stock held over for subsequent seasons is more difficult. Often such material may be a sizable portion of the entire inventory. The plant may fully recover and be perfect the following season. In some cases, if its growth were somewhat stunted, this could be a benefit to the grower. In these cases assessment is very difficult. After the stock has been sold and planted in a yard, park, or cemetery, the concept of economic value loses its meaning. That blue spruce in the yard may be scrubby, showing red spider and winter injury, as well as sulfur dioxide injury. It could easily be replaced for 20 dollars except for the fact that it was planted on Johnnie's first birthday and is therefore irreplaceable! In such cases the injury is not so much to the leaves of the plant as to the emotions of the persons concerned.

B. Hidden Injury and Physiological Effects

The question of hidden injury—injury to the plant without visible injury to the leaves—is an old one. Much of the work done by the group at the American Smelting and Refining Company (*13, 30*) was stimulated by the hidden injury claims of Stoklasa (*31*). Hill and Thomas (*29*), and others following their lead, have quite adequately answered the question in respect to sulfur dioxide. As noted above, these workers showed that the degree of alfalfa yield reduction was proportional to the degree of leaf surface destroyed. The yield was altered to the same degree, whether the leaf area was destroyed by sulfur dioxide or by clipping. While sulfur dioxide will affect photosynthesis slightly without visible injury, the effect does not seem to be sufficient to significantly alter the growth of the plant (*6*). Hill and his co-workers (*32*), using a similar approach in carefully measuring growth under controlled conditions, have presented a strong case against hidden injury from fluorides, at least for the tomato. Yet the hidden injury question is still with us.

The question of hidden injury in the strict sense of the term may be purely academic. As noted above, the important point is whether the air pollutant has affected the growth, yield, or survival of the plant. Certainly, some of the effects on growth reported for the oxidant type smog (*27*) could be considered hidden injury in the strict sense. Some of the apparent effects of fluoride on citrus growth which have been observed in controlled fumigations (*33*) are not consistent with the degree of leaf injury.

The possible effects of fluoride have received much attention (*32*). It is known to be an enzyme poison. There would seem to be evidence developing which would indicate that fluoride could alter the respiration pathway of plant tissue at leaf concentrations that would not cause leaf markings. The significance of these developments is still subject to the questions of Hill *et al.* (*32*): Do these effects significantly affect the intact plant as used?

The growth effects, noted by Brewer, in citrus (*33*) which developed a chlorosis during fumigation, may be the result of upsets more fundamental than the visible leaf injury; however, much more work is needed to confirm this hypothesis. At the present time, we cannot tell with any degree of certainty what effect on yield, growth, or survival results from the chlorosis observed on fumigated citrus trees. The large field project at the University of California, Riverside (*34*) may in time give an answer to some of these problems, as well as those concerning the smog type of pollutant. Taylor (*27*) has reported some of the observed physiological upsets in trees, due to smog. Others (*7, 8, 11, 28*) have indicated general poor growth, as well as early senescence, due to smog. At the present time we have no basis for accurately evaluating the significance of these observations. Much basic work, such as that of Freebairn (*35*), on the effects of smog type oxidants on the mitochondria fragments from cells, will be required before we can begin to evaluate these possible physiological effects in terms of the intact plant. The reporting of peroxyacetyl nitrite (PAN) as one of the phytotoxicant components of smog causing leaf injury similar to the field-observed injury may be a step in helping evaluate the basic physiological effects. It must be remembered, however, that this may be only one of the phytotoxicants of this complex.

A report by Guderian, Van Haut, and Stratmann (*35a*) expresses the philosophy of the German approach to the general problem of effects of air pollutants on vegetation. In this the authors make a distinction which is much in keeping with the writers' views. They distinguish between "injury," implying all the physiological upsets arising from an air pollutant, and "damage," referring to those effects which affect the usefulness of the plant. Stratmann (*35b*) has amplified these views with special reference to his recent studies with sulfur dioxide.

V. Surveys

Since vegetation develops characteristic symptoms when exposed to low concentrations of certain air pollutants, it can serve as a useful tool in field surveys. While the injury symptoms developed in a specific variety by a specific pollutant may be characteristic, they are not necessarily definitive of cause. Disease, insects, cultural conditions, and so forth, singly or in combination, as noted above, may produce similar, if not identical, injury patterns as does an air pollutant. To attribute any other than these known effects of specific pollutants to a nonspecific complex of urban pollution, as is sometimes done, is understandable but unsound. Considerable caution must be exercised in attributing nonspecific complaints of poor growth and general abnormality to air pollution. Recent reviews (*8, 9, 36*) outline the limitations as well as the potentialities of the use of vegetation injury as an air pollution field survey technique.

Field surveys of vegetation have a significant place in air pollution assessment and monitoring. The approach to be taken and the interpretations of the observations depend upon the purpose of the survey. Surveys are generally designed either for assessment and definition of a problem or for monitoring known air pollution sources.

An assessment survey, at its simplest, tries to answer the question: Does this area have a significant air pollution problem? Often this is somewhat in the category of confirming the obvious, since a survey would not be initiated unless there were subjective reasons for assuming that the answer would be an affirmative. In such cases the surveys are designed to produce objective data.

Any attempt to establish a hypothetical base line which would include all of the variables of environment except air pollution, and to compare the vegetation of the area to this base line, would obviously be an impossibility. We must, then, enter an area with the hypothesis of specific pollutants rather than of general air pollution. We will usually have some prior knowledge of the possible air pollutants of an area. Knowing these and knowing from prior work what effect, if any, they have upon vegetation, we can examine the area for a relatively few characteristic symptoms.

Given only a set of visible symptoms of foliar injury, it will not be possible to deduce with a high degree of confidence the amount, or sometimes even the nature, of exposure to an injurious pollutant. A competent observer must, therefore, make a series of guesses. Any individual guess is subject to a high degree of uncertainty, which arises from the age of the tissue, the site, the weather conditions, and the entire prior history of a given plant. But through a series of these guesses concerning different materials in different stages of growth, a competent observer is often able to put a rather high degree of creditability upon the observation, "this area has been fumigated with this pollutant."

Note the use of the term, "competent observer." This is not meant to imply that only those with a long prior history of field observation of air pollution effects on vegetation are competent. The competency required is not so much in the field of air pollution effects as it is in the detailed knowledge of local vegetation. Any plant pathologist completely familiar with the vegetation of a given area would probably diagnose sulfur dioxide fumigation correctly even though he had never seen it before in the field. An equally competent plant pathologist who was unfamiliar with an area would have some hesitance in making such a diagnosis until he had done some laboratory work or spent sufficient time to bring himself up to date on the vagaries of the locality. The limitations of this approach are rather obvious. First, by observation of vegetation we are at present able to identify only five major pollutants: fluoride, sulfur dioxide, ozone, smog, and ethylene. Secondly, we are dependent upon the existence of susceptible varieties, at a susceptible stage of growth, at the time of a fumigation which is sufficiently intense to affect them. Thirdly, the presence of a competent observer is needed in the field at the appropriate time to observe the symptoms after they have developed and before they have become obscured by other changes. The interpretation that is put upon the observations collected in this way is dependent upon the frequency or the extent of the observed fumigation. But more important, it must rest finally with the observer. It must always be kept in mind that, since the vegetation is a receptor of variable response depending upon a host of prior conditions, the observation that the conditions of the vegetation of an area are in keeping with the cultural conditions of the area by no means denies the hypothesis of a significant air pollution problem.

An entirely different type of survey develops around the use of vegetation as an air pollution monitor. Once the existence of a definite air pollution effect upon the vegetation of a given area has been proved, this effect can often be used as a monitoring system for air pollution conditions in the area. Noble (*8*) has described the use of this type of system in Los Angeles, and Cole (*36*) has described the problem from the standpoint of specific source monitoring. The designs of the survey, of course, is limited to the climate and vegetation in the area. The use of specially grown plants, as used in the Los Angeles area, overcomes some of these difficulties. Again, the significance placed upon the data is dependent upon the reliability assigned it by the observer and upon the frequency of the observations.

A specialized type of vegetation monitoring is used in the case of fluorides. This problem does not concern the direct effects of fluorides upon vegetation, although this can be a problem, but rather deals with the levels of fluorides in forages and with their effect upon the foraging animals. The approach thus becomes essentially similar to that of sampling any vegetation for minor element analysis. Fluoride content will vary markedly with age, species, and even variety. If the survey program is for monitoring an area, a single species will often suffice to indicate the distribution over the area, the change with season, and the changes from year to year. If the concern is with the hazard to grazing animals, the samples must be reasonably representative of all the vegetation eaten by the animal. A similar caution applies if the vegetation is to be harvested for hay or silage. In either case, sufficient samples should be taken at each location so as to obtain some estimate of the "normal" variance. Also, because of the small quantities of fluoride present (40–50 p.p.m. can cause trouble), care must be taken to insure against contamination and loss during sampling, sample preparation, and analysis. This has been the subject of much discussion for all the trace elements in plants, as well as in air pollution (*37, 38*).

Acknowledgments

The author has been fortunate in having had the opportunity, during the last few years, of visiting most of the workers in this field in the United States and of discussing in detail these problems of the effects of air pollution on vegetation. These discussions have been extremely helpful in the preparation of this chapter, as well as in many other respects. This has, however, presented a problem in that it has been difficult to determine what information has been published and what information was gained through personal talks. It would be impossible to acknowledge all the workers who have directly or indirectly contributed to this review. The author must make special acknowledgment, however, to Dr. Moyer D. Thomas and Dr. John T. Middleton, of the University of California, Riverside; Dr. A. C. Hill, Columbia Geneva Steel, Provo, Utah; Dr. B. L. Richards, Salt Lake City, Utah; and the late Dr. P. W. Zimmerman, Boyce Thompson Institute, Yonkers, New York, for their patience and assistance.

References

1. C. A. Cameron, *Garden Chron.* **1,** 274–275 (1874).
2. E. Haselhoff and G. Lindau, "Die Beschädigung der Vegetation durch Rauch." Bornträger, Leipzig, 1903.
3. C. R. Hursh, *U. S. Dept. Agr. Circ.* **774** (1948).
4. K. J. Seigworth, *Am. Forests* **49,** 521–523, 558 (1943).
5. G. Bredeman, "Biochemie und Physiologie des Fluors." Akad. Verlagsges., Berlin, 1951.
6. M. D. Thomas, *Agron. J.* **50,** 545–550 (1958).
7. J. T. Middleton, E. F. Darley, and R. F. Brewer, *J. Air Poll. Control Assoc.* **8,** 9–15 (1958).
8. W. M. Noble and L. A. Wright, *Agron. J.* **50,** 551–553 (1958).
9. E. F. Darley, *J. Air Poll. Control Assoc.* **10,** 198 (1960).
10. J. T. Middleton and A. J. Haagen-Smit, *J. Air Poll. Control Assoc.* **11,** 125 (1961).
11. J. T. Middleton, personal communication (1960).
12. D. F. Adams, *A.M.A. Arch. Ind. Health* **14,** 229–245 (1956).
13. M. D. Thomas, *Ann. Rev. Plant Physiol.* **2,** 293–322 (1951).
14. M. D. Thomas and R. H. Hendricks, *in* "Air Pollution Handbook" (Magill,

Holden, and Ackley, eds.), Chapter 9. McGraw-Hill, New York, 1956.
15. P. W. Zimmerman, *Boyce Thompson Inst. Plant Research Professional Paper* **2,** 124–145 (1955).
15a. M. D. Thomas, *in* "Air Pollution," W. H. O. Monograph Series No. 46, pp. 233–278. World Health Organization, 1961.
15b. K. Garber, *Angew. Botan.* **34,** No. 2, 65–103 (1960).
16. M. D. Thomas and G. R. Hill, *Plant Physiol.* **10,** 291–307 (1935).
16a. R. Guderian, *Staub* **20,** No. 9, 334–337 (1960).
16b. R. Guderian, *Staub* **21,** No. 2, 60–61 (1961).
16c. R. Zahn, *Staub* **21,** No. 2, 56–60 (1961).
16d. H. Van Haut, *Staub* **21,** No. 2, 52–56 (1961).
17. E. G. Brennan, I. A. Leone, and R. H. Daines, *Plant Physiol.* **25,** 736–747 (1950).
18. B. L. Richards, J. T. Middleton, and W. B. Hewitt, *Agron. J.* **50,** 559–561 (1958).
19. H. E. Heggestad and J. T. Middleton, *Science* **129,** 208–210 (1959).
20. M. C. Ledbetter, P. W. Zimmerman, and A. E. Hitchcock, *Contribs. Boyce Thompson Inst.* **20,** 275–282 (1959).
21. J. T. Middleton, J. B. Kendrick, Jr., and H. W. Schwalm, *Plant Disease Reptr.* **34,** 245–252 (1950).
22. R. A. Bobrov, *Proc. 2nd Natl. Air Poll. Symposium, Stanford Research Inst., Los Angeles, Calif.* pp. 129–134 (1952).
23. W. M. Noble, *J. Agr. Food Chem.* **3,** 330–332 (1955).
24. J. T. Middleton, A. S. Crafts, R. F. Brewer, and O. C. Taylor, *Calif. Agr.* **10,** 9–12 (1956).
25. W. C. Hall, G. B. Truchelut, C. L. Lainweber, and F. A. Herrero, *Physiol. Plantarum* **10,** 306–317 (1957).
26. I. W. Wander and J. J. McBride, Jr., *Science* **123,** 933–934 (1956).
27. O. C. Taylor, *Agron. J.* **50,** 556–558 (1958).
28. W. M. Noble, personal communication (1959).
29. G. R. Hill and M. D. Thomas, *Plant Physiol.* **8,** 223–245 (1933).
30. M. D. Thomas, *J. Air Poll. Control Assoc.* **5,** 205–208 (1956).
31. J. Stoklasa, "Die Beschädigung der Vegetation durch Rauchgase und Fabriksexhalationen." Urban & Schwartzenberg, Berlin, 1923.
32. A. C. Hill, L. G. Transtrum, M. R. Pack, and W. S. Winters, *Agron. J.* **50,** 562–565 (1958).
33. R. F. Brewer, personal communication (1960).
34. B. L. Richards and O. C. Taylor, *J. Air Poll. Control Assoc.* **11,** 125 (1961).
35. H. T. Freebairn, *J. Appl. Nutrition* **12,** 2–13 (1959).
35a. R. Guderian, H. Van Haut, and H. Stratmann, *Z. Pflanzenkrankh. u. Pflanzenschutz* **67,** 257–264 (1960).
35b. H. Stratmann, *Staub* **21,** No. 2, 61–64 (1961).
36. G. A. Cole, *Agron. J.* **50,** 553–555 (1958).
37. R. D. Cadle, P. L. Magill, A. A. Nichol, H. C. Ehrmantraut, and G. W. Newell, *in* "Air Pollution Handbook," (Magill, Holden, and Ackley, eds.), Chapter 10. McGraw-Hill, New York, 1956.
38. J. H. Yoe and H. J. Kock, Jr., "Trace Analysis." Wiley, New York, 1957.

CHAPTER 9

Effects of Air Pollution on Animals

HERBERT E. STOKINGER

Toxicology Section, Division of Occupational Health, United States Public Health Service, Department of Health, Education, and Welfare
Cincinnati, Ohio

Experimental investigations designed specifically to determine the effects of air pollutants on animals have been undertaken only recently; on the other hand, field studies have been made sporadically for many years. These latter studies have provided sufficient evidence to show that unregulated airborne contaminants in the vicinity of industrial operations can seriously affect the well-being of livestock and wildlife. The goal of the field studies has been to find the etiologic agent of some local affection in domestic or wild animals; the aim of the laboratory studies has been to determine whether a health hazard exists for man. Lesser effort is being made to determine the specific effects of polluted atmospheres on domestic animals.

In the few years that laboratory studies have been pursued, not only has the toxic potential of certain critical air pollutants, such as sulfur dioxide, ozone, and nitrogen dioxide, been given sharper definition, but the study of toxicological interactions among various air pollutants has also demonstrated important instances of both synergism and antagonism. These findings in turn are leading to new concepts in toxicology and are opening new and promising paths for exploration whereby natural protective mechanisms against the effects of air pollution may be enhanced. Sufficient studies have already been done to indicate that particulates in engine exhausts and simulated smogs themselves are carcinogenic for rodents, both in the lung and on superficial areas of the body. These findings in simulated smog point to a new group of potential cancerigenic substances of an aliphatic, oxygen-bearing character that now must be considered along with the more familiar polycyclic hydrocarbons in smog.

Interesting and diverse as are these new findings, air pollution research is not yet sufficiently advanced to permit a summarizing of its progress as unified concepts; rather the approach of this chapter is to present toxicological information according to specific pollutant. Consideration is confined to those substances which are either of known or of potential air pollution significance. A survey of the pertinent literature to May 1960 has been made.

A few compilations of the effects of air pollutants on animals have already appeared. "Air Pollution Handbook" (*1*) contains a section that gives a toxicological review of the effects of arsenic, fluoride, and lead on farm animals, with 78 references, through 1951, many of which had not been previously assembled. An annotated bibliography (*2*), prepared by the library staff of the Kettering Laboratory, contains 790 critically abstracted reports, up to 1957, of experiments with toxic agents of possible air pollution interest. Few of the reports abstracted, however, are oriented to air concentrations of air pollution interest. An earlier annotated bibliography (*3*) was prepared by Heimann *et al.* in 1950. Reference is made in Marsh's book, "Smoke" (*4*), to the effects of air pollution on the health of birds at the London zoo and to ewes and hares fed vegetation damaged by smoke. The "Proceedings of the First U. S. Technical Conference on Air Pollution" contains a few chapters dealing with the effects of fluorides on livestock (*5*). The above sources will not be re-reviewed further here.

References to current literature sources may be found in the *Veterinary Bulletin,* a monthly publication of abstracts of research articles and books. Original articles on experimental research with air pollutants on animals appear principally in the *A.M.A. Archives of Environmental Health, Industrial Medicine and Surgery, British Journal of Industrial Medicine, Journal of Applied Physiology, Journal of the American Industrial Hygiene Association, Journal of the Air Pollution Control Association,* and numerous journals dealing with veterinary and agricultural sciences.

I. Field Investigations

A. Acute Effects on Domestic Animals and Animals in Captivity

Animals subjected to acute smog episodes tend in general to manifest signs and symptoms of exposure resembling those in man, as the following review of four episodes indicates. Because of the *ex post facto* nature of acute studies and their frequent dependence on the validity of lay impression and recollection, the reliability of certain reports (Donora, Poza Rica) is far less than that of reports of chronic exposures. Of the acute episodes, the Donora report (*6*) presents the greatest detail. Table I, adapted from the report, indicates the canary as the most susceptible species, and the dog next in susceptibility. Cattle, horses, sheep, and swine were reported not to have been significantly affected; milk production did not decline. The response of the canary appears to be consistent with the recognized susceptibility of this animal to toxic inhalants and anoxia (*7*) and with its response in the Poza Rica incident. The marked response of the dog, however, is difficult to understand; the recognized resistance of this animal to respiratory tract irritants has excluded its use in the numerous studies of sulfur dioxide (SO_2), the chief component implicated in the Donora smog (*6*). As the report indicates, dog distemper may have clouded the picture and, in the absence of animal mortality and morbidity statistics normal for the area, the dog data must be considered unreliable. Certainly it would appear so from more recent information on dog response to oxidant smog. Similarly, it is difficult to reconcile the lack of effects, particularly on cattle, when this species was notably affected by the smogs of the Meuse valley, both in the 1911 and 1930 episodes, and in the London smogs of 1873 and 1952, all instances in which SO_2 was prominently involved. It is therefore impossible to estimate the relative susceptibility of man and animals in this instance at least, and in general it must be concluded that statistical data on animal effects from acute episodes of requisite reliability, are difficult to obtain *ex post facto*.

TABLE I
ESTIMATED SMOG MORBIDITY AND MORTALITY RATES FOR DOMESTIC ANIMALS BY SPECIES[a, b]

Animal species	No. households with 1 or more species	Estimated no. animals	Animals affected		Animal deaths attributed to smog	
			No.	%	No.	%
Canary	17	20	4	20	2	10
Dog	229	245	38	15.5	10	4.1
Fowl	43	550	60	10.9	7	1.3
Cat	131	165	12	7.3	3	1.8
Pigeon	4	25	0	0	0	0

[a] Based on 1028 households.

[b] Adapted from Table 23 of Report. [H. H. Schrenk and others, Air Pollution in Donora, Pa., *U. S. Public Health Bull.* **306,** (1949).]

A brief paragraph is all that is given in the report on the effects on animals of the Meuse valley episode in 1930 (*8*). In translation, "respiratory difficulties encountered strongly recall those presented by man; some complications of the digestive tract are also seen." The effects described refer to sick or slaughtered cattle, and it was concluded that the effects were "due to the local action of an upper respiratory tract irritant," a fact consistent with the closely reasoned, but analytically unsupported, conclusion that SO_2 was the chief offending agent. It should be added that later reports of the incident (*9, 10*) adduced equally convincing evidence that hydrogen fluoride was the etiological agent. It now seems odd that no one apparently envisioned the possibility that a mixture of these substances might have been involved.

Even less attention was given to the effects of air pollution on animals in the report of the Poza Rica episode, 1952 (*11*). A cursory investigation disclosed that the animal population had been affected, in that an undetermined number of canaries, chickens, cattle, pigs, geese, ducks, and dogs either died or were made ill by the exposure. Although it was estimated that 50% of the exposed species (other than canaries) died from the air pollution, all of the canaries in the area died. This latter finding would be most informative if one were certain of the responsible air pollutant. Although hydrogen sulfide (H_2S) was unquestionably involved, the extent of involvement of associated organic thiols, (some of whose acute toxicity is remarkably high) is far from clear. Lest one conclude that canaries might serve as an indicator species for thiols for man, it should be noted that, after considerable experience, the U. S. Bureau of Mines many years ago rejected this animal for this purpose (*12*).

Somewhat more informative was a report of the London fog of December, 1952, in which a number of prize cattle were reported to have been severely affected (*13*). In 351 animals grouped for exhibition at the Smithfield Cattle Show on the ground floor, acute respiratory distress developed, from which 5 died; 9 were eventually slaughtered and 52 others developed signs of severe affection attributable to the smog. The characteristic signs were marked respiratory distress, profuse salivation, and elevated temperature. By contrast, the sheep and swine, which were on the first floor, showed no effects. Oddly, the dense London fog of 1873 occurred also at the time of the Smithfield Fair, and the cattle, especially the Shorthorns, showed similar effects; but the sheep and swine showed none, although they were exhibited on the same floor as the cattle. The dairy cattle in neighboring London at this time showed 48 affected of 360 exposed. Post-mortem examinations of the cattle affected in 1952 revealed acute bronchitis, emphysema, and right-heart failure. Inasmuch as sulfur dioxide again was considered the chief offending agent, the finding of bronchiolitis would appear to indicate that SO_2 was carried to the deeper portions of the respiratory tract, probably adsorbed to some aerosol. Another contribution of these reports seems to consist in indicating that increased stress associated with the rapid deposit of the considerable amount of fat to be found on "show" animals so alters the cardiorespiratory functions of cattle that increased susceptibility to air pollutants of the upper-respiratory irritant type occurs.

In connection with the affection of the prize cattle in the fog of 1952, it should be noted that there was no increased morbidity among horses at the Life Guards' Barracks or among those used by the British Railways in London. Nor did the Royal Veterinary College, London, find evidence of increased illness attributable to the smog in the small, large, or old animals treated there. At the Zoologic Gardens in London, however, there was an increased incidence of bronchitis and pneumonia in primates. Diseases of the chest were also more common among the unacclimated animals, the very young, the old, or those with a history of pulmonary disease, irrespective of species. In recalling similar remarks on London zoo animals made above (*4*), referable to an earlier date (1936), the impression is given that animals in captivity have a marginal physiological reserve and are thus more susceptible to the action of air pollutants. It is obvious also that in certain aspects such as age and respiratory characteristics, the effects in animals resemble closely those in man. Unfortunately, as with most acute smog episodes, the etiological agents in these cases remain conjectural.

B. Chronic Effects on Livestock and Wild Animals

Here will be summarized a few instructive animal epidemiologic studies that deal with chronic poisoning of livestock and wild animals which have not received the attention they merit. They are confined to relatively few substances: arsenic, lead, molybdenum, and fluoride. It should be noted that, in general, the effects of air pollutants are much more accentuated in foraging animals than in man because of (1) the accumulation of the pollutant on or in the forage and (2) the quantity of forage consumed by the animal.

1. *Airborne Arsenic Poisoning*

One of the earliest reports on this subject, by Harkins and Swain (*14*), deals with widespread poisoning of cattle, horses, and sheep, which first became noticeable in 1902 at Anaconda, Montana. The epizoobiologic evidence was the following: 625 sheep, of a flock of 3500, died after feeding on vegetation 15 mi. from a copper smelter after having been brought into the area from 28 mi. distant. Analysis of the grass and moss on which the animals fed showed 52 and 405 p.p.m. As_2O_3 respectively. Furthermore, horses kept in an area remote from the smelter but which fed on hay grown in a location on which smelter fumes had fallen, died. Arsenic analysis of the hay showed 285 p.p.m. As_2O_3. The liver of the animals showed 1.3 mg. As_2O_3/100 gm. of tissue. Finally, arsenic was found in large quantities (10–150 p.p.m.) on all types of vegetation near the smelter; copper analysis of the same vegetation showed equally high values (128–1800 p.p.m.). Analysis of 82 specimens comprising 8 tissues from calves, cows, sheep, and horses feeding in the area showed values for arsenic ranging from traces (liver) to several hundred parts per million (hair). By the method of analysis used, control tissues failed to show the presence of arsenic. Although there was a real question of the involvement of copper in the poisoning cases, the signs and symptoms of poisoning which were most carefully evaluated agreed in all details with those of acute and chronic arsenic poisoning, and the diagnosis was confirmed as well by both gross and microscopic pathology. Experimental verification was also made by feeding animals graded doses of arsenic and then analyzing the tissues. A complete organ analysis of a horse chronically administered As is given. From 0.2 to 5.7 p.p.m. As_2O_3 was found in 9 samples of milk from cows that had been feeding in that area. The arsenic content of ulcers of the nose of horses from the smelter regions showed values as high as 1015 p.p.m. The tail hair of a horse feeding in the Anaconda region showed 58 p.p.m. As_2O_3; that of a colt, 605 p.p.m. The content of the liver and bone was from $\frac{1}{10}$ to $\frac{1}{100}$ that of the hair.

A similar epidemiological study of poisoning of animals by air pollution was made by Prell (*15*) as a result of having found peculiar injuries to the hair in game animals in Saxony. Neither parasites, sarcoptids, nor fungi could be found as pathogenic agents. Histological examination of the skin of completely bare red deer showed thickening of the stratum corneum. The key to the solution of the problem was a strange mortality among bees some years preceding, in an area in which no infection could be discovered as the cause, which was traced ultimately to factory fumes. Analysis of pollen showed as much as 88 μg. As/gm. and 1 μg. As/bee. Interestingly, the minimal lethal dose (MLD) of As for bees is 0.1–0.2 μg. or, assuming a bee weighs 100 mg., 2 mg./kg., a dose identical to the MLD for man. With this clue, arsenic determinations were made of the stomach, intestinal contents, liver, kidney, and hair of 41 red deer, 102 roe deer, 27 horses, and a number of foxes. Arsenic values varying from traces to 42 mg./kg. were found. The signs and symptoms paralleled those of arsenic poisoning in all its many details, such as scleroderma, malformation of the horns, thickened joints, emaciation, etc. The author suggested that bees might serve as "merktier" ("warning animal") for man in reference to arsenic poisoning.

2. *Airborne Fluorides*

Both the acute and chronic effects of fluorides on animals have been amply and repeatedly documented (*1, 2, 3, 5, 10, 16*). Moreover, the fluoride contamination problem is far from new; fluorosis was noted in bones in Iceland, from volcanic eruptions thousands of years ago (*5*).* The subject has been perennially investigated, osseous structures analyzed, and the entire problem treated without the originality requisite for advances in our knowledge of the more important basic mechanisms involved in the abnormal calcification of bone and tooth or in the decreased milk production caused by fluoride overexposure in farm animals. Greenwood and associates recently have written extensively on the subject of their researches on the effects of fluoride in cattle, and have described chronic bovine fluorosis (*17*), as well as the effect of various levels of

* Discussion of Dr. Huffman, p. 63 in (*5*).

sodium fluoride on growing turkeys (*18*), and have recommended practices whereby fluorosis in livestock and poultry may be reduced (*19*). The levels of different fluoride sources nonproductive of fluorosis in animals is given in Table II. In addition, the subject of fluoride poisoning in animals has been repeatedly detailed in the toxicological and dental research literature, and would thus appear to require no further review here. For example, the acute and subchronic effects of exposure of laboratory animals to hydrogen fluoride and to elemental fluorine gas has been described by Stokinger in (*20*), in which references to prior toxicological work with gaseous fluorine compounds may be found. Smith (*21*) assembled in 1951 an annotated bibliography of the 1393 pharmacological and toxicological references to fluorine and its compounds; regrettably, it is not indexed. Kettering Laboratory, Cincinnati, has published references which cover the world literature on the subject through 1957 (*22*). Thus far, organic fluorine compounds do not represent an air pollution problem.

TABLE II

SAFE LEVELS OF FLUORINE IN TOTAL RATION OF LIVESTOCK [a]

	Fluorine Source	
Species	NaF or other soluble F (p.p.m.)	Phosphatic limestone or rock phosphate (p.p.m.)
Dairy cow	30–50	60–100
Beef cow	40–50	65–100
Sheep	70–100	100–200
Swine	70–100	100–200
Chicken	150–300	300–400
Turkey	300–400	—

[a] Taken from H. Phillips, D. A. Greenwood, C. S. Hobbs, and C. F. Huffman, The fluorosis problem in livestock production, *Natl. Acad. Sci.—Natl. Research Council, Publ. No.* **381** (1955).

3. *Poisoning by Airborne Lead*

In 1955 Hupka (*23*) reported from Germany an illness affecting cattle and horses at pasture within a radius of 5 km. of each of two lead and zinc foundries, which shows that metal poisoning of cattle is still occurring today throughout the world, despite earlier recognition of the problem. The affection was characterized by poor bodily condition, emaciation, and pronounced swelling of the limb joints, causing severe lameness and necessitating slaughter. Post-mortem examination revealed an increased volume of synovial fluid in the affected joints and detachment of the articular cartilage from the bone. Paralysis of the recurrent nerve was unusually prevalent in the affected areas. The author suggested that the peculiar clinical picture of the poisoning was due probably not to lead alone but to its combination with another toxic agent, presumably zinc.

The condition was reproduced by feeding 2 foals samples of dust collected in the vicinity of the foundries. One sample contained 45% lead and 5% zinc; the other, 17% lead and 23% zinc. Only traces of arsenic and fluoride were present. The liver of cattle and horses grazing on polluted pastures contained abnormally high amounts of lead (up to 25 mg. %)* or zinc (up to 3000 mg. %) or both. Phillips in (*1*) has described the acute, chronic, and cumulative action of lead as an air pollutant in farm animals, and the effect of dietary calcium on lead storage. The difference in Phillips' description of lead poisoning from that discussed above is consistent with the interpretation that some agent in addition to lead caused the response.

Despite the huge quantities of leaded gasoline consumed today (250 million pounds in the United States), the attrition of lead paint on buildings, and contributions from soil and other sources, the lead pollution of the atmosphere from these sources is of the order of a few micrograms per cubic meter of air even in urban areas and is not calculated to add appreciably as yet to the the toxic body burden of this element, the lead intake from food being far greater. Sayers *et al.* (*24*), in an exhaustive study of ethyl gasoline and its combustion products, showed in 1927 that laboratory animals, including the dog and monkey, upon repeated daily 3-hour exposures, 6 days weekly, for 8 months, to the combustion products failed to show either appreciable storage of lead or characteristic pathological lesions when usual amounts of ethyl fluid were used. Experiments using fivefold the commercial concentration of lead tetraethyl in the fuel resulted in lead accumulation in some but not all species, but no signs of lead poisoning. Exposure concentrations of lead were 14 $\mu g./m.^3$ and 140 $\mu g./m.^3$.

There are few toxic agents that have been given such unremitting study, yet the mechanisms by which lead exerts its toxic action, is transported and sequestered in the body, and is liberated from its storage sites are still unknown. Borsook (*24a*) has reported the first intimation that lead's toxic action may be effected by inhibiting the incorporation of amino acids into the red cell. Kehoe and associates, Kettering Laboratories, have written extensively on numerous aspects of

* Milligrams of metal per 100 grams of wet tissue.

lead exposure, as have Fairhall and Aub. Kantarow and Trumper have published a book on the subject of lead poisoning (*25*).

4. *Poisoning by Airborne Molybdenum*

Hallgren *et al.* (*26*) in 1954 described molybdenum (Mo) poisoning in cattle in western Sweden that had grazed in a pasture contaminated with smoke from a steel plant about 0.1 km. away. The smoke contained molybdenum, and analysis of the vegetation in the pasture revealed up to 230 mg. Mo/kg. of dry matter, compared with the normal of approximately 1.5 mg./kg. Although only one cow died, many others were affected but recovered on Mo removal from the contaminated pasture. The cow, on autopsy, showed fatty degeneration of the liver and hyperemia of the jejunal mucosa; the Mo content of the blood serum was 0.7 mg./l. Like the horses in the 1952 London smog, 2 horses grazing on the same pasture were not affected, although the Mo content of their blood serum was greater than 1 mg./l. The authors stated that the Mo content of the blood of the affected cattle was 25 times that of normal cattle from an uncontaminated pasture.

It now appears established from the work of Dick (*27*) and others that Mo and copper (Cu) act as metal antagonists in the body, high dietary Mo levels (5 p.p.m.) leading to Cu deficiency and low Mo intake (0.1 p.p.m. on forage) to rapid accumulation of Cu in the liver, which could result in chronic Cu poisoning and ultimate death (sheep). In chicks and poults it has been shown by Kratzer (*28*) that added Cu in the diet can prevent Mo poisoning. More recently, inorganic sulfate has been shown to increase the toxicity of Mo in monogastric animals on a low Cu diet (*29*), but in those on a high Cu diet, orally administered sulfate, thiosulfate, cystine, and methionine exerted a protective effect against Mo (*30*). During investigation of the possible enzyme systems involved in sulfur metabolism in rat liver and kidney, Mills *et al.* (*31*) showed that liver sulfide oxidase activity was markedly depressed in Mo toxicity, but liver cysteine desulfhydrase, kidney aryl sulfatase, and the oxidation of cysteine sulfinate were unaffected. No evidence was obtained that Cu-dependent enzymes were involved in Mo toxicosis. Current interest in Mo metabolism stems from its discovery in the flavoprotein enzymes, xanthine and aldehyde oxidases.

II. Laboratory Investigations

Currently in the United States, laboratory studies on the biological effects of chemical air pollutants are for the most part oriented, rightly or wrongly, toward the products of incomplete combustion of liquid and gaseous fuels, including the substantial influence of completely unburned fuels and related hydrocarbons that leak or evaporate into the air. This is based on the finding that the irradiation of such materials accounts for all the manifestations, thus far observed, of the oxidant-type smog—the eye irritation, plant damage, reduced visibility—and for the fact that oxidant smog, typical of Los Angeles, is also becoming typical of other urban areas throughout the United States. In Great Britain, where coal burning predominates, biological studies have been directed almost entirely toward an elucidation of the effects of SO_2, both alone and in admixture with coal smoke components. Some research on SO_2 in the United States is also being performed.

Both types of smog have within them components which are consistent with the epidemiological and laboratory findings of increased incidence of lung cancer among the human population. In this connection, one of the most outstanding demonstrations of recent air pollution research is the finding of Tebbens and collaborators (*32*) that all carbonaceous matter, of whatever source—coal, oil, wood, or gas—will, if incompletely burned, give rise to polycyclic aromatic hydrocarbons (arenes) and certain of their oxidation products, many of whose structures have been linked with carcinogenic effects. Moreover, as a result of the work of Kotin, Falk, and others, it is becoming clear that cancerigenic sources need not be confined to complex polycyclic hydrocarbon structures but may also encompass broad groups of substances of carcinogenic or cocarcinogenic potential of aliphatic oxygen-bearing character.

Laboratory studies on the effects of air pollution on animals, for the present purposes, may be divided most conveniently into studies of (1) complex and unknown mixtures, (2) single, known agents, and (3) simple mixtures.

III. Complex and Unknown Mixtures

A. Engine Exhausts

From 1954 to 1959 Kotin and his colleagues published 10 studies on the relation of engine exhausts and ozonized gasoline to carcinogenicity, and to exposed animal survival and reproduction. Their early work shows that the particulate phase of gasoline engine exhausts contains aromatic hydrocarbons whose benzene extracts produced 44% skin papillomas, and, among these, 58% skin cancers, in C57 black mice (*33*); no skin tumors were seen in control mice. Extracts of diesel engine exhausts showed far fewer tumors (2 of 33) in C57 mice and a somewhat higher incidence in other strains of mice (*34*). No skin tumors were seen in any of the control mice. Leiter, Shimkin and Shear had previously produced subcutaneous tumors in mice with tars extracted from atmospheric dusts (*34a*).

Pattle *et al.* (*35*) studied the acute toxicity of diesel engine fumes at high concentration under four different operating conditions. Guinea pigs were more susceptible than mice and rabbits. Significantly different responses occurred at different operating conditions; light loads produced no deaths, but moderate loads produced deaths of some animals and light loads with restricted air intake resulted in death of all animals in a 5-hour exposure, presumably from carbon monoxide. Evidence of irritation to respiratory tract from aldehydes and nitrogen oxides was noted. At the high exposure concentrations tested no other results would be expected. The work of Sayers *et al.*, many years ago, on the effects of combustion products of leaded and nonleaded gasolines, showed marked irritation to occur in animals only at excessive exposures (*24*). Mittler (*36*) reported inability to demonstrate skin tumors in mice exposed to diesel exhausts, although 76% of the animals developed tumors from gasoline engine exhausts, 1 of 36 mice, from coal soot, and none from oil soot. Possible reasons for the discrepancy may lie in the smaller number of animals used by Mittler, coupled with the low tumor incidence of diesel exhaust and the wide variation in carcinogen output among different operating conditions of the engine.

Hueper *et al.* (*36a*) have shown that subcutaneously injected solvent fractions of air particulates of 8 cities yielded cancerous growths in mice; cancer yield varied with the fraction and the city from which the particulates were obtained.

B. Bactericidal Action

The bactericidal action of oxidant smog has been demonstrated by Goetz and Tsuneishi (*37*) in preliminary experiments, using a collecting device known as a Concentrometer. The test was developed as a bacteriological analogue for the measure of eye irritation from smog aerosols. Bacteria of uniform density are exposed to a concentration of smog varying along one direction to a constant flow of aerosol. The bacteriostatic effect is defined by the reduction of growth along this direction. Although a sufficient number of tests had not been made, at the time of this report, to establish a quantitative relation between results obtained from the concentrometer technique and from eye irritation, there are indications that the procedure will prove a simple, sensitive, and inexpensive method of establishing the presence of irritant substances in spot smog samples. Smog concentrations as low as 0.125 p.p.m. of hydrocarbons from exhaust of certain gasoline fuels has proved bacteriostatic for common bacteria used for such tests.

C. Simulated Oxidant Smogs: Ozonized Gasoline Products

Using ozonized gasoline of a relatively high oxidant content (several p.p.m.), Kotin and associates have demonstrated the production of (1) skin tumors in C57 black mice (*38*), (2) induction of pulmonary tumors in strain A mice (*39*), and (3) pulmonary tumors and changes in respiratory epithelium in C57 black mice (*40*). Two of 52 black mice developed skin papillomas; 4 of 50 A mice, cancers, indicating a very low cancerigenic potential of ozonized gasoline products. Of greater significance was the production in C57 black mice of pulmonary tumors and hyperplastic and metaplastic response of the respiratory epithelium. Of interest is the apparent inhibitory effect of the ozonized gasoline smog on spontaneous extrapulmonary tumors in the test animals, compared with controls. In all this work it should be noted that relatively high smog levels were evidenced by reduced growth rate. Still highly important, nevertheless, is the demonstration that oxidant substances of aliphatic nature, unrelated to polycyclic hydrocarbons, can induce neoplastic growth; these substances include epoxides, peracids, aldehydes, peroxides, ozonides, ketenes, and other substances which are either free radicals or have free radical potential. Of particular interest also is the report by Kotin and Thomas (*41*) which shows a remarkable, depressing effect on reproduction and offspring survival of mice exposed to ozonized smog. Table III

TABLE III
Total Births and Survival until Weaning

	Smog air	Los Angeles air	Washed air
Number of litters	17	38	45
Total mice born	106	254	325
Total mice surviving until weaning	4	161	215
Total surviving (%)	3.8	63	66

gives the reduction in the number of litters in total mice born and those surviving to weanling age in ozonized gasoline atmosphere, in comparison with those in Los Angeles air and in washed air. This is a most interesting experimental corroboration of the observation, made many years earlier, of reduced propagation of ewes exposed to urban "smoke" (*4*).

D. Ultraviolet Irradiated Gasoline-Nitrogen Oxide Mixtures

A basic biochemical approach to the evaluation of effects of simulated oxidant smog on animal and human cellular material has been made by

Gast and Estes (*42*) using *in vitro* techniques. Gast's smog recipe was a gasoline of exceptionally high (65%) olefinic content with 15% aromatics at a level of about 200 p.p.m., mixed with about 1.6 p.p.m. of nitrogen dioxide, and irradiated with an ultraviolet source, to yield between 1.5 and 3 p.p.m. oxidant as measured by the phenolphthalein method for ozone. By exposing white blood cells of guinea pigs in a suitable medium to a continuous flow of this smog, a 50% reduction in oxygen uptake was recorded at 90 min., compared with air-exposed control cells. A very slight reduction (9%) was also noted when the smog was bubbled through the buffer and the white cells were subsequently added, which indicates the transient nature of the biologically active smog ingredients and the marked susceptibility of the short-lived white blood cell. The smog was far less effective in reducing O_2 uptake of *Escherichia coli* cells (15% in 1 hr.) during the log growth phase, but the rate of multiplication was reduced 30% after a 2-hr. exposure. Both the tone and amplitude of contraction, as well as changes in rhythmicity, of isolated guinea pig ileum segment resulted from 1- or 2-min. exposures to the smog, indicating the irritant nature of the smog for smooth muscle. Similar, though less, irritation was produced by nonirradiated smog. The smog was without measurable effect on the following systems: P^{32}-labeled phosphate uptake by human red cells; production of methemoglobin in human red cells; modification of the glutathione SH, or total SH content, of the red cell.

The significance of these *in vitro* changes in cellular respiration should be clearly recognized. Such studies as those just cited, and to be cited later, represent the classic approach of biochemistry to an understanding of the basic mechanisms involved when cells are exposed to noxious agents. Such studies are capable of identifying the "biochemical lesion" while it is still reversible, and of indicating the precise site and mechanism involved in the metabolic derangement. The *in vitro* technique has serious experimental and theoretical limitations, however. Experimentally, the requirement of an aqueous medium makes extremely difficult the precise evaluation of actual exposure concentration, because the distribution coefficient between the gas or gas-adsorbed aerosol and the liquid phase varies with each substance. Theoretically, it is impossible to gage the degree of impact of the biochemical lesion on the organism as a whole, with its complex of defenses both circulatory and nervous, and the various shunt mechanisms that come into play upon development of the lesion. At the same time, this limitation is precisely the strength of the *in vitro* technique, for it isolates the system unencumbered by a complex of bodily defenses, permitting direct identification of the metabolic alteration involved.

If any significance may be attached to these preliminary studies of Gast and Estes, the reduction in O_2 uptake caused by their smog would indicate a possible cancerigenic potential, according to a recent theory of the origin of cancer cells of Warburg (*43*). After decades of study, involving the same *in vitro* measurements of cellular respiration, it now appears, according to the theory, that as the respiration of the cell changes from one of aerobic oxidation to anaerobic glycolysis (lactic acid production), the change to a malignant cell type occurs. Evidence of the change is reduced oxygen uptake. In any interpretation of the current work of Gast it must be noted that the ambient smog concentrations appear to be unrealistically high, although it is still conjectural what the actual exposure concentrations to the cell were. Whatever the actual situation, Kotin's closely related ozonized gasoline-smog has a demonstrated carcinogenic potential for mice.

IV. Inorganic Gases

The number of inorganic compounds and types of organic compounds, whose effects have been studied in animals expressly because of their air pollution interest, is small, i.e., less than a dozen. Moreover, few compounds have been identified and characterized from smog atmospheres on which there was not already a considerable body of prior toxicological information. Therefore air pollution-related research, particularly on the inorganic substances, has been confined to eliciting new details of unusual aspects of the biological action of a few of the characteristic smog constituents, such as SO_2, NO_2, and O_3, and of their behavior in concentrations lower than those of prior 8-hour per day, 5-day per week occupational exposure. A few new compound types, however, among the organic substances have been investigated as candidate air pollutants, chief among which are the organic peroxides and hydroperoxides, aliphatic and aromatic thiols, nitro olefins, and ketenes. Research on these substances is still in its preliminary stages, most of the work dealing with acute or subchronic aspects of their toxicity. Under consideration for study are such substances as the peracyl nitrates, peroxyaldehydes, nitrosyl chloride, and carbon suboxide. Such substances have been demonstrated either to be components of oxidant smog or postulated from kinetic studies as reasonable components.

A. Ozone

No other chemical air pollutant has received such varied and detailed toxicological investigation as has ozone. Ozone's importance stems from two sources: (1) Haagen-Smit in 1951 (*43a*) showed ozone to be a key component of oxidant smog derived from atmospheric hydrocarbons and sunlight, and (2) ozone is a gas of outstanding irritancy, a characteristic of oxidant smog. Review of ozone toxicology in 1953 by Stokinger (*44*) called attention to two points: (1) ozone's high toxicity, and (2) the lack of precise information on its physiological response in man and animals, despite the recognition of its effects for more than 100 years. Twenty-five references to earlier work on the biological effects of ozone were included.

1. *Acute Toxicity*

Determination of acute toxicity of ozone, reported by Mittler *et al.* (*45*) and Stokinger (*46*), showed, contrary to common opinion at the time, that ozone was highly injurious and even lethal to laboratory animals in a single exposure of a few hours' duration. The minimal lethal 4-hr. concentration (LC_{50})* of O_3 for mice and rats approximates 6 p.p.m. Using the factor of ¼, determined earlier by Jordan and Carlson as the amount of ozone reaching the lungs from the exposure atmosphere, 4 μg. O_3 constitutes a lethal dose for the mouse, and 50 μg. for the rat—two species of about equal susceptibility. Diggle and Gage (*47*) also found similar susceptibilities for these two species. Cats, rabbits, and guinea pigs were increasingly less susceptible in that order, and dogs were relatively resistant. Animals died of acute pulmonary edema and hemorrhage. Day-old chicks, hatching in an incubator containing 1–4 p.p.m. O_3 died after 5 days of continuous exposure, Quilligan *et al.* (*48*), indicating this species to be the most susceptible yet tested. These findings classify ozone among the most highly toxic gases. All investigators generated ozone by electric discharge in purified air or O_2 and all LC_{50} values were in remarkable agreement, if account is taken of differences in exposure time and methods of analysis. (The factor for converting ozone concentrations determined by the alkaline KI method to that by the neutral KI method is 1.54).

The bactericidal action of ozone for *E. coli* suspensions has been characterized by Fetner and Ingols (*49*) as an all-or-none response; at 1°C., 0.4–0.5 mg./l. O_3 was the critical lethal concentration. This differs markedly from the action of chlorine, which kills in a geometrically progressive fashion. The report is of considerable interest in relation to the previously mentioned work of Gast (*42*) and of Goetz and Tsuneishi (*37*).

2. *Factors Affecting Acute Ozone Toxicity*

Because levels of oxidant in the Los Angeles smog, of which O_3 is a significant part, had reportedly reached, on occasion, values in excess of

* LC_{50}, a concentration of a toxicant that is lethal for 50% of an exposed group.

1 p.p.m., and because pulmonary injury from ozone had been reported for the first time among welders (*50*), considerable study has been given to factors that may affect the acute toxicity of O_3. Stokinger (*46*) drew attention to 6 factors that may accentuate, reduce, or abolish the acute toxic response to ozone.

a. Age. Young animals (mice) were found more susceptible to the acute toxic effects of O_3 than old animals. This natural resistance appears to progress throughout life and amounts to a factor as great as two- or threefold in very old animals, as compared with weanlings.

b. Intermittent Exposures. The mortality in young adult animals from an acute exposure to ozone was appreciably reduced when a 30-min. exposure was interrupted with a 20-min. exposure to air, as compared with animals exposed continuously to the same total time.

c. Disease. Ozone appears capable of "bringing out," or activating, latent respiratory infection in animals, which may terminate fatally for reasons not associated with the direct action of ozone. Such responses are observed commonly in subchronic or chronic exposures to ozone but occasionally are observed in survivors of acute exposures (*46*).

d. Intermittent Exercise. The acute toxicity of ozone has been demonstrated to be strikingly enhanced if animals during exposure to noninjurious levels of ozone are concurrently subjected to intermittent exercise (*51*).

e. Temperature. Experiments with rats and mice indicate that the susceptibility to the toxic effects of ozone may be doubled by a rise of 15°F. (from 75°F. to 90°F.). The lethal dose in summer (90°F.) for rats was 2.6 p.p.m. O_3 by volume for a 4-hour exposure, while it was 6–8 p.p.m. for a 6-hour exposure in the winter (75°F.).

f. Effect of Reducing Agents and Drugs. Prophylactic administration of reducing agents, such as ascorbic acid alone and in combination with cysteine, and glycuronate, substantially reduced the toxic effects of ozone. Pantothenate in suitable combination with these agents resulted in the most effective prophylactic combination. Thus it would appear that certain dietary constituents in optimal proportions exert a beneficial effect on the acute pulmonary response from inhaled ozone. The inhibition of activity of mitochondrial preparations from liver by ozone was abolished by ascorbic acid or by reduced glutathione in part or completely, according to Freebairn (*52*). Partial to very slight protection was found by Mittler (*53*) to be afforded mice exposed to lethal amounts of O_3, by ascorbic acid and atropine, hexamethonium chloride, sodium nitrite, and sodium thiosulfate; no effect was observed with glutathione; *p*-aminopropiophenone worsened the effect. Ascorbic acid was likewise shown by Matzen (*54*) to reduce the mortality of mice exposed to ozone. Pulmonary edema did not develop to the same extent as that found in untreated ozone-exposed mice, as shown by the lowered water content of the lungs. Hydrocortisone even in large doses, however, offered no protection against ozone, although it has been found to benefit the response to oxygen at high pressures. Serotonin, however, in large doses (1 mg.) in the mouse, has been found by the same worker to reduce pulmonary edema and mortality from lethal exposures to O_3 (*55*). Mittler (*56*), on the other hand, was unable to find any benefit from therapeutic administration of antifoaming agents, silicone aerosols, and alcohol vapor in similar exposures.

3. *Tolerance Development*

A most unusual tolerance to ozone was developed in laboratory animals from prior exposure to subinjurious concentrations. The tolerance was marked by its rapid development, demonstrable in 24 hr.; its persistence for from 4 to 6 weeks in rats and as long as 100 days in mice; as shown by survival from challenging exposures of lethal magnitude; and by the absence of the characteristic pulmonary edema and hemorrhage that regularly follows such exposures. Matzen (*57*) confirmed the findings of tolerance by Stokinger *et al.*, and refined the measurement of the reduction in pulmonary edema by precise determination of the water content of the lung. Henschler (*57a*) subsequently made similar findings and in addition showed cross-tolerance among ozone, phosgene, and nitrogen oxides.

4. *Subchronic Toxicity*

The toxicity of ozone for rats has been reported by Mittler (*58*) for interrupted and continuous subchronic exposures, at levels found by him to be nondamaging to the lung in single, acute exposures. On a 4-day/week schedule, damage to the pulmonary tissue was not observed until after 64 hr. of cumulative exposure. There was less damage after 144 hr. of exposure than at earlier intervals, indicating tolerance to ozone. Continuous exposures of rats for 241 hr. at this level showed (1) reduced weight gains, (2) decrease in food utilization efficiency, (3) 20% mortality, and (4) gross hemorrhage and edema of the lung. Unfortunately, no histological examination was made of the lungs. It would appear, however, from these findings that both intermittent and continuous exposures to ozone concentrations that are noninjurious in single, short exposures, result in cumulative effects, referable to the lung, that may end fatally. This is consistent with the data of Stokinger *et al.* (*59*) on long-continued exposures at lower concentrations.

5. *Characterization of Ozone Injury*

In a comprehensive attack on the problem, Scheel, Mountain, *et al.* (*60*) have characterized the response of the animal lung by examining the effect of O_3 on the immunochemical response and on certain enzyme systems, and by correlating these with changes in respiratory function and pathology. A finding of outstanding importance was the apparent demonstration of increasing titers of antibody following O_3 exposure in rabbits whose sera was reacted with ozonized egg albumin used as antigen. With this analogue of lung protein, O_3 was shown to denature egg albumin by several criteria. Immunological cross reaction with heat-denatured egg albumin and sera from ozone-exposed rabbits was shown, further indicating the nature of the reaction of O_3 and protein. Such findings call attention to an area of immunochemistry that has been almost completely overlooked, namely, the immune response of the lung to inhaled substances, in particular to respiratory irritants having the capacity to react with lung protein. Eventually this finding may have practical application in the demonstration of exposure to specific air pollutants.

Parallel with these studies exploration was made of *in vivo* effects of O_3 on lung enzymes as another early sensitive indicator of low-grade exposure to respiratory irritants. It was found that, whereas alkaline phosphatase activity of rat lung decreased after exposure to O_3, the total alkaline phosphatase activity of the serum increased immediately after exposure to ozone, the greater part of the increase being observable in the magnesium-activated fraction. The decrease in activity of lung enzyme paralleling its increase in the serum was interpreted as a release of enzyme from tissue cells into interstitial fluid and into the circulation. Furthermore, a direct relation between changes in enzyme activity and O_3 tolerance was shown; lung alkaline phosphatase was only lowered to 63% of control values in the tolerant group as compared with a lowering in the phosphatase activity to 40% of control levels in the nontolerant group. This correlation at the enzymatic level with gross observation of tolerance and associated mortality is most informative, because it points to a basic mechanism possibly involved in the pulmonary tolerance phenomenon. In this connection it is interesting that 5-nucleotidase activity showed no appreciable differences in the two groups, indicating no association of this enzyme with tolerance phenomena.

Repeated acute injury from the respiratory oxidant, O_3, was observable also in both altered respiratory function and morphology. From measurements of oxygen consumption and tidal volume in relation to histological change made before and after each acute exposure, an irregular respiratory pattern developed as the first observable sign; later inhibition of respiration was found to be the factor that limited tidal volume, apparently as a result of an altered Hering-Breuer reflex due to increased irritation of lung tissue. Repeated exposures showed progressive dimunition of minute ventilation and oxygen consumption; values in rabbits after the 10th 1-hr. weekly exposure showed a minute ventilation reduced to 20% of its control, and oxygen consumption reduction to 23%. Respiration rate was 130% of that of the control. Associated with these physiological changes were progressive fibrotic changes in the lung that were indistinguishable histologically at the 49th 1-hr. weekly exposure from those observed in animals receiving O_3 6 hr. daily for one year at a lower level.

At the year's end of the repeated acute injuries, evidence of premature aging was observed, consisting of premature calcification of sternocostal cartilage, unthrifty appearance and coarseness of the pelage, and severe depletion of body fat. The aging effect was interpreted as a result of generalized stress response initiated by the repeated acute O_3 injury. Such effects grossly resemble chronic effects of low-grade radiation injury. Attention has been called to the possible radiomimetic* effects of ozone in a report by Brinkman and Lamberts (*61*), in which they adduce among other evidence that O_3 and ultraviolet irradiation alike cause a defect in oxygen desaturation of oxyhemoglobin. Moreover, the finding of a similar mechanism of protection by sulfur compounds from either O_3 or irradiation brings further evidence to bear on ozone's radiomimetic potentialities. On the other hand, ozone does not act in all respects like ionizing radiation; substances reported to be effective against acute radiation injury such as β-mercaptoethylamine, glutathione, and others have been shown to be either without effect in acute ozone poisoning or to worsen the reaction (*46, 53*).

6. *Chronic Fibrosis of the Lung*

Because it was questionable whether chronic effects on health can occur from exposure to urban air pollutants, a study was made by Stokinger *et al.* (*59*) to determine whether the respiratory irritant, ozone, would produce such effects. Chronic injury to the lungs in the form of chronic bronchitis and bronchiolitis was observed in all the smaller animal species exposed daily to O_3 at 1 p.p.m. by volume as determined by the alkaline potassium iodide method; the dog, however, showed none of the deep lung changes seen in the smaller animals but only mild irritation of the trachea and the major bronchi. The difference in the reaction of the dog is attributed to the differences in the dimensions of the respiratory tract. These irreversible fibrotic changes in the lung thus appear to give evidence for one respiratory irritant at least that chronic changes in the lung can occur from repeated low-grade exposures, or as noted above, by infrequent repeated acute injuries from

* Mimicking the effects of ionizing radiation in biological material.

O_3 exposure. The study, moreover, shows that the two processes, tolerance to the acute effects, and the insidiously developing fibrotic changes, go on simultaneously, may actually be interrelated.

7. *Ozone as a Lung-Tumor Accelerator*

The free radical potential of O_3 suggested it as a candidate tumorigenic agent. Such a possibility was realized in $CxAF_1$ mice in finding a tumor (adenoma) incidence of 85% in the ozone-exposed mice as against 38% in the control unexposed mice after 15 mo. of daily exposures to 1 p.p.m. O_3 (*62*). The average number of tumors/mouse was 1.9 as against 1.5 in the controls. The toxic effects of ozone on the host at this level were not considered to be of such a degree as to influence the tumor development appreciably; mortality was not appreciably different in the two groups although it was somewhat higher in the ozone-exposed group.

B. Nitrogen Oxides

Of the six commonly encountered oxides of nitrogen, N_2O (nitrous oxide; NO (nitric oxide); NO_2 (nitrogen dioxide); N_2O_3 (nitrogen trioxide); N_2O_4 (nitrogen tetroxide); and N_2O_5 (nitrogen pentoxide), NO_2 is considered of the greatest air pollution interest for three reasons. (1) All other oxides of nitrogen react in air in such a way that the principal product is NO_2. (2) NO_2 is believed to be the key substance in the chain of ultraviolet reactions with hydrocarbons in the engine exhausts that leads to oxidant smog. (3) NO_2 results as a major end product of the burning of fuel in engines and furnaces because of air oxidation of the NO formed by high combustion temperatures. Because of the low relative toxicity and air pollution significance of N_2O, N_2O_3 and N_2O_4, only the toxicology of NO_2, NO and N_2O_5 will be discussed.

1. *Nitrogen Dioxide* (NO_2)

Early studies, begun in 1877, of the acute effects of NO_2 on laboratory animals, indicate a surprisingly low toxicity for this substance, compared with results obtained in recent years by Gray *et al.* (*63*) who found LC_{50} values for a 30-min. exposure of rats to be 138 p.p.m.; Pflesser, (*64*) on the other hand, as late as 1935, reported 3500 p.p.m. to be the lethal dose for mice, a species of about equal susceptibility. Scrutiny of the observations detailed by Pflesser, in seeking the cause of this major discrepancy, revealed that the method of allowing the animals to remain exposed to NO_2 until death unquestionably resulted in the animals' receiving multilethal doses; delayed, not immediate, death is a characteristic of NO_2 response. Earlier experimenters reported similar low acute toxicity, probably for other reasons, such as impurities in the NO_2. Although Gray *et al.* used fuming red nitric acid as a source of NO_2, their acute toxicity values were in substantial agreement with those found by Stokinger (*46*) using 98%-pure tank NO_2. Thus it would appear that the acute, toxic dose of NO_2 is approximately 15 times that of ozone, which it resembles in producing acute pulmonary edema and death.

To develop acute pulmonary edema in man with death in 48 hr., concentrations of NO_2 of 500 p.p.m. or higher are required (*65*); at 300–400 p.p.m. there is edema with bronchopneumonia and death in 2–10 days; at 150–200 p.p.m., bronchiolitis fibrosa obliterans develops, which is fatal in 3–5 weeks; and at 50–100 p.p.m. bronchiolitis with focal pneumonitis with recovery in 6–8 weeks. All responses occur following exposures of a few months in animals or man. The smoke of cigarettes, pipe tobacco, and cigars contains approximately 300, 950, and 1200 p.p.m. NO_2 respectively, as analyzed by the Saltzman method. Presumably, the intermittent nature of the exposures and antagonistic components of the smoke reduces or abolishes the otherwise injurious effects of NO_2.

The chronic toxicity of NO_2 for small animals is also of a lower order than that of O_3, according to the work reported by Gray *et al.* (*63*). These workers found that, whereas exposure of experimental animals 4 hr./day, 5 days/week for 6 weeks at concentrations ranging between 9 and 14 p.p.m. by volume produced pulmonary injury, a 6-month exposure to an average concentration of 4 p.p.m. resulted in no toxic manifestations, as determined by their criteria. From this a tentative threshold limit of 5 p.p.m. NO_2 for an 8-hr. working day was established by the Committee on Threshold Limits of the American Conference of Governmental Industrial Hygienists. The safety of 5 p.p.m. NO_2 for daily exposures is felt not to be rigorously established, for certain technical reasons, particularly in the light of a claim of Russian workers (*66*) that exposure of workmen for from 3 to 5 years at concentrations generally below 2.8 p.p.m. resulted in chronic changes in the lung. Accordingly, the uncertainty surrounding the "no effect" level of NO_2 for repeated daily exposures permits no decision as to whether current or attainable air pollution levels of NO_2 are harmful. In this connection, it should be noted that NO_2 is one of the few stable free radicals. Current theories of carcinogenesis involve the action of free radicals. If ultimately NO_2 should prove cancerigenic, levels less than 1 p.p.m. might be of concern. Certainly at levels of a few (10–15) p.p.m. inhalation of NO_2, as of most respiratory irritants, could result in chronic bronchitis and bronchiolitis, ending in pulmonary emphysema.

2. *Nitric Oxide (NO)*

This gas per se, is of little toxicological interest as an air pollutant because of its relatively rapid conversion in the atmosphere to NO_2. Kinetic theory shows that 4000 p.p.m. NO is 50% oxidized to NO_2 in approximately 1 min., lower concentrations requiring relatively longer times for oxidation. It is possibly for this reason that no cases of human poisoning strictly from NO have been reported. For this reason also it is impossible to obtain the true inhalation toxicity of NO in animals, because of their oxygen requirements. All such tests must of necessity involve mixtures of NO with varying amounts of NO_2. Toxicologists have recognized this, and within these limits have reported that NO (1) possesses no irritating properties (as opposed to NO_2), (2) produces a rapidly developing cyanosis by direct combination with blood hemoglobin (nitrosohemoglobin), which results in a progressive depression of the central nervous system, asphyxial convulsions, and sudden central paralysis, if inhaled concentrations are sufficiently high (*64*). In this latter respect NO resembles N_2O, but at far lower concentrations, 0.45 vol.% vs. 90 vol.% for N_2O. Its toxic action is mediated probably through the indirect mechanism of methemoglobin formation and not directly on the central nervous system. After an hour's exposure 320 p.p.m. NO is reported to be lethal to mice (*64*). Thus, NO is at least 5 times less acutely toxic than NO_2, assuming minimal contamination and no synergistic effects of NO_2.

3. *Nitrogen Pentoxide* (N_2O_5)

Air pollution interest in this gas stems from the presence of NO_2 and ozone in oxidant smog, and the probable interaction of these gases to produce N_2O_5. Toxicological interest in this gas was also stimulated in the early 1950's, when the view unfortunately became widespread that the toxicity of O_3 is increased in the presence of nitrogen oxides, which would indicate N_2O_5 as the cause. Toxicological study was given to these questions by Diggle and Gage (*67, 68*) in England, and by Byers and Saltzman (*69*), and Stokinger (*46*) in the United States. The work of these investigators left no doubt that NO_2 and O_3 react to form N_2O_5, at least at levels of a few p.p.m.; discrepant findings on the toxicity of N_2O_5 between the English and American workers, however, were reported. Diggle and Gage (*67*) concluded from a study of rats that N_2O_5 was approximately 3 times more toxic than O_3; Byers and Saltzman did not confirm this finding (*69*); indeed, they found N_2O_5 to possess an LC_{50} for white mice of approximately 75 p.p.m. or a toxicity of about 1/15 that of ozone. They attributed the greater apparent toxicity found by the English workers to their method of administering N_2O_5 as a solution in chloroform. Byers and Saltzman demonstrated the lower toxicity both from mixtures of NO_2 and O_3 and from vapors of solid N_2O_5. Neither rats nor mice succumbed to 4-hr. exposures of 50 p.p.m. N_2O_5 vapor. Moreover, Stokinger (*46*) found lower toxicity in mice from exposure to mixtures of NO_2 and O_3 than from exposure to O_3 alone. Nitric acid, a possible product of N_2O_5 and water vapor, in two 8-hr. exposures was shown to have an approximate LC_{50} for rats greater than 500 p.p.m. In another study of NO_2 and O_3 mixtures, Diggle and Gage (*68*) again concluded that N_2O_5 was more toxic than O_3, but scrutiny of their supporting data permits of other conclusions. In all instances in which toxic effects occurred from their mixtures, O_3 was of sufficient concentration to account for the effects.

Thus, until further evidence is forthcoming, it would appear that N_2O_5 possesses an acute toxicity for small animals, about equal to that of NO_2. The chronic toxicity of N_2O_5 has not been studied.

C. Sulfur Dioxide (SO_2)

Presentation of the very considerable amount of information on the toxicological effect in animals of this gas, one of the more important of the air pollutants, may be conveniently made in three parts; (1) summarization of the toxicological information obtained from studies related to this gas as an occupational inhalation hazard, (2) later studies stimulated by air pollution interest, and (3) studies of combined effects of SO_2 and other air pollutants.

The toxicological effects of SO_2, based on animal studies which began in 1884 and continued to 1940, have been critically reviewed in 1954 by Greenwald (*70*). The following may be generally concluded from this review:

(1) Under most conditions of exposure SO_2 acts chiefly as an upper respiratory tract irritant because of its high solubility in body fluids. The action of SO_2 is acute; no chronic or cumulative effects on animal lungs stemming directly from the inhalation of SO_2 per se at reasonable concentrations (below 20 p.p.m.) have ever been observed.

(2) Species vary greatly in susceptibility to SO_2 by inhalation; rats are the most resistant; guinea pigs, the most susceptible. (Man, it was concluded, was much more sensitive than the guinea pig.) Rabbits and guinea pigs tolerated daily 6 to 7-hr. exposures for 30 days at 50 p.p.m., a concentration far in excess of any attainable community air pollution. Mice inhaled without effect 25 p.p.m. for more than 1100 hr. Lower concentrations repeated daily for prolonged periods in other species failed to reveal any histological changes in the lungs.

(3) Repeated exposures of animals to high concentrations of SO_2 (100–500 p.p.m.) lowered their resistance to infection from a variety of microorganisms and reduced their capacity to form antibodies; exposures of 50 p.p.m. SO_2 had no such effect.

(4) Neither the tolerance nor the hypersensitivity reported in man appears to have been detected in animals; young animals appeared more susceptible than old.

It would seem that the patently clear conclusion that everyone should have gathered from the work done up to 1940, namely, that SO_2 alone is without injurious effect at any attainable community air pollution level, was apparently unacceptable to most workers, for studies on pure SO_2 continued as if some new property would eventually emerge that would explain the disasters of the Meuse, Donora, and London smogs. Much of the work, fortunately, is unpublished. Dalhamn (*71*) observed the influence of SO_2 on mucous flow and ciliary activity of rats, and showed a considerably increased amount of mucus, and reddened mucosa of the trachea. The average exposure concentration of SO_2 required to produce these changes approximated 11 p.p.m. for 18 days. There was no change in ciliary beat until 25 p.p.m. SO_2 was obtained. Subsequent observation of the rats following SO_2 exposure showed a considerably retarded flow of mucus; some animals showed no measurable mucus transportation, an important clearing mechanism of the respiratory tract. On the other hand, ciliary activity rapidly commenced following cessation of exposure, and the animals later showed no tolerance, "habituation," or hypersensitive reactions upon re-exposure.

Factors called "compliance" and "resistance" of the lungs of guinea pigs were decreased and increased respectively at levels increasing from 26 to 835 p.p.m. SO_2 inhaled for 1 hr. (*72*). Tidal volume was increased, but minute volume was reduced, showing greatly slowed breathing. The SO_2 concentrations responsible for these effects were unrealistically high by air pollution standards. Disturbances in reflex activity and respiratory patterns have also recently appeared in the Russian literature (*73*). The lowest concentration of SO_2 that produced reflex disturbances in the rabbit was between 1.2 and 3.7 p.p.m. Changes in respiratory pattern occurred at 1 p.p.m. These concentrations are more realistic, but the significance of the changes in reference to health maintenance is in doubt.

In an attempt to trace the routes of penetration of inhaled SO_2 in the animal by tracer-labeled SO_2, a Russian worker (*74*) found that SO_2 was carried rapidly by the blood throughout the animal and retained in the organs for periods as long as 11 days or more, depending upon the concentration of the SO_2 in inhaled air. The distribution in the various organs was not uniform; preferential localization appeared in the lungs. Repeated inhalation of SO_2 resulted in an accumulation of sulfur metabolites. The final conclusion of the authors, however, that this work permits, the suggestion that daily inhalation of even small amounts of SO_2 can lead to the development of pathological symptoms in an animal, does not seem warranted from the data and is contrary to all past experience. It would appear that the extremely trivial amounts (a few microcuries) of radioactive tracer used may have been responsible for the apparent general distribution of SO_2, which may not have occurred had more physiological amounts been used. Stokinger (*75*) has pointed out some years ago the errors in interpretation that can result from tracer studies, when attempts are made to relate the results to doses of toxicological interest. The establishment of toxicity requires more than demonstrating the presence of an agent in the tissues; it requires demonstration of an untoward response from the agent. Sulfate is a normal metabolite of the body, and the finding of trace amounts in addition to the general pool is unimpressive.

The combined effects of aerosols and SO_2 are presented in Section VIII,A.

D. Ammonia (NH_3)

This gas is presently of only minor air pollution interest toxicologically, because of its questionable existence in most urban atmospheres, except in combination with such acidic ions as sulfate or chloride. In these combinations its concentration in urban air averages from 0.01 to 0.2 p.p.m. In circumstances in which free ammonia exists in the atmosphere it has the following toxicological characteristics:

Because of its high aqueous solubility, its physiological activity is confined almost entirely to the upper respiratory tract, only a few per cent of an inhaled dose reaching the lungs in inhalable concentrations. At extremely high concentrations NH_3 acts as a powerful asphyxiant by constricting air passages, owing to its extreme irritancy. Although an irritant gas, the least amount producing immediate irritation of eyes, nose, and throat is from 400 to 700 p.p.m., and ammonia does not become dangerous (asphyxiant) until concentrations of 2500–6500 p.p.m. (0.25–0.65 volumes per cent) are attained.

Therefore, NH_3 is not a serious health menace in acute exposures in urban atmospheres, except in concentrations far above those encountered in community air pollution; it is not dangerous in prolonged repeated exposures. Weatherby (*76*) found that exposures of male guinea pigs to 170 p.p.m. NH_3 for 18 weeks, 6 hr./day, 5 days/week was required to produce mild changes in spleen, kidneys, adrenals, and liver, but that no changes were seen at 12 weeks. Dalhamn (*71*), however, found far lower concentrations of NH_3 caused cilia of the upper respiratory tract of rats to cease beating, but that recovery of motility was rapid. NH_3 concentrations of 3 p.p.m. stopped ciliary beating in 8 to 9 min., 20 p.p.m., in 20 sec.; and 90 p.p.m., in 5 sec. It would thus appear that if rat cilia have a susceptibility to ammonia similar to those of the guinea pig, cessation of ciliary mobility has little effect on the general health of guinea pigs. On the other hand, the experimental guinea pigs used by Weatherby may not have been subject to the stress of infectious agents, in which the role of the ciliary activity plays an important part in combating the initiation of infection. Under these circumstances the action of ammonia on ciliary activity may be significant. In summing up the effects of NH_3 as an air pollutant, Pattle (*77*) concluded that the greatest effectiveness of ammonia as an air pollutant is the partial neutralization of acidic airborne constituents such as SO_2, with consequent reduction in irritant activity of each consitutent.

E. Carbon Monoxide (CO)

No other gaseous air pollutant with such a toxic potential as CO exists at such high relative concentrations in urban atmospheres. If the ratio of toxic concentration to normal air level for CO is about 20, that for O_3, NO_2, and SO_2 ranges respectively from approximately 50, to 375, and 2500. However, it is extremely doubtful that CO of itself will ever exert a serious effect on urban populations, because attainment of injurious concentrations represents extremely large additions of CO to the atmosphere. Moreover, CO is "safe" at 100 p.p.m. for repeated daily 8-hr. exposures. At slightly more than 10-times this level CO is rapidly fatal; all intermittent levels are without permanent effect provided exposure is not prolonged. It is characteristic of gases such as CO not to accumulate indefinitely in the body but to attain an equilibrium level in the blood and tissues at a value dependent on the partial pressure of the inhaled CO and the relative affinity of CO and O_2 for hemoglobin. Thus 24-hr. continuous exposures will never result in a blood CO level of indefinitely high value, no matter how indefinitely prolonged the exposure.

The combination of CO with blood hemoglobin and its secondary effect on the central nervous system are so well known and amply recorded (*78*) as to need no recounting here. That these two effects do not comprise the entire physiological action of CO, however, is suggested by certain inconsistencies in the behavior of CO, unexplained by the older literature. More recent studies of guinea pigs poisoned with CO showed indeed that another component may be involved. Cytochrome C of heart was reduced to almost indeterminable levels in acute CO poisoning; in subacute poisoning the reduction was equivalent to the severity of the intoxication; and in chronic intoxication the reduction was less conspicuous but noticeable (*79*).

V. Inorganic Mists (Sulfur Trioxide and Sulfuric Acid)

Sulfur Trioxide (SO_3) and Sulfuric Acid (H_2SO_4) Mists. It is not possible at the present time to assess the toxicological potential of these irritant aerosols in urban atmospheres, because no analytic distinction has been made generally between these aerosols and SO_2 in atmospheric surveys. Thus no data on the SO_3 mist burden in the air relative to other urban air pollutants are available. (SO_3 in atmospheres around industrial plants, however, is from 1/100 to 1/50 that of SO_2.)

Sulfuric acid mists have been repeatedly shown, during the last decade, to be highly lethal to guinea pigs at relatively low concentrations (5 p.p.m.) and for short exposures (2–3 hr.). Other laboratory species are far more resistant, surviving more than double the concentration for prolonged, repeated exposures (Treon *et al.*) (*80*). Thus the toxicity of H_2SO_4 mists for guinea pigs is of the order of that of O_3 for small laboratory animals. The effects upon the respiratory tract have been reported to be dependent upon (1) the age of the animal—the younger animals being more susceptible (*81*); (2) particle size—particles slightly below 1 μ mean diameter being more injurious than smaller or larger particles (*82*), although size effect may be somewhat dependent on concentration (*81, 83*); and (3) temperature—subnormal temperatures lowering the toxicity. The above conclusion on particle-size effect appears at odds with that of Pattle (*77*), who finds larger sizes (2.5–2.7 μ MMD)* to be more injurious. It should be noted, however, that particle-size expression in terms of MMD tends to accentuate size both above and below 1 μ measured diameter in proportion to the distribution frequency, *if particles differ in density significantly from unity.* Thus Pattle's finding of greater injuriousness of 2.7 μ MMD particles may in reality represent particles close to 1 μ (measured diameter), and thus no real conflict in findings exists. Regrettably, it is not possible to calculate the mean diameter from the MMD of Pattle, as no standard deviation was given.

Amdur (*72*) has shown that H_2SO_4 mist, starting at a level of 2.5 p.p.m. and 2–2.5 μ MMD, produced immediately increased airway resistance of the lung and reduced alveolar ventilation of guinea pigs.

Lethal or near-lethal concentrations result in degenerative changes in the epithelium of the respiratory tract, pulmonary hyperemia and edema,

* Mass-Median Diameter.

and focal pulmonary hemorrhages. Atelectatic and emphysematous areas in the lung also occur.

Although there is no question of the severity of the lung changes in animals exposed to these irritants at high concentrations for short periods, it is important to note that fibrosis of the lung did not develop in guinea pigs exposed continuously for 18–140 days to approximately 1 p.p.m. (4 mg./m.^{3}), according to Thomas *et al.* (*82*). The exposure, moreover, was one in which concentrations accidentally reached peaks as high as 75 p.p.m. for short periods. Furthermore, only slight effects in guinea pigs, the most susceptible species, resulted from continuous exposure of more than 3 mo. to 0.5 p.p.m. H_2SO_4 mists. Apparently at these lower concentrations insignificant amounts of the mists reach the pulmonary alveolar tissue owing to solubility of the mists. Medium-size particles (about 1 μ mean diameter) were more injurious than either the coarse (4 μ) or fine (0.59 μ). It would appear, therefore, that SO_3, like SO_2, does not give rise to chronic irreversible changes in the lung from repeated or continuous daily exposures at any attainable air pollution concentration. Thus it differs markedly from ozone in this respect. Particularly interesting was the finding that the changes produced by the H_2SO_4 mist on the lung parenchyma were acute in nature and that the apparent lack of changes suggestive of chronic processes indicates that the acute lesions become completely resolved (*82*).

VI. Organic Mists (Oil Mists)

Oil Mists. Oil mists have been used to study the toxicological behavior of mists in general, and in particular, to characterize further the lipid pneumonia described in 1925 by Laughlen (*84*) as resulting from inhalation of certain oil mists. In general, vegetable oils, apart from those which are specific irritants such as chaulmoogra and croton oils, are readily metabolized by lipase activity of the lung and body fluids and thus create no specific pathological effects. Some fish oils, such as cod liver oil, have immediate and specific irritating and necrotizing effects on lung tissue. Refined liquid petrolatum "mineral oil" and motor oil, which it closely resembles chemically, behave in the lung as a neutral foreign body, stimulating the typical "foreign body" reaction of the lungs characterized by the appearance of numerous macrophages. If the inhaled concentration of these oils is sufficiently high and prolonged—a few grams per cubic meter, for a few weeks, well above the usual air pollution levels—localized pneumonitis generally results, accompanied by an outpouring of polymorphonuclear cells and followed by pulmonary fibrosis. A survey of the fate of various kinds of oil mists, including motor oil, in the lung of the mouse exposed by inhalation has been made by Shoshkes *et al.* (*85*). Although initial concentrations of all oil droplets were similar as were the median particle sizes (0.8–1.6 μ), only motor oil and mineral oil remained in the lung essentially unchanged; the quantity of the edible oils (peanut, corn, and cod liver) remaining, progressively decreased. Following heavy exposures of a few gm./m.^{3} for periods of from 2 to 4 weeks, only motor and mineral oil retention result in localized foreign body reactions of moderate severity, with infrequent patches of lipid pneumonia. Other workers with oils have made similar findings. For various technical reasons, the authors felt that these results in the mouse lung were directly applicable to man. Thus it would appear that repeated exposures to motor oil mists alone in high concentrations can give rise to acute changes (pneumonitis) and chronic changes (fibrosis) as well.

VII. Organic Vapors

A. Formaldehyde (HCHO) and Homologues

With the exception of formaldehyde, which is a recognized sensitizing agent and highly irritant to the mucous membranes of the eyes, nose, and throat, the higher aliphatic homologues of formaldehyde are probably of no toxicological significance per se at present air pollution concentrations. Unsaturated aliphatic aldehydes such as acrolein and crotonaldehyde are more highly irritating than HCHO. Kotin (*86*) exposed exteriorized rat and rabbit trachea and ciliated epithelium of the frog's esophagus to formaldehyde and a number of higher aldehydes, and found inhibition of ciliary action and of mucus flow immediately on exposure to 22,000–66,000 mg./m.^{3}. Acetaldehyde and *n*-butyraldehyde produced immediate stimulation at about 10,000 mg./m.^{3}, whereas propionaldehyde and isobutyraldehyde showed no immediate effect. 2-Furfuraldehyde behaved like formaldehyde at first but later stimulated ciliary activity at somewhat higher concentrations. Interestingly, each aldehyde showed a characteristic response when measured after 1 and 16 min. and at 6 hr. exposure. Dalhamn (*71*), in testing concentrations of formaldehyde of 22, 10, 3, and 0.5 p.p.m. on the ciliary movement of the respiratory tract of anesthetized rats with opened trachea, found that movement ceased and thus cessation of mucus transport at 10, 30, 50, and 150 sec., respectively. Ciliary movement recommenced in 10–30 sec. after exposure to formaldehyde was stopped. Cralley (*87*) had previously shown similar effects in roughly the same time interval on the *excised* trachea of rabbits. It is not known whether ciliary activity would remain depressed for long periods after prolonged depression of such activity. Ciliary activity is an important mechanism for clearing the respiratory tract of harmful particulates such as bacteria, which, if infectious, may lead to secondary complications in the respiratory tract from exposure to such air pollutants.

The sensitizing action of formaldehyde is well known but not documented with sufficient evidence to permit an estimate of what order of concentration is required to produce hypersensitivity. HCHO reacts directly with free amino groups, thus altering the character of protein, which could account for the hypersensitivity in some persons. The lowest concentration giving detectable odor is said to be 0.8 p.p.m., and the lowest concentration causing throat irritation, 5 p.p.m.

B. Ketones

The monoketones as a group have no known toxicological significance at atmospheric levels now encountered; health effects are not incurred until levels of a few hundred p.p.m. are attained for considerable periods. Halogenated ketones, particularly the aromatic type, are potent irritants and lacrimators, but their presence in community atmospheres has not been noted. Alpha diketones are likewise potent irritants, as are the conjugated unsaturated ketones. The former unquestionably occur in oxidant smog in small amounts as a result of chain reactions of free radicals developed from the ozonolysis of olefins, but their quantitative significance has not yet been determined; similarly, no measurements of conjugated unsaturated ketones have been reported in urban atmospheres.

C. Ketenes (RCH=C=O)

These substances have been shown by Scott *et al.* (*88*) to result from the action of ozone on olefins. Toxicological information on one, the first member of the series, ketene ($CH_2=C=O$), shows it to be among the most irritant and lethal of chemical substances. Death in mice follows exposures of only 10-min. duration to 17 p.p.m. equivalent to 6 μg. per mouse, assuming a 20-ml. minute volume and 75% effectiveness of the inhaled ketene. Considerable difference in species susceptibility to ketene has been reported by Treon *et al.* (*89*); although monkeys were almost as susceptible as mice, rabbits were found considerably more resistant, and cats, rats, and guinea pigs showed intermediate susceptibility. As in the case of phosgene, which it exceeds in toxicity, the lung is the organ affected, with the development of severe alveolar epithelial damage resulting in acute congestion and edema on short exposures. It would appear, from the work of Treon also, that the acute toxic response bears little relation to the chronic response; in this respect it resembles ozone. Rabbits, which were the most resistant to effects of acute high exposure, succumbed in greater numbers to the effects of daily, repeated low-grade (1 p.p.m.) exposures than did mice and monkeys, the most susceptible species in acute exposures. Treon also drew attention to the reduced toxicity of ketene upon repeated exposures. Later work by Mendenhall and Stokinger (*90*) showed indeed that, not only does prior low-grade exposure result in appreciable tolerance in mice to subsequent lethal exposure to ketene, but it also provides tolerance to acute lethal exposure to O_3. They moreover showed that prior exposure to ozone cross-protected mice subsequently exposed to lethal concentration of ketene. These findings may have considerable public health significance as far as acute exposures are concerned, and may even be responsible for chronic effects.

D. Organic Hydroperoxides and Peroxides

These substances, which comprise a large and varied group of chemically related substances, have been shown by Scott and co-workers (*88*) to result from the interaction of ozone on olefins, and have long been suspected in oxidant smog. Part of the oxidant determined by the neutral potassium iodide analytic method has been attributed to organic peroxides. The general structure of the hydroperoxide is R_3COOH, and that of the peroxide is R_3COOCR_3. These substances are used widely in industry as catalysts and as intermediates in synthesis. No information exists on the potential of this group of substances in producing chronic effects on health at levels of air pollution interest. Some information, however, has been recorded by Floyd and Stokinger (*91*) on acute and subchronic effects of four typical peroxides, namely, methyl ethyl ketone peroxide, cumene hydroperoxide, *t*-butyl hydroperoxide, and di-*t*-butyl peroxide in laboratory animals. None of the peroxides compares in acute toxicity with that of ozone or ketene as respiratory irritants. The hydroperoxides, however, are more toxic than peroxides by a factor of several times. All are skin and eye irritants, except di-*t*-butyl peroxide, albeit at solvent dilutions of to 1 to 35%. A finding of possibly considerable significance was the demonstration that repeated sublethal doses (1/5 LD_{50}*, either orally or intraperitoneally) resulted in cumulative effects and finally in the death of some of the animals. Whether cumulative effects will occur from repeated exposures at air pollution levels is regrettably not known. Although the peroxides convert blood hemoglobin to methemoglobin *in vitro*, no methemoglobin was demonstrated in rats given repeated daily doses either by inhalation or intraperitoneally. Cross-tolerance to hydrogen peroxide only was demonstrated in mice

* LD_{50} is the dose of a toxicant that will kill 50% of an exposed population.

previously exposed to cumene hydroperoxide, but not to O_3, NO_2 or, oddly, to cumene hydroperoxide itself. No changes in serum protein patterns occurred in animals on repeated high-level exposures.

E. Organic Sulfur Compounds from Petroleum

The majority of sulfur present in crude oil is organic, the total quantity of which is relatively large in distillates from high sulfur petroleums. Past estimates for thiols (RSH) alone place the quantity lost per day at 150–200 tons from naphthas refined in this country. Until very recently very little attention had been given the organic sulfur compounds in the air. Most of the toxicological reports of a rather cursory nature originated from Europe (Ljunggren *et al.* (*92*) DeRekowski (*93*), and others). The first investigators described the toxicity of dimethyl sulfide, dimethyl disulfide, and methyl mercaptan, but disagreed on the toxicity of methyl mercaptan relative to that of hydrogen sulfide. Conflicting toxicity reports and the little available information on these substances have prompted a detailed study of the acute toxicity of 7 aliphatic and 2 aromatic thiols in animals by Fairchild and Stokinger (*94*). The 9 compounds tested were benzene-, methylheptane-, α-toluene-, ethane-, hexane-, butane-, propane-, 2-methyl-2-propane, and 2-methyl-1-propanethiol. Several routes of administration were used, including that of inhalation and eye. Of the 9 compounds tested by inhalation, in rats, rabbits, and mice benzenethiol and methylheptanethiol were the most toxic. The 48-hr. and 15-day LC_{50}'s respectively for benzenethiol were 59 and 33 p.p.m. and the 24-hr. LC_{50} for methylheptanethiol was 51 p.p.m. for a single 4-hr. exposure, evidence of a remarkably high acute toxicity. Very large differences in acute toxicity among the various thiols, however, exist. For example, the 48-hr. LC_{50} for propanethiol by comparison was 7300 p.p.m., the 15-day LC_{50} for 2-methyl-2-propanethiol, 22,200; and more than 25,000 p.p.m. for 2-methyl-1-propanethiol; ethane-, butane-, and hexane-, thiols were intermediate. All thiols, except methylheptanethiol and propanethiol, produced a considerable number of rodent deaths among the exposed animals; after 2 weeks, however, all of those animals that had not died at that time survived. All thiols also had the common toxicological property of being soporific, ranging in degree from producing mild stupor to heavy sedation. Methylheptanethiol was an exception in that it produced a powerful central nervous system stimulation.

Acute thiol poisoning produced a uniform pattern of central depression and respiratory paralysis, death ensuing from respiratory failure. The methylheptanethiol, however, inhaled in combination with a respiratory depressant thiol, counteracted this depression but was unable to counteract the toxic effects associated with maximal lethal exposures. Toxic sublethal or lethal doses of methylheptanethiol induced clonic and tonic seizures ending like other thiols in central respiratory failure and death.

Repeated administration of the most toxic thiols, unlike that of the organic peroxides, for 3 to 4 weeks, 3 times per week, at approximately one-third the LD_{50}, were tolerated by rats, thus providing evidence of lack of cumulative toxic effects as well as indicating no apparent tolerance development.

Splenic enlargement was the only gross pathological change produced with consistency. Benzenethiol produced injury to the cornea and conjunctivae of rabbits, and lethal doses of methylheptanethiol frequently produced petechiae in the lungs. Thiol-exposed rats and mice commonly showed latent pulmonary infection and/or pneumonia. Liver and kidney damage occurred from intraperitoneal, inhalation and, particularly, from oral administration, but at relatively high levels. Inhalation at high levels produced slight to severe irritation of the respiratory tract, the degree dependent on the thiol; benzenethiol was the only compound producing significant pathological conditions at lower levels of thiol exposure.

Considerably less toxicity information is available on the organic nonthiol S compounds, the sulfides and disulfides. Dimethyl sulfide [$(CH_3)_2S$] is less acutely toxic to rodents by inhalation and intraperitoneally by a factor of 1.5–2 than the corresponding methylthiol; in contrast, dimethyl disulfide ($CH_3S—SCH_3$) is more toxic by a factor of 3 or 4 than methylthiol, but diphenyl disulfide ($C_6H_5SSC_6H_5$) is only slightly more toxic by the intraperitoneal route than the corresponding benzenethiol (*95*). The cyclic S compound, thiophene, is reported to have an acute toxicity distinctly greater than that of benzene by inhalation (*96*). The work was done at a time when benzene contained appreciable amounts of thiophene, and thus should be repeated with pure materials. Evidence on thiophene metabolism in the animal body involves breakdown to ethylthiol.

F. Conjugated Nitro Olefins $\left(\begin{array}{c} NO_2 \\ | \\ R_1—C{=}CHR_2 \end{array}\right)$

Toxicological information is available on a rather large series (12 compounds) of 2-nitro-2- and 3-nitro-3- olefins,* largely from the studies of Deichmann and co-workers (*97, 98*). Interest in these com-

* Toxicological investigation of nitro olefins has been made at Army Chemical Center but is not in the open literature.

pounds as air pollutants arose from the likelihood of their presence in oxidant smog, from the work of Haagen-Smit, and from the known eye irritancy of the conjugated types from the work of Brown (*99*).

All such compounds from C_4 to C_9 exhibit similar toxicological responses. Marked eye irritation is the first observable response upon exposure; rabbits and chicks were the more sensitive, rats less so. Upon continued exposure at high concentrations, the conjunctiva, sclera, and eyelid become inflamed, and direct application of a drop in a rabbit's eye results in marked local irritation of the mucous membranes; subsequently the cornea becomes whitened or "burned," indicating coagulation of the protein of the epithelial layer of the cornea. With more intense exposures, a sloughing of the superficial layers of the cornea occurs within a day. Irritation of the mucous membrane of the respiratory tract is also conspicuous, with marked secretion of mucous in nose and throat. Dyspneic breathing and cyanosis increases with increased exposure, and animals die with asphyxial convulsions. Rabbits are the first to succumb; levels of from fifty to a few hundred p.p.m. produced death within 1 hr. to 1 day for the various compounds; all animals survived single, 5-hr. exposures, however, of less than 50 p.p.m. (1–6 millimoles) of nitro olefins. The LC_{50} values were not determined for any nitro olefin.

LD_{50} values were determined, however, for acute oral doses, and intraperitoneally and cutaneously administered nitro olefins (*97*).

Eye irritation determined on human volunteers in two separate laboratories with different testing procedures (*98*) showed 2-nitro-2-butene and 2-nitro-2-hexene to produce eye irritation at concentrations between 0.1 and 0.5 p.p.m. in 3 min.; and the corresponding nonene derivative at concentrations greater than 1 p.p.m. The important finding was made that repeated exposure to nitro olefins resulted in increased sensitivity to the eye-irritating effects. It was further noted that brief ultraviolet exposures destroyed the lacrimators. Thus on the basis of the eye-irritation data it would appear that the lower molecular weight nitro olefins may be likely candidates as eye-irritating air pollutants in oxidant smog. The presence of conjugated nitro olefins has not yet been positively demonstrated in such smog.

VIII. Simple, Known Mixtures

Experimental attention has been given only recently to the physiological effects of mixtures of candidate chemical air pollutants, after sifted evidence from acute episodes had appeared to indicate that the effects observed on health could not be explained by the action of single substances alone at the concentrations encountered. Exposure to mixtures of substances has been tried since the beginning of pharmacology and clinical medicine, when attempts were made to surpass the effects of the single components. Out of such trials emerged the findings of (1) antagonism (reduced effects), (2) synergism (enhanced effects), and (3) simple additive effects. Despite the serious analysis of effects of mixtures begun in 1910 by Burgi (*100*), no complete explanation of the means by which these effects are brought about has been found. Veldstra (*101*), in an impressive review of synergism and potentiation containing 366 references, concludes that although many questions must remain unanswered for the present, a large proportion of instances may be explained as a competition between the substance and the synergist at various "sites of loss." Sites of loss are defined as points of nonspecific adsorption, such as storage at unreactive sites, or as loci at surfaces of active enzymes involved in the ordinary metabolism and detoxication, or as excretory mechanisms. The value of this hypothesis, it would appear, is that it is broad enough to account for the phenomenon of antagonism, of which synergism may be considered a special case, in that both are competitive for active sites, the opposing effects resulting from different sites of action. Antagonists act mainly at sites of direct action, synergists at sites not directly involved with the effect observed but at sites of destruction or loss. Recent statistically designed experiments have been reported (*102*) that validate the sites of loss hypothesis as far as the acute synergistic effect of malathion and EPN (another insecticide) by mouth are concerned. It is of considerable practical importance to note that synergism has not been observed upon chronic administration of these related insecticides and is not to be expected for chronic exposures because of dosage-size considerations.

A demonstration of a possible mechanism of synergistic action consistent with the above hypotheses was reported by Murphy and DuBois (*103*); EPN inhibited the enzyme system that detoxifies malathion, thus providing an explanation for the observed potentiation of toxicity. This work represents the first "breakthrough" in this hitherto obscure toxicological response.

The theories of antagonism have been given mathematic expression by Gaddum (*104*). Four types have been identified: (1) antagonism by neutralization, (2) competitive reversible antagonism, (3) noncompetitive antagonism, and (4) independent antagonism. Unfortunately, these quantitative expressions cannot be applied with assurance to the inhalation of mixtures, because they are predicated on the assumption of attainment of equilibrium, a condition that usually is not met. Their usefulness therefore is confined to the experimental determination of the mechanism of antagonism in isolated systems.

A further word of caution should be voiced regarding application of the concepts of synergism and antagonism to inhalation of air pollutant mixtures, in order to avoid loose and uninhibited use of the terms. If one accepts the terms synergism and antagonism as meaning the competition for sites of action as defined above, then one must exclude the terms from consideration for such enhanced or reinforced effects as are produced in conjunction with heat, humidity, light, or effects of physiological stress (activity); other terms had best be coined for these phenomena.

Some may consider the present mechanistic concepts of synergism and antagonism too limited. They are limited for two reasons: (1) The experience from which they have evolved concerns organic chemical compounds, drugs, metabolites, insecticides, and related substances; and (2) Physical agents, mechanical factors, and various types of superimposed physiological stress result in a grossly altered host (abnormal test animal), an altered dose, or both. Basing the theories on organic substances will exclude inorganic substances only in so far as their fate in the body does not resemble that of organic substances. In general, however, the fate of inorganic substances is dissimilar to that of organic substances. In particular, many of the so-called "metal antagonisms" would not be considered true antagonisms according to present theory; the mechanism of many metal antagonisms involves rendering the active metal unavailable to the body by converting it to an insoluble substance; some, however, represent true competition for active sites on enzymes and coenzymes and thus may be subject to consideration according to the theory.

It will become clear in what follows that few demonstrations to date of the effects of inhalation of mixtures may be classed unequivocally as cases of synergism or antagonism. Often this is not because they do not occur but because of improper experimental design. On the other hand, practically all the studies of inhalation of mixtures appear to show effects not predicted on a simple additive basis. If this is surprising considering the relatively few known cases of enhancement by other routes of exposure (for example, oral), it is understandable when it is noted that, added to the usual means of substance interaction and metabolism, the inhalation route presents the additional possibilities of adsorption effects, mechanical transport on particles, catalysis, and pulmonary nerve and local cellular response.

The reader may wonder why more research dealing with the effects of air pollutant mixtures has not been done, in view of its recognized importance. The difficulties, both experimental and theoretical, of working with single substances are compounded manyfold when working with mixtures: experimentally, quantitative analysis of trace amounts of one substance in the presence of others often presents a problem of great magnitude; theoretically, the question of the precise mechanism often remains unanswered, owing to the incomplete nature of the pertinent theory.

A. Mixtures of Particulate with Gas or Vapor

Dautrebande, long an investigator of the fate of airborne substances in the respiratory tract, was among the first to recognize and study the interaction of solid aerosols on gases and vapors as an air pollution problem. His paper (*105*), appearing in 1951, drew attention to the effect of particulate matter (NaCl and silica dust) on eye irritation produced by the volatile irritants, sulfur dioxide, formaldehyde, and nitric acid vapor; and the importance of particle size in connection with air pollutant exposures. The aerosols of NaCl and silica approximated 0.1 μ in mean diameter. Irritation was greater from the aerosol mixed with the vapors than from the vapors alone. In 2 of 3 cases irritation generally disappeared immediately after the end of exposure. The results were not felt to be quantitatively reliable, however; considerable variation was noted from subject to subject and from one exposure to another.

LaBelle *et al.* (*106*) criticized Dautrebande's results on the basis of their subjective nature, and performed experiments with mice (6 per group) on a variety of solid aerosols and oil mists in combination with each of the vapors of formaldehyde, acrolein, and nitric acid, in which 50% survival time from a single brief exposure was used to provide requisite objectivity. Of the 9 aerosols tested (5 solids and 4 liquids) with formaldehyde, death occurred sooner in 6 cases than with formaldehyde alone; survival was prolonged with 7 aerosols used in conjunction with nitric acid vapor; but, oddly, with acrolein the aerosols effected no appreciable change in survival time in 6 of the 9 combinations tested. Increases in lung-to-body weight ratio, an evidence of pulmonary injury, paralleled fairly well the survival times from formaldehyde and the aerosols. On the assumption that increased toxicity resulted from deeper transport of the vapor into the respiratory tract by adsorption on the aerosol, and its converse, the prediction agreed with findings in 19 of 27 tests, or 70%. From this degree of agreement and from the small number of mice (six used/test group), although replicate tests were made, it is not possible to conclude whether the assumed mechanism of gaseous transport on the aerosol is the one to account for the observed effects, or whether the mechanism is incorrect and the cause of the disagreement resides in the variation in animal response. LaBelle *et al.* appear to have shown that a wide variety of aerosols of relatively large particle size (1.8–3.3 μ MMD) can materially alter the pulmonary response of mice to respiratory irritant vapors when administered together with the vapors at relatively high concentrations (50–2,920 mg./m.^{3}). Thus, like Dautrebande for the eye, LaBelle has demonstrated an enhancement of effect by particulates for a different site of action, the lung; in addition, he has shown with certain mixtures a reduced effect and, with others, no observable effect.

In work demonstrating the combined effect of aerosols and irritant gases, the physiological effects of a mixture of SO_2 and NaCl have been determined by Amdur *et al.* (*107*) in unanesthetized guinea pigs at near air pollution levels by measuring intrapleural pressure, tidal volume, and the rate of gas flow in and out of the respiratory system. From these measurements, resistance to air flow and compliance of the lung was calculated. Resistance was selected because it was felt to be the most simple and expressive measure of irritant effect. At SO_2 concentrations of 2–250 p.p.m. and NaCl at 12 mg./m.^{3} and of submicronic size (about 0.04 μ diameter), the increase in pulmonary resistance was greater than that for the corresponding concentration of SO_2 used alone. The degree of enhancement was related to the SO_2 concentration; a 27-fold increase in effect occurred at 2.6 p.p.m. SO_2, which diminished to a value of 3- or 4-fold when concentrations of SO_2 exceeded 8 p.p.m.; NaCl alone was without effect on the measurement. The effect of NaCl aerosol and SO_2 together, however, was of longer duration than that of SO_2 alone. Like SO_2, acetic acid and formaldehyde gave prolonged effects with NaCl, but only formaldehyde produced enhancement. These studies are highly suggestive of a means by which exacerbated effects of SO_2 in individuals are believed to have occurred, apart from those with cardiorespiratory debilitation. The exact mode by which the combinations act, however, is still conjectural.

Goetz (*108*) has developed a physicochemical theory to explain the altered physiological effects of combinations of vapor and aerosol. Stated in its most elementary form, the physicochemical considerations that govern the final toxicological outcome are: (1) the degree of adsorption or absorption of the vapor on or in the particle, (2) the degree of chemical or catalytic interaction of vapor and particle, (3) the relative rate of desorption of the substance from the particulate onto the biological surface, and (4) the toxicity of the new combination, if such occurs.

This theory finds considerable support in the result of LaBelle (*106*) and Amdur (*107*), and may be used to explain not only synergism but antagonism between aerosol and vapor. For if adsorption of vapor on particulate occurs with a resulting new chemical compound of lesser toxicity (e.g., NO_2 on iron oxide to form iron nitrate), a lesser effect is predictable. On the other hand, if a vapor such as SO_2 which because of upper respiratory absorption normally does not penetrate into the lung, is adsorbed on a particle of respirable size, it will be carried to the deeper portions of the lung in very highly localized concentration. If the adsorbed layer is then desorbed onto the mucous surfaces, a synergistic effect may be anticipated. All gradations in response are predictable from this theory, depending upon the degree to which the four physicochemical conditions, enumerated above, operate.

Undoubtedly, similar conditions operate to explain the enhanced effects of sulfuric acid mist when inhaled with SO_2, as shown by Amdur (*109*) in guinea pigs; 8 mg./m.^{3} H_2SO_4 mist and 89 p.p.m. SO_2 inhaled as a mixture produced more marked effect on growth, lung tissue changes, and respiration than was predicted from the simple added effects of each.

Attempts to evaluate the role of kerosene-carbon smoke, when mixed with SO_2, have been made by Pattle and Burgess (*110*) by subjecting guinea pigs and mice to exceedingly high concentrations of (1) SO_2 in smoke, (2) SO_2 alone, (3) smoke followed by SO_2, and (4) SO_2-desorbed smoke. SO_2 concentrations ranged from approximately 1000 to 4000 p.p.m.; approximate smoke concentrations, from 50 to 135 mg./m.^{3}. No difference was observed between the response (time of death) from SO_2 and smoke mixtures and from SO_2 alone at high concentrations, but real increases in mortality were found at lower smoke concentrations, compared with sulfur dioxide alone. Interestingly, smoke seemed to lessen the effects of SO_2 when given prior to SO_2 exposures. Smoke itself produced no acute effects, as it was shown in another experiment that the LD_{50} for mice was 1500 mg./m.^{3} for a 200-min. exposure, a dosage outside the range of present consideration. Kerosene smoke was considered to be toxicologically inert at air pollution levels and, when inhaled with SO_2, produced histological changes in the lung that did not resemble those from sulfuric acid mist. Thus it would appear that the particulates in kerosene smoke are unable to oxidize SO_2 catalytically. Of interest also is the protection offered by smoke against pulmonary edema; similar protection was found by Stokinger *et al.* (*111*) from oil mists used against a respiratory irritant, which may indicate involvement of a common basic mechanism. Pattle and Burgess believe that there was no evidence from their studies to support the hypothesis that adsorption of SO_2 was an important factor in increasing the injurious action of smokes. It is quite probable that the kerosene-generated carbon particles already possess an adsorbed oil layer and thus present a surface unfavorable for adsorption of SO_2.

B. Oil Mists and Oxidant Gases

Because oil mists are constituents of combustion engine exhausts, either by direct discharge or by secondary reactions of oxidant smog components, it is important to know what their role might be in affecting the irritant action of the more important simple oxidant gases, O_3 and NO_2. The only available information to date is that derived from pulmonary studies following acute exposures of rodents to either motor or mineral oil mists by Stokinger and co-workers (*111*). These studies show that the acute lethal effects of ozone on mice are materially reduced, and those of NO_2 completely abolished, some hours after exposure to the mists. Both ordinary motor oil and mineral oil mists of low or high viscosity are similarly effective. The mists provide slight but measurable protection when given in sequence, but no appreciable reduction in mortality when inhaled along with the respiratory oxidants; indeed, some synergism occurred when the mixture of aerosol and gas was inhaled concurrently, a finding in agreement with LaBelle's report (*106*). The lowest concentration of oil mist found to be effective against ozone toxicity was of the order of 8.5 p.p.m. for 6 hr.; for NO_2, the effective oil concentration was 0.5 p.p.m. (about 7 mg./m.^{3}). The protective effect was still measurable at 9 days but could not be demonstrated after 12 days.

A study of the effect of a number of other variables related to oil aerosols for protection against lethal doses of O_3 showed that: (1) No protective effect occurs if oil and irritant are simultaneously administered; (2) Particle size of the mists are diminishingly effective outside the limits of 0.5–1.5 μ diameter; (3) Condensation nuclei, Na^+ and Cl^-, appear to have no measurable influence on action of the oil mists, as nebulized aerosols and LaMer-generated aerosols were equally effective; (4) Neither viscosity nor the antioxidant properties of the oils are a major determinant in the protective effect; and (5) Among hydrocarbon oils protection appears to be confined to cycloparaffinic structures. Thus it would appear that certain fractions of oils of petroleum origin have an extraordinary capacity to reduce or abolish the acute irritant properties of at least two of the more important gases in oxidant smog.

C. Beryllium Sulfate ($BeSO_4$) Mist and Hydrogen Fluoride (HF) Vapor

The fatal air pollution cases that occurred in an area surrounding a beryllium processing plant, the "neighborhood cases" (*112*), represent the first recorded *chronic* air pollution episode in which the etiological agent (Be) has been determined. On the basis of an *ex post facto* study of the plant materials balance, and the Be distribution of the plant effluent "fallout" calculated from the equations of Bosanquet and Sutton, the phenomenally low air pollution level of Be was tentatively set at 0.01 μg./m.^{3}, the first established limit for an air pollutant. Because this level was surprisingly low, compared with that set for daily, 8-hr. industrial exposures to Be (2 $\mu g./m.^3$), an experimental study of the possible potentiating action of fluoride, a substance involved in Be production, was made by Stokinger and co-workers (*113*). The study, made in rats exposed on alternate days to $BeSO_4 \cdot 6H_2O$ mist and HF, at levels of 0.38 mg. $Be/m.^3$ and 8 $mg./m.^3$ HF, with the requisite control exposures, resulted in enhanced effects in the mixed exposure group over those in a corresponding group exposed to the agents singly. Mortality was greater than that expected for the time exposed, as were the histological changes in the lung; body weight showed greater depression and fluoride deposition in various osseous structures exceeded by 14 to 23% that found in corresponding controls exposed to each agent singly. Although the enhanced toxicity was but a small fraction of that implied in the difference between the air pollution and plant levels, it should be noted that the experimental study was acute in nature, whereas neighborhood cases were chronic, involving unquestionably several months or years of exposure. Thus, in addition to demonstrating certain potentiation of a vapor by a particulate, the study is believed important for another reason: it showed that enhanced toxic effects may occur from substances not necessarily inhaled together but in sequence with one another.

IX. Mixtures of Gases and Vapors

A. Ozone and Hydrogen Peroxide (H_2O_2)

The presence of H_2O_2 in oxidant smog atmosphere in small concentrations is likely, as the result of an interaction of 2 hydroperoxy radicals (*114*), or as a secondary reaction product of ozone on living tissue. A study of the toxicological interaction of H_2O_2 and O_3 in animals, by Svirbely *et al.*, (*115*), showed the combination to be remarkably toxic; concentrations above 1.5 p.p.m. H_2O_2 with 1 p.p.m. O_3 were lethal to mice following a 4-hr. exposure. These concentrations are noninjurious when the substances are inhaled singly. (The 4-hr. LC_{50} of H_2O_2 by inhalation in mice approximates 200 p.p.m.; of O_3, 6 p.p.m.) H_2O_2 proved similarly synergistic for rats but at a somewhat higher concentration (above 3 p.p.m.) when O_3 levels were maintained at about 1 p.p.m.

O_3 and H_2O_2 showed other interesting toxicological interactions. Repeated exposures of mice to H_2O_2, or a single dose of about ⅕ the lethal dose, conferred protection (tolerance) on mice that were subsequently challenged with acute lethal doses of O_3. The reverse cross tolerance was also demonstrable. Cumene hydroperoxide likewise afforded protection against challenging doses of H_2O_2, and finally H_2O_2 provided a tolerance to subsequent lethal exposures of itself. This phenomenon of cross tolerance among these respiratory irritants indicates a common basis for at least part of their action in the respiratory tract.

B. Ozone and 100% Oxygen

The exposure of rodents to ozone in the presence of 100% O_2 reduced the toxicity of O_3 for the mouse (3-hr. LC_{50} ozone, at 12.6 p.p.m. versus 33 p.p.m. for the mixture) but resulted in no observable change in acute lethality in the rat and guinea pig, according to Mittler *et al.* (*116*). What inference one may draw from these results for man is not clear.

C. Ozone and Carbon Dioxide

When a mixture of O_3 in 2% CO_2 was administered in a single, 3-hr. exposure to rodents, the acute toxicity of O_3 was slightly enhanced for the guinea pig (24.7 p.p.m. vs. 19.2 p.p.m. for the mixture; 13.1 and 10.2 p.p.m. respectively for the rat); no effect of the 2% CO_2 on O_3 lethality was noted in the mouse, however (*116*). Ozone in these experiments was determined by the neutral KI method, which gives values approximately 1.6 times greater than does the alkaline KI method at these concentrations.

D. Ozone and Nitrogen Dioxide

The acute lethal effects of O_3 for mice was slightly reduced by the addition of NO_2 in a single, 4-hr. exposure (*46*), presumably by the formation of N_2O_5 which has a lesser acute toxicity for rodents than has ozone.

E. Carbon Monoxide and Gaseous Synergists

For no other air pollutant has synergistic action been reported so generally as for carbon monoxide (*78*). It is regrettable, however, that demonstrations were made at unrealistically high air concentrations, for it is not at present possible to state with assurance whether the synergism observed at high levels also occurs at air pollution levels. With the limited amount of information available on the mechanism of action of synergists, one would be inclined to conclude that the enhanced effects seen at high levels would not necessarily occur at extremely low levels, on the basis that critical enzyme inhibition would be slight at extremely low air pollution levels and that thus the "sites of action or loss" would not be reduced, one of the requirements for synergistic action.

A variety of agents increase the toxicity of CO; none is reported that decreases its toxicity, with the possible exception of alcohol, which

Pecora (*116a*) reported slightly reduced the HbCO (carboxyhemoglobin) concentration in the blood of dogs breathing 100 p.p.m. CO.

Many investigators have found illuminating gas to be more toxic than expected on the basis of its percentage concentration in CO, and explain this effect by the presence of various contaminants whose nature has not been determined but among which may be benzene.

Hydrogen sulfide (H_2S) at a concentration of 0.04% (400 p.p.m.) materially increases the toxicity of 0.5% CO. A 10-min. exposure of the mixture was fatal to mice, whereas the same exposure to each gas singly was not; however, exposure to the mixture at one-half the concentration of each gas for longer periods was also fatal. This effect is possibly one of true synergism, although H_2S at this concentration stimulates respiration and thus increases intake of CO. In contrast to H_2S, CO is not rapidly fatal, and thus simple additive effects of each gas would not be expected to be observed. Hydrogen cyanide (HCN) is similarly synergistic with CO; a mixture of 1000 p.p.m. CO and 18 p.p.m. HCN produces as severe a paralysis in cats as is produced by a mixture containing 2.5 to 3 times the concentration of each gas.

Possibly of greater importance to air pollution is the apparent synergistic action of nitrogen oxides with CO. Admixture of 240–250 p.p.m. of nitrogen oxides and 1600–1700 p.p.m. CO proved fatal to cats in 90 min., whereas concentrations of 430 p.p.m. nitrogen oxides and 4000 p.p.m. CO, singly, for 70–80 min. were required for fatality. The mechanism of the enhanced effect is believed to be the interference with CO expiration caused by the pulmonary edema from the nitrogen oxides.

Other suggestive but less definite enhancement of CO toxicity has been noted. Rabbits with anthracotic lesions in the lung were more susceptible to CO than normal animals. It is a clinical impression that individuals suffering from tuberculosis and silicosis succumb more readily to CO; longer periods for recovery from CO poisoning were also found among persons so afflicted; alcohol has been similarly implicated, but this has not been borne out by studies on dogs. It is probable also that altered effects would occur from exposure to CO in individuals who have abnormalities of the blood or of the blood-forming organs. And, inasmuch as one of the actions of CO is on the peripheral blood vessels, diseases that affect these structures should result in enhanced CO effects.

F. Sulfur Compounds and Oxidant Gases

A number of the oxidant gases of air pollution interest—ozone, nitrogen dioxide, ketene and others—appear to be radiomimetic or to have radiomimetic potentialities (*52, 117, 118*). Because certain sulfur-containing organic molecules have been found effective in protecting animals against acute lethal effects of X-irradiation (*119, 120, 121*), the potential of sulfur compounds from petroleum in conferring protection against certain oxidant gases was tested in mice and rats by Fairchild *et al.* (*122*). Both organic thiols and disulfides, but not organic sulfides, were highly effective in antagonizing the acute lethal action of either NO_2 or O_3 when inhaled along with the oxidant gases. Table IV shows the

TABLE IV
EFFECT OF SULFUR COMPOUNDS ON THE TOXICITY OF NITROGEN DIOXIDE AND OZONE FOR MICE[a]

Sulfur compound	Average conc. (p.p.m.)	Oxidant (average conc. p.p.m.)		Mortality			
				S-treated		Control	
		NO_2	O_3	24 hr.	72 hr.	24 hr.	72 hr.
Hexanethiol	145	78	—	0/20	1/20	10/20	11/20
	115	—	4.1	1/20	2/20	10/20	10/20
Methanethiol	65	—	4.8	2/15	2/15	9/15	9/15
Dimethyl disulfide	45	83	—	5/20	5/20	10/20	11/20
	21 mg./kg.[b]	80	—	4/20	4/20	13/20	13/20
	21 mg./kg.[b]	—	4.6	2/20	2/20	10/20	12/20
Hydrogen polysulfide	20 mg./kg.[b]	105	—	8/25	8/25	16/25	18/25
Benzenethiol	14	76	—	1/20	1/20	10/20	10/20
	9	—	6.1	1/20	3/20	11/20	12/20
Hydrogen sulfide	11	—	4.9	7/35	7/35	17/35	18/35
	1.5	82	—	1/20	2/20	10/20	10/20

[a] Mortality at 24 and 72 hr. is indicated by deaths per number of mice tested.
[b] Administered by intraperitoneal injection.

results of some of the more effective sulfur compounds tested. In general, the sulfur compounds were more effective against NO_2 than O_3, but aromatic as well as aliphatic types were protective. The most effective sulfur compound thus far found was a technical grade of H_2S that presumably contained some polysulfide; here the effective mole ratio was 1 to 55 moles NO_2; benzenethiol was next in order of effectiveness with a mole ratio of 1 to 5.4 moles NO_2. Against ozone the molar ratios for H_2S and benzenethiol were respectively 1/2 and 1/1.5. Both organic and inorganic polysulfides also afforded protection; hydrogen polysulfide and dimethyl disulfide offered substantial protection.

The antagonism against oxidant toxicity by sulfur compounds is physiological, and not the result of chemical combination prior to inhalation to form a less active compound. Analyses of chamber atmosphere for oxidant gas showed essentially no change upon addition of sulfur compounds. Moreover, protection was equally conferred by injected sulfur compounds. Histopathological examination of pulmonary tissue showed degrees of tissue change that paralleled the protective effect; pulmonary edema and cellular infiltration—characteristic responses of oxidant exposure—were markedly inhibited in the protected groups.

The mechanisms involved in the protection are not entirely clear, but apparently the functional unit is —SH and/or —SS, but not —S—; dimethyl sulfide was ineffective. Significantly, —SH and —SS are characteristic of compounds conferring protection against ionizing radiation (*119, 120*); for optimal protection, however, an amino group separated by not more than three carbon atoms from the S is required (*119*). Against O_3 and NO_2, however, amino sulfur compounds provided less than optimal protection. MEG (2-mercaptoethylguanidine · HBr), highly protective against irradiation effects at 200 mg./kg., gave only modest protection against 80 p.p.m. NO_2 (mortality: 8/20 protected as against 12/20 with NO_2 alone). Thus similarity, but not identity, of action in protective compounds favors strongly the view that the mechanism of action of the oxidants O_3 and NO_2 mimics that of X-irradiation.

Brinkman and Lamberts (*117*) have called attention to the possible radiomimetic properties of O_3 by showing that O_3 and irradiation produced the same defect in O_2 consumption of the skin of the finger; also cysteamine was equally protective against the effects of both agents. Likewise Fetner (*118*) has shown a similar capacity of O_3 and x-rays to produce chromosomal aberrations in *Vicia faba*. The action was presumably mediated through the OH and HO_2 radicals formed from the aqueous decomposition of O_3; the separate effects of O_3 plus irradiation were fully additive.

Several highly attractive mechanisms have been proposed for the action of radiation-protective thiols and disulfides (*119–121*) which may prove applicable to these findings. The oxidant-protective compounds studied may act as radical traps providing a "radical-buffering" defense in protecting the —SH and —SS— groups of target molecules, thus diminishing the tissue damage from free radical-generating O_3 (*118*) and the free radical NO_2.

It is felt that the noted antagonism displayed by certain sulfur compounds is highly significant for an insight into possible mechanisms of protection against air pollutants and also into the hitherto unexplained toxic action of oxidants.

X. Conclusion

In briefly concluding this chapter, it should be apparent that, although a considerable insight has been gained into the effects of certain of the more prominent air pollutants in animals, knowledge of the toxic potentialities of some of the currently more unusual or exotic air pollutants, such as peroxyacyl nitrates, ketenes, free radicals or radical formers, and air ions, is grossly incomplete and unsatisfactory. Similarly, only a beginning has been made in the more important area of toxicological interactions in which the presence of one air pollutant may, at one extreme, completely abolish the effects of another or, at the other extreme, enhance the effects out of all proportion to the toxicity of either alone. This beginning, however, is most impressive not only from the viewpoint just mentioned, but also because studies thus far indicate the contributions that may be made to our understanding, both of the relation of the action of certain types of air pollutants to radiation effects and of the basic physiological actions of the lung in particular, and the body in general.

References

1. "Air Pollution Handbook," (P. L. Magill, F. R. Holden, C. Ackley, eds.), Section 8. McGraw-Hill, New York, 1956.
2. I. R. Campbell and others, Annotated Bibliography, The Effects of Atmospheric Pollution on Man, Part IV. Kettering Laboratory, Cincinnati, Ohio (1957).
3. H. Heimann, H. M. Brooks, and D. G. Schmidt, Biological Aspects of Air Pollution, An Annotated Bibliography. Federal Security Agency, Washington, D. C. (1950).
4. A. Marsh, "Smoke, The Problem of Coal in the Atmosphere," pp. 69, 70, 91, 92. Faber and Faber, London, 1947.
5. L. C. McCabe, "Air Pollution," Proc. 1st U. S. Tech. Conf., Chapters 5, 6, 12. McGraw-Hill, New York, 1952.
6. H. H. Schrenk, H. Heimann, G. D. Clayton, W. M. Gafafer, and H. Wexler, "Air Pollution in Donora, Pennsylvania," Public Health Bulletin No. 306. U. S. Public Health Service, Washington, D. C., 1949.
7. W. P. Yant, F. A. Patty, H. H. Schrenk, and L. B. Berger, The response of Japanese waltzing mice and canaries to carbon monoxide and to atmospheres deficient in oxygen, *U. S. Bur. Mines, Rept. Invest.* **3040** (1930).
8. J. Mage and G. Batta, Résultats de l'expertise judiciare sur la cause des accidents survenus dans la vallée de la Meuse, *Chim. & Ind. (Paris)* **27,** 961 (1932).
9. J. Mage and G. Batta, Le role de l'acide fluorhydrique dans la nocivité du brouille de la Meuse en 1930. *Chim. & Ind. (Paris)* **30,** 787 (1933).
10. K. Roholm, The fog disaster in the Meuse Valley, 1930: A fluorine intoxication, *J. Ind. Hyg. Toxicol.* **19,** 126 (1937).
11. L. C. McCabe and G. D. Clayton, Air pollution by hydrogen sulfide in Poza Rica, Mexico, *A.M.A. Arch. Ind. Hyg. & Occup. Med.* **6,** 199 (1952).
12. *U. S. Bur. Mines Inform. Circ. No.* **6983** (1938). Some pertinent information about mine gases, 1938.
13. H. Collumbine, R. E. Pattle, and F. Burgess, The Toxicity of Fog, United Kingdom Scientific Mission, (Porton, England) (Oct. 1956).

14. W. D. Harkins and R. E. Swain, The chronic arsenical poisoning of herbivorous animals, *J. Am. Chem. Soc.* **30,** 928 (1908).
15. H. Prell, Die Schädigung der Tierwelt durch die Fernwirkungen von Industrieabgasen, *Arch. Gewerbepathol-Gewerbehyg.* **7,** 656 (1937).
16. J. N. Agate *et al.,* Industrial fluorosis, A study of the hazard to man and animals near Ft. Williams, Scotland, *Med. Research Council (Brit.) Mem. No.* **22,** (1949).
17. J. L. Shupe *et al.,* Pathology of chronic bovine fluorosis, *Proceedings Book, Am. Vet. Med. Assoc.* **92,** 125 (1955).
18. J. O. Anderson, *et al.,* Effect of feeding various levels of sodium fluoride to growing turkeys, *Poultry Sci.* **34,** 1147 (1955).
19. Recommended practices to reduce fluorosis in livestock and poultry, *Utah State Agr. Coll. Agr. Exptl. Sta. Circ.* **130** (1952).
20. H. E. Stokinger, *in* "Pharmacology and Toxicology of Uranium Compounds," (C. Voegtlin and H. C. Hodge, eds.), Part II, pp. 1042–1057. McGraw-Hill, New York, 1949.
21. F. A. Smith and G. J. Cox, An Annotated Bibliography of the Literature on the Pharmacology & Toxicology of Fluorine and Its Compounds Including Effects on Bones & Teeth. UR-154 Revised, Univ. Rochester Atomic Energy Project, Jan. 1952.
22. I. R. Campbell and E. M. Widner, with the assistance of I. P. Kukainis, Annotated Bibliography, The Occurrence and Biologic Effects of Fluorine Compounds, Vol. 1, Kettering Laboratory, Cincinnati, Ohio (1958).
23. E. Hupka, Über Flugstaubvergiftungen in der Umgebung von Metallhütten, *Wien. Tierärztl.* **42,** 763 (1955).
24. R. R. Sayers, A. C. Fieldner, W. P. Yant, and B. C. H. Thomas, Experimental studies on the effect of ethyl gasoline and its combustion products, *U. S. Bur. Mines, Monograph* No. 2 (1927).
24a. H. Borsook, E. H. Fischer, and G. Keighley, Factors affecting protein synthesis *in vitro* in rabbit reticulocytes, *J. Biol. Chem.* **229,** 1059 (1957).
25. A. Kantarow and M. Trumper, "Lead Poisoning," Williams & Wilkins, Baltimore, Maryland, 1944.
26. W. Hallgren, N. Kerllson, and G. Wramby, Molybdenosis in cattle, *Nord. Veterinärmed.* **6,** 469 (1954).
27. A. T. Dick and L. B. Bull, Some preliminary observations on the effect of molybdenum on the copper metabolism in herbivorous animals, *Australian Vet. J.* **21,** 70 (1945).
28. F. H. Kratzer, Effect of dietary molybdenum on chicks and poults, *Proc. Soc. Exptl. Biol. Med.* **80,** 483 (1952).
29. A. T. Dick, Molybdenum in animal nutrition, *Soil Sci.* **81,** 229 (1956).
30. R. Van Reen and M. A. Williams, Studies on the influence of sulfur compounds on molybdenum toxicity in rats, *Arch. Biochem. Biophys.* **63,** 1 (1956).
31. C. F. Mills, K. J. Monty, A. Ichihara, and P. B. Pearson, Metabolic effects of molybdenum toxicity in the rat, *J. Nutrition* **65,** 129 (1958).
32. B. D. Tebbens, J. F. Thomas, and M. Mukai, Hydrocarbon synthesis in combustion, *A.M.A. Arch. Ind. Health* **13,** 567 (1956); Aromatic hydrocarbon production related to incomplete combustion, *ibid.* **14,** 413 (1956); B. D. Tebbens, J. F. Thomas, E. N. Sanborn, M. Mukai, Hydrocarbon synthesis in combustion. II. *Am. Ind. Hyg. Assoc. Quart.* **18,** 165 (1957).
33. P. Kotin, H. L. Falk, and M. Thomas, Aromatic hydrocarbons, II. Presence in

particulate phase of gasoline-engine exhausts and the carcinogenicity of exhaust extracts, *A.M.A. Arch. Ind. Hyg. Occup. Med.* **9,** 164 (1954).

34. P. Kotin, H. L. Falk, and M. Thomas, II. Presence in the particulate phase of diesel-engine exhausts and the carcinogenicity of exhaust extracts, *A.M.A. Arch. Ind. Health* **11,** 113 (1955).

34a. J. Leiter, M. B. Shimkin, and M. J. Shear, *J. Natl. Cancer Inst.* **3,** 155, 167 (1942).

35. R. E. Pattle, H. Stretch, F. Burgess, K. Sinclair, and J. A. G. Edginton, Toxicity of fumes from diesel engine under 4 different running conditions. *Brit. J. Ind. Med.* **14,** 47 (1957).

36. Note in *Chem. Eng. News* **31,** 2866 (1956).

36a. W. C. Hueper, P. Kotin, E. C. Tabor, W. W. Payne, H. Falk, and E. Sawicki, Carcinogenic bioassays of air pollutants, *Proc. 53rd Ann. Meeting Air Poll. Control Assoc.* Paper No. 33 (1960).

37. A. Goetz and N. Tsuneishi, Bacteriologic analogue for eye irritation by aerosols, *A.M.A. Arch. Ind. Health* **20,** 167 (1959).

38. P. Kotin, H. L. Falk and M. Thomas, I. Production of skin tumors in mice with oxidation products of aliphatic hydrocarbons, *Cancer* **9,** 905 (1956).

39. P. Kotin and H. L. Falk, II. The experimental induction of pulmonary tumors in strain A mice after exposure to atmosphere of ozonized gasoline, *Cancer* **9,** 910 (1956).

40. P. Kotin and H. L. Falk, III. The experimental induction of pulmonary tumors and changes in respiratory epithelium in C_{57} BL mice following exposure to ozonized gasoline, *Cancer* **11,** 473 (1958).

41. P. Kotin and M. Thomas, Effects of air contamination on reproduction and offspring survival in mice, *A.M.A. Arch. Ind. Health* **16,** 411 (1957).

42. J. H. Gast and F. L. Estes, Biochemical effects of air pollutants. II. Experimental evaluation by *in vitro* techniques. *Proc. Ann. Meeting Air Poll. Control Assoc., Philadelphia, Pennsylvania* (1958).

43. O. Warburg, On the origin of cancer cells, *Science* **123,** 309 (1956).

43a. A. J. Haagen-Smit and C. E. Bradley, Ozone formation in photochemical oxidation of organic substances, *Ind. Eng. Chem.* **45,** 2086 (1953).

44. H. E. Stokinger, Ozone toxicity—A review of the literature through 1953, *A.M.A. Arch. Ind. Hyg. Occup. Med.* **9,** 366 (1954).

45. S. Mittler, D. Hedrick, M. King, and A. Gaynor, Toxicity of ozone. I. Acute toxicity, *Ind. Med. and Surg.* **25,** 301 (1956).

46. H. E. Stokinger, Evaluation of the acute hazards of ozone & oxides of nitrogen, *A.M.A. Arch. Ind. Health,* **15,** 181 (1957).

47. W. M. Diggle and J. C. Gage, Toxicity of ozone in presence of oxides of nitrogen, *Brit. J. Ind. Med.* **12,** 60 (1955).

48. J. J. Quilligan, R. D. Boche, H. L. Falk, and P. Kotin, Toxicity of ozone for young chick, *A.M.A. Arch. Ind. Health* **18,** 16 (1958).

49. R. H. Fetner and R. S. Ingols, A comparison of the bactericidal activity of ozone and chlorine against *E. coli* at 1°, *J. Genl. Microbiol.* **15,** 381 (1956).

50. M. Kleinfeld and C. P. Giel, Clinical manifestations of O_3 poisoning: report of a new source of exposure, *Am. J. Med. Sci.* **231,** 638 (1956).

51. H. E. Stokinger, W. D. Wagner, and P. G. Wright, Studies in ozone toxicity. I. Potentiating effects of exercise and tolerance development, *A.M.A. Arch. Ind. Health* **14,** 158 (1956).

52. H. T. Freebairn, Reversal of inhibitory effects of ozone on oxygen uptake by mitochondria, *Science* **126,** 303 (1957).

53. S. Mittler, Protection against death due to ozone poisoning, *Nature* **181,** 1063 (1958).
54. R. N. Matzen, Effect of Vitamin C and hydrocortisone on the pulmonary edema produced by O_3 in mice, *J. Appl. Physiol.* **11,** 105 (1957).
55. R. N. Matzen, Effects of serotonin on pulmonary edema produced by O_3 in mice, *Guthrie Clin. Bull.* **29,** 102 (1959).
56. S. Mittler, Toxicity of ozone. IV. Silicone aerosols and alcohol vapor therapy in O_3 poisoning, *Ind. Med. and Surg.* **27,** 43 (1958).
57. R. N. Matzen, Development of tolerance to ozone in reference to pulmonary edema, *Am. J. Physiol.* **190,** 84 (1957).
57a. P. Henschler, Protective effect of pretreatment to low concentrations of gas against lethal lung edema, *Arch. Exptl. Path. Pharmakol.* **238,** 66 (1960).
58. S. Mittler, M. King, and B. Burkhardt, Toxicity of ozone, *A.M.A. Arch. Ind. Health* **15,** 191 (1957).
59. H. E. Stokinger, W. D. Wagner, and O. J. Dobrogorski, Ozone toxicity studies. III. Chronic injury to lungs of animals following exposure at a low level, *A.M.A. Arch. Ind. Health* **16,** 514 (1957).
60. L. D. Scheel, O. J. Dobrogorski, J. T. Mountain, J. L. Svirbely, and H. E. Stokinger, Studies on pulmonary irritants, I. Physiologic, biochemical, immunologic and pathologic changes following ozone exposure, *J. Appl. Physiol.* **14,** 67 (1959).
61. R. Brinkman and H. B. Lamberts, Ozone as a possible radiomimetic gas, *Nature* **181,** 1202 (1958).
62. H. E. Stokinger, W. D. Wagner and O. J. Dobrogorski, unpublished results.
63. LeB. Gray, S. B. Goldberg, F. M. Patton, E. Kaplan, Toxicity of the Oxides of Nitrogen. II. *A.M.A. Arch. Ind. Hyg. Occup. Med.* **10,** 418 (1954); III. *ibid.* p. 423 (1954).
64. G. Pflesser, Die Bedeutung des Stickstoffmonoxyds bei ver Vergiftung durch Nitrose Gase, *Arch. exptl. Pathol. Pharmakol. Naunyn-Schmiedeberg's* **179,** 545 (1935).
65. R. R. Grayson, Silage gas poisoning: Nitrogen dioxide pneumonia, a new disease in agricultural workers, *Ann. Internal. Med.* **45,** 393 (1956).
66. N. A. Vigdortschik, E. C. Andreeva, I. Z. Matussevitsch, M. M. Nikulina, L. M. Frumina, and V. A. Striter, The symptomatology of chronic poisoning with oxides of nitrogen, *J. Ind. Hyg. Toxicol.* **19,** 469 (1937).
67. W. M. Diggle and J. C. Gage, The toxicity of nitrogen pentoxide, *Brit. J. Ind. Med.* **11,** 140 (1954).
68. W. M. Diggle and J. C. Gage, The toxicity of ozone in the presence of oxides of nitrogen, *Brit. J. Ind. Med.* **12,** 60 (1955).
69. D. H. Byers and B. E. Saltzman, Toxicity studies of nitrogen dioxide-ozone mixtures and nitrogen pentoxide, Presented before the Air Pollution Section of the Am. Chem. Soc. Annual Meeting, Atlantic City, June 1956.
70. I. Greenwald, Effects of inhalation of low concentrations of sulfur dioxide upon man and other mammals, *A.M.A. Arch. Ind. Hyg. Occup. Med.* **10,** 455 (1954).
71. T. Dalhamn, Mucous flow and ciliary activity in the trachea of healthy rats and rats exposed to respiratory irritant gases, *Acta Physiol. Scand.* **36,** *Suppl.,* 123, pp. 1–161 (1956).
72. M. O. Amdur, Effect of irritant gases and aerosols on respiratory system of the guinea pig, C.W.L. Tech. Memo No. 27-16, U. S. Army Chem. Warfare Laboratories, Army Chem. Center, Maryland (August 1957).

73. N. V. Volkova, The effect of sulfur dioxide on the organism, *Trans. Leningrad Saint-Gigien. Med. Inst.* **26,** 59 (1956). (Seen in Abstract only: *Referat. Zhur., Khim. Biol. Khim.* Abstr. No. 24077, 1957.)
74. T. A. Bystrova, Some aspects of the action of sulfur dioxide studied by the labeled-atoms method, *Gigiena Sanitariya* **22,** 30 (1957).
75. H. E. Stokinger, Size of dose—its effect on distribution in the body, *Nucleonics* **11,** 24 (1953).
76. J. H. Weatherby, Chronic toxicity of ammonia fumes by inhalation, *Proc. Soc. Exptl. Biol. Med.* **81,** 300 (1952).
77. R. E. Pattle and H. Collumbine, Toxicity of some atmospheric pollutants, *Brit. Med. J. No.* **4998,** 913 (1956).
78. W. F. von Oettingen, Carbon monoxide, its hazards and the mechanism of its action, *U. S. Public Health Bull. No.* **290** (1944).
79. N. Costellino, Cytochrome C in experimental carbon monoxide poisoning, *Folia Med. (Naples)* **38,** 838 (1955).
80. J. F. Treon, F. R. Dutra, J. Cappel, H. Sigmon, W. J. Younker, Toxicity of sulfuric acid mist, *Arch. Ind. Hyg. Occup. Med.* **2,** 716 (1950).
81. M. O. Amdur, R. Z. Schulz, and P. Drinker, Toxicity of sulfuric acid mist to guinea pigs, *A.M.A. Arch. Ind. Hyg. & Occup. Med.* **5,** 318 (1952).
82. M. D. Thomas, R. H. Hendricks, F. D. Gunn, and J. Critchlow, Prolonged exposure of guinea pigs to sulfuric acid aerosol, *A.M.A. Arch. Ind. Health* **17,** 70 (1958).
83. M. O. Amdur, Respiratory response of guinea pigs to sulfuric acid mist, *A.M.A. Arch. Ind. Health* **18,** 407 (1958).
84. G. F. Laughlen, Studies on pneumonia following nasopharyngeal injections of oil, *Am. J. Pathol.* **1,** 407 (1925).
85. M. Shoshkes, W. G. Banfield, and S. J. Rosenbaum, Distribution, effect and fate of oil aerosol particles retained in lungs of mice, *A.M.A. Arch. Ind. Hyg. Occup. Med.* **1,** 20 (1950).
86. P. Kotin, Unpublished results (1957).
87. L. V. Cralley, Effects of irritant gases upon the rate of ciliary activity, *J. Ind. Hyg. Toxicol.* **24,** 193 (1942).
88. W. E. Scott, E. R. Stephens, P. L. Hanst and R. C. Doerr, Presented at 22nd Midyear Meeting, Am. Petrol. Inst. Div. of Refining, Philadelphia, Pennsylvania, May 14, 1957.
89. J. F. Treon, H. E. Sigmon, K. V. Kitzmiller, F. F. Heyroth, W. J. Younker, and J. Cholak, Physiologic response of animals exposed to airborne ketene, *J. Ind. Hyg. Toxicol.* **31,** 209 (1949).
90. R. M. Mendenhall and H. E. Stokinger, Tolerance & cross-tolerance development to the atmospheric pollutants, ketene and ozone. *J. Appl. Physiol.* **14,** 923 (1959).
91. E. P. Floyd and H. E. Stokinger, Toxicity studies of certain organic peroxides and hydroperoxides, *Am. Ind. Hyg. Assoc. J.* **19,** 205 (1958).
92. G. Ljunggren and B. Norberg, On the effect and toxicity of dimethyl sulfide, dimethyl disulfide and methyl mercaptan, *Acta Physiol. Scand.* **5,** 248 (1943).
93. L. DeRekowski, Sur l'action du methyl mercaptan, *Arch. sci. biol. (U. S. S. R.)* **2,** 206 (1893).
94. E. J. Fairchild and H. E. Stokinger, Toxicologic studies on organic sulfur compounds. I. Acute toxicity of some aliphatic and aromatic thiols, *Am. Ind. Hyg. Assoc. J.* **19,** 171 (1958).

95. E. J. Fairchild, Unpublished results (1958).
96. F. Flury and F. Zernik, Über die Giftigkeit des Thiophens, *Chem. Ztg.* **56,** 149 (1932).
97. W. B. Deichmann, M. L. Keplinger, and G. F. Lanier, Acute effects of nitro-olefins upon experimental animals, *A.M.A. Arch. Ind. Health* **18,** 312 (1958).
98. K. F. Lampe, T. J. Mende, W. B. Deichmann, *et al.,* Evaluation of conjugated nitro-olefins as eye irritants, *Ind. Med. and Surg.* **27,** 375 (1958).
99. J. F. Brown, The infrared spectra of nitro- and other oxidized nitrogen compounds, *J. Am. Chem. Soc.* **77,** 6341 (1955).
100. E. Burgi, Die Wirkung von Narcotica-Kombinationen, *Deut. med. Wochschr.* **36,** 29 (1910).
101. H. Veldstra, Synergism and potentiation, *Pharmacol. Revs.* **8,** 339 (1956).
102. J. P. Frawley, E. C. Hagan, O. G. Fitzhugh, H. N. Fuyat, and W. I. Jones, Marked potentiation in mammalian toxicity from simultaneous administration of 2 anticholinesterase compounds, *J. Pharmacol. Exptl. Therap.* **119,** 147 (1957) (Abstract).
103. S. D. Murphy and K. P. DuBois, Quantitative measurement of inhibition of the enzymatic detoxication of malathion by EPN, *Proc. Soc. Exptl. Biol. Med.* **96,** 813 (1957).
104. J. H. Gaddum, *in* "Drug Antagonism," A Symposium Presented at 20th Intern. Physiol. Congr., Brussels; *Pharmacol. Revs.* **9,** 211 (1956).
105. L. Dautreband, J. Shaver, and R. Capps, Studies on aerosols. XI. Influence of particulate matter on eye irritation produced by volatile irritants, *Arch. intern. Pharmacodynamie* **85,** 17 (1951).
106. C. W. LaBelle, J. E. Long, and E. E. Christofano, Synergistic effect of aerosols, *A.M.A. Arch. Ind. Health* **11,** 297 (1955).
107. M. O. Amdur, The physiologic response of guinea pigs to atmospheric pollutants, *Intern. J. Air Pollution* **1,** 170 (1959); also *Am. Ind. Hyg. Assoc. Quart.* **18,** 149 (1957).
108. A. Goetz, An interpretation of the synergistic effect of aerosols based upon specific surface action of airborne particles, *U. S. Public Health Service Final Rept. No.* SAph-69557 Part B (1958).
109. M. O. Amdur, Effect of a combination of SO_2 and H_2SO_4 on guinea pigs, *U. S. Public Health Rept.* **69,** 503 (1954).
110. R. E. Pattle and F. Burgess, Toxic effects of mixtures of sulfur dioxide and smoke, *J. Pathol. Bacteriol.* **73,** 411 (1957).
111. W. D. Wagner, O. J. Dobrogorski, and H. E. Stokinger, Antagonistic action of oil mists on air pollutants, *Arch. Envir. Health* **2,** 534 (1961).
112. M. Eisenbud, R. C. Wanta, C. Dustan, L. T. Steadman, W. B. Harris, and B. S. Wolf, Non-occupational berylliosis, *J. Ind. Hyg. Toxicol.* **31,** 282 (1949).
113. H. E. Stokinger, N. J. Ashenburg, J. De Voldre, J. K. Scott, and F. A. Smith, Acute inhalation toxicity of beryllium, II. The enhancing effect of the inhalation of hydrogen fluoride vapor on beryllium sulfate poisoning in animals, *A.M.A. Arch. Ind. Hyg. Occup. Med.* **1,** 398 (1950).
114. P. A. Leighton and W. A. Perkins, Photochemical secondary reactions in urban air, *Air Pollution Foundation, San Marino, California, Rept.* **24,** (Aug. 1958).
115. J. L. Svirbely, O. J. Dobrogorski, and H. E. Stokinger, Enhanced toxicity of ozone-hydrogen peroxide mixtures. *Am. Ind. Hyg. Assoc. J.* **22,** 21 (1961).

116. S. Mittler, D. Hedrick, and L. Phillips, Toxicity of ozone II. Effect of oxygen and carbon dioxide upon acute toxicity, *Ind. Med. and Surg.* **26,** 63 (1957).

116a. L. J. Pecora, Physiologic effects of ethyl alcohol and CO, *Am. Ind. Hyg. Assoc. J.* **20,** 235 (1959).

117. R. Brinkman, and H. B. Lamberts, Ozone as a possible radiomimetic gas, *Nature* **181,** 1202 (1958).

118. R. H. Fetner, Chromosome breakage in *Vicia faba* by ozone, *Nature* **181,** 504 (1958).

119. D. G. Doherty, W. T. Burnett, and R. Shapira, Chemical protection against ionizing radiation. II. Mercapto alkylamines and related compounds with protective activity, *Radiation Research* **7,** 13 (1957).

120. R. Shapira, D. G. Doherty, and W. T. Burnett, III. Mercaptoalkylguanidines and related isothiouronium compounds with protective activity, *Radiation Research* **7,** 22 (1957).

121. L. Eldjarn and A. Pihl, Abstract of paper presented at Intern. Congr. Radiation Research, Burlington, Vermont, August 1958.

122. E. J. Fairchild, II, H. E. Stokinger, and S. D. Murphy, Protection against ozone and nitrogen dioxide poisoning by sulfur compounds, *Science* **130,** 861 (1959).

CHAPTER 10

Effects of Air Pollution on Humans

JOHN R. GOLDSMITH

Air Pollution Medical Studies, Bureau of Chronic Diseases, California State Department of Public Health, Berkeley, California

I. Introduction

A. Importance of Air to Health

The average adult male requires about 30 lb. of air each day compared with about 2¾ lb. of food and about 4½ lb. of water. Compared with the other necessities of life, obligatory continuous consumption is a unique property of air. The insensible, intimate interpenetration of air which courses in and out from the lungs gives to air pollution its essential importance. It has been estimated that a man can live for 5 weeks without food, for 5 days without water, but for only 5 min. without air. Air is essential to the sense of sight, smell, and hearing, and its pollution assaults the first two of these.

B. Classification of Health Effects

Natural variability in responsiveness to air pollution is observed in all populations. Generally speaking, susceptibility is great among premature infants, the newborn, the elderly, and the infirm. Those with chronic diseases of the lungs or heart are thought to be at particular risk. Because of the wide variation in sensitivity to air pollution of different groups in the population, data concerning health effects on healthy persons may not be as important as the responses of the individuals most likely to be sensitive. The control of air pollution, to the extent that it is based on health effects, should be based on the most sensitive groups of persons. This principle requires that these sensitive groups be definable in terms of age and/or medical status.

The effect of air pollution on personal or community health are:

(1) Acute sickness or death.

(2) Insidious or chronic disease.

(3) Alteration of important physiological function, such as ventilation of the lung, transport of oxygen by hemoglobin, or dark adaptation (the ability to adjust eye mechanisms for vision in partial darkness).

(4) Untoward symptoms, which in the absence of an obvious cause, such as air pollution, might lead a person to seek medical attention and relief.

(5) Discomfort from air pollution sufficient to lead individuals to change residence or place of employment.

Today, medicine and public health can no longer satisfy the demands of the public if their concern is confined to diagnosed disease states. This has had its most succinct expression in the definition of health by the World Health Organization as "A state of complete physical, mental, and social well-being and not merely the absence of disease or infirmity." The public will not wait for the demonstration that an unpleasant atmosphere causes disease. They will insist that the air of metropolitan cities be free of substances which interfere with visibility, have a bad odor, or cause irritation. There is no doubt, however, that the urgency with which steps are taken to improve air quality will depend very much on how severe or serious a health problem air pollution becomes.

C. Relation of Air Pollution Effects to Other Exposures

1. *Occupation*

Many common air pollutants are also substances to which persons are exposed in their occupations. This is true, for example, of sulfur dioxide, carbon monoxide, and lead, as well as of smoke and many dusts. The downtown traffic policeman, the automobile mechanic, and the truck driver in large metropolitan areas may all have substantial exposures to carbon monoxide and lead in association with their occupations. Since these substances may also be found in community pollution, cessation of work does not necessarily terminate the occupational exposure. Therefore, such individuals have an unusually great risk from exposure to community air pollution.

Workers in the fields of occupational medicine and industrial hygiene have given us a wealth of information about the effects on human health of specific substances in specific concentrations (*1–3*). This information has been organized and evaluated in establishing the so-called threshold limits or maximum allowable concentrations (MAC), which are really neither thresholds, nor allowable (*4*). Table I indicates the threshold limits for industrial exposure and the maximal reported air pollution levels for selected pollutants. There are several good reasons why these limits must be cautiously applied to community air pollution exposures. An occupational exposure is limited in area. It is almost always possible to reduce the effects of occupational exposure. Persons exposed to occupational air pollution are generally in good health, are usually men, and if there exists among them any with an idiosyncrasy for a given type of exposure, such a person could presumably find employment elsewhere. Finally, the occupational exposure is for roughly 40 out of the 168 hr. in the week, and these hours of exposure are intermittent.

In contrast, exposures to community air pollution are relatively cumbersome to control and relatively difficult for the exposed person to avoid, even though during air pollution episodes it is usually possible for persons who may be adversely affected to reduce their exposure by the simple expedient of staying indoors. The population exposed to

TABLE I

Comparison of Industrial Threshold Limits (MAC) with Maximal Air Pollution Values

Substance	Industrial threshold limits (MAC)[a]		Maximal air pollution levels	Place and date where observed
	p.p.m.	mg./m.^{3}		
Gases				
Acrolein	0.5	1.2	0.011 p.p.m.[b]	Los Angeles, California, 1960
Carbon monoxide	100	110	72[c] p.p.m.	Los Angeles, California, 1959
Fluoride (as HF)	3.0	2.5	0.08[d] p.p.m.	Baltimore, Maryland, 1950
Formaldehyde	5	6	1.87[c] (aldehydes as formaldehyde) p.p.m.	Pasadena, California, 1957
Gasoline	500	2000	4.66[c] (total hydrocarbons) p.p.m. (Gasoline, Heptane, Hexane)	Los Angeles, California, 1957
Heptane (*n*-heptane)	500	2000		
Hexane	500	1800		
Hydrogen sulfide	20	30	0.9[d] p.p.m.	Santa Clara, California, 1949–1954
Nitrogen dioxide	5	9	1.3[c] p.p.m.	Los Angeles, California, 1958
Ozone	0.1	0.2	0.90[c] p.p.m.	Los Angeles, California, 1955
Sulfur dioxide	5	13	3.16[d] p.p.m.	Chicago, Illinois, 1937
Particulates				
Arsenic	—	0.5	0.00141[e] mg./m.^{3}	Philadelphia, Pennsylvania, 1954
Beryllium	—	0.002	0.00011[f] mg./m.^{3}	Pennsylvania, 1958
Lead	—	0.2	0.042[d] mg./m.^{3}	Los Angeles, California, 1949–1954
Sulfuric acid	—	1	—	—
Vanadium				
dust	—	0.5	0.0004[d] mg./m.^{3} (dust and fume)	Cincinnati, Ohio, 1946–1951
fume	—	0.1		

[a] "Threshold Limit Value for 1960," American Conference of Governmental Industrial Hygienists. *A.M.A. Arch. Environmental Health* **1,** 140 (1960).

[b] W. L. Faith and N. A. Renzetti, "Seventh Technical Progress Report," Air Poll. Foundation Report No. 33. San Marino, California, 1961.

[c] Los Angeles Air Pollution Control District Reports.

[d] Stanford Research Institute Final Report, "Literature Review of Metropolitan Air Pollutant Concentrations—Preparation, Sampling and Assay of Synthetic Atmospheres," Menlo Park, California, 1956.

[e] Air Pollution Measurements of the National Air Sampling Network, *Public Health Service Publ.* No. 637 (1958).

[f] V. H. Sussman, J. Lieben, and J. G. Cleland, *Am. Ind. Hyg. Assoc. Quart.* **20,** 504 (1959).

community air pollution includes the newborn, children, adults (in whatever state of health), and the elderly. Finally, though exposure to air pollution varies from hour to hour, by its nature it is continuous. Many of the levels for industrial exposures depend upon detoxification of pollutants by the body. These are inapplicable to air pollution since continuous exposures do not give the same possibilities for excretion or detoxification of pollutants during times when none are being absorbed.

2. *Cigarette Smoking*

The products of tobacco combustion are similar to the products of combustion of other fuels. Both include carbon monoxide, oxides of nitrogen, and tars of a complex sort which contain a potent substance [benzo(*a*)pyrene] capable of causing cancer in experimental animals (*5*).

Whether or not he smokes is decided by each individual: he does not have the same opportunity to exercise control over the inhalation of air polluted by the activities of others.

Occupational and community air pollution have been found to be associated with the same types of diseases associated with cigarette smoking—cancer of the lung, pulmonary emphysema, and bronchitis. On the basis of present data, the strength of the associations is greater for cigarette smoking than for community air pollution. Therefore, in evaluating air pollution effects in a community, both the proportion of persons with occupational exposure to these pollutants and the proportion of persons with cigarette-smoking exposures must be taken into consideration.

3. *Radiation*

A portion of all inhaled particles is radioactive, from either natural radioactivity or fallout (Chapter 24). If nuclear bomb testing is ever stopped, fallout should decrease (*6*). However, those particles which are radioactive because of radon decay and similar natural causes will always be a part of our atmosphere. Since radon and stratospheric fallout will, to a considerable extent, be adsorbed on particles and since they will largely be attached to otherwise nonradioactive particles, it follows that the size distribution of the radioactive particles will replicate that of the nonradioactive particles in the atmosphere. The site in the respiratory tract where radioactive particles will deposit will thus be determined in part by the size distribution of nonradioactive particulates in the atmosphere (see pp. 349–351).

It has been clearly shown that inhalation of radioactive particles can produce lung cancer in experimental animals (*7*).

Some have postulated that the effects of air pollution resemble those of radiation—that they are radiomimetic (*8*). For example, the effects of ozone in accelerating pulmonary fibrosis is similar to that of radiation. Air pollution effects are neutralized in experimental animals by the same sorts of substances which tend to protect against radiation. Finally, certain types of air pollutants may contain fairly extensive amounts of free radicals. These energy-containing chemical fragments are thought to be the mechanism through which radiation exerts its biological effect on man and animals.

II. Acute Air Pollution Episodes

A. Characteristics Common to Episodes

Several disastrous episodes have focused attention upon air pollution as a health problem. These episodes have made it obvious that the air quality of a community may deteriorate enough to menace the health of its citizens.

The observed relationship of air pollution disasters to the presumptive exposures permits several general conclusions. The toll of excess mortality and morbidity in disasters has usually not been appreciated at the time; therefore, protective measures had not been taken. They have always occurred under extraordinary meteorological conditions which reduced the effective volume of air in which the pollutants were mixed. Most have occurred under circumstances in which small water droplets were present, and, therefore, it is likely that a combination of aerosols and gaseous pollutants was involved.

B. Meuse Valley, Belgium, 1930

On Monday, December 1, 1930, the narrow valley of the Meuse River in Belgium was afflicted by an unusual and widespread weather condition which persisted the remainder of the week. In this narrow river valley 15 mi. in length with hills about 300 ft. high on either side, a thermal inversion confined emitted pollutants to the air volume contained in the valley. There were a large number of industries, including coke ovens, blast furnaces, steel mills, glass factories, zinc smelters, and sulfuric acid plants. On the third day of this unusual weather a large number of people became ill with respiratory tract complaints, and before the week was over, sixty had died. In addition, as discussed in the preceding chapter, there were deaths in cattle. Older persons with previously known diseases of the heart and lungs had the greatest mortality; however, illness affected persons of all ages and was best described as an irritation of all exposed membranes of the body, especially those of the respiratory tract. Chest pain, cough, shortness of breath, eye and nasal irritation were the most common symptoms. Treatment with antispasmodic drugs was of some help. Frequency of symptoms decreased strikingly on December 5, but fatalities occurred both on December 4 and December 5. Autopsy examinations showed only congestion and irritation of the tracheal mucosa and large bronchi. However, there was some black particulate matter in the lungs, mostly within the phagocytes.

The chemical substances responsible for the illness and fatalities have been disputed. In the original report on the episode (*9*) it was estimated (since no measurements had been made during the event) that the sulfur dioxide content of the atmosphere was from 25 to 100 mg./m.^{3} (9.6 to 38.4 p.p.m.). Assuming, as is unlikely, complete oxidation of the sulfur dioxide, sulfuric acid mist concentrations of 38 to 152 mg./m.^{3} might theoretically have resulted. Some have raised the question as to whether fluorides were possibly the cause of the episode (*10*). It is generally felt now that a combination of several pollutants may have been associated with this, as well as with other community disasters. Certainly, strong suspicion attaches to sulfur dioxide, but it is more likely that this substance, when dissolved or otherwise combined with water droplets, and in the presence of a multiplicity of other pollutants, oxidizes to sulfuric acid mist with a particle size sufficiently small to penetrate deeply into the lung.

Firket remarked prophetically that "the public services of London might be faced with the responsibility of 3200 sudden deaths if such a phenomenon occurred there" (*9*).

C. London, England, 1952

From December 5 through December 9, 1952, most of the British Isles were covered by a fog and temperature inversion. One of the areas most severely affected was London, which is located in the broad valley of the Thames. During this period an unusually large number of deaths occurred and many more persons were ill. The illnesses were usually sudden in onset and tended to occur on the third or fourth day of the episode (*11*). Shortness of breath, cyanosis, some fever and rales were observed. Most of those seriously ill were in the older age groups. Admissions to hospitals for the treatment of respiratory diseases were increased markedly, but so were admissions for heart disease. An increase in mortality among all ages was observed. However, the very old, those in the seventh and eighth decades, had the highest increment. The most frequent causes to which deaths were ascribed were chronic bronchitis, bronchopneumonia, and heart disease. Of particular interest was the fact that mortality remained elevated for several weeks after the weather had improved. The total excess was between 3500 and 4000 deaths, distributed as shown in Fig. 1.

Measurements were available for the amount of suspended smoke and sulfur dioxide. The highest values reported were 4.46 mg./m.^{3} of smoke and 1.34 p.p.m. of sulfur dioxide.

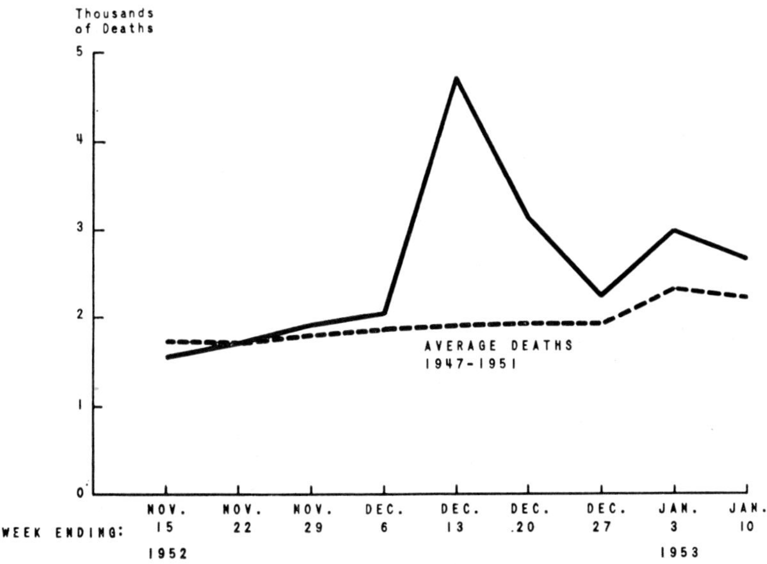

FIG. 1. Deaths registered in Greater London (London fog: December 5–8). [Source: Ministry of Health, Reports on Public Health and Medical Subjects No. 95, Table 1, p. 2. Her Majesty's Stationery Office, London, 1954.]

Autopsy examination did not reveal any characteristic mode of death other than evidence of respiratory tract irritation. Search of the past records of meteorology and mortality indicated that periods of excessive mortality had occurred previously. Three hundred excess deaths occurred in the winter of 1948; detectable increases in mortality associated with fog were found in December 1873, January 1880, February 1882, December 1891, and December 1892. A subsequent episode has occurred in 1959 (*12*). None of the other episodes, however, was quite as severe as the one in 1952.

D. Donora, Pennsylvania, U.S.A., 1948

The impact of the Donora disaster has been eloquently described by Breton Rouèche (*13*). "The fog closed over Donora on the morning of Tuesday, October 26th. The weather was raw, cloudy, and dead calm, and it stayed that way as the fog piled up all that day and the next. By Thursday, it had stiffened adhesively into a motionless clot of smoke. That afternoon it was just possible to see across the street, and except for the stacks, the mills had vanished. The air began to have a sickening smell, almost a taste. It was the bittersweet reek of sulfur dioxide. Everyone who was out that day remarked on it, but no one was much concerned. The smell of sulfur dioxide, a scratchy gas given off by burning coal and melting ore, is a normal concomitant of any durable fog in Donora. This time it merely seemed more penetrating than usual." During this period, again, temperature inversion and foggy weather affected a wide area. Donora is located on the inside of the horseshoe-shaped valley of the Monongahela River. The city contained a large steel mill, a sulfuric acid plant, and a large zinc production plant, among other industries. The hills on either side of the valley are steep, rising to several hundred feet. At the time there were about fourteen thousand people living in the valley. A meticulous health survey of the population was made within a few months of the episode (*14*). The investigation was directed at the health effects which occurred among people and animals, the nature of the contaminants, and the meteorological conditions. Interviews were obtained from persons who were ill and from physicians in the community. Roentgenograms and blood tests were taken, and teeth, bone, and urine samples were studied to determine whether fluorides might have been involved. These studies indicated that 43% of the population was made ill during the episode. Curiously, a large number of the persons who were not ill were unaware of the extent of ill health. Cough was the most prominent symptom, but all of the respiratory tract and the eyes, nose, and throat were irritated. Many complained of chest constriction, headache, vomiting, and nausea. There was a relationship observed between the frequency and severity of illness and the age of the population. Most of those who became ill did so on the second day of the episode; of the twenty deaths, most occurred on the third day. Among the fatalities, pre-existing cardiac or respiratory system disease was common. From examinations made for fluorides it was felt that fluorine was probably not involved. Retrospective examination of mortality indicated that a similar event might have occurred in April of 1945. Autopsy examinations from the 1948 fatalities were again nonspecific, but there was abundant evidence of respiratory tract irritation. Environmental measurements had not been made during the episode, but it was inferred that sulfur dioxide had ranged between 0.5 and 2.0 p.p.m. Particulate matter was undoubtedly present. The calls for medical assistance in Donora ceased rather abruptly on Saturday evening despite the fact that the fog remained quite dense. This suggests that some change in the physical nature of the fog droplets may have occurred; for example, the particles may have increased sufficiently in size so that they were deposited in the upper airway instead of penetrating deeply into the lung.

The population affected was restudied in 1952 and 1957 and was found to have a less favorably mortality and morbidity experience than persons not affected in 1948 (*15*).

E. Poza Rica, Mexico, 1950

Another type of community disaster resulting from the discharge of a toxic gas from a single source befell the small town of Poza Rica, Mexico (*16*). Here a new plant for the recovery of sulfur from natural gas put a portion of its equipment into operation on the night of November 21, 1950. One of the steps in the process was the removal of hydrogen sulfide from natural gas. In order to do this, the hydrogen sulfide was concentrated in a system in which it was intended to be burned. During the night of November 23 and 24, the flow of gas into and through the plant was increased; the weather was foggy with weak winds and a low inversion layer. Between 4:45 A.M. and 5:10 A.M. of November 24, hydrogen sulfide was released inadvertently and spread into the adjacent portion of the town. Most of the nearby residents were either in bed or had just arisen; many were afflicted promptly with respiratory and central nervous system symptoms. Three hundred twenty were hospitalized and twenty-two died. The characteristic manner in which the hydrogen sulfide affected these individuals was to produce loss of sense of smell and severe respiratory tract irritation. Most of the deaths occurred in persons who had such central nervous system symptoms as unconsciousness and vertigo. A number of the affected individuals also had pulmonary edema. Persons of all ages were affected and pre-existing disease did not seem to have much influence on which persons were afflicted.

F. Yokohama, Japan, 1946

In the winter of 1946 American service men and their dependents in the Kanto Plains area of Yokohama, Japan reported an unusual frequency of respiratory tract irritation with a predominance of asthmatic symptoms (*17*). The preceding year many of the same personnel had had a mild bronchitis. Most of those afflicted had no history of allergy, and pollen counts were relatively low during the episodes. These attacks tended to occur during a period of light winds and relatively high air pollution levels. This problem has continued to be troublesome. Among some Japanese, similar symptoms have been reported and a not-dissimilar situation has been also reported from Okinawa. The cause of these episodes is yet to be determined, but investigations concerning particulate and sulfur dioxide levels in Japanese cities suggests that perhaps there is some association with particulate or sulfur dioxide type of pollution.

G. New Orleans, Louisiana, U.S.A., 1958

In 1958 a series of unusual episodes of increased frequency of asthma was reported in certain districts of New Orleans. Gentle winds, usually from the same direction, have been associated with these episodes. The investigation is continuing, but it is thought that a single or closely grouped source is likely to be involved because of the geographic distribution of cases.

III. Experimental Exposures in Animals and Man

By exposure of animals to various pollutants a great deal has been learned about the fundamental mechanisms by which air pollution interferes with health. However, there are certain obvious limitations of this method. In many respects the manner of response to a given exposure by an animal cannot be thought to mimic the response to the same pollutant for the same period of time by man. For example, the experimental production of lung cancer in animals after exposure to the same substances which are epidemiologically associated with lung cancer in man has been quite unrewarding. The effects of some pollutants are related to the ventilatory pattern and to the size and other functional properties of the respiratory tract. This obviously differs among the several species in relationship to body size; species variability of some consequence also occurs in the mucous glands, being, for example, more abundant in the rat than in the mouse. There are obvious metabolic and anatomic differences between animals and man which cast some doubts on the ability to extrapolate to human health some of the findings in animal exposures. Despite these limitations, animal experiments carefully done have contributed a great deal to our knowledge of the effects of air pollutants on humans.

In the case of experimental animals, with proper planning, exposures to a large number of compounds of varying concentrations can be and have been carried out. To undertake the same type of work in humans is ethically impossible. This does not mean that there is not a place for experimental human exposures, but merely that their role is limited.

Several general principles can be developed which should provide guides for experimental human exposures. One of the simpler and more obvious principles is that when accidental or unplanned exposures to humans occur, suitable opportunities should be taken to make the necessary relevant observations. A second principle holds that when planned or experimental exposures are undertaken, they should be undertaken with such pollutants and at such levels that it is as certain as possible that no lasting harm will occur. The corollary of this principle is that the effects of pollutants which are most important to determine by human exposure are those very effects which are transient and which are characteristic of humans, such as the effects on judgment, on sensation, on reflex activity, or on subclinical responses such as alterations of airway resistance. In studying human responses the most sensitive available methods ought to be used in order to use the lowest possible concentration of pollutants capable of producing a reliable response.

Another principle which can be used as a guide in experimental human air pollution exposure is that the concentrations should resemble those likely to occur under conditions of natural pollution. Under these circumstances there may be some benefit to the experimental subject, since his measured response under laboratory conditions will permit him to know whether subsequent exposure to natural pollution is likely to result in any ill effects. On the basis of this concept, there are some who feel that experimental exposure of persons who have substantial impairment of the cardiopulmonary system is indicated because of its prognostic and potentially prophylactic importance.

Legal reviews of this problem have suggested that when the subjects are hired for this purpose, the relationship becomes a complex one. It is generally held that written waivers of responsibility under most circumstances provide inadequate protection against possible liability of the experimenter. It is more satisfactory if the subjects for human exposures are true volunteers (unpaid), patients to whom the information concerning their reaction to exposure is important, or are themselves the investigators. In the latter case methods of detecting human responses should be insensitive to voluntary influence by the subject investigators.

IV. Dilemmas

In some cases, several pollutants have very nearly the same effects on humans; for example, irritation may be the predominant effect of sulfur dioxide, formaldehyde, and acrolein, and, to some extent, of chlorine and ozone. In addition, the physiological response of increased airway resistance is common to many irritants and is also produced by inert dusts (*18*).

It is known that, at least *in vitro,* nitrogen oxides interfere with the oxygen transport function of hemoglobin by altering the hemoglobin molecule. This has not been observed *in vivo*. As is well known, carbon monoxide produces this effect both *in vitro* and *in vivo*. Thus, several pollutants likely to occur together may have common effects.

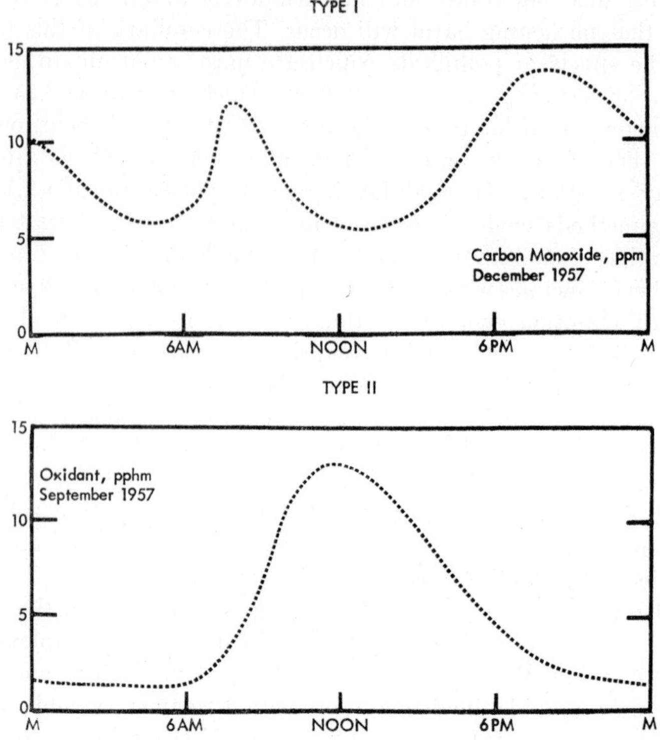

FIG. 2. Los Angeles basin average data. Examples of Type I and Type II diurnal curves. Type I: Primary pollutants have two diurnal peaks at approximately 7:00 A.M. and 8:00 P.M.; have an annual peak in winter. Carbon monoxide, hydrocarbons, nitrogen dioxide, particulates, sulfur dioxide are examples of Type I pollutants. Type II: Secondary pollutants have one diurnal peak at approximately 12:00 noon; have an annual peak in autumn. Aldehydes, eye irritant, oxidant, ozone, plant toxicant are examples of Type II pollutants. [Source: W. J. Hamming, R. D. McPhee, and J. R. Taylor, *J. Air Poll. Control Assoc.* **10**, 7 (1960).]

Experimental exposures have usually been conducted with level concentrations for stipulated periods of time; in contrast to these are the fluctuating exposures which occur with natural air pollution. For substances such as lead, whose toxicity is related to the accumulated body burden, in addition to studying the effect of level doses over long periods of time, it becomes necessary to estimate what the effect of fluctuating exposures might be since it can be assumed that the body has a limited capacity to detoxify or excrete such compounds. Therefore, if the exposure occurs at a rather low level during 16 or more hours of the day and a relatively high level for 8 hr. a day, this effect may be substantially different than the time-weighted average of these. This fact has been cited by Kehoe as one reason why no extrapolations should be made for lead from 8-hr. working day exposures to community air pollution exposures.

Most realistic air pollution exposures occur to multiple pollutants. Therefore, exposure of animals or even humans to single pollutants scarcely provides an adequate basis for estimating the simultaneous effect of several. Under natural conditions the several pollutants may vary in concentration from time to time. Figure 2 illustrates the fluctuation of multiple pollutants in Los Angeles (*19*).

There is already sufficient evidence that particulate pollutants may tend either to augment or, in some cases, to impair the effects of simultaneous exposure to pollutant gases (*20, 21*). These and other dilemmas have been extensively reviewed by Heimann (*21a*).

In view of these dilemmas, it is important to increase experimental work in which the time course of concentrations is altered in order to represent that likely to occur in realistic pollution situations, and to devise experiments utilizing realistic combinations of pollutants.

V. Effects of Particulate Pollutants

A. General Effects

There are at least two different fates for inhaled particulates. On the one hand, the larger particulates probably are impacted by aerodynamic forces upon the mucous lining of the upper airway and, if insoluble, are carried by ciliary action to the pharynx where they are swallowed. The smaller particulates usually impinge on the deeper structures in the lung where no mucous blanket exists. There they produce their effects directly or, if sufficiently insoluble, may be absorbed by the body's scavenger cells, from which the particles may be deposited in the lymph glands. The level and theoretical proportion of retention of some particulates are shown in Fig. 3 (*22*). The mucous and ciliary lining of the airway is found in the bronchi and above, but this defensive system is absent in the lower bronchioles, alveolar ducts, and alveoli.

For a given weight of particulate substance, the total surface area increases in inverse proportion with the mean particle radius. Particulates concentrate material on their surface and in their interstices and thus tend to produce a locally high concentration of an otherwise very dilute substance. This mechanism has been postulated to account for the fact that natural air pollution produces more eye irritation than can be accounted for by its gaseous constituents. Aqueous droplets may dissolve such gases as sulfur dioxide and permit their hydration to sulfurous acid, or, if oxidized, to sulfuric acid. Organic particulates, such as those from heated fats and oils, may have the capacity to facilitate the analogous reactions of organic substances. It is possible, also, that

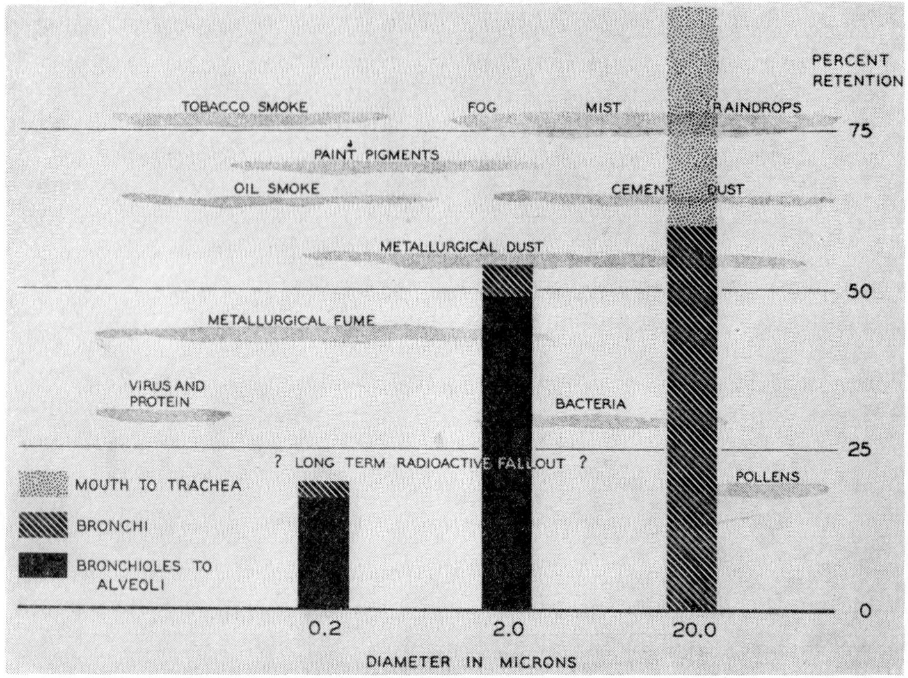

FIG. 3. Relationship between particle size, origin, and pulmonary retention. [Source: *Calif. Health* **18,** No. **7** (1960).]

many natural particulates are complex combinations of organic and aqueous materials. There is evidence that some particulates are aqueous droplets surrounded by an organic surface layer which is relatively insoluble in water.

Because the respiratory tract is usually at a higher temperature than the air and is saturated with water vapor, the inhalation of any particle which is capable of absorption of water causes that particle to increase in size as it progresses down the respiratory tract. This complex relationship needs further study since it is not clear whether the particle growth occurs with sufficient rapidity to prevent submicronic hygroscopic particles from reaching the deeper portions of the lung.

It is interesting to speculate on the possibility that particulates carry biologically active energy in the form of free radicals. Radiation effects are thought to be mediated by the formation of free radicals within cells. It is quite possible that the free radicals within the interstices of a particle may be incorporated into the cell. The effects of these free radicals would depend, in part, upon where the energy carried by them is dissipated.

It is known that in animal exposures the presence of sodium chloride aerosols greatly increases sensitivity of animals to a number of inhaled irritants and that an increase in airway resistance occurs in humans on exposure to a number of inert particulates, including the particulates in cigarette smoke (*23*).

B. Soot

Observations in Great Britain have indicated the importance of smoke or soot in aggravating symptoms of persons with chronic bronchitis. Paradoxically, the particles which fall out of a polluted atmosphere into an open container and are measured as "sootfall" are particles of the sizes least likely to deposit in the respiratory tract. These large particles are either filtered out in the nose and throat or are trapped in the mucous blanket. It is the smaller particles that are likely to be deposited in the deeper portions of the lung which constitute the greatest hazard to human health. These minute particles are not estimated by simple sootfall devices. However, they can be detected rather well by the paper strip or glass fiber filter type of sampler.

Most soots are highly porous structures made up of agglomerates of irregular carbonaceous particles. The porosity of these particles of carbon tends to make them avid adsorbers of other substances. This property is even more important since most soots are generated by combustion processes which also generate the complex polycyclic hydrocarbons (such as benzo[*a*]pyrene) which are known experimentally to produce cancer. Falk *et al.* (*24, 25*) have studied the adsorption onto soots of carcinogenic hydrocarbons and their removal by various biological solutions, particularly serum. They found a slow release of hydrocarbons to serum from small soots (about 80 mμ) and a more rapid elution from soots of 500 mμ. Nau *et al.* (*26*) found that in very small particles benzo[*a*]pyrene was tightly bound to soot and could not be eluted by human serum or gastric juice. They used channel black of about 5 to 35 mμ in size.

The observation that the lungs of city dwellers, on autopsy, are blackened is probable evidence that some of the inhaled sooty materials are retained in the lung. However, a clear distinction should be made between occupational exposures to such things as coal dust, which has been shown to produce coal workers' pneumoconiosis (*27*) and the exposure to soot in community air pollution. No disease has, as yet, been clearly related to community exposures to soot alone. The action of soot is most likely that of a carrier of pollutants into the deeper portions of the lung. However, experimental inhalation of India ink and other inert aerosols has been shown to be capable of producing increased airway resistance in man (*28*).

C. Sulfuric Acid

It is possible that sulfuric acid mist was the substance principally responsible for the health effects associated with the air pollution disasters in the Meuse Valley, Donora, and in London. Experimental work has shown that on a molar basis sulfuric acid produces from four to twenty times the physiological response in animals as does sulfur dioxide. It probably does so in man as well. The immediate response to sulfuric acid mist is essentially the same as, but greater than that to sulfur dioxide. However, its effect is greatly influenced by the size of the mist particles. The particle size of greatest effectiveness appears to be about 1 μ or slightly less. Larger particles probably impinge upon the upper airway, and may very well be buffered and thus produce little effect. On the other hand, it is possible that irritants in the upper airway produce reflex bronchoconstriction. This problem is just beginning to be studied. Unfortunately, there is relatively little data concerning levels and particle sizes of sulfuric acid as a community air pollutant.

Sulfuric acid in experimental animal exposures is capable of producing lung damage roughly proportional to the product of the concentration times the time of exposure. It is difficult to know whether or not such a relationship occurs in humans.

The concentration which is known *not* to produce any effect in human subjects is 0.12 mg./m.^{3}, or 0.03 p.p.m. A concentration of 0.25 mg. of sulfuric acid per cubic meter will produce no ill effects on healthy persons; however, there may be some effects of such a concentration on persons who are ill or who have chronic respiratory tract disease. Detectable responses in humans begin to occur at about 0.25 mg./m.^{3}, assuming the particle size is about 1 μ. This is equivalent to 0.06 p.p.m. (*29*).

Bushtueva (*30*) reports on the alteration of light sensitivity upon inhalation of sulfuric acid, without specifying the particle size. No effect was observed with 0.6 mg./m.^{3}; 0.7 to 1.3 mg./m.^{3} increased light sensitivity; more than 2.0 mg./m.^{3} decreased sensitivity.

D. Lead

Lead is a well-known industrial pollutant which in high enough doses causes severe acute symptoms. In levels likely to be found in air pollution, its effects (if any) will probably be confined to chronic intoxication. Lead is known to interfere with the development and maturation of red blood cells. The presence of sufficient lead is also associated with the excretion of certain porphyrins, which are precursors of hemoglobin (*31*). In chronic lead poisoning the red blood cells may be stippled and show an increased mechanical fragility, but also a decreased osmotic fragility. These effects have not yet been observed in persons exposed to community air pollution alone. It is generally agreed that the most conservative index of possible chronic lead toxicity would be the increase in storage of lead in the various organs of the body. Under metabolic stress, stored lead is mobilized.

Much of the lead ingested by mouth is excreted without ever being absorbed—only about 5–10% is absorbed; however, of that which is inhaled and deposited in the deeper parts of the lung, a much larger

TABLE II

Mean Blood Lead Values in Urban and Rural Population Samples Tabulated by Sex and Age[a]

	Urban areas		Rural areas	
Sex and age	Number of observations	Mean blood lead (mg./100 gm.)	Number of observations	Mean blood lead (mg./100 gm.)
Sex groups				
Male	566	0.021	113	0.016
Female	169	0.016	49	0.011
Age groups (years)[b]				
15–30	297	0.019	50	0.015
30–45	283	0.020	71	0.014
45–60	148	0.021	38	0.014

[a] Source: D. Hofreuter, Paper presented at *4th Air Poll. Med. Research Conf.* (*Calif. State Dept. of Public Health*), *San Francisco, 1960*.

[b] Age data for all subjects were not available.

proportion is absorbed. Much of the particulate material inhaled is deposited on the mucous layer of the larger airways. By ciliary action this material is moved toward the pharynx and ultimately swallowed. For insoluble substances such as lead, therefore, much of this material is actually passed through the intestinal tract. For this reason it is felt

TABLE III

MEAN BLOOD LEAD AND URINE LEAD LEVELS AMONG MEN WITH CERTAIN OCCUPATIONAL EXPOSURES[a]

	Blood			Urine			Occupational exposure level	
Occupation	Number of observations	Mean lead (mg./100 gm.)	Standard deviation	Number of observations	Mean lead (mg./l.)	Standard deviation	Mean concentration (μg./m.^{3} of air)	Range
Auto inspectors	28	0.030	±0.007	28	0.041	±0.021	14.8	8.88–19.98
Garage mechanics	52	0.031	±0.009	49	0.046	±0.025	21.0	5.22–131.6
Control Data							Atmospheric levels, outside garage	
Male residents								
Urban areas	566	0.021	—	—	—	—	2.08	0.91–3.84

[a] Source: D. Hofreuter, Paper presented at *4th Air Poll. Med. Research Conf.* (*Calif. State Dept. Public Health*), *San Francisco, 1960.*

TABLE IV

MEAN BLOOD LEAD LEVELS IN SMOKERS AND NONSMOKERS IN URBAN AND RURAL AREAS[a]

Group	Urban areas			Rural areas		
	Number of observations	Mean blood lead (mg./100 gm.)	Range	Number of observations	Mean blood lead (mg./100 gm.)	Range
Smokers	471	0.021	0.005–0.060	90	0.017	0.010–0.038
Nonsmokers	264	0.017	0.003–0.044	69	0.012	0.001–0.036

[a] Source: D. Hofreuter, Paper presented at *4th Air Poll. Med. Research Conf.* (*Calif. State Dept. Public Health*), *San Francisco, 1960.*

that the particle size of lead in community air pollution determines, to a large extent, how much lead is actually absorbed. The effects of lead in community air pollution can be estimated by urine or blood determinations. Recent studies have shown (*32*) that persons who live in urban areas have higher blood lead levels than persons who live in rural areas, as shown in Table II. Also, persons with occupational exposure to automobile exhaust tend, on the average, to have higher values than the average of other males, as shown in Table III. A slight increase is also observed in blood lead levels of cigarette smokers as compared with nonsmokers, as shown in Table IV. This is consistent with the fact that lead, as well as arsenic, is found in cigarette smoke. The apparent source is residues of lead arsenate sprays which, though no longer used, have sufficiently contaminated the soil so that tobacco plants and leaves absorb these metals (*33*).

Substantial amounts of lead occur in the food supply and in some beverages. For this reason the amount which may be absorbed from community air pollution may represent only a small fraction of the total exposure. In a few individuals, community air pollution exposures may be sufficient to result in increased lead storage or in chronic lead poisoning. However, this has not been demonstrated conclusively, and lead as a community air pollutant must be considered to have potential, rather than proven, health effects.

E. Beryllium

Exposure to small amounts of beryllium or its compounds has been shown to be associated with a chronic disease, which may be delayed in its onset for 4 to 6 years after exposure. The symptoms are weight loss, weakness, shortness of breath, cough, and sometimes, bone changes. Characteristic chest X-ray pictures also occur and it is usually possible to find beryllium in the blood, urine, or the body tissues (*34*). The effects of beryllium are to produce a diffuse pulmonary fibrosis with interference in the diffusion of gases from the lung alveoli into the blood vessels. In addition, beryllium affects other organs of the body.

A substantial portion of the cases have been found among persons living in the neighborhood of factories using beryllium. In one community study, most of the affected persons lived within ¾ mi. of the plant, though one patient lived about 2 mi. from the plant; in this case, however, a workman with occupational exposure also lived in this household and it was felt that exposure had occurred during laundering of his clothes. It is felt that the amount of beryllium in the air in the neighborhood of these plants was about 0.1 μg./m.^{3} (*35*). The possibility has been raised by Eisenbud *et al.* (*36*) that the reason the neighborhood cases were so frequent was that the particle size of beryllium at some distance from the plant was particularly likely to lead to retention on inhalation.

VI. Effects of Gaseous Pollutants

A. General Effects

The attempts to relate the measured levels of gaseous pollutants to the observed effects of pollution have not been entirely satisfactory. The concentrations of gaseous pollutants capable of experimentally causing observed effects are usually substantially higher than are naturally measured levels.

Most pollutants are studied experimentally by diluting the pure pollutant with air. It has recently become apparent how difficult it is to obtain high concentrations, approaching purity, of certain types of pollutants in gaseous or vaporous form. This is particularly true for the active agents found in Los Angeles photochemical air pollution. In high concentrations such substances as peroxyacyl nitrate (PAN) or nitro-olefins may be either so explosive or so irritating as to be hazardous for laboratory personnel to handle. In any event, it is clear that concepts based on high concentrations of gases or vapors may be invalid in the air pollution range of 1 p.p.m. and less. Thus it is possible that observed effects in community air pollution are due to the presence of substances which, on the basis of chemical studies at high concentrations, were thought to be transient or nonexistent.

Another possible basis for the discrepancy between observed natural pollution effects and experimental exposures may lie in the fact that it is assumed that the gases are intimately and completely intermixed; in fact, it is quite possible that in the presence of particulates of certain sorts, a microscopic cloud of a given contaminant may exist at a relatively high concentration in the very tiny volume surrounding the particulate. Thus, the concentrating effects of simple particles such as mist may be very substantial.

Even though the concentration of gaseous pollutants is minute, the amount which may be absorbed by the body can be appreciable. For example, if air polluted with 1 p.p.m. of ozone is inhaled by an average person for 24 hr., the resulting dose of ozone is about 15 mg., or $\frac{1}{4}$ of a grain.

Just as knowledge concerning the biological fate of particles is beginning to accumulate in a meaningful fashion, so we are also beginning to recognize that the biological fate of gases depends somewhat on their solubility in the fluids which line the respiratory tract, or in the case of eye irritants, in the tears. Dalhamn (*37*) and Balchum *et al.* (*38*) have shown that in rabbits virtually all of the sulfur dioxide which is inhaled through the nose is dissolved or removed in the upper airway before the nasopharyngeal level is reached. It is quite likely that solution in the upper airway tends to protect the lungs from the effects of some air pollutants. Certain interesting consequences follow from this assumption. It may be that persons with upper respiratory tract disease who are permanently or temporarily required to breathe through their mouths may be peculiarly susceptible to gaseous or even particulate air pollution because of the lack of this defense mechanism.

Gaseous pollutants interact with the surfaces of clothing and of the furnishings and woodwork of houses. For this reason, among others, substantial protection from atmospheric pollution is afforded to persons who stay indoors.

B. Carbon Monoxide

Carbon monoxide is a nonirritating, odorless gas whose primary effect on human health is based on its very great affinity for hemoglobin. It tends to combine with hemoglobin two hundred and ten times as readily as oxygen, thus effectively preventing the hemoglobin from performing its most important function, the transport of oxygen from the lungs to the tissues. Recent findings suggest (*39*) that there may be effects of carbon monoxide exposure on the eye and on the nervous system, but its effect on hemoglobin is the one about which most is known.

At low concentrations about half the carbon monoxide is absorbed from the inspired air. On cessation of exposure, the carbon monoxide which is combined with hemoglobin is spontaneously released and the blood is cleared of carbon monoxide in an exponential fashion with a half-time of 3 to 4 hr., a slightly shorter period being observed in women than men.

The earliest symptoms of carbon monoxide intoxication are headache, dizziness, and lassitude. At higher levels, which have not been seen in community air pollution, more serious symptoms can occur. In most persons symptoms are first observed at carbon monoxide concentrations of about 100 p.p.m.

Because the effects depend upon the amount actually within the body, it may take several hours for the effects of low level exposure to be detectable. This is especially true for concentrations below 100 p.p.m. It has been estimated (*40*) that for each 1 p.p.m. of carbon monoxide with which the human body is in equilibrium, 0.16% of the body's hemoglobin will be inactivated by the formation of carboxyhemoglobin. This relationship holds only at rather low concentrations. The rate of absorption, as well as the rate of disassociation of carbon monoxide and hemoglobin depends in part on the rapidity of gas exchange; that is, the frequency and depth of breathing (*41*).

It seems likely that the most serious effects of carbon monoxide are to be expected in persons with chronic heart and lung diseases. This group is one upon which little experimental work has been done, but they are expected to be most vulnerable to interference with oxygen transportation. At carboxyhemoglobin levels corresponding to equilibration with low ambient air concentrations, detectable effects of carbon monoxide on visual sensitivity occur; whether these detectable effects are of any practical importance will require additional research. Though the mechanisms of effects are somewhat different, the exposure to about 30 p.p.m. of CO at equilibrium (which requires 4–6 hr.) is roughly comparable in terms of oxygen saturation of the blood to altitudes of about 6000 ft.

Carbon monoxide is such a common pollutant that exposures to it occur in many occupations; cigarette smokers may have carboxyhemoglobin levels as high as 8%. It seems likely that the addition of 5% of carboxyhemoglobin by community air pollution to that possible from other sources may be sufficient to pose a serious risk to the health of sensitive persons. Such a level may be produced by exposures to 30 p.p.m. for 4–6 hr., or exposure to 120 p.p.m. for 1 hr. (*42*).

C. Ozone

This gas, which formerly had been thought to have some beneficial effects, and even has been used as an agent for odor suppression, is now known to be a highly irritating and toxic substance. However, the effects of ozone are quite complex. It is known that on experimental exposure to 1¼ p.p.m. for about 1 hr. there is an increase in the residual volume of the lung and a decrease in the breathing capacity (*43*). Higher levels tend to produce pulmonary edema, hemorrhage, and interference with diffusion of gases from the lung alveoli into the blood. In animal exposure studies, levels of about 1 p.p.m., repeated for 8 hr. a day over a year or so, has produced bronchitis, fibrosis, and bronchiolitis in some but not all species of rodents. This suggests the possibility that ozone may have a similar effect in man. The ozone levels in Los Angeles air pollution are commonly 0.2 to 0.3 p.p.m. and have been as high as 0.9 p.p.m. No demonstrable effect that can be related specifically to community air pollution levels of ozone has been shown for humans. A possible reason for the lack of effects on humans may be postulated from the work of Stokinger (Chapter 9) in which oil mists tended to protect animals from the acute effects of ozone. Pre-exposure to lower levels also seems to protect animals from subsequent, otherwise lethal, levels. Whether oil mists or intermittent exposures protect man from chronic effects is not known. The importance of ozone is heightened by the probability that hydrocarbon emissions from automobile exhaust will be controlled within a few years, thus substantially reducing some effects of the photochemical complex, but possibly not reducing the concentration of ozone as much. Further investigation of the effects on humans of exposures to ozone at low levels is urgently needed.

D. Sulfur Dioxide

The principal effect of sulfur dioxide at low concentrations, such as may be expected in community air pollution, is upon airway resistance. Increased resistance increases the effort required to move air into and out of the lung. The effects of sulfur dioxide have been shown in animals to be potentiated by simultaneous exposure to at least certain types of particulates (*44*).

The least amount of sulfur dioxide detected by odor is about 3 p.p.m. However, there are reports that concentrations as low as 1 p.p.m. produce a discernible physiological response in man (*45*). This finding, however, has been disputed by others (*46*). It is readily agreed that a concentration of 0.6 p.p.m. will produce no detectable response in healthy human subjects. Some of the disagreement concerning the lowest concentration producing a physiological effect is probably related to variability in human sensitivity to sulfur dioxide as well as to the fact that for some experiments, a small number of human subjects were used.

It is generally agreed that in the range between 1 and 5 p.p.m. most human subjects will begin to show a detectable response. The more sensitive individuals will be found in the lower portion of this range, and the less sensitive in the upper portion. There is considerable evidence from occupational exposures that persons with repeated exposure to concentrations of 5 p.p.m. and above tend to become relatively insensitive to the detection of these concentrations by odor or by the production of respiratory tract irritation. Dubrovskaya (*47*) reports that the odor threshold may be as low as 1.6 mg./m.^{3} (0.56 p.p.m.) and that light sensitivity of the eye is increased by exposure to 0.6 mg./m.^{3} (0.21 p.p.m.). There is no good evidence that chronic exposures to concentrations below 5 p.p.m. of sulfur dioxide have any ill effects upon healthy persons.

Experimental work on animals has indicated adverse effects of sulfur dioxide on the rate of ciliary activity. The cilia are the whiplike fibers which occur in the respiratory tract, and by rhythmic beating, they fulfill an important role in clearing the respiratory tract of inhaled particles and irritants. An adverse effect has also been shown by Reid (*48*) on the proliferation of mucous glands. These findings are particularly relevant to the general problem of chronic bronchitis in man and its relationship to community air pollution, since the increased size of mucus-secreting glands and the characteristic finding of increased expectoration in chronic bronchitis seem logically related to the stimulus of sulfur dioxide and associated irritants. However, research on the mechanisms by which the lung clears inhaled particles and irritants is in its early stages.

Lawther (*49*) has studied the relationship of symptoms of persons with chronic bronchitis to atmospheric levels of sulfur dioxide and smoke. The data on the clinical changes in these persons were obtained through a diary and some of the data is shown in Fig. 4. Data such as

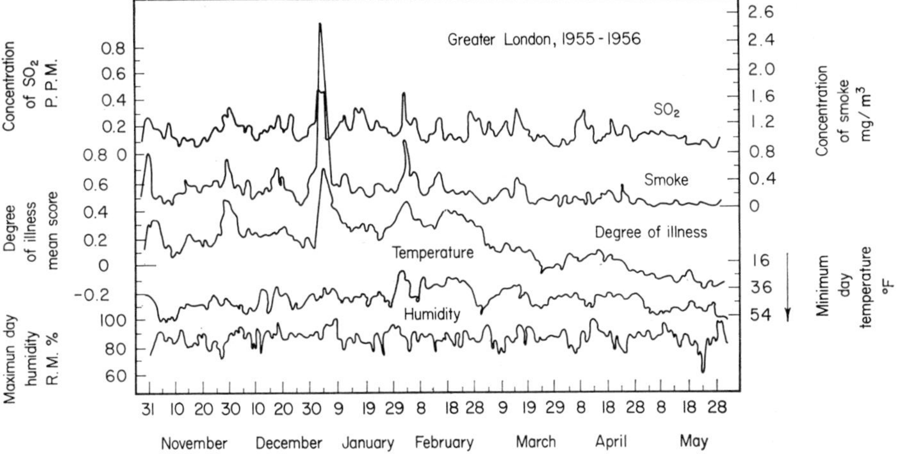

FIG. 4. Graph showing degree of illness of a group of 180 patients in Greater London with chronic bronchitis plotted with smoke and SO_2 concentrations, temperature, and humidity. [Source: P. J. Lawther, *Proc. Roy Soc. Med.* **51,** 262 (1958).]

this have been interpreted as indicating that both smoke and sulfur dioxide need to be present in order to aggravate the symptoms of these sensitive individuals. The approximate concentrations producing this effect have been estimated to be: 0.4 p.p.m. of sulfur dioxide, and 0.2 mg. of soot per cubic meter of air (*50*).

Possible sensitization to sulfur dioxide is suggested by the studies of Sim and Pattle (*51*) in which several of the human subjects had a protracted period of cough and expectoration of sputum following experimental exposures; in addition, the symptoms of wheeezing and cough lasted well beyond the duration of exposure, and low exposure seemed to produce an exaggerated response in these subjects. There is evidence that some individuals, upon repeated exposure, develop increased sensitivity, and others decreased sensitivity to sulfur dioxide. In any event, there is consensus of agreement upon the fact that bronchodilator drugs are effective in both the relief of symptoms and the prevention of effects of sulfur dioxide and other inhaled irritants (*52*).

Studies of human response to inhaled sulfur dioxide have also been reported by Frank *et al.* (*53*), as well as by Wright and Lloyd (*54*). These findings appear to be in conflict, in that Frank *et al.* have detected in their subjects an effect upon airway resistance of exposures at about 5 p.p.m., while Wright and Lloyd have not. However, the experiments of Frank *et al.* were conducted using a technique in which changes of airway resistance and exposure to sulfur dioxide were promptly measured under rather carefully controlled laboratory conditions. The work of Wright and Lloyd was conducted under less favorable conditions. A delay of up to 20 min. occurred between the termination of exposures and the measurement of airway resistance. The former group of subjects were breathing through the mouth, while the latter were not.

An ingenious way of counteracting the effects of sulfur dioxide has been developed based on the observations of animals exposed during the severe London smog attack in 1952. Here the animals which received relatively less attention and hence whose pens were contaminated with urine and feces did not show any ill effects, while those which were kept scrupulously clean suffered much harm. This led to the suggestion that perhaps the ammonia produced by excreta was capable of neutralizing sulfur dioxide in the atmosphere. Experimentally, ammonia does counteract the effects of sulfur dioxide and sulfuric acid (*55*). This finding has subsequently been applied by the development of an "airwick" type of dispenser for dilute ammonia vapor which is said to be quite effective. One observer pointed out that a somewhat neglected infant with wet diapers in a room might provide an effective antidote to sulfur dioxide exposure!

Since most natural exposures to sulfur dioxide occur in conjunction with other pollutants, the capacity of these other substances to facilitate the oxidation of sulfur dioxide to sulfur trioxide, the anhydride of sulfuric acid, assumes some importance. Johnstone (*56*), in particular, has conducted studies on the effect of manganese as a catalyst, and it seems likely this may have some role. With the possible exception of work in the Soviet Union (*47*), there are regrettably few simultaneous measurements both of sulfur dioxide and sulfuric acid.

In summary, it may be said that the threshold for detectable physiological response of humans is in the neighborhood of 1 p.p.m. of sulfur dioxide. The response, however, may differ readily in the presence of particulates and is influenced by individual sensitivity. Five parts per million is known both to be detectable by most subjects and to produce an unequivocal physiological response. Ten parts per million is quite unpleasant for most subjects.

E. Oxides of Nitrogen

Nitrogen dioxide is known to be an acutely irritating substance, but in some occupational exposures it has a latent period of several hours; in addition, it has been shown experimentally to produce chronic lung disease in animals, and there is some evidence that the exposure to nitrogen dioxide associated with filling of silos also produces a chronic pulmonary condition (*57*). It is not known for sure whether nitrogen dioxide produces increased airway resistance, but it is known that acute pulmonary edema does result from exposure to high levels. Men have died of a "chemical" bronchopneumonia following relatively high exposures. However, exposures of this severity do not occur in community air pollution. As pointed out by Gray (*58*), many occupational exposures and some experiments reported are to mixtures of nitrogen oxides and ozone. Thus, the toxicology of pure nitrogen oxides is still obscure. In the Soviet Union chronic toxicity to nitrogen dioxide has been reported from exposures for from 3 to 5 years at concentrations below 2.8 p.p.m. (*59*).

Nitric oxide (NO) commonly occurs with nitrogen dioxide. Human poisonings with nitric oxide are unknown. It is capable *in vitro* of combining with hemoglobin, but has not yet been shown to do so *in vivo*. In animal exposures, nitric oxide is about one-fifth as toxic as nitrogen dioxide. At the present time the effect of nitrogen oxides at levels observed in community air pollution must be thought of as being potentially irritating and potentially related to chronic pulmonary fibrosis, but there is no good evidence of its quantitative relationship to these effects.

F. Formaldehyde

Formaldehyde has been suggested as one of the major irritants in the photochemical complex in Los Angeles (*60*). It is a well-known substance in experimental and occupational exposures. Its irritant properties are likely to constitute its major (if not its only) effect on human health.

Formaldehyde is important for two reasons: First, it is a substance whose effect is known to be similar to that of sulfur dioxide in experimental exposures, and it has been used as a basis for comparison of the eye-irritating effects of air pollution from the photochemical complex. Second, ethylene, a common pollutant produced from motor vehicles and other combustion sources, may possibly be oxidized in the atmosphere to produce formaldehyde.

A linear relationship of the logarithm of total aldehyde concentration to the response of an eye irritation panel (probit scale) has been reported for natural Los Angeles smog *(60a)*. The relationship is such that about 25% of the panel noted eye irritation above an aldehyde level of 0.11 p.p.m. Formaldehyde, acrolein, and peroxyacyl nitrate (PAN) were also measured. Associations between these substances and eye irritation were not as clear cut as between total aldehydes and eye irritation.

G. Acrolein

Acrolein is a substance for which few atmospheric measurements have been made; however, its effect in occupational exposure is rather well known and it has been suggested as one of the irritants produced in the photochemical complex. Acrolein has been used in human experiments on eye irritation; concentrations of 0.1 p.p.m. have been shown to produce eye irritation effects comparable to exposure to irradiated automobile exhaust or natural photochemical air pollution.

Acrolein measurements in natural Los Angeles smog show that an eye irritation maximum seems to occur at a concentration of about 0.01 p.p.m. *(60a)*. Higher and lower concentrations were associated with less eye irritation.

H. Hydrogen Sulfide

Hydrogen sulfide is a colorless gas having a characteristic disagreeable odor often described as that of rotten eggs. The presence of low concentrations of hydrogen sulfide is evidenced by its odor, the discoloration of some paints, and the tarnishing of brass fixtures and silver. Exposures for short periods can apparently result in fatigue of the sense of smell, which is particularly serious in industrial exposures because the sense of smell is lost after 2 to 15 min. of exposure to 100 p.p.m. or more *(42a)*.

Hydrogen sulfide is also an irritating substance at concentrations considerably above those that cause odors. At still higher concentrations it produces systemic effects and can result in death. At levels less than those producing marked systemic effects it exerts an irritant action on the respiratory mucous membranes which resembles that of chlorine. In subacute or chronic poisoning the main symptoms are irritation, particularly of the eyes, and to a lesser degree, of the respiratory tract, as well as irritability, insomnia, loss of appetite, nausea, and vomiting.

Irritation of the mucosa is thought to be based on formation of sodium sulfide. It is felt that the gas is absorbed as the sulfide ion. After absorption, the ion is partly hydrolyzed by the blood. Hydrogen sulfide is readily absorbed by the lungs and gastrointestinal tract. In the blood it is partly free and partly present as sulfides; the free hydrogen sulfide is thought to be the only form in which neurotoxicity is manifested.

The air pollution problem resulting from the presence of hydrogen sulfide is largely associated with nuisances from odors and discoloration of some paints and metals at very low concentrations of the gas. Levels of hydrogen sulfide sufficiently high to cause vegetation damage, irritation of the eyes and respiratory system, systemic effects, or death are unlikely to be encountered in the atmosphere. It is expected that these higher concentrations result from accidental industrial discharges from point sources rather than from community-wide emissions. Unlike what is known of the photochemical eye irritants, hydrogen sulfide causes inflammation and edema of the conjunctiva.

VII. The Photochemical Mixture Known as Los Angeles Smog

The health effects of air pollution in Los Angeles first brought forth public clamor and concern in 1946. The effect first noted, eye irritation, has yet to be satisfactorily ascribed to a specific pollutant. The severity of air pollution in Los Angeles increased rapidly during the next 10 years. Serious concern was felt in 1954 following a series of unusually severe episodes of air pollution, which led the question to be raised: "Can this smog kill us?" Responsibility for answering this question led to a review of mortality data which failed to support the hypothesis that the smog might have been lethal; however, the possibility could not be entirely dismissed.

In late August and early September, 1955, in connection with a severe heat wave with temperatures above 100° for over a week, a severe bout of air pollution occurred; at the same time a substantial increase in daily mortality was also recorded (*61*). The relevant data for persons over 65 are shown in Fig. 5. The available data have been carefully analyzed, and it is generally thought that the rise in mortality was associated with the high temperature rather than with the high air pollution levels. This finding was supported by the fact that a proportionately great increase in mortality occurred in September 1939, in connection with a similar episode of high temperature, but during a period in which air pollution was known not to be inconsequential

The California State Health Department has set up a surveillance scheme under which all nursing homes in Los Angeles County with twenty-five or more beds report each week the deaths by day, as well as the transfers to hospitals, of the residents in these homes. This frail segment of the population has an unusually low resistance to any environmental stress. This scheme has two purposes—one, to permit

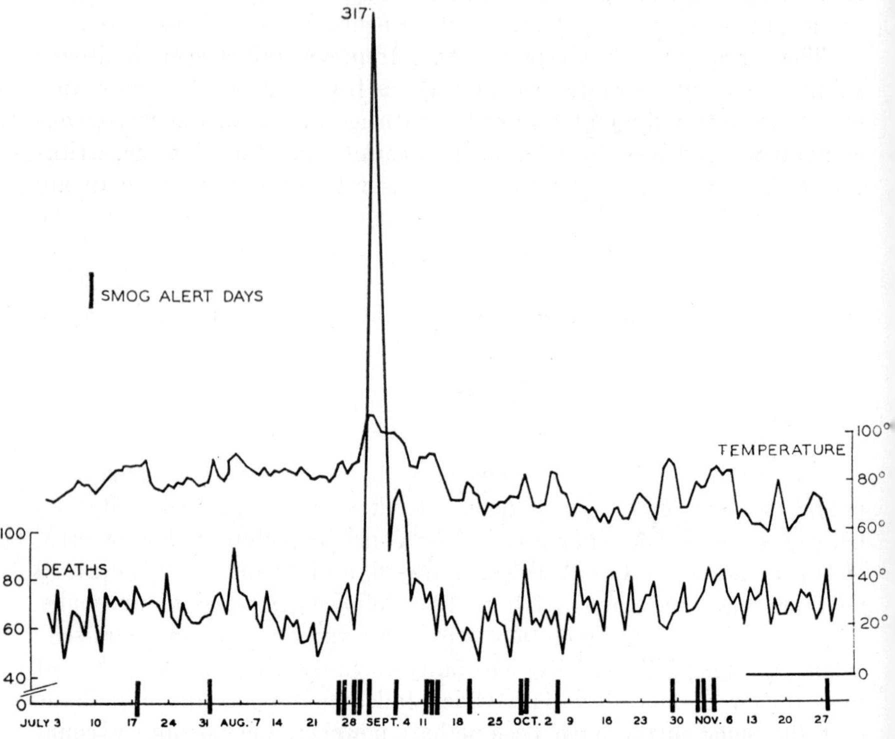

FIG. 5. Deaths of persons 65 years and over and maximum daily temperature. Los Angeles County, July 1–November 30, 1955. [Source: J. R. Goldsmith and L. Breslow, *J. Air Poll. Control Assoc.* **9,** 129 (1959).]

the detection as early as possible of any adverse change which might be associated with environmental factors; two, to provide a means of analyzing the cumulative effects of air pollution on mortality. To date, there have been no clear-cut evidences of increased mortality in this group due to air pollution; the only two substantial rises were in 1955 in association with the heat wave, referred to above, and in early 1960 in association with an epidemic of influenza.

Schoettlin (*62*) has carried out a study of the onsets of attacks of asthma among a group of patients with asthma in Pasadena. He also obtained data concerning oxidant levels, particulates, pollens, temperature, and humidity. On the basis of a careful statistical analysis, it was concluded that there was no substantial influence of air pollution on the time of onset of asthma attacks. There was, however, a low but statistically significant correlation between attacks of asthma on a given day and the oxidant levels for that day. This suggests that there may be a few persons among such a group who are reactive to air pollution exposures.

There is substantial concern about the possibility of chronic disease being caused by air pollution exposure in Los Angeles. This concern is supported by the finding of Motley *et al.* (*63*) that patients with severe emphysema during smoggy weather had improved lung function when placed in rooms whose air supply was filtered through activated charcoal.

TABLE V
CORRELATION OF EYE IRRITATION WITH SIMULTANEOUS OXIDANT IN ORDER OF DECREASING EYE IRRITATION SCORE FOR A NUMBER OF STATIONS IN THE LOS ANGELES BASIN[a]

Station	Number of daily observations	Correlation D (or r^2)	Average eye irritation score	Average oxidant (parts per hundred million)
5	25	0.88	26.2	13.0
8	29	0.68	22.0	10.0
4L	24	0.76	21.9	21.1
2	30	0.06	21.3	11.1
3	67	0.56	18.2	15.0
4E	66	0.65	13.0	17.0
All	344	0.18	18.8	13.6

[a] Source: Air Poll. Foundation Report No. 9. San Marino, California, 1955.

While concern has been growing about the chronic disease potential of air pollution in Los Angeles, eye irritation remains the most troublesome effect on man's health. Despite the fact that ozone is very prominent in photochemical air pollution, ozone itself at the observed levels does not produce irritation of the eyes and respiratory membranes. It seems well established that eye irritation is most closely statistically associated with the concentration of oxidant; that is, the extent to which the atmosphere when bubbled through alkaline potassium iodide solution releases iodine. This relationship is shown in Table V and Fig. 6. The possibility that the irritant is a mixture of acrolein and formaldehyde has been suggested (*60*).

There is some dispute concerning whether irritation of the eyes and respiratory tract is associated with the presence of particles in the air.

The reason this question has been raised is that the concentration of known gaseous irritating substances in the smog mixture has not been felt to be sufficiently high to account for the effects observed. In one report, removal of particles did not eliminate eye irritation (*64*). In opposition to this, it has been suggested that only the larger particles were removed in this experiment and that submicronic particles may have "recaptured" some of the eye irritant stripped off the larger particles.

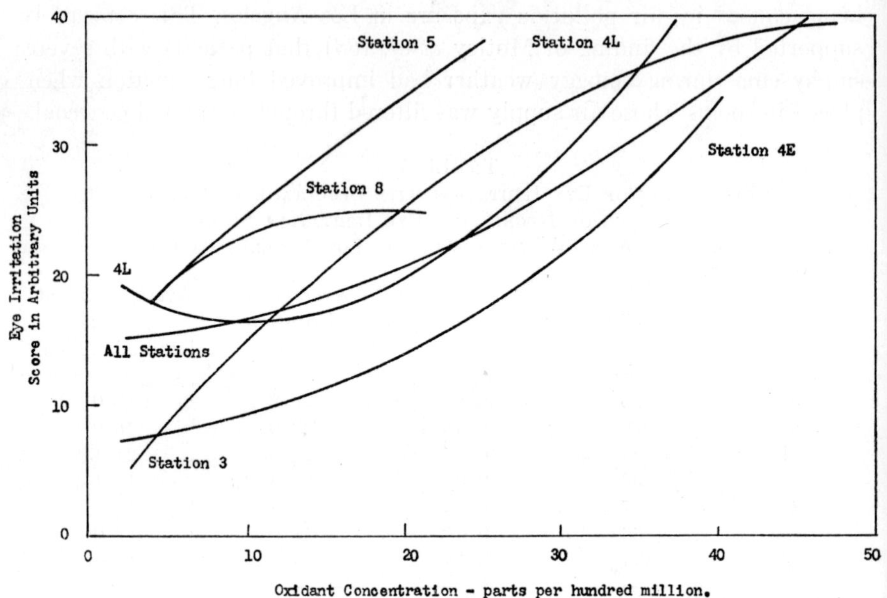

FIG. 6. Regression curves relating eye irritation and simultaneous oxidant concentrations from a number of stations in the Los Angeles Basin. [Source: Air Poll. Foundation Report No. 9. San Marino, California, 1955.]

Though eye irritation affects almost three-quarters of the population in the metropolitan areas of Southern California (*65*), a number of studies by eye specialists have failed to indicate that repeated irritation results in any permanent eye injury (*66*). A complex relationship exists between eye irritation and the atmospheric concentration of olefinic hydrocarbon and oxides of nitrogen. However, when one or the other is particularly low, a decrease in the concentration of the more prevalent substances does not proportionately decrease eye irritation, as shown in Fig. 7.

The relationship of photochemical pollution to a variety of com-

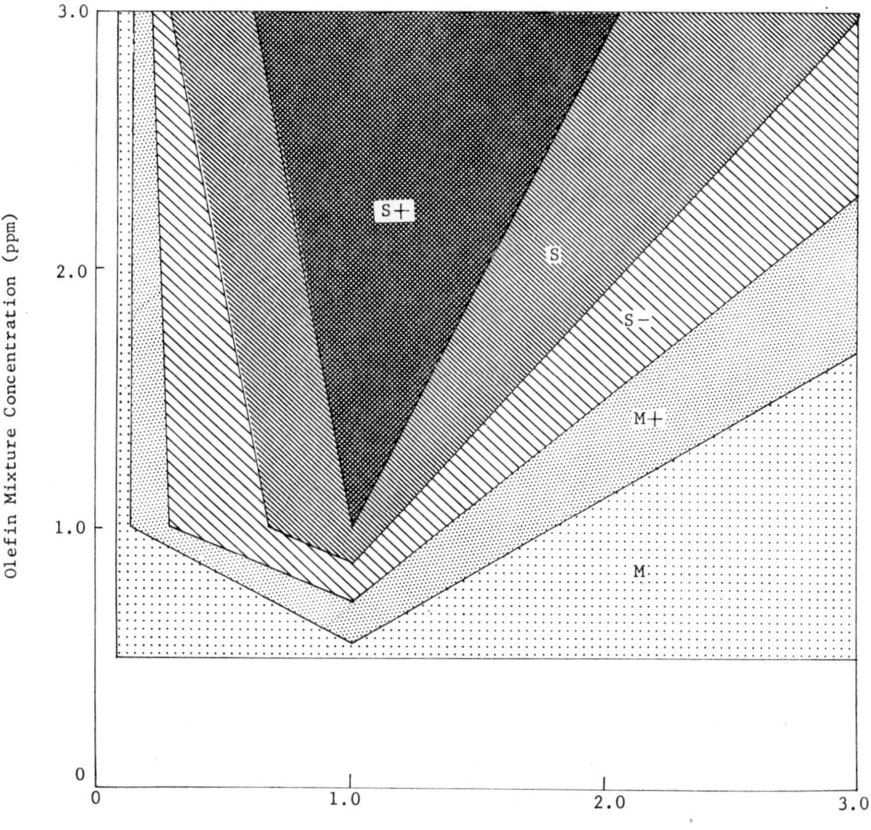

FIG. 7. Expected eye irritation as a function of olefin and nitrogen dioxide concentrations from 2-hr. irradiation of an olefin mixture. Key: M = medium; S = severe. [Source: Air Poll. Foundation Report No. 31, p. 49, San Marino, California, 1960.]

plaints is shown by data obtained in population surveys (*65*). The proportion of adults in a random sample of California residents who reported that they were bothered by air pollution is shown in Fig. 8. A number of these persons, particularly in Los Angeles, report that they have seriously considered changing jobs because of air pollution. This is shown in Fig. 9.

Each respondent who had suffered during the year from a specific chronic condition was asked: "Does it (the chronic condition) bother you more on some days than others?" If the answer was "yes," they were further asked: "What is it about these times that makes you feel worse?" Until this time in the interview the respondent had not been

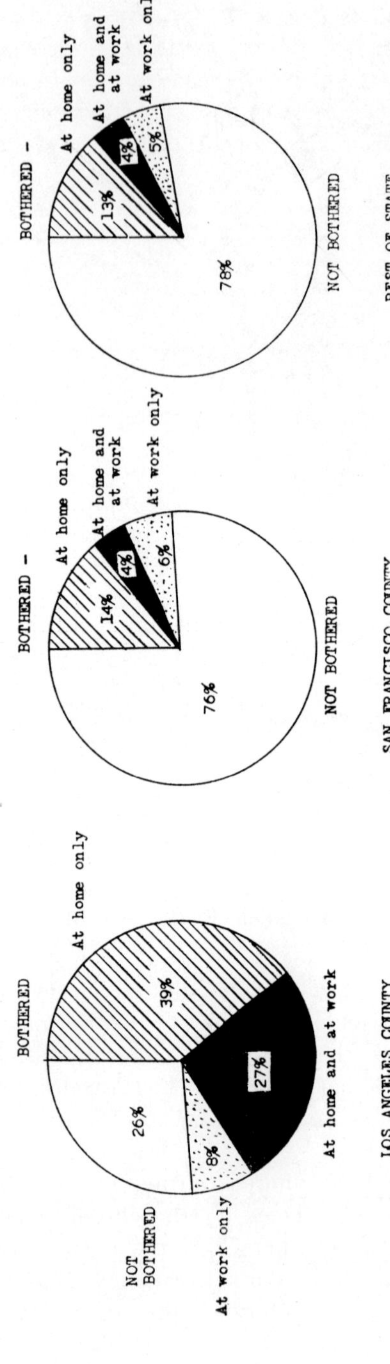

FIG. 8. Proportion of workers bothered by air pollution. Note: workers constitute only 55% of the population interviewed. [Source: California State Department of Public Health, "Air Pollution Effects Reported by California Residents." Department of Public Health, Berkeley, California, 1960.]

directly questioned about air pollution; he had been told that the purpose of the interview was to gather health data. Also the interviewers had been definitely instructed not to mention either air pollution or smog until after these questions had been answered. The per cent of all those reporting a change in condition who attributed the change to air pollution and to other weather conditions is shown in Fig. 10.

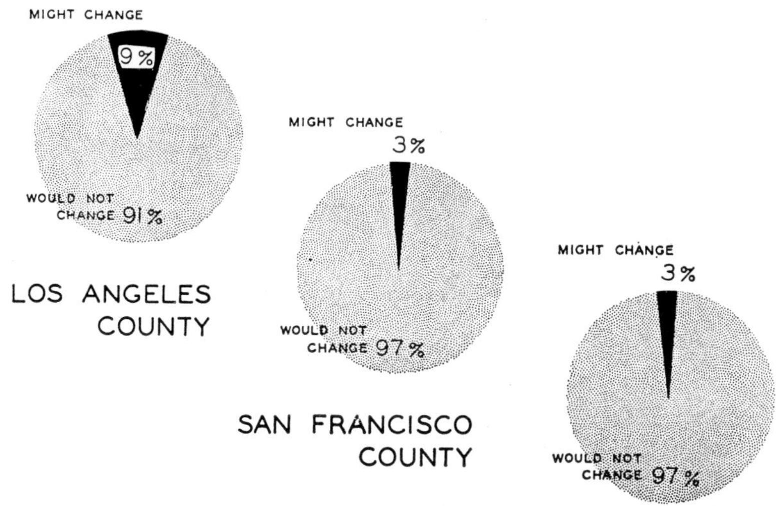

FIG. 9. Proportion of workers bothered by air pollution who have seriously considered changing jobs. [Source: California State Department of Public Health, "Air Pollution Effects Reported by California Residents." Berkeley, California, 1960.]

In summary, the mixture of pollutants which afflicts Los Angeles has:

(1) Not so far been shown to produce fatalities.

(2) Not produced acute disease, except possibly in a small minority of asthmatics.

(3) Possibly produced interference with lung function or aggravation of chronic respiratory conditions.

(4) Been suspected of a role in chronic pulmonary disease and lung cancer.

(5) Produced widespread eye irritation.

(6) Caused some persons to move their places of residence or employment.

Los Angeles air pollution has been characterized as a serious threat to health, including physical and social well-being (*61*).

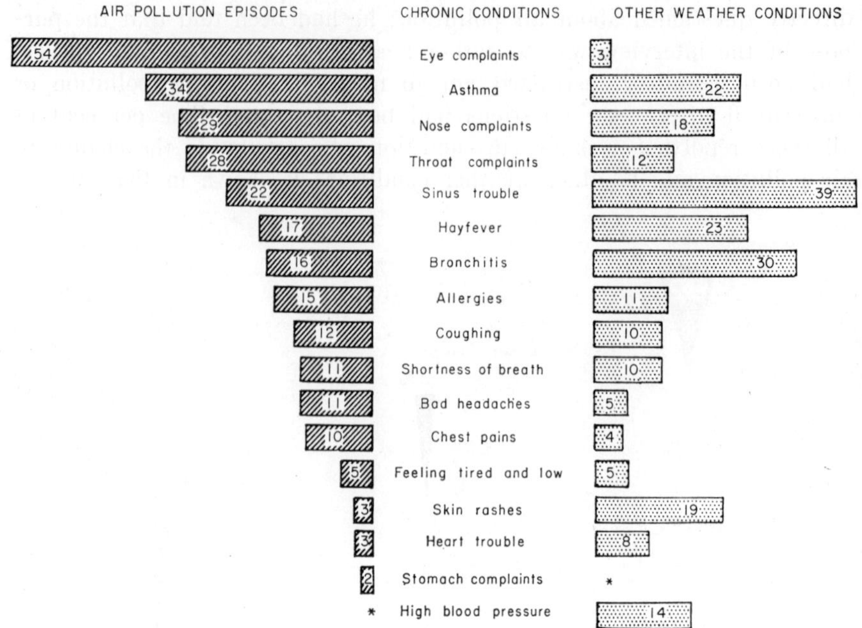

FIG. 10. Changes in chronic conditions related to air pollution and other weather factors. Numbers indicated in bars indicate per cent reporting a change in condition. Asterisk represents less than 1%. [Source: California State Department of Public Health, "Air Pollution Effects Reported by California Residents." Berkeley, California, 1960.]

VIII. Air Pollution as a Factor in Chronic Pulmonary Diseases

A. LUNG CANCER

The very striking increase in cancer of the respiratory tract (Fig. 11) has led naturally to the question as to whether inhaled pollutants may be in part responsible. Lung cancer is a more frequent cause of death in urban areas than in suburban and rural areas, as is shown in Fig. 12 (*67*). This has led to the hypothesis that part of the difference is due to community air pollution. There can be little doubt that there is some "urban" factor, but its exact nature is not entirely clear.

Dean (*68*) and also Eastcott (*69*) have demonstrated that, compared to that for natives, an increased lung cancer rate is observed in persons who emigrated from Great Britain to South Africa and New Zealand, respectively. The association of this increase with their exposure to polluted air prior to their emigration has been suggested.

Exposure to cigarette smoke has been shown to be related to in-

TABLE VI

LUNG CANCER DEATH RATES[a] OF MEN IN RURAL, MIXED, AND URBAN AREAS CLASSIFIED ACCORDING TO PAST SMOKING HABITS[b]

Smoking category	Ages 45–54			Ages 55–64			Ages 65–74			S.D.R. 45–74[c]		
	Rural	Mixed	Urban	Rural	Mixed	Urban	Rural	Mixed	Urban	Rural	Mixed	Urban
Nonsmokers	0	0	31	0	0	147	70	0	336	14	0	131
Pipe smokers	0	0	104	34	59	143	145	26	232	41	0	143
Cigarette smokers												
Light	69	57	112	70	224	378	154	259	592	87	153	297
Moderate	90	83	138	205	285	386	362	435	473	183	132	287
Heavy	117	214	205	626	362	543	506	412	588	363	303	394
Number of deaths	16	26	124	25	56	232	27	36	183	68	118	539

[a] Mean annual per 100,000 from mid-1952 to mid-1954.

[b] Source: P. Stocks and J. M. Campbell, *Brit. Med. J.* **ii,** 923 (1955).

[c] Standardized death rate based on Liverpool population. The number of deaths upon which the rates are based is shown in the bottom line.

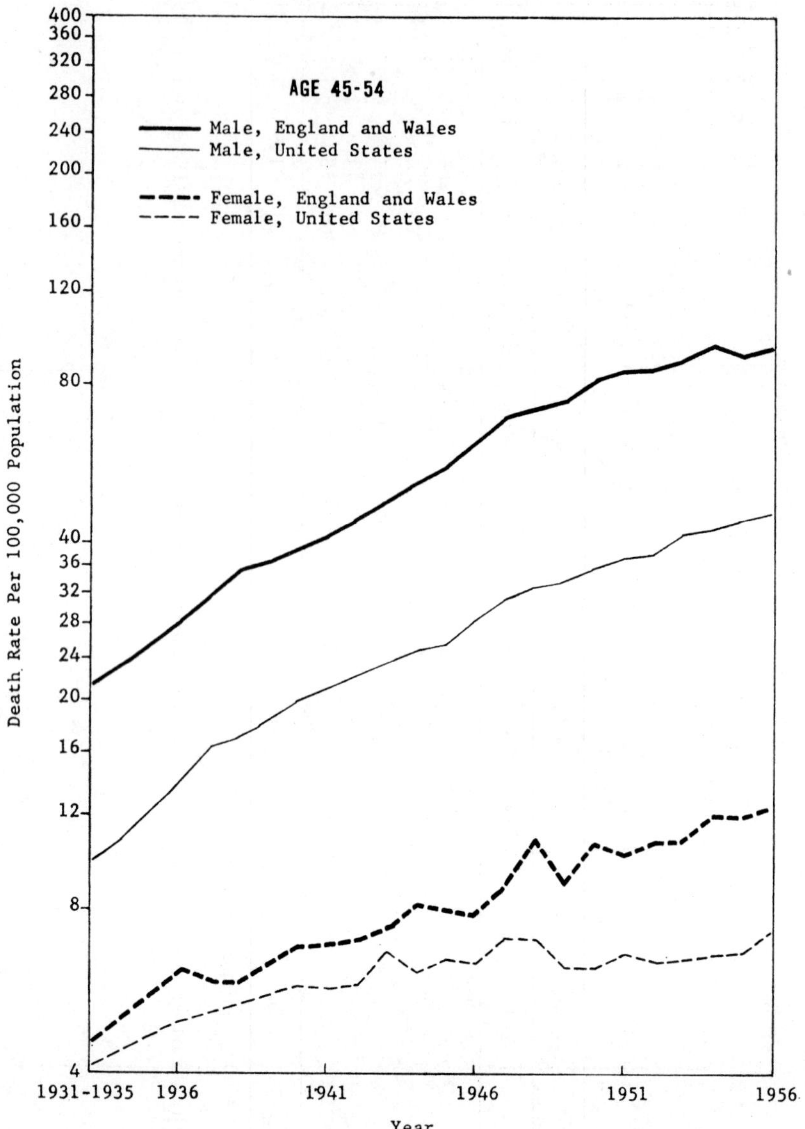

FIG. 11. Lung cancer death rates, by sex, at selected ages for England and Wales and the United States (white population) in 1931–1935 to 1956. [Sources: Registrar-General of England and Wales and United States National Office of Vital Statistics.]

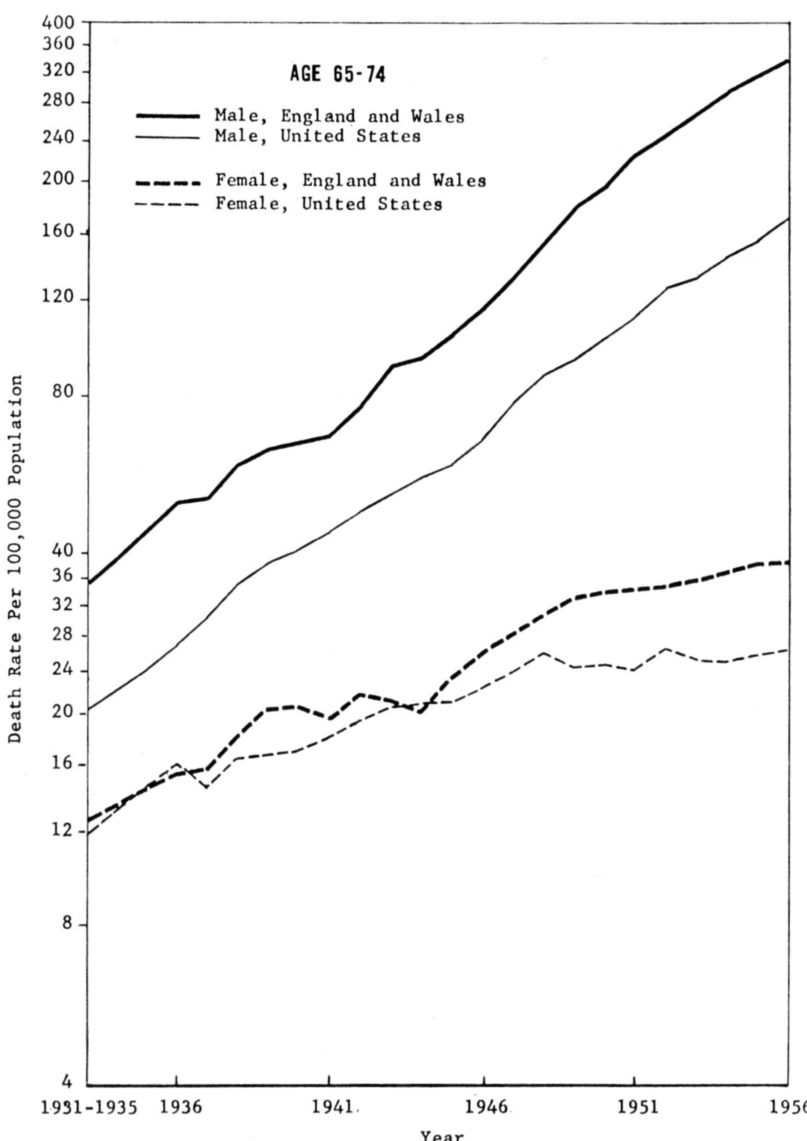

FIG. 11 (continued; for legend see p. 374)

creased incidence of lung cancer. In reviewing reported studies, it is clear that, for large heterogeneous populations, smokers have from nine to forty times as much lung cancer as nonsmokers, whereas persons exposed to community air pollution have from 1.3 to two times as much lung cancer as comparable groups of nonexposed persons. It is likely that both types of exposure are important. Indeed, it is difficult to see how the lung can discriminate between the several sources of pollution—its response is essentially indifferent to the source and is only influenced by the chemical and physical nature of the pollutants.

There is no doubt that the atmosphere of many polluted areas contains substances which are experimentally capable of producing cancer in animals. It has been stated (*70*) that carcinogens may be found in any polluted atmosphere which is analyzed with sufficiently sensitive methods. What is not known is whether these substances are present in sufficient amounts to produce cancer in man through inhalation.

Lung cancer has been produced experimentally by exposing mice simultaneously to ozonized gasoline, a form of simulated smog, and to influenza virus (*70a*). This work by Wisley and co-workers opens up a new approach to work both on the role of viruses and of air pollutants.

Two classes of carcinogens have been detected in polluted atmospheres: (1) The organic carcinogens, such as benzo[*a*]pyrene, dibenzanthracene and related compounds. (2) Potentially carcinogenic metals and metal compounds. The magnitude of pollution with benzo[*a*]pyrene is substantially greater in cities whose pollution sources are primarily the combustion of coal in comparison with those whose pollution is primarily from petroleum combustion (*71*).

Stocks and Campbell (*5*) have shown a relationship between lung cancer mortality rates, urbanization, and atmospheric levels of benzo[*a*]pyrene. They were careful to control their data with respect to differences in consumption of cigarettes. Table VI shows the death rates for several categories of smokers living in various areas of Great Britain.

In a study of lung cancer, bronchitis, and pneumonia mortality, by areas of Great Britain in which measurements of smoke, polycyclic hydrocarbons, and trace metals were available, Stocks (*71a*) found lung cancer to be strongly correlated with smoke density. The relationships are only partly explained by social differences in the populations. A similar relationship holds for bronchitis and pneumonia in males, and bronchitis in females. In some geographic areas, cancer of the stomach and intestine are significantly related to smoke. For lung cancer and bronchitis benzo[*a*]pyrene (i.e., benzopyrene) has the most important association. Of the trace metals, associations of lung cancer with beryllium and molybdenum are of some consequence, with arsenic, zinc, and vanadium showing weaker associations.

There is also evidence of the effects of arsenic, chromium, nickel, and other metallic carbonyls on the incidence of lung cancer on occupational exposures (*72*). The levels of these substances in community air pollution are substantially less than those in occupational exposure.

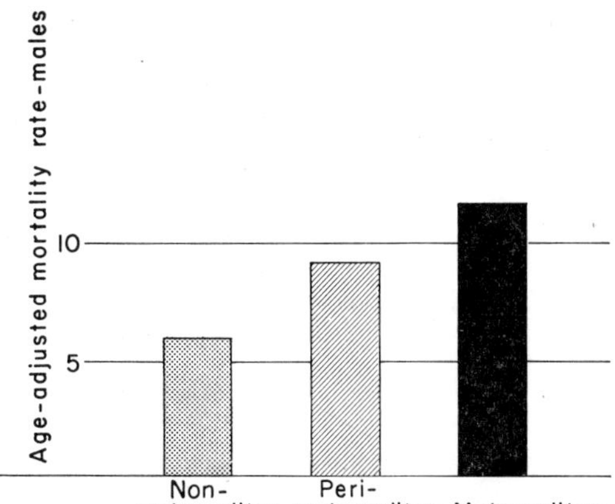

FIG. 12. The association of lung cancer with urbanization of county of residence. [Source: N. Manos, *Public Health Service Publ.* No. 562 (1957).]

However, several occupations have been shown in a case-control study to have excessive lung cancer rates (*73*). These are shown in Fig. 13. Hueper (*74*) states that lung cancer in nonoccupational groups has been caused by arsenic. Attention has also been called to the arsenic

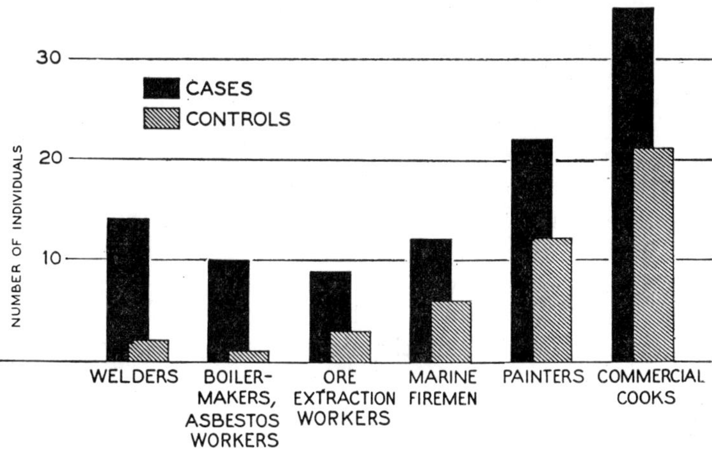

FIG. 13. Occupations with a high lung cancer rate. [Source: L. Breslow, L. Hoaglin, G. Rasmussen, and H. K. Abrams, *Am. J. Public Health* **44,** 171 (1954).]

content of cigarette smoke (*75*). It seems somewhat less likely that human cancer is produced by the metallic group of potential carcinogens than from the organic group. However, there may be local community sources of pollution which lead to rather high levels of some of these substances, and since so little environmental measurement is being done for them, they could pass unnoticed.

B. Chronic Obstructive Respiratory Diseases (Asthma, Bronchitis, and Emphysema)

Also increasing rapidly and with a similar epidemiologic pattern to lung cancer are a group of respiratory diseases best exemplified by pulmonary emphysema in the United States and chronic bronchitis in Great Britain. Data for California is shown in Fig. 14. It is not possible to make a clear distinction between the deaths in the United States ascribed to pulmonary emphysema and those ascribed to asthma, bronchiectasis, bronchitis, or pulmonary fibrosis (*76*). Therefore, it is considered proper to combine these groups of diseases as shown in Fig. 14; however, the increase is most striking in emphysema. A number of explanations for the increased frequency of emphysema are possible, including increased physician familiarity with the diagnosis. Another suggestion is that this increase is primarily associated with the increased number of elderly persons. However, the increase has occurred at the same relative magnitude in several age groups. The frequency of this group of diseases is substantially greater in Great Britain than it is in the United States; so, also, is the volume of research on the possible relationship of air pollution.

The evidence concerning the relationship of air pollution to chronic pulmonary disease is quite strong in Great Britain. Reid and Fairbairn (*77*), in particular, have shown that mortality from chronic bronchitis is statistically associated with the amount of air pollution, and they have also shown that morbidity from chronic bronchitis among postmen is related to the amount of pollution to which they are exposed. The magnitude of this problem in Great Britain is very great—chronic bronchitis is the second most common cause of death in men from 40 to 55, and is the leading cause of disability. British investigators have looked in vain for comparable findings in other countries (*78*). It is possible that a good deal of chronic pulmonary disease elsewhere is either overlooked, or is represented on death certificates by other causes of death. British investigators are particularly interested in the possibility that some of the persons certified in the United States as dying of coronary heart disease might possibly have been certified in Great Britain as having died of chronic bronchitis or emphysema.

Recent studies reported by Reid (*79*) and Gilson (*80*) give strong support to the relationship between emphysema and exposure to polluted air. Also of some importance is the finding of dust or soot particles surrounding the dilated air spaces on pathologic examination of the early lesions of emphysema, even before the illness is well developed (*81*). The association of this pigment and the early emphysema lesions

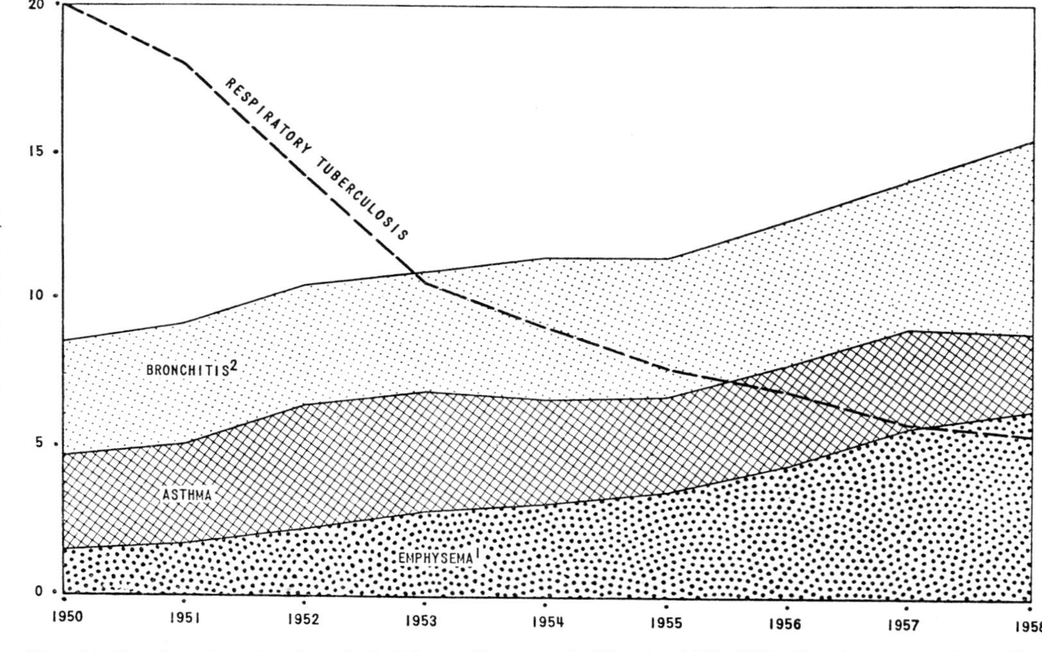

FIG. 14. Death rates due to selected lung diseases, California, 1950–1958. Emphysema and cardio-respiratory disease. [Source: J. R. Goldsmith, *Am. Rev. Resp. Diseases* **82,** 485 (1960).]

[1] Emphysema with bronchitis is included with emphysema.

[2] Bronchitis includes acute bronchitis, bronchitis unqualified, chronic bronchitis, bronchiectasis, and other chronic interstitial pneumonia.

does not necessarily prove that the pigment was the cause of these lesions.

At the Third Conference on Research in Emphysema in Aspen, Colorado (*82*), it was stated that emphysema may originate from one or more of the following factors: (1) chronic recurrent irritation; (2) chronic and/or recurrent infection; (3) recurrent, temporary or permanent diffuse or patchy paralysis of the cilia; (4) overproduction and increased viscosity of bronchial mucus; (5) abnormally prolonged retention of various inert and/or chemically active atmospheric pollutants; and (6) acquired or congenital defect or (7) injury from violent coughing. Of these possible factors the first, irritation; the third, alteration of function of the cilia; the fourth, increased production of mucus; and the seventh, effects of coughing may all be secondary effects of the air pollution exposure, while the fifth is directly related to pollutant exposures. Nevertheless, many persons with very serious and prolonged

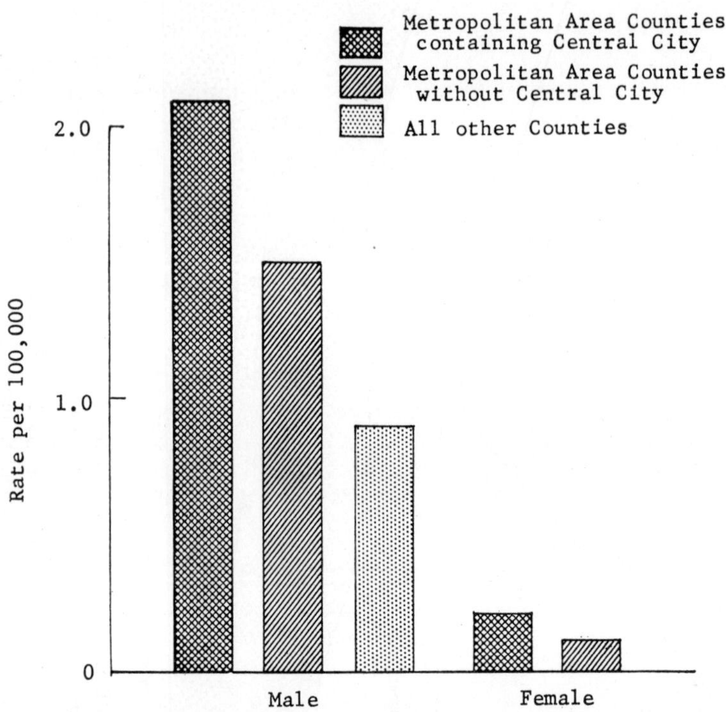

FIG. 15. Age-adjusted mortality rates by degree of urbanization in the United States, white population, by sex, 1949–1951. Emphysema, no mention of bronchitis. [Source: N. Manos, *Public Health Service Publ.* No. 562 (1957).]

exposures to a variety of pollutants do not develop the disease. It should be noted that emphysema, rather than asthma, chronic bronchitis, or obstructive ventilatory disease, has been discussed. Epidemiological studies of emphysema are not as readily undertaken as they are for obstructive disease which includes asthma and bronchitis as well.

In the United States emphysema is more common in metropolitan than in suburban and rural areas, as shown in Fig. 15. This rural-urban difference cannot be detected in California, but this is likely to be due to the fact that most of the residents in California migrated to the state and now do not live in the same types of communities as those in which they were born and reared. In chronic respiratory disease, too, an important role is played by exposure to cigarette smoke. Work on this problem is at a somewhat less advanced state than is the case in cancer of the lung.

It is, therefore, felt likely that future investigation will show some role of community air pollution in chronic lung disease in the United States. Present evidence suggests that community air pollution exposures alone probably will not account for all of the increase and that a substantial contribution will be ascribed to cigarette smoking.

IX. Prevention and Treatment of Air Pollution Effects

Obviously the ultimate prevention of effects from air pollution depends on controlling the emission of pollutants. While there can be no compromise with this ideal, the universal achievement of air of satisfactory quality is a goal for the future. So long as air pollution is likely to affect humans, it is important to stress a few principles which will help to prevent manifestations, and which may be helpful in treating any possible effects.

Community air pollution produces relatively less concentrations inside dwellings and buildings than in the outside, circumambient, air. For this reason substantial protection against the possible effects of air pollution can be obtained by staying indoors during periods when air pollution is likely to be severe. In addition, recent advances in air conditioning have led to general agreement that for enclosed spaces filtration of air supplied through activated charcoal filters will remove most noxious pollutants. Such filters can, with relative ease, be included in standard air conditioning equipment and should be given serious consideration when such equipment is planned for use in hospitals or nursing homes in communities where air pollution is prevalent. Filters conventionally used in household ventilating systems are not adequate for this purpose and should not be relied upon. Specific neutralization of pollutants remains a possibility but, except for the neutralization of sulfur dioxide and sulfuric acid by dilute ammonia vapors, there has been little demonstration of its effectiveness.

The sum total of experience indicates that there are a few people in most populations who are unusually susceptible to irritating air pollution. Such individuals deserve special consideration. It seems clear that the judicious use of bronchodilator drugs such as isopropylarterenol may be valuable in treatment of such persons, or in prophylaxis.

Some have suggested the advisability of making oxygen available for the particularly susceptible persons in the event of serious air pollution. Though added oxygen under medical supervision may be lifesaving, it is also possible that when oxygen is used injudiciously, it may be lethal. For this reason, widespread use, even during emergencies, should be carefully controlled according to sound physiological and medical principles.

References

1. D. Hunter, "The Diseases of Occupations." Little, Brown, Boston, 1955.
2. F. A. Patty, "Industrial Hygiene and Toxicology." Interscience, New York, 1948.
3. R. T. Johnstone and S. E. Miller, "Occupational Diseases and Industrial Medicine." Saunders, Philadelphia, 1960.
4. Smyth, H. F., Jr., Hygienic standard for daily inhalation. *Am. Ind. Hyg. Assoc. Quart.* **17,** 129 (1956).
5. P. Stocks and J. M. Campbell, Lung cancer death rates among non-smokers and among pipe and cigarette smokers. *Brit. Med. J.* **ii,** 923 (1955).
6. E. A. Martell and E. A. Drevinsky, Atmospheric transport of artificial radioactivity. *Science* **132,** 1523 (1960).
7. H. Cember, J. A. Watson, and A. A. Spritzer, Bronchogenic carcinoma from radioactive cerium fluoride. *A.M.A. Arch. Ind. Health* **19,** 14 (1959).
8. H. E. Stokinger, Themes and variations in experimental toxicology. Paper presented at *4th Air Poll. Med. Research Conf. (Calif. State Depart. Public Health), San Francisco, 1960,* to be published in Proceedings.
9. J. Firket (Secretary), "Sur les causes des accidents survenus dans la vallee de la Meuse, lors des brouillards de decembre 1930. Resultats de l'expertise judiciaire faite par MM. Dehalu, Shoofs, Mage, Batta, Bovy, et Firket. *Bull. acad. roy. med. Belg.* **11,** 683–741 (1931).
10. K. Roholm, The fog disaster in the Meuse Valley, 1930: A fluorine intoxication. *J. Ind. Hyg. Toxicol.* **19,** 126 (1937).
11. Ministry of Health, "Mortality and Morbidity During the London Fog of December 1952," Reports on Public Health and Related Subjects No. 95. Her Majesty's Stationery Office, London, 1954.
12. A. E. Martin and W. H. Bradley, Mortality, fog and atmospheric pollution. *Monthly Bull. Ministry of Health and Public Health Lab. Service* **19,** 56 (1960).
13. B. Rouèche, "Eleven Blue Men." Little, Brown, Boston, 1953.
14. H. H. Schrenk, H. Heimann, G. D. Clayton, W. M. Gafafer, and H. Wexler,

"Air Pollution in Donora, Pennsylvania." Public Health Service Bulletin No. 306. U. S. Public Health Service, Washington, D. C., 1949.
15. J. Thompson and A. Ciocco, Sickness, change of residence and death: I. General results of follow-up in two population groups. *Brit. J. Preventive & Social Med.* **12,** 172 (1958).
16. L. C. McCabe and G. D. Clayton, Air pollution by hydrogen sulfide in Poza Rica, Mexico. *Arch. Ind. Hyg. Occupational Med.* **6,** 199 (1952).
17. T. E. Huber, S. W. Joseph, E. Knoblock, P. L. Redfearn, and J. A. Karakawa, New environmental respiratory disease (Yokohama asthma). *Arch. Ind. Hyg. Occupational Med.* **10,** 399 (1954).
18. J. R. Goldsmith, *Proc. Natl. Conf. on Air Poll. Public Health Service Publ.* No. 654, 214 (1959).
19. W. J. Hamming, R. D. McPhee, and J. R. Taylor, Contaminant concentrations in the atmosphere of Los Angeles County. *J. Air Poll. Control. Assoc.* **10,** 7 (1960).
20. M. O. Amdur, The response of guinea pigs to inhalation of formaldehyde and formic acid alone and with a sodium chloride aerosol. *Intern. J. Air Poll.* **3,** 201 (1960).
21. Stokinger, H. E., Toxicologic interactions of mixtures of air pollutants: Review of recent developments. *Intern. J. Air Poll.* **2,** 313 (1960).
21a. H. Heimann, Effects on human health, *in* "Air Pollution," W. H. O. Monograph, pp. 159–220. World Health Organization, Geneva, 1961.
22. J. R. Goldsmith, Effects of air pollution on health. *Calif. Health* **18,** No. 7 (1960).
23. J. A. Nadel, D. F. Tierney, and J. H. Comroe, Jr., Effect of inhalation of cigarette smoke and broncho-active aerosols on airway conductance (Abstract). *Federation Proc.* **19,** 378 (1960).
24. P. Kotin, H. Falk, and A. Miller, Removal of 3,4,benzpyrene from soot by proteins (Abstract). *Federation Proc.* **17,** 1741 (1958).
25. H. Falk, P. Kotin, and A. Miller, Polynuclear hydrocarbons in polluted atmosphere and factors concerned with carcinogenic activity. *Intern. J. Air Poll.* **2,** 201 (1960).
26. C. A. Nau, J. Neal, and A. Stanbridge, A study of the physiological effects of carbon black: III. Absorption and elution potentials; Subcutaneous injections. *A.M.A. Arch. Environmental Health* **1,** 512 (1960).
27. W. H. Anderson, G. L. Hamilton, and B. E. Dossett, A comparison of coal miners exposed to coal dust and those exposed to silica dust. *A.M.A. Arch. Environmental Health* **1,** 540 (1960).
28. A. B. Dubois and L. Dautrebande, Acute effects of breathing inert dusts and of carbachol aerosol on the mechanical characteristics of the lung in man; changes in response after inhaling sympathomimetic aerosols. *J. Clin. Invest.* **38,** 1746 (1959).
29. California State Department of Public Health, "Technical Reports on Air Quality Standards and Motor Vehicle Exhaust," Chapter V, pp. 61–68. Berkeley, California, 1960.
30. K. A. Bushtueva, *in* "Limits of Allowable Concentrations of Atmospheric Pollutants" (V. A. Ryazanov, ed.), Book 3, p. 20. Medgiz, Moscow, 1957. Transl. by B. S. Levine; distr. by Office of Technical Services, U.S. Dept. of Commerce, Publ. No. 59–21175).
31. S. S. Pinto, C. Einert, W. J. Roberts, G. S. Winn, and K. W. Nelson, Copropor-

phyrinuria: Study of its usefulness in evaluating lead exposure. *Arch. Ind. Hyg. Occupational Med.* **6,** 496 (1952).

32. D. Hofreuter, Review of some epidemiological studies to evaluate the health hazards of exposure to lead and carbon monoxide. Paper presented at the *4th Air Poll. Med. Research Conf. (Calif. State Dept. Public Health), San Francisco, 1960,* to be published in Proceedings.
33. H. S. Saterlee, The arsenic poisoning epidemic of 1900; Its relation to lung cancer in 1960: An exercise in retrospective epidemiology. *New Engl. J. Med.* **263,** 676 (1960).
34. J. Cholak, The analysis of traces of beryllium. *A.M.A. Arch. Ind. Health* **19,** 205 (1959).
35. V. H. Sussman, J. Lieben, and J. G. Cleland, An air pollution study of a community surrounding a beryllium plant. *Am. Ind. Hyg. Assoc. J.* **20,** 504 (1959).
36. M. Eisenbud, R. C. Wanta, C. Dustan, L. T. Steadman, W. B. Harris, and B. S. Wolf, Non-occupational berylliosis. *J. Ind. Hyg. Toxicol.* **31,** 282 (1949).
37. T. Dalhamn, Studies on the effect of sulfur dioxide on ciliary activity in rabbit trachea *in vivo* and *in vitro* and on the resorptional capacity of the nasal cavity. *Am. Rev. Respiratory Diseases* **83,** 566 (1961).
38. O. J. Balchum, J. Dybicki, and G. R. Meneely, The dynamics of sulfur dioxide inhalation. *A.M.A. Arch. Ind. Health* **21,** 564–569 (1960).
39. M. H. Halperin, R. A. McFarland, J. I. Niven, and F. J. W. Roughton, Time course of the effects of carbon monoxide on visual thresholds. *J. Physiol.* **146,** 583 (1959).
40. J. R. Goldsmith and L. H. Rogers, Health hazards of automobile exhaust. *Public Health Repts. (U.S.)* **74,** 6 (1959).
41. W. H. Forbes, F. Sargent, and F. J. W. Roughton, The rate of carbon monoxide uptake by normal men. *Am. J. Physiol.* **143,** 594 (1945).
42. California State Department of Public Health, "Technical Report of California Standards for Ambient Air Quality and Motor Vehicle Exhaust." pp. 69–73. Berkeley, California, 1960.

42a. M. B. Jacobs, "The Analytical Chemistry of Industrial Poisons, Hazards, and Solvents," 2nd Ed., Interscience, New York, 1949.

43. H. G. Clamann and R. W. Bancroft, Toxicity of ozone in high altitude flight. *Advances in Chem. Ser.* No. 21, 352 (1959).
44. M. O. Amdur, *Proc. 2nd Air Poll. Med. Research Conf. (Calif. State Dept. Public Health), Berkeley, 1958,* p. 42 (1959).
45. M. O. Amdur, W. W. Melvin, Jr., and P. Drinker, Effects of inhalation of sulfur dioxide in man. *Lancet* **ii,** 758 (1953).
46. P. J. Lawther, Effects of sulfur dioxide on respiration and pulse rate in normal subjects. *Lancet* **ii,** 745 (1953).
47. F. I. Dubrovskaya, *in* "Limits of Allowable Concentrations of Atmospheric Pollutants" (V. A. Ryazanov, ed.), p. 37. Medgiz, Moscow, 1957 (transl. by B. S. Levine; distr. by Office of Technical Services, U.S. Dept. of Commerce, Publ. No. 59–21175).
48. L. Reid, Measurement of human bronchial glands in chronic bronchitis: experimental study of the response of the bronchial tree to irritation; Types of emphysema in chronic bronchitis. *Am. Rev. Respiratory Diseases* **83,** 416 (1961).
49. P. J. Lawther, Climate, air pollution and bronchitis. *Proc. Roy. Soc. Med.* **51,** 262 (1958).
50. J. A. Scott, Fog and atmospheric pollution in London, Winter 1958–59. *Med. Officer* **1,** 191 (1959).

51. V. M. Sim and R. E. Pattle, Effect of possible smog irritants on human subjects. *J. Am. Med. Assoc.* **165,** 1908 (1957).
52. J. A. Nadel, *Proc. 3rd Air Poll. Med. Research Conf. (Calif. State Dept. Public Health), Los Angeles, 1959,* p. 66 (1960).
53. N. R. Frank, M. O. Amdur, J. Bartlett, and J. L. Whittenberger, Respiratory responses to sulfur dioxide in controlled human exposures. Paper presented at *3rd Air Poll. Research Seminar (U.S. Public Health Service), New Orleans, 1960,* p. 26 (1960).
54. G. W. Wright and T. Lloyd, The pulmonary reaction of normal and emphysematous persons to the inhalation of SO_2, fly ash, and moisture. Paper presented at *3rd Air Poll. Research Seminar (U.S. Public Health Service), New Orleans, 1960,* p. 27 (1960).
55. R. E. Pattle and H. Collumbine, Toxicity of some atmospheric pollutants. *Brit. Med. J.* **ii,** 913 (1956).
56. H. F. Johnstone and D. R. Coughanowr, Absorption of sulfur dioxide from air. *Ind. Eng. Chem.* **50,** 1169–1172 (1958).
57. T. Lowry and L. M. Schuman, Silo-filler's disease; A syndrome caused by nitrogen dioxide. *J. Am. Med. Assoc.* **162,** 153 (1956).
58. E. LeB. Gray, Oxides of nitrogen: Their occurrence, toxicity, hazard. *Arch. Ind. Hyg. Occupational Med.* **10,** 418 (1959).
59. N. A. Vigdortschik, E. C. Andreera, I. Z. Matussevitsch, M. M. Nikulina, L. M. Frumina, and V. A. Striter, Symptomatology of chronic poisoning with oxides of nitrogen. *J. Ind. Hyg. Toxicol.* **19,** 469 (1937).
60. E. A. Schuck and G. J. Doyle, "Photooxidation of Hydrocarbons in Mixtures Containing Oxides of Nitrogen and Sulfur Dioxide." Air Poll. Foundation Report No. 29. San Marino, California, 1959.
60a. "Seventh Technical Progress Report," Air Poll. Foundation, Report No. 33. San Marino, California, 1961.
61. J. R. Goldsmith and L. Breslow, Epidemiological aspects of air pollution. *J. Air Poll. Control Assoc.* **9,** 129 (1959).
62. C. Schoettlin and E. Landau, Air pollution and asthmatic attacks in the Los Angeles area. *Public Health Repts. (U.S.)* 76:6, p. 545 (1961).
63. H. L. Motley, R. H. Smart, and C. I. Leftwich, Effect of polluted Los Angeles air (smog) on lung volume measurements. *J. Am. Med. Assoc.* **171,** 1469 (1959).
64. "Fourth Technical Progress Report," Air Poll. Foundation Report, No. 22, p. 23. San Marino, California, 1958.
65. California State Department of Public Health, "Air Pollution; Effects Reported by California Residents," Berkeley, California, 1960.
66. C. H. Hine, M. J. Hogan, W. K. McEwen, F. H. Meyers, S. R. Mettier, and H. K. Boyer, Eye irritation from air pollution. *J. Air Poll. Control Assoc.* **10,** 17 (1960).
67. N. Manos, Comparative mortality among metropolitan areas of the United States—102 causes of death. *Public Health Service Publ.* No. 562 (1957).
68. G. Dean, Lung cancer among white South Africans. *Brit. Med. J.* **ii,** 852 (1959).
69. D. F. Eastcott and M. B. Lond, The epidemiology of lung cancer in New Zealand. *Lancet* **i,** 37 (1956).
70. P. Kotin, Paper presented at the *4th Air Poll. Med. Research Conf. (Calif. State Dept. Public Health), San Francisco, 1960,* to be published in Proceedings.
70a. D. V. Wisley, P. Kotin, Fowler, and Trived, The combined effect of repeated viral infection and exposure to carcinogenic aerosols on pulmonary tumor induction in C-57 Black mice. *Proc. Am. Assoc. Cancer Research* **3,** 278 (1961).

71. E. Sawicki, W. C. Elbert, T. R. Hauser, F. T. Fox, and T. W. Stanley, Benzo(a)pyrene content of the air of American communities. *Am. Ind. Hyg. Assoc. J.* **21,** 443 (1960).

71a. P. Stocks, On the relations between atmospheric pollution in urban and rural localities and mortality from cancer, bronchitis, and pneumonia, with particular reference to 3,4-benzopyrene, beryllium, molybdenum, vanadium, and arsenic. *Brit. J. Cancer* **14,** 29 (1960).

72. F. W. Sunderman, A. J. Donnelly, B. West, and J. F. Kincaid, Nickel poisoning: IX. Carcinogenesis in rats exposed to nickel carbonyl. *A.M.A. Arch Ind. Health* **20,** 36 (1959).

73. L. Breslow, L. Hoaglin, G. Rasmussen, and H. K. Abrams, Occupations and cigarette smoking as factors in lung cancer. *Am. J. Public Health* **44,** 171 (1954).

74. W. C. Hueper, Epidemiologic, experimental and histological studies on metal cancers of the lung. *Acta Unio Intern. contra Cancrum* **15,** 424 (1959).

75. R. H. Holland, R. H. Wilson, A. R. Acevedo, M. S. McCall, D. A. Clark, and H. C. Lanz, A study of arsenic in regular sized unfiltered and filtered cigarettes. *Cancer,* **11,** 1115 (1958).

76. J. R. Goldsmith, Epidemiologic studies of obstructive ventilatory disease of the lung: I. A review of concepts and nomenclature. *Am. Rev. Respiratory Diseases* **82,** 4 (1960).

77. D. D. Reid and A. S. Fairbairn, The natural history of chronic bronchitis. *Lancet* **i,** p. 1147 (1958).

78. H. C. Olson and J. C. Gilson, Respiratory symptoms, bronchitis and ventilatory capacity in men. *Brit. Med. J.,* **i,** 450 (1960).

79. D. D. Reid, Environmental factors in respiratory disease. *Lancet* **i,** 1237–1289 (1958).

80. J. C. Gilson, Recent epidemiologic evidence from the United Kingdom on the relationship of atmospheric pollution and coal-dust exposure to chronic nonspecific lung disease. *Am. Rev. Respiratory Diseases* **83,** 407 (1961).

81. R. R. Wright, Pathologic changes in the elastic tissue in bronchi in chronic pulmonary emphysema. *Am. Rev. Respiratory Diseases* **83,** 425 (1961).

82. R. S. Mitchell, *et al.,* Third Conference on Research in Emphysema. *Am. Rev. Respiratory Diseases* **83,** 402 (1961).

PART III

Measuring and Monitoring Air Pollution

CHAPTER 11

Air Sampling

E. R. HENDRICKSON

Air Pollution Research Laboratory, University of Florida, Gainesville, Florida

I. General Sampling Considerations

Devices and techniques for determining the concentration of pollutants in the atmosphere are important for three main reasons: (1) to establish hazardous levels in the environment; (2) to determine the efficacy of ameliorating measures; and (3) to appraise contamination from a process or source. Accurate and adequate sampling is thus at the very heart of air pollution control and investigation.

Although "standard" procedures may not be desirable in all instances, it is essential that the theory and limitations of the various combinations of devices and techniques be thoroughly understood if results are to be meaningful. Each investigator must assure himself that the combination of sampling units and procedures selected by him will provide results of known accuracy. Failure to consider the effect of a single item, such as the material of the inlet tube, may result in errors of several hundred per cent.

It might be well at the start to define two terms commonly encountered in sampling—precision and accuracy. Quite often, the two words are used interchangeably. However, as used in this work, the term precision refers to the reproducibility of an observation, and the term accuracy refers to the truth of an observation. It is possible that a device or technique may be precise although not accurate, and vice versa. Some devices and techniques may be accurate and precise and others may be neither.

A. Problems Encountered in Sampling

There are several stages involved in making quantitative determinations of atmospheric pollutants. These include collection of the sample, refinement of the collected sample, analysis, and calculation of the results. In carrying out these various stages, a number of problems may be encountered, as discussed in ASTM Standard D1357-57 (*1*). Included are:

1. *Size of Sample*

The quantity of air which it is necessary to sample in any given situation must be known. To do this requires knowledge of the minimum pollutant concentration of interest as well as the sensitivity of the analytical technique. For some effects, such as vegetation damage, the minimum concentration of interest may not be known for a number of common pollutants assumed to cause damage.

2. *Rate of Sampling*

The permissible rate of sampling is determined by the collection device selected and is dependent upon the allowable head loss in that device, as well as on the experimentally determined optimum flow rate. Most units for sampling gaseous constituents have a permissible flow rate of 0.028 cu. m./min. The optimum and maximum flow rate for any given type of unit can be determined only experimentally. Units which depend on inertial forces to remove certain size ranges of particulates must be operated only at the prescribed rate if they are to function properly. A unit capable of efficient operation at a high flow rate is essential where a short duration is desirable.

3. *Duration of Sampling*

An important decison concerning the actual sampling procedure is the duration. A duration should be selected which will provide the information desired for each specific problem. Any sampling period will indicate the average concentration during that period of time (Figs. 1, 2, and 3). In each case, the actual pollutant concentration (which is purely arbitrary in this case) is shown by the solid line. If a sampling

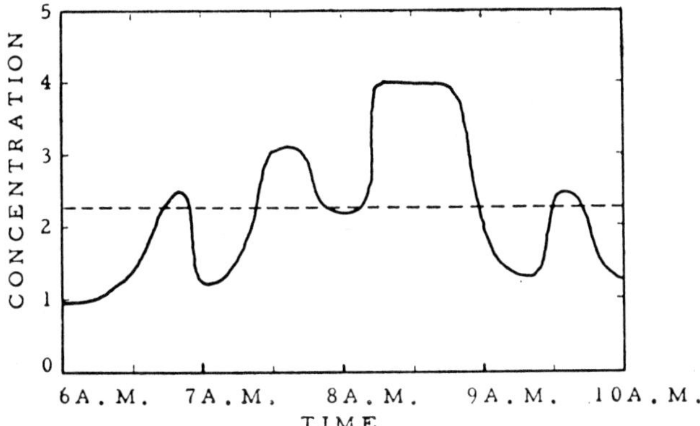

FIG. 1. Apparent pollutant concentration resulting from a sampling period of four hours duration is shown by the dashed line.

period of 4 hours duration is selected, the average concentration will be that shown in Fig. 1. Reducing the duration of sampling to a series of four 1-hour periods while holding the sampling rate fixed will produce the results shown by the dashed line in Fig. 2. This more closely approx-

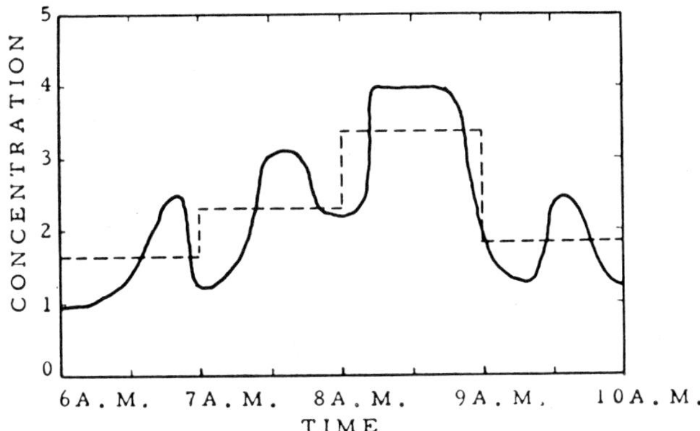

FIG. 2. Apparent pollutant concentration resulting from a series of sampling periods of one hour duration is shown by the dashed line.

imates the actual condition. The effect of further reducing the duration to a series of 15-minute intervals is shown in Fig. 3. If it is known that exposure to a concentration of 3 for a period of 15 minutes produces a certain undesirable condition, only the latter duration or less could be used to identify a cause and effect relationship.

Since peaks of fumigant concentrations may be the only significant values, the shortest sampling period generally reveals the most valuable information. The length of sampling period, however, is not a purely arbitrary decision. Factors which affect the minimum possible duration

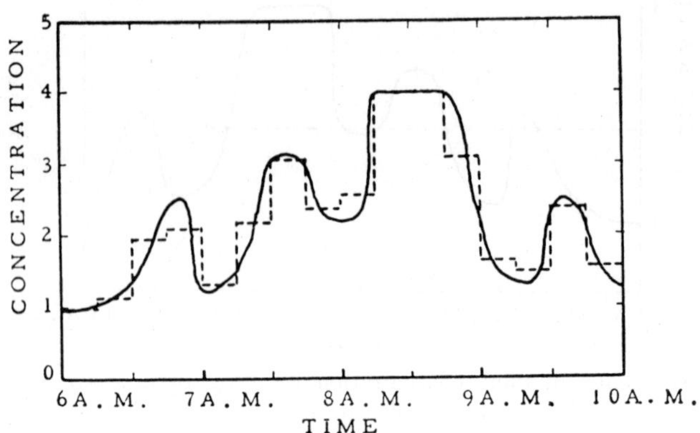

FIG. 3. Apparent pollutant concentration resulting from a series of sampling periods of 15 minutes duration is shown by the dashed line.

include: (1) the expected significant concentration to be encountered; (2) permissible rate of sampling; and (3) the lower limit of the analytical procedure to be used. Where very short durations are required, the use of automatic recording instruments of high sensitivity is indicated. Selection of an optimum sampling period requires consideration of the fact that very short durations result in a rapidly fluctuating record which may be difficult to read. In the case of intermittent sampling, the use of very short durations presupposes the collection of a continuous series of samples, if the results are to have meaning.

4. *Collection Limitations*

To be effective, each collection device must be assembled from units found to be most suitable for the specific pollutant involved. It is not necessary that the collector be 100% efficient, but the efficiency must be known and reproducible. An efficiency below about 75% is generally not suitable for air pollution sampling (*2*).

Numerous basic sampling devices for aerosols and gases have been in use for some time. Certain basic information on their use, however, is still lacking. For many units, there is a dearth of reliable information concerning the maximum flow rates for a variety of contaminants, the efficiency of collection at various flow rates, and the effect of low concentrations encountered. Information is urgently needed for many devices on the variation of efficiency with such factors as rate of sampling, concentration of a variety of compounds, and the nature of the collecting reagent. The assumption that the collection efficiency of a given unit is the same for variations in these factors is untenable. More and more sampling devices are being used for which such basic data are not available. This throws considerable doubt on the accuracy of the results. For example, when a midget impinger is used for collecting samples of a gaseous contaminant, even though it is operated at the optimum flow rate, it cannot be considered to have the same efficiency of collection as it is known to have for the dusts for which it was designed. A change in the reacting agent will undoubtedly alter the efficiency of collection of any device.

All gaseous samplers have a threshold value below which their efficiency drops to practically zero. This threshold value is different for different types of collectors and must be determined for the conditions under which sampling is to be conducted.

In the case of collecting devices for particulate matter, a variety of limitations may be cited. These will be discussed when the units themselves are described. It should be pointed out, however, that the term collection efficiency must be defined by the method used for determining the efficiency. Collection efficiency may be determined on the basis of weight of particles removed, count of particles removed, or reduction in discoloration effects. If the test aerosol contains a variety of particle sizes, the efficiency of removal on a weight basis may be very high, because large particles which make up the majority of the weight of a mixture are removed. Efficiency on the basis of total particle count is the most severe measure of efficiency. It may be possible to have an efficiency of 99.99% on a weight basis and only 40 or 50% on a total particle count basis. The method of determining efficiency will depend upon the use to which the results are to be put. If fine particles are particularly undesirable, the particle-counting method will probably be used. If, however, it is necessary to remove only the large particles, efficiency by weight will probably be satisfactory. Particles may be altered by coalescence or disintegration during sampling, depending on the method of collection. Thus, particles collected may not be representative of those present in the atmosphere.

In the final analysis, the effectiveness of a sampling procedure is measured by the accuracy and precision of all of its elements in proper combination. The only way this can be determined is by trial, on a reproducible synthetic atmosphere under controlled conditions. A discussion of the use of exposure chambers for this purpose is beyond the scope of this chapter, except to say that the investigator must assure himself that the atmosphere being sampled actually contains the concentrations it is believed to contain (*3*). It would be well to point out that the use of two similar sampling devices in series is not a satisfactory method of determining the efficiency of one of them. The fact that little or no material is collected in the second device is not necessarily a reliable indication that the first unit is highly effective, because the same portion passing through the first unit will be passing through the second. A particulate collector, for example, is effective only over a certain range of particle sizes. When sampling an atmosphere containing a wider spectrum of particle sizes, the first device may collect all of the particles for which it is effective, the second will show no collection because it is effective over the same range, but all of the particles will not be removed from the sampled air stream. Because of the threshold concentration level of gaseous collectors, the same line of reasoning may be applied.

5. *Analytical Limitations*

Reliable microanalytical procedures are presently available for practically all of the compounds of interest in air pollution episodes. Details of these methods will be found in Chapter 13.

Particular care must be taken to ensure that the interfering substances are not present or that the effects of interfering substances are eliminated. It is not necessary that the analyst personally collect the sample. It is desirable, however, that the analyst have sufficient knowledge of the sampling program in order to know what interferences may be present. This does not relieve the person making the collection of the responsibility of keeping complete notes on any unusual condition occurring during the sampling period which may have some bearing on the analytical procedure. Many times, interfering substances can be eliminated by distillation or ion exchange.

6. *Alteration of Constituents*

Cognizance should be taken of the fact that compounds which cause damage by their presence in the atmosphere may not be the same ones which were discharged from a source. Compounds which are collected in a sampler may not be the same ones present in the atmosphere, and materials received in the analytical laboratory may not be the same ones which were originally collected in sampling. A great variety of conditions may result in alteration of the sample, and it may be impossible to identify compounds originally discharged. In instances where it is necessary to identify specific compounds, rather than groups or classes of compounds, precautions must be taken to prevent alteration of the sample after it is collected. This will generally involve selection of a specific sampling technique by which alteration is minimized.

7. *Effect of Storage*

To reduce the effect of possible variation introduced by the interval between collection and analysis, that interval should be kept as short as possible and, preferably, always of the same duration. The sample should be protected from exposure to heat and light, and extra precautions should be taken to prevent leaks. Changes in the sampled compounds may be brought about by interaction between the various components of the collected sample. The effect of the container on the sample over a period of time must be determined for each type of sample and over a range of concentrations. This is of particular importance if the samples are to be shipped to a laboratory and if a considerable period of time has elapsed. Many different types of plastic, glass, and other containers are available, not all of which are compatible with the scrubbing solution that may be used, or with the polluting compounds which may be collected in the solution. Alteration of the sample may occur by adsorption or reaction with the walls of the container, or by dissolving the container material in the scrubbing solution. Thus, for each sampling technique a sampling container must be selected which has been determined to have no adverse effect on the stored sample. If it is impossible to obtain a suitable container material, the exact effect must be noted, and storage conditions must be controlled so that corrections may be made.

8. *Accuracy and Precision Required*

Frequently, an unreasonable degree of accuracy and precision in measurement is specified. There is no need to obtain a concentration to the nearest 0.01 unit if differences between effects are not noticeable to the nearest unit or 10 units. Each increase in precision and accuracy means an increase in cost of obtaining and analyzing the sample. In many instances, the variations in atmospheric concentration will not justify extremely accurate results. The degree of accuracy required must be determined on the basis of use to which the data will be put. In establishing cause and effect relationships in the laboratory, a greater degree of accuracy may be justified than in field monitoring of this same relationship. It is unnecessary to obtain exactitude in sampling which is greater than the sensitivity of the analytical procedures, and vice versa.

The concentration of contaminants at various places in the atmosphere, representing many different distances and intermediate conditions from a source of pollutants, may range over a wide scale. Variations also occur with time. Difficulty is thus experienced in sampling because there is no way of knowing what concentration may be present at any given time and location. This fact, coupled with the variation in efficiency exhibited by collectors when operated over a wide range of concentration, can create a serious trap for the unwary. The experienced individual recognizes this as a possible source of inaccuracy in his results. When some initial data are available, it is possible to vary rate or duration in the collection of the sample. This is of particular importance where very low concentrations may be encountered. The limitations of analytical procedures are such that it is necessary to collect a certain minimum amount of material before it can be detected.

9. *Collecting versus Recording Samplers*

To obtain the most reliable information concerning the variation of pollutant concentration in the atmosphere, continuous sampling is essential. For some purposes, however, samples collected intermittently at a number of locations will provide data of more value than will a continuous record at a few locations. A complete intermittent sampler usually includes a source of vacuum, a device for measuring the quantity of air sampled, and some type or combination of collectors. An interval timer may be used to shut off the equipment after a given period of sampling. The use of an automatic programer to collect a continuous series of cumulative samples makes this type of equipment of greater value. When so equipped, the combination of units is referred to as a sequential sampler. Some of these devices are intended to collect a series of samples of fixed duration. Others permit a variable program of starting, stopping, and different durations of sampling. Sequential samplers are limited in the number of individual collectors only by the number of vacuum and electrical circuits in the unit.

The series of collectors may be a part of, or separate from, the programing unit. Collectors may be of a variety of types, including impingers, filters, and fritted-glass scrubbers. The period of operation of an individual collector is controlled either by automatically connecting it to the vacuum source, or by automatically operating an inlet valve. One example of the former type of control utilizes a motor or ratchet-operated rotary valve actuated by a cam timer. The source of vacuum is connected to the rotor of the valve, and the individual collectors to the various openings on the stator. Another approach to the same type of control utilizes a series of solenoid-operated valves (one for each collector) connected to a vacuum manifold (*4*). These are actuated consecutively by a cam timer. This method potentially provides more flexibility in operation, particularly in respect to varying the duration of, and intervals between, sampling. Some valve arrangements of this nature use flexible rubber tubing for the valves, which are opened and closed mechanically by cams and lifters. An example of the inlet valve type of control has the individual collectors mounted on the perimeter of a rotating circular table. The table is rotated one position at a time by a ratchet device. Each collector is equipped with an inlet stopper valve which is held closed by a parallel table mounted above the rotating one. When the collector is moved to the proper position, the valve expands into a sampling well cut in the upper table, and opens. All of the collectors are under vacuum continuously but they sample only when the inlet stopper valve is open.

Another valuable accessory which may be used to control the operation of intermittent samplers is a wind vane controller. Mechanical controllers have been used for fallout jars but only the electrical type will be discussed here. A wind vane controller can be used to operate a sampling unit or units only when the wind is coming from a certain sector. A time meter may be wired to the sampler motor to record the total time of operation. Commercial or homemade wind vanes of the contact type, rather than the selsyn type, are used. It is generally desirable to use a low voltage hookup to the vane, operating a relay to actuate the sampler motor. Because of the effects of gustiness in swinging the vane back and forth over a contact, time delays should be included in the control circuits.

Devices of the types described serve merely as collectors, and quantitative analysis must take place in the laboratory. The units have the advantage that, by proper combination of collection technique and analytical procedure, they can be made very specific for many polluting materials. Each complete unit may cost a few hundred dollars. Such units, however, are very expensive in time and man power. For an extensive sampling problem, many man-hours may be required in making collections, maintaining the units, and performing the necessary analyses. A fixed duration of sampling must be selected and the results will show the average concentration over that interval of time.

To avoid some of the disadvantages of the intermittent collectors, recording instruments have been developed for several of the common pollutants (*5*). For an extensive and continuous program, the available recording instruments may prove to be more economical, since analysis is performed in the unit. It should be borne in mind, however, that the existing instruments are expensive in initial cost, many are temperamental in operation, and it may be difficult to eliminate interfering substances. The fact that analysis and recording of the results are performed in the instrument does not necessarily mean that the unit is a continuous sampler. Some recording instruments provide a continuous series of cumulative samples, with the duration of an individual sample being as long as 30 minutes.

10. *Units of Expression*

A casual examination of the literature on air pollution will reveal a great variety of units for expressing the results of sampling. This mixture of units is a natural result of the variety of disciplines which have been working on various phases of the problem. Each worker has calculated results in terms most familiar to him and most meaningful to his professional group. Many times, results are expressed in confusing

TABLE I
RECOMMENDED UNITS FOR REPORTING AIR POLLUTION MEASUREMENTS

Item measured	Recommended units	Observed ranges
Particle fallout		
Count	Number per square centimeter per time interval	—
Weight	Milligrams per square centimeter per time interval	0.5 to 135 mg./sq. cm./mo.
Airborne particulates		
Count	Number per cubic meter	10×10^6 and up particles/cu. m.
Weight	Micrograms per cubic meter	10 to 5000 μg./cu. m.
Gases and vapors	Micrograms per cubic meter	Varies greatly
Instantaneous light transmission	Per cent transmitted	0 to 100%
Visibility	Kilometers	—
Volume emission rates	Cubic meters per minute	1.5 to 300+ cu. m./min.
Sampling rates	Cubic meters (decimeters or centimeters) per minute	10 cc./min. to 3 cu. m./min.
Temperature	Centigrade scale	—
Time	0000 to 2400 hours per day	—
Pressure	Millimeters of mercury	—
Velocity	Meters per second	0 to 100 m./sec.
Gas volumes	Reported at 760 mm. Hg and 10°C.	—

proportional units with no indication as to whether the proportion is by weight or volume, and, even more important, the temperature and pressure conditions to which the calculations were adjusted are not given. Standardized procedures are definitely and urgently needed in calculating and reporting the results of analyses for air pollution surveys. Similar proposals have been presented by several investigators (*6*).

Terraglio *et al.* have made a comprehensive study and evaluation of the units used in the air pollution literature (*7*). Recommended units and the range which might be expected in the outdoor atmosphere are given in Table I.

11. *Computation of Results*

If expressed in the units recommended above, little actual computation is involved. All air volumes should be converted from the conditions of sampling to 760 mm. mercury and 10°C. For all practical purposes, in the range encountered while sampling the atmosphere, the PV/T relationship of the ideal gas law is applicable.

B. Common Equipment Needs (*8–10*)

1. *Vacuum Sources*

To operate one of the collection devices, it is necessary to draw a known volume of air through the unit. In a few instances, a pump discharge is used for collection of samples, but the shortcomings of this procedure are rather obvious. Therefore, a source of vacuum is necessary for the operation of any air-sampling device. The most commonly used sources of vacuum include:

a. Motor-driven vacuum pumps
  (1) Rotary
  (2) Cycloid
  (3) Reciprocating
  (4) Diaphragm
  (5) Centrifugal
b. Hand-operated vacuum pumps
c. Aspirators
d. Automobile vacuum

The sampling device should always be the first unit in a sampling train and the air should be drawn into it; that is, the pump should be on the downstream side. In sampling, continuous operation is often essential, and sampling intervals may extend over several hours. Various rates of flow are frequently desirable. For these reasons, a motor-driven pump is generally most suitable. The pump may operate on a battery, on line voltage, or from a gasoline engine-driven generator. If the latter is used, care must be taken that the exhaust does not interfere.

a. Motor-Driven Pumps. Of the pumps most frequently used in air sampling, the five which have been listed are the most common. The rotary pump is shown in Fig. 4. This type of pump has the advantage of being a positive displacement unit, of having low maintenance costs, and of providing a pulseless flow. The pumps are available in a wide range of sizes and capacities. Some manufacturers make oilless pumps in which the pump vanes are made of graphite instead of fiber, and lubrication is provided by the wear of the graphite vanes. The graphite vanes, however, are brittle and may be easily broken. In the case of the

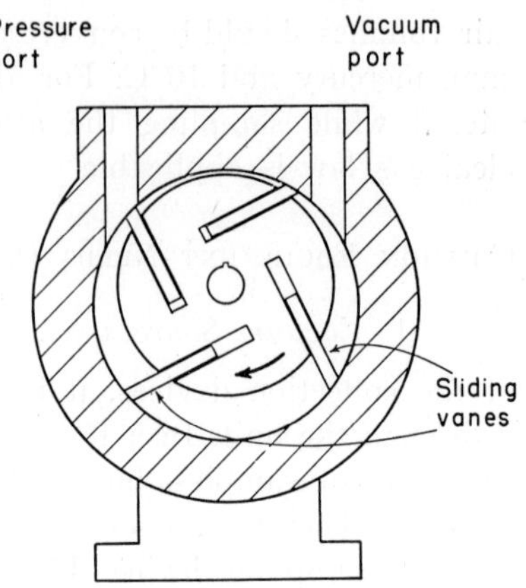

FIG. 4. Section through a rotary vacuum pump.

lubricated type rotary, difficulty is sometimes experienced in providing proper lubrication, especially at low vacuum. These pumps are usually lubricated by a wick-fed oiler having a small orifice. If the head loss through the orifice is greater than the vacuum being pulled on the system, the pumps will get little or no lubrication. This difficulty may be eliminated by providing the pump with a positive action oil device or by enlarging the orifice in the vacuum oiling device.

The cycloid pump is shown in Fig. 5. It also is a positive displacement unit which provides pulseless flow. It is generally made in larger sizes, although some smaller units suitable for air sampling are available. The major disadvantages of this type of pump are that it is more expensive than the one previously described and that it cannot pull as great a vacuum because of slippage between the cycloids.

Reciprocating pumps, except in small sizes, are not generally used in air sampling. They cause frequent difficulties because of the many working parts, such as check valves and piston rings. The flow which is obtained from a reciprocating pump, even a two-cylinder one, is not uniform. In small sizes, the reciprocating pumps for aquarium aeration are sometimes used.

In small units, diaphragm pumps are used. These are generally of the type used for pumping gasoline in automobiles. The diaphragms are usually of metal and the pump is driven electrically. The flow rate for a diaphragm pump of this type is rather low, being limited to about 1000 cc./min. For larger flows, the rubber diaphragm pumps used in some paint sprayers may be suitable.

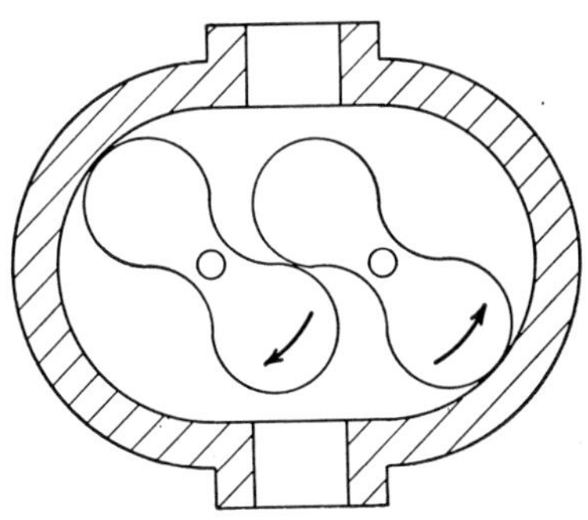

FIG. 5. Section through a cycloid vacuum pump.

Centrifugal compressors are used in air samplers where a large volume of flow is required at low head loss. The centrifugal compressor operates on the same principles as the centrifugal pump for water. The unit manufactured for tank-type vacuum cleaners, which is used in the Public Health Service high volume sampler, is of this type. This unit may provide air flow up to 2.8 cu. m./min. against a few inches of water vacuum.

Where vacuum pumps or centrifugal compressors are used to power collection devices such as filters, in which a pressure loss may build up during sampling, the use of some constant flow device is desirable. One such device was described by Schmidt and Wiltshire (*11*). In this unit, which can be applied to any vacuum pump, a vacuum-operated control valve is placed in series with the collection device to maintain a constant total suction at the intake. For centrifugal compressors such as those used on the high-volume sampler, several different approaches have been used. In one commercial unit the air, after passing through the filter, flows through an orifice mounted on a spring-loaded diaphragm. As filter resistance builds up, the pressure ahead of the orifice decreases, permitting the diaphragm to move slightly and contact a double throw switch, which activates a damper motor. A bypass damper is closed, thus increasing the total suction on the filter. A unit described by Harrison and Nader (*12*) may be attached to the standard high volume filter utilized by the Public Health Service. The unit consists of a spring-loaded piston valve providing an annular opening between its circumference and the tapered wall of the regulator body. A build-up of air flow resistance through the filter is counteracted by a corresponding change in resistance through the orifice opening.

b. Hand-Operated Vacuum Pumps. Hand-operated vacuum pumps are not too frequently used in air pollution sampling. Those which are used are mostly of the small hand-operated bicycle type, and only small samples can be drawn, with a great expenditure of energy. A few samplers are provided with this type of prime mover. Some commercial-type samplers are provided with a squeeze bulb pump, but these are used mostly in industrial hygiene work.

c. Aspirators. Aspirators operate on the venturi principle. They may use water, steam, or compressed air for providing the vacuum. The ordinary laboratory aspirator using water is limited to a few liters per minute. A recent innovation utilizes the discharge from a pressure container of Freon to operate an aspirator. Care must be taken that the Freon does not interfere with the analysis. Larger aspirators using steam, compressed air, or water are available to rates of several cubic meters per minute. In places where a surplus of air, steam, or water under high pressure is available, an aspirator provides a good means of furnishing the vacuum for air pollution sampling.

d. Automobile Vacuum. The vacuum connection used to operate windshield wipers and other devices on an automobile may be used for providing a source of vacuum for air pollution sampling. The flow, however, is limited to a few liters per minute, and the amount of vacuum produced is rather small. The automobile engine, of course, must be in operation during the time the vacuum is used, and this provides a possible source of contamination for the samples.

2. *Metering Devices*

In order to provide a quantitative measure of the amount of pollutant found in a given volume of air, a precise and accurate measurement must be made of the quantity of air drawn through the sampling device. The flow measurement should be downstream from the sampling device, between it and the prime mover. The flow should be measured into the pump rather than out of the pump. Since this places the flow measurement device at some pressure condition other than atmospheric, a manometer and thermometer must be used in the line so that the proper volume may be calculated.

There are two general types of flow measurement devices used in air pollution sampling:

a. Rate measurement
- (1) Pitot tubes (with differential pressure measurement)
- (2) Orifices (with differential pressure measurement)
- (3) Nozzles (with differential pressure measurement)
- (4) Rotameters

b. Quantity measurement
- (1) Dry test gas meter
- (2) Wet test gas meter
- (3) Cycloid gas meters

a. Rate Measurement. Rate measurement devices have the advantage of being compact and generally inexpensive. They have the disadvantage, however, of measuring only the instantaneous rate of flow, and must be checked frequently during the period of sampling to obtain a proper indication of the total flow.

The orifice, nozzle, and venturi section provide a loss of head which can be measured by a closed manometer. These can readily be calibrated to provide good accuracy in measuring the rate of air flow. Techniques and equipment for the calibration and use of these devices may be obtained from the ASME Power Test Codes (*13*).

A convenient device of undetermined accuracy, which is frequently used in air-sampling devices, is the critical orifice. This is an orifice usually having rounded upstream edges and designed to be of such size that large increments of pressure differential will not produce any appreciable difference in flow. This condition occurs when the critical pressure is considerably greater than the pressure at the nozzle outlet. If the absolute pressure in the low pressure region is less than about 53% of the pressure at the inlet, critical flow occurs. Temperature and pressure corrections must still be made, however.

The rotameter has a self-contained scale. A rotameter consists of a float mounted in a tapered tube. The air flow enters the lower end of the tube and causes the float to rise until the area between the float and the tube is such that the pressure drop is just sufficient to support the float. In effect, a variable orifice is provided. The tube is usually glass and has etched upon it a scale on which the position of the float can be read. By means of a calibration curve, the flow for any given float position can be determined. The rotameter is a very handy rate measurement device frequently used in air pollution sampling.

b. Quantity Measurement. Quantity-measuring devices record the total flow passing through them, which is most useful in air pollution work. They have the disadvantage, however, of being rather bulky. The dry test meter consists of a pair of bellows, a system of bell cranks, and a pair of sliding valves. The bellows are alternately filled and emptied and, in this operation, operate the bell cranks to turn a geared indicating dial. These meters are suitable for field use and are quite accurate. The error is about $\pm 1\%$. The meter provides a positive displacement measurement. The construction is shown in Fig. 6.

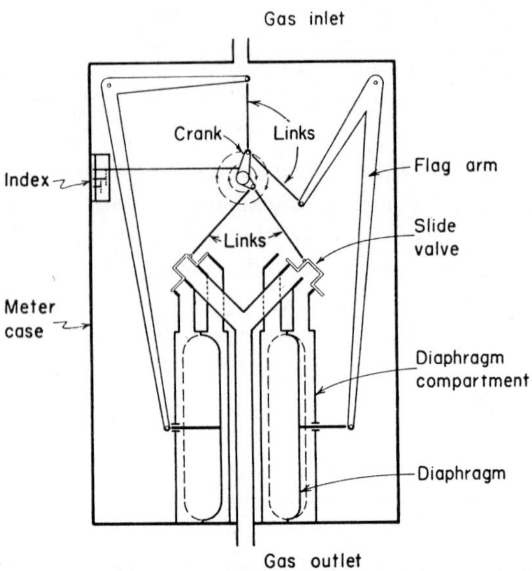

FIG. 6. Schematic drawing of the mechanics of operation of a dry test gas meter.

The wet test meter is more accurate than the dry test meter, generally having an error of $\pm 0.5\%$. This type of meter, because of its construction, is not too suitable for field use but is quite suitable for laboratory use in calibrating other flow measurement devices. The construction is shown in Fig. 7.

A cycloid-type meter, similar in construction to the cycloid-type pump previously described, is available. This is a positive displacement meter which is somewhat more expensive than the two previously described meters.

It should be borne in mind that any flow measurement device should be calibrated before use and at intervals during use. The scales on some flow-measuring devices are calibrated to read results far beyond the accuracy of the measuring device itself. A word of caution should prevent anyone from falling into this trap.

Several methods are available for calibrating flow-measuring devices. The basic calibration method is by displacement of some fluid such as water. Commercial "meter provers" are available but are not generally

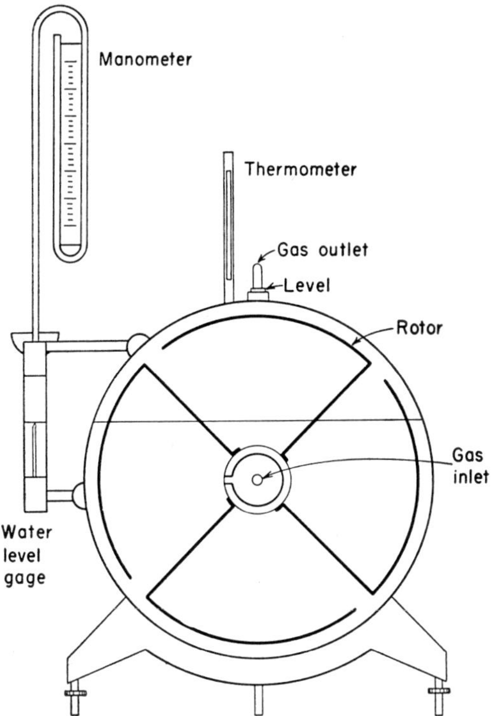

FIG. 7. Wet test gas meter (front face removed).

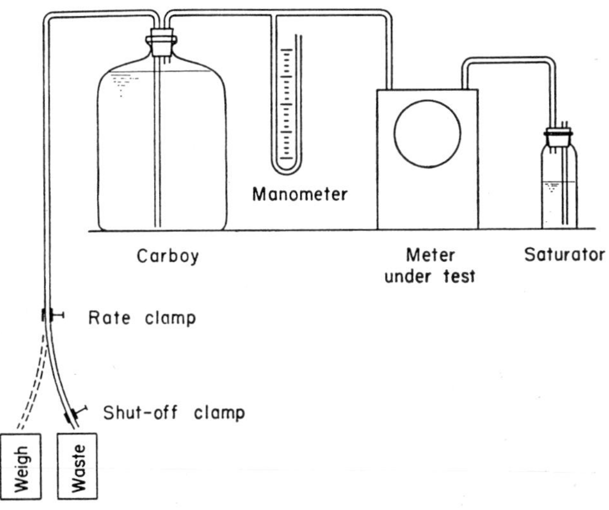

FIG. 8. Method of calibration for gas meters suggested by ASTM.

found in the ordinary laboratory. It may be possible to obtain the use of one from a gas company.

Another simple way of calibrating measuring devices is as shown in Fig. 8. The amount of displaced water is collected in a bottle and measured volumetrically or gravimetrically. By determining and making adjustments for the temperature and pressure, accurate calibrations may be made. The calibration should be performed at constant operating conditions and the beginning and end of the dial movement should be excluded from the observation. This permits the slack in the gear train to be taken up. The ASTM standard for this method of calibration is D1071-55, Measurement of Gaseous Fuel Samples (*14*).

3. *Essential Supplementary Devices*

In order to determine the concentration of a pollutant in the air, it is necessary to assemble the units which have been described into a complete sampler. The usual organization of a sampler is:

(a) Inlet tube
(b) Collection device
(c) Overflow trap (if necessary)
(d) Manometer and thermometer
(e) Flow-measuring device
(f) Valves
(g) Prime air mover

The inlet tube should be of some material that will not react with the contaminant being sampled. In general, this means glass, plastic, or stainless steel. For most contaminants, glass is probably the most satisfactory insofar as its inertness is concerned. For sampling HF this may not be the case. The big disadvantage of using glass tubing on the inlet is its fragility and rigidity.

For most inlet tubes, therefore, plastic seems to be a suitable material. Polyethylene is inert to most common pollutants. It is attacked, however, by hydrocarbons and has the disadvantage of being destroyed when exposed to sunlight, heat, and air for long periods. A more suitable plastic is polytetrafluoroethylene or polychlorotrifluoroethylene. It is more expensive than most other plastics, however. Polyvinyl chloride should also be suitable as an inlet tube for many of the common contaminants. Both polyvinyl chloride and rubber have been found to be unsuitable for SO_2 and HF. Many of these plastics may be obtained with a pigment such as carbon black, which gives them greater resistance to destruction by exposure to light and heat. It must be remembered that modifiers are used to accentuate certain desired properties of many plastics. Therefore, tubing fabricated of a given plastic resin may not always have the same properties. Some of these modifiers are volatile and may contaminate a sample or react with the pollutant being sampled (*15, 16*).

If it is necessary to use a metal inlet tube as might be the case, for example, in stack sampling at high temperatures, the appropriate type of stainless steel should be used to minimize loss by reaction before the sample reaches the collection device.

For particulate sampling, chemical resistance may not be as important as resistance to abrasion. In most instances, an inlet tube material should be selected which does not have and which will not develop a static charge.

Most gas collection devices are constructed of glass or plastic. Many of these devices are readily available from chemical supply houses.

After the collection device, little concern need be given to tubing other than to be sure that its diameter is large enough to prevent unnecessary head loss and that, in portable samplers, it is light enough. Rubber, plastic, or aluminum tubing, and wrought-iron pipe are all satisfactory.

For determining the temperature and pressure conditions of the air flow being measured, sensing devices should be installed in the line near the inlet of the metering unit. A mercury open manometer or sensitive vacuum gauge is suitable for the pressure measurement. The most convenient thermometer is probably the all stainless-steel dial thermometer with a stem of about eight inches. Breakage is less than that which occurs when using mercury-in-glass thermometers, and some types are equipped with a calibration screw.

For convenience in operation, most samplers should be provided with a timing device. The simplest of these is a common interval timer such as is used in the kitchen, but provided with a switch instead of a bell. The sampler can be placed in operation by setting the timer, and will automatically be switched off at the end of the time interval.

A more versatile unit may be constructed as described by Raynor (*4*). This unit provides for great versatility in a number of different operations.

II. Sampling Aerosol Contaminants

A. General Considerations

Most of the devices which will be described are merely collectors. Analysis must be done separately. Since changes in materials and equipment are being made rapidly, it behooves the investigator to study the

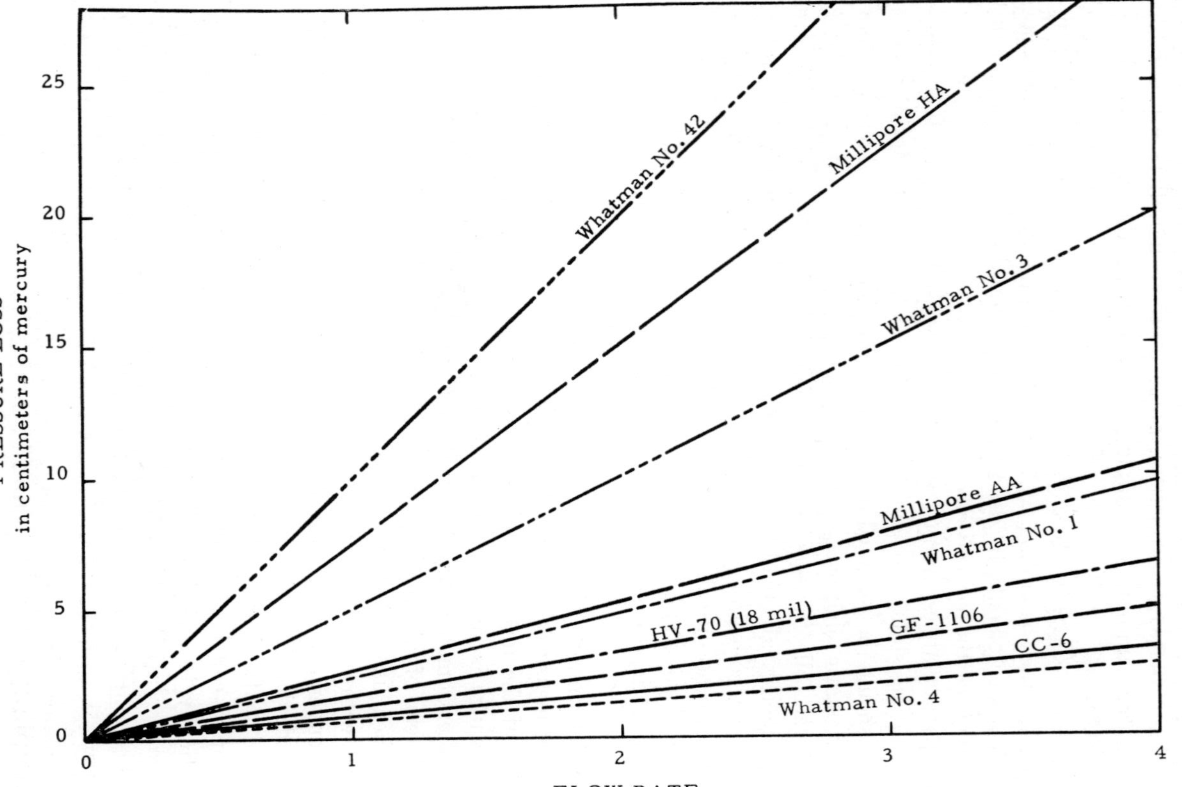

FIG. 9. Head-loss characteristics for various types of common filter media.

trade and contemporary literature carefully. In many instances a series combination of some of these devices will be found most satisfactory. Care must be taken, however, that particulates in the sampled air stream do not collect on the wall of the inlet and connecting tubing. Particular care must be taken if an aerosol sampler is used preceding a gas sampler. In many instances, the gas of interest may be adsorbed on the surfaces of the particles and collected in the aerosol collector. In other instances, the gas of interest may react with the material of the aerosol collector and result in an apparently low gas concentration.

B. Filtration (see also Chapter 29)

Filters are among the most commonly used aerosol collection devices. An air filter is made up of a porous bed through which the air must pass along tortuous paths. In most filters the air is forced to change direction many times in an abrupt fashion, so that inertial forces or direct collision will bring the particles into contact with a relatively large surface area provided by the filter material. In some instances, large particles collect on the surface of clean filters and rapidly accumulate to reduce the size of the filter opening. This enables the filter to collect matter much smaller than the original opening. For certain types of filtering materials an electrostatic charge may be built up, or may exist, to attract the particle out of the air stream. Various types of filtering material may operate on different principles or, more accurately, certain filter mechanisms may predominate in certain types of filters. Head loss characteristics for a variety of filters are shown in Fig. 9.

After collection, analysis may be performed by weighing, determining the chemical composition, or by particle sizing. Practically all of the types of filtering materials described are suitable for the first two methods. Fibrous and granular filters, however, are not too satisfactory for the third method of analysis because of the difficulty in separating collected material from the sampling medium. Three types of filtration devices are generally available.

1. *Fiber Filters*

Examples of these include wood fiber paper of various grades; papers or mats made of other cellulose fibers, mineral wool, plastic, or glass fibers; and asbestos mats. The filter paper ordinarily used in the analytical laboratory is not too suitable for air sampling. Most of the fibers are of too large a size and of the wrong shape, and it is difficult to conduct particle size analysis on the collected sample. However, special papers are reasonably efficient for a wide range of particle sizes.

In general, such papers are not suitable for collecting particles of less than about 0.5 to 1.0 μ. Paper thimbles have similar limitations. The characteristics of several common papers are given in Table II. None of these devices can be used at high temperature or under conditions of high moisture. Of course, the effectiveness of a filter must be examined in the light of its resistance to air flow as well as of its efficiency of particle removal. Some special fiber filters utilizing glass or mineral fibers are effective for particles as low as 0.3 μ in diameter and at a low head loss. Some of these can be used at temperatures as high as 800°C. Some of the newer glass fiber media utilize fibers of less than 1 μ in diameter and are effective for particle sizes as low as 0.05 μ. Many of the newer ultra-efficient media, because of low mechanical strength, require uniform support, usually in the form of a fine wire mesh or fritted material. A summary of efficiencies of various filter media is given in Table III.

TABLE II
COLLECTION EFFICIENCY BY PARTICLE SIZE FOR SELECTED FILTER PAPERS[a, b]

	Flow rate: 0.1 linear meter per minute				
Particle diameter (μ)	Whatman #1	Whatman #4	Whatman #41	Whatman #42	MSA Type "S"
Less than 0.4	57[c]	23[c]	23[c]	99[c]	48[c]
0.4–0.6	58	24	31	97	47
0.6–0.8	67	25	59	98	77
0.8–1.0	92	77	74	99	92
1.0–2.0	94	63	63	99	93
More than 2.0	100	100	100	100	100

[a] From Smith and Surprenant (*17*).
[b] Efficiency for particle retention is in per cent by count. Particles greater than 0.4 μ collected by high-speed cascade impactor.
[c] DOP test values used for particles below 0.4 μ diameter.

2. *Granular Filters*

Examples of granular filters include porous ceramics, fritted glass or metal, and sand. Where it is desirable to recover the sampled particulates, soluble granular materials such as the crystals of sugar or salicylic acid have been used (*18*). Since granular materials may be obtained in a great variety of sizes, the effectiveness of collection also covers a wide range of particle sizes. In general, however, granular filters are not suitable for collecting particles of less than about 1 μ in diameter.

TABLE III

COLLECTION CHARACTERISTICS OF SELECTED FILTER MEDIA[a]

Filter medium	Flow rate: 0.1 linear meter per minute — Atmospheric dust count efficiency (%)[b]	Flow rate: 0.1 linear meter per minute — DOP efficiency (%)
Whatman 1	50.0	57.0
Whatman 4	15.0	23.0
Whatman 32	99.1	99.5
Whatman 40	85.1	84.0
Whatman 41	26.5	23.0
Whatman 41H	24.0	19.0
Whatman 42	98.8	99.2
Whatman 44	97.0	98.6
Whatman 50	92.0	97.0
Whatman 540	67.0	65.0
S & S 640	13.0	15.0
HV 70, 9 mil	96.5	96.5
HV 70, 18 mil	99.5	99.3
MSA Type "S"	46.0	48.0
Millipore Type HA	↑	99.9+
Millipore Type AA		99.9+
S & S Ultrafilter		—
Glass fiber paper		99.99+
CC-6	No particles found after 6 hours' running	99.9+
AEC-1		99.9+
AEC glass asbestos		99.9+
AEC all-glass	↓	99.9+

[a] From Smith and Surprenant (*17*).

[b] Dust particles were 1 μ and smaller. Efficiency was determined by particle count, using a sonic impactor. Values are an average of four tests.

3. *Controlled Pore Filters*

These are the filters commonly known as membrane or molecular filters (*19, 20*). They are composed of cellulose esters and can be manufactured with uniformly controlled pore size. A recent innovation reinforces the sheet with a nylon mesh for greater mechanical strength. The types commonly used for air sampling have a pore size of about 0.45 to 0.8 μ, depending on the type. The pores constitute 80 to 85% of the volume of the filter. Because of the effect of electrosatic forces, and by building up a precoat of collected particles on the surface, these filters can collect particles down to about 0.1 μ in diameter. They are particularly suited for particle sizing since most of the particles collected are retained on or near the surface. The filter may be made transparent with mineral oil and the collected particles made clearly visible. For other uses, the filtering material may be dissolved with methanol, esters, or ketones, or may be ashed. Filters of this type cannot be used at temperatures above about 125°C. Techniques are not presently available for collecting viable organisms from the air on these filters. Bacteria are usually killed during collection by desiccation.

C. Impingement (see also Chapter 31)

Several different types of impingement apparatus are commonly used in collecting solid or liquid aerosol contaminants. These may either impinge on a surface submerged in a liquid, in which case they are described as wet impingers, or may impinge on a surface exposed to the air, in which case they are called dry impingers. Dry impingers are sometimes referred to as impactors. When an air stream containing particulates in suspension is deflected around a body, the particles, because of their greater mass and inertia, tend to resist the change in direction and to collect on the body. Since impingement relies on the inertia of the particle in continuing in a straight direction until it strikes a surface, it follows that impingement efficiency is related to the difference between the mass of the particle and the mass of the gas molecules from which it is to be separated. Very small particles, because of their relatively small mass and inertia, may tend to follow the stream lines of the gas and thus be carried around the obstacle. Good collection efficiencies, however, are obtained by impingement for particle sizes down to about 2 μ. With the high impact velocities generally used in impinging devices, large agglomerated particles may separate, and consequently an erroneously high number of fine particles may be found in the sample. At the high velocities in dry impingers, moisture in the atmosphere tends to condense on the collecting surfaces. It has been reported that when operated at sonic velocities, high collection efficiency for particles as small as 0.1 μ may be obtained in wet impingers.

After collection in a wet impinger, analysis may be performed on the basis of weight, particle size, or chemical constituents. Samples collected on the cascade impactor are ideal for direct examination under the microscope. The Andersen sampler impinges on solid media in standard Petri dishes and is thus generally used for collecting and counting bacteria.

1. *Wet Impingers*

Wet collectors usually consist of a glass tube ending in an orifice with the air flow impinging on a flat surface. The flat surface may be a piece of glass welded below the orifice tube or the flat bottom of a collection tube. Collected particles are retained by water or some other liquid in the bottom of the collection tube. The Smith-Greenburg impinger and midget impingers are examples of this type of equipment (Fig. 10) (*21, 22*). In the former, 0.028 cu. m./min. of air is drawn

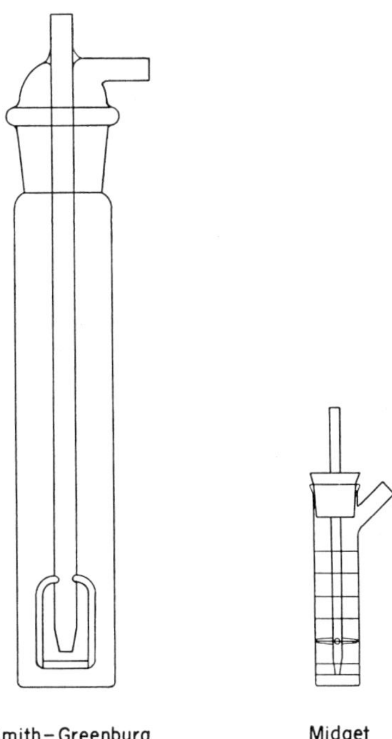

FIG. 10. Two types of wet impingers.

through an orifice 2.3 mm. in diameter and impinges against a flat surface 5 mm. distant. Under these conditions the jet velocity is estimated to be 113 m./sec. In the midget impinger, 2800 cc./min. is drawn through an orifice 1 mm. in diameter and impinges against a flat surface 5 mm. distant. The jet velocity here is estimated to be about 60 m./sec. Under some conditions (as will be reported later) impingers may be used as absorbers for collecting gas samples.

2. *Dry Impingers*

Commercial versions of dry impingers, or impactors, usually consist of a series of progressively smaller size jets impinging on standard microscope slides (*23, 24*). This results in progressively higher jet speeds and in the collection of progressively smaller size particles. An example of this type of equipment is the cascade impactor, shown in Fig. 11.

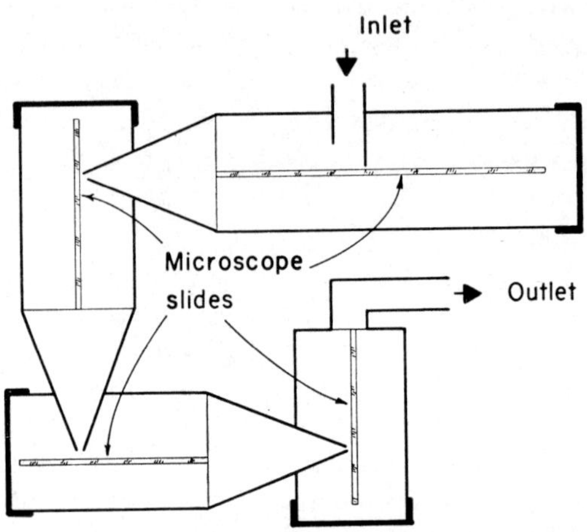

FIG. 11. A common type of cascade impactor.

D. SEDIMENTATION

This technique is suitable only for the collection of larger particle sizes. The procedure depends for its effectiveness on the natural sedimentation of particles from the air stream. In still air, sedimentation devices are quite satisfactory for particles larger than about 5 μ. Table IV shows the rate of fall of spherical particles in still air. It can be

TABLE IV
RATE OF FALL OF SPHERICAL PARTICLES IN STILL AIR

Particle diameter (μ)	Rate of fall (cm./sec.)
100	30
10	0.3
1	0.003
0.1	0.00009

seen from the table that for the smaller particles even a slight air current will cause a deflection of the particle and possibly prohibit its settling.

Collection is further complicated by the effects of wind eddies which transport particles at velocities higher than their fallout velocity.

Sedimentation devices take a number of forms. Frequently used are battery jars and Mason jars with a plastic funnel having an area at the open end of about 930 sq. cm. Plastic and metal containers have also been used with success. To prevent collected material from being blown out of the jar, water or some other liquid is sometimes placed in the bottom. Below-freezing weather requires the use of antifreeze in the water. Recent work by Nader (*25*) has indicated that wet-bottom collectors and collectors equipped with a special deflector are no more efficient than plain containers with straight sides. In use, these devices are properly exposed over a wide area. Periodically, say once a month, the jars are collected, the inside surfaces rinsed, and the liquid evaporated. The total material collected is weighed and is usually expressed in terms of weight per unit of area. This technique is used principally in determining dustfall or sootfall, and as such is an indication of the general dirtiness of a community. It is claimed to give comparative measures of the amount of dustfall in a particular area over a period of time. This is accomplished by expanding the results manyfold and, at the same time, expanding all of the inaccuracies inherent in the method. It must be remembered that the rate of settling of very fine particles is small compared to that of large particles and, therefore, large particles will tend to predominate in the dustfall jar. Both APCA and ASTM have standards covering this method of sampling, to which the reader is referred (*26, 27*).

There are numerous sources of inaccuracies in dustfall samples. Included are such items as the agglomeration of particles, adherence to the wall of the container or the funnel, streamline deflection effects of the container, wind eddies which result from nearby objects, and other factors which affect the collection of rainfall samples.

E. Electrostatic Precipitation (see also Chapter 30)

Electrostatic precipitators may be of several designs, but they all operate on the same basic principle (*28*). A high difference of electrical potential is maintained between two spaced electrodes, and a current flow is thus established. Potential differences of 12,000 to 30,000 volts d.c. are involved. Many ions are liberated and maintained in the area between the electrodes. As particle-laden air passes through this space, suspended particles in the air stream collide with the charged ions and are thus made to assume a charge. The force exerted on the charged particles by the electric field causes them to be transported to the collecting electrode, where the charge is neutralized and the particles collected. It should be recognized that an electrostatic precipitator is effective only against particulates on which a charge can be impressed. An electrostatic precipitator will not remove gases; nor will it remove solids or liquids which volatilize below the temperature at which the precipitator is operated. Precipitators will work for either liquid or solid aerosols. It should be obvious that no type of electrostatic precipitator is suitable for collecting samples in an explosive atmosphere.

The efficiency of particle collection is a function of the size, shape, and type of electrodes; electrode spacing; velocity and time of exposure of particles; electrical energization; and electrical resistivity of the particle. Electrostatic precipitators are nearly 100% effective for particles in the range of 0.01 to about 10 μ. Efficiencies decrease somewhat as particle size increases and contact time decreases. Higher efficiencies usually result from higher electrical energy. The highest voltage permissible in a precipitator depends on the electrode spacing and the breakdown or arcing voltage for the gas system involved. The discharge electrode is usually negative, and the maximum voltage which will just prevent arcing is impressed on the system.

One commercial type of electrostatic sampler consists of a central wire negative electrode and a positive concentric electrode, which is a removable aluminum tube 1½ in. in diameter and 7 in. long. The high voltage d.c. current is furnished by means of a special power pack built into the carrying case. The sampling rate, which is set at the factory, is 0.085 cu. m./min. After collection, the particles can be removed from the tube and analyzed chemically, by weight, or by counting and sizing.

Another commercial electrostatic precipitator uses, as the positive electrode, a microscope slide or a Petri dish containing solid media. This latter type is particularly suitable for direct microscopic examination or for collection of viable organisms directly on growth medium.

F. Thermal Precipitation (see also Chapter 30)

A thermal force is defined as a force greater than that caused by convection, which acts on a body suspended in a gas not in thermal equilibrium. It is a force of this type that causes the migration of small particles suspended in a gas from a zone of high temperature to one of low temperature. This is the principle on which the thermal precipitator operates. The magnitude of the force of thermal repulsion is relatively small and can only be observed when it is acting on objects of small mass suspended in a low viscosity fluid. The currently accepted explanation for the motion of a suspended particle in a thermal gradient presumes that the fluid actually flows around the particle from the colder side to the warmer side. It is the reaction to this fluid creep which causes the motion of the particle toward the cooler zone. In general, the thermal force is negligible if the gradient is less than about 750°C./cm. Many commercial models operate with a thermal gradient above 3000°C./cm. The effect of thermal repulsion is greatly reduced for particles with high thermal conductivity, such as some crystalline substances.

Thermal precipitators are claimed to have nearly 100% efficiency over a wide range of particle sizes. High efficiency is noted for particles from 0.001 to 100 μ. Particular caution must be observed, however, for particles above about 5 μ in diameter since they may fail to adhere to the collecting slide. Samples collected by thermal precipitation are particularly desirable for direct microscopic examination. The disadvantage of most precipitators of this type is the low flow rate involved.

Several commercial versions of the thermal precipitator consist of a hot wire suspended near a glass microscope slide with the air flow directed between them. Low flow rates, of 10 or 20 cc./min., are provided by a vacuum pump or by water displacement.

Another type consists of an electrically heated plate suspended above a water-cooled plate on which a glass disk is placed (*29*). The air flow enters in the center of the heating disk and flows radially to the edges. The unit is self-contained with a cooling pump, air pump, and flow meter. This model has a design flow of 500 cc./min. It may be used to collect viable bacteria or liquid aerosols by limiting the temperature gradient to about 320°C./mm. All thermal precipitators have the advantage of a gentle precipitating force, thus preventing shattering or disaggregation of particles.

G. Centrifugal Methods (see also Chapter 28)

For the most part, samplers which fall into this category are midget cyclones. The primary field of application is in sampling for large particles such as fly ash. They may be readily constructed, of metal or glass, in the laboratory or shop. When properly designed, they have good efficiency for removal of particles of more than about 5 μ. Submicron particles are usually not captured at all.

Goetz (*30*) described an instrument for the quantitative separation and classification of airborne particulate matter. The unit consists of a rapidly rotating helical channel with a removable cone-shaped cover. Flow within the channel is provided by the motion of the helix and is kept in the laminar range. In operation, a high centrifugal acceleration (about 20,000 g) is imposed on the collected aerosol and individual particles, following Stokes' law, are deposited on the inside of the cone. The position of their deposition is predictable. The device is effective for particle sizes down to 0.2 μ.

III. Sampling Gaseous Contaminants

A. General Considerations

A variety of gases and vapors may be involved in air pollution episodes. In general, gases and vapors behave alike when discharged into the air. The only significant difference between the two is that vapors are liquids at ordinary temperatures. The main reason for differentiating between the two is that different collection techniques may be used in sampling. A vapor may frequently be collected by simple condensation. Gases and vapors are readily diffused and mixed with the air upon discharge, and rapidly lose the identity of such physical properties as density. Their chemical properties, however, may produce undesirable conditions even when these compounds are present in very minute quantities. Several basic techniques are available for sampling gases and vapors. Not all of the techniques are suitable for all sampling conditions. Sampling devices which are very efficient for high concentrations of gases may not be suitable, without modifications, for sampling a contaminant such as hydrogen fluoride, which may cause undesirable effects in concentrations as low as 5 μg./cu. m. of air. Some gases, such as carbon dioxide, aldehydes, and nitrogen oxide, are inefficiently collected in an absorber containing aqueous solutions when the gases are present in low concentration.

Many of the general considerations previously discussed are applicable here as well. Particular care must be taken if an aerosol sampler is used preceding a gas sampler. An apparently low gas concentration may result, owing to the presence of the aerosol sampler. It is also desirable when sampling for gases and vapors to observe the temperature and pressure conditions of the air mass from which the sample is collected.

B. Adsorption (see also Chapter 33)

Adsorption is probably less frequently used for collecting gases and vapors than other methods. Gas adsorption is an operation in which a gas or vapor comes in contact with a solid so that its molecules adhere to the surface of the solid. The solid material is known as the adsorbent and the gas to be collected, the adsorbate. Since adsorption is largely a surface phenomenon, the amount of adsorbate which may be collected is dependent upon the specific surface or total surface per unit mass of the adsorbent. Other factors which control the removal capacity include the nature of adsorbent and adsorbate, geometric state of the adsorbent, temperature, velocity of the air stream, concentration of the gas of interest as well as of the other gases in the stream, and how far adsorption has proceeded. An adsorption bed operates at high efficiency until just before the capacity of the bed is reached.

A variety of solids of an extremely porous nature have been developed, each with a selective preference for certain gases or vapors. These preferences can only be determined by reference to the literature or by experiment. All of the common adsorbents are more or less granular in form and usually supported in columns through which the air to be sampled is drawn. The depth of bed may range from several inches to several feet, depending on the factors which have been indicated as controlling adsorption capacity. Most of the common adsorbents have a capacity of 15 to 30% of their weight. The ideal adsorbent is granular and of such size and shape as to offer low resistance to flow, has high effective adsorptive capacity, is inert, resists breakage and other deterioration in use, is noncorrosive, is readily reactivated, and provides easy release of adsorbate. Materials which are commonly used as adsorbents include charcoal, silica gel, lithium chloride, alumina, fuller's earth, and bauxite. Practically all of these may be "activated" by heating or steaming with chemicals to increase their capacity manyfold. The adsorptive capacity of an adsorbent closely parallels the critical temperature of the gas. For example, the adsorptive capacity of charcoal at 15°C. is shown in Table V.

TABLE V
ADSORPTIVE CAPACITY OF CHARCOAL AT 15°C. FOR SELECTED GASES

Gas	Critical temperature (°K.)	Volume adsorbed (cc./gm.)[a]
N_2	126	8
CO_2	304	48
H_2S	373	99
SO_2	430	380

[a] Gas volumes reduced to 0°C. and 760 mm. Hg.

Sampling by adsorption is not complete with the collection. The adsorbate must usually be removed from the column for analysis. This may be accomplished by heating the column (usually to 100 to 150°C., although sometimes higher), blowing air through it, and collecting the gas of interest by absorption. In some instances, steam may be passed through the column and the effluent vapor condensed, or the adsorbate may be stripped with a liquid solvent. Vacuum removal has been favorably reported as a desorbing method (*31*). In some devices, the adsorbent contains an indicator which is specific for the compounds to be measured and which changes color when the granules are saturated (*2*). The length of the colored column in this case is a measure of the concentration.

C. Absorption (see also Chapter 31)

Absorption is one of the most frequently used methods for collecting gases. Gas absorption is an operation in which a soluble component of a gas mixture is dissolved in a liquid or hygroscopic solid. The absorbent, which is the collecting agent, may change either physically or chemically or both during the absorption process. The absorbent may be either reactive or nonreactive.

Recent work on small gas absorbers has been reported by Calvert and Workman (*31a*). They note the various factors which contribute to absorber efficiency and confirm that gas-phase diffusivity, liquid-phase diffusivity, residence time, reciprocal of bubble size, and solubility are of greatest importance. When the solubility of a gas in an absorbent is low, the efficiency of absorption tends to be low. This condition can be improved by using a chemically reactive absorbent. Although Calvert and Workman (*31b*) describe a method for predicting the efficiency of bubbler-type absorbers, the prediction can only be considered an estimate. If very accurate knowledge of collector efficiency is required, the information must be obtained as indicated in the section of this chapter on collection limitation.

In the choice of absorbent, consideration is given to liquids with high solubilities for the solutes to be absorbed. The solubility of a gas in a liquid depends upon the partial pressure of the gas in the atmosphere, the temperature, and on the purity of the absorbent. The ideal solvent is relatively nonvolatile, inexpensive, noncorrosive, stable, nonviscous, nonfoaming, and nonflammable. Distilled water fulfills many of the characteristics of an ideal solvent and is frequently used in collecting some gases. Its suitability for various common gases can be seen in Table VI. It can be seen that water will be quite suitable for sulfur dioxide but is not recommended for the others. Other solvents, such as alkaline solutions for acid gases and acid solutions for alkaline gases, may be used. In these cases, not only solubility but reactivity come into importance. Special chemical solutions may be used for special purposes or in anticipation of the use of a specific method of analysis. For example, straw oil may be used to collect hydrocarbons. An alkaline zinc acetate solution is used in one method of sampling for hydrogen sulfide in which the sulfide precipitates as the zinc salt. If the gas does not react chemically with the absorbent, its solubility is defined by Henry's law. If reaction does occur, the usual laws of chemical reaction apply.

As small a quantity of liquid absorbent as is necessary to cover the dispersion tube adequately should be used. Too much liquid dilutes the

TABLE VI
SOLUBILITY OF SELECTED GASES IN DISTILLED WATER AT 20°C.

Gas	Volume absorbed per volume of water[a]
Nitrogen	0.015
Oxygen	0.031
Nitric oxide	0.047
Carbon dioxide	0.878
Hydrogen sulfide	2.582
Sulfur dioxide	39.374

[a] Gas volumes reduced to 0°C. and 760 mm. Hg.

sample and may cause difficulties in the subsequent analysis. Losses by evaporation and by foam and mist carry-over must be considered. The effect of oxidation by the air being drawn through a reactive solution must be determined before sampling.

Devices used for sampling by absorption include the following: fritted glass scrubbers, impingers, packed columns, countercurrent scrubbers, and atomizing scrubbers.

1. *Fritted-Glass Scrubbers*

A great variety of sizes and shapes of these devices is available. A few are shown in Fig. 12. In general, units of this type provide the most efficient collection for gases. In addition to the readily available commercial devices, homemade units may be constructed using the gas dispersion tubes available from most glass supply houses. These units may be available in the form of a disk or a cylinder, and in a range of pore sizes. Coarse or extra-coarse frits provide effective gas dispersion at relatively low head loss. The head-loss characteristics for a variety of scrubbing devices are shown in Fig. 13. It is to be emphasized that these data cover only the individual units tested. However, the shape of the curves probably applies to all similar units.

The efficiency of collection of gases will depend on a variety of factors previously described. Most fritted-glass scrubbers, however, under optimum conditions of flow rate and reagents, have an efficiency in excess of 90%. At the end of the sampling period the liquid reagent should be surged back and forth through the frit several times before a sample is withdrawn for analysis.

Since coarse-fritted ware has a pore size of about 50 μ, the units may gradually clog with use. They may be cleaned by surging the appropriate cleaning solution back and forth through the frit and then rinsing several

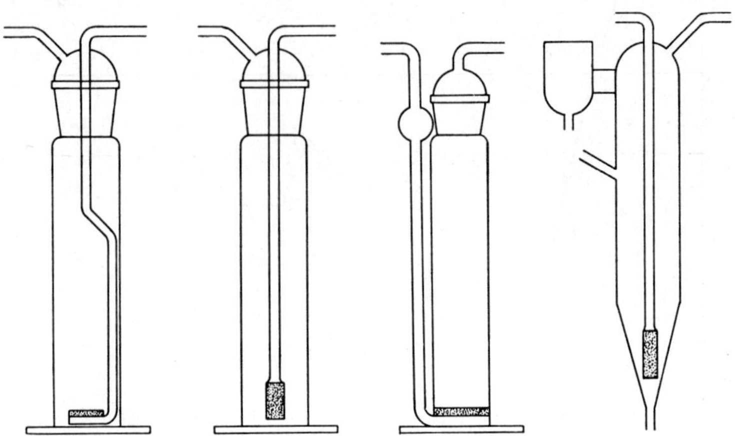

FIG. 12. Several types of fritted-glass scrubbers used in sampling for gases.

times with distilled water in the same manner. Dirt can be removed with hot concentrated hydrochloric acid, fatty materials with carbon tetrachloride, and organic matter with hot concentrated sulfuric acid containing a few drops of sodium nitrite. Dichromate cleaning solution may permanently stain the frit and should not be used.

2. *Impingers*

Impingers have frequently been used for collecting samples of gases and vapors in the same manner as have fritted glass scrubbers. Several types of impingers are shown in Fig. 10. Work done in the laboratories at the University of Florida and at Southwest Research Institute (*32*) indicates that impingers may be somewhat less efficient for collection of gas samples than are fritted-glass scrubbers. In the low concentration commonly encountered in air pollution sampling, and when all types of collectors were operated at the optimum sampling rate, midget impingers were found to have an efficiency less than that of a fritted-glass scrubber. The threshold concentration level for the midget impinger was also found to be considerably higher than for several types of fritted-glass scrubbers. The lowest sulfur dioxide concentration at which the fritted-glass collectors exhibited reasonable efficiency was about one third of

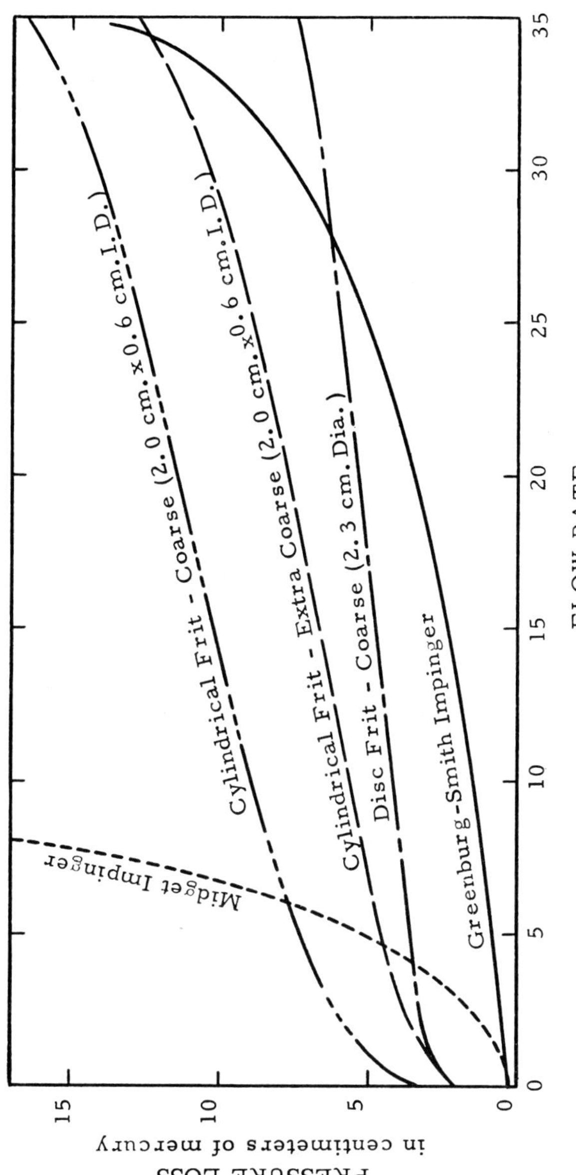

FIG. 13. Head-loss characteristics for several types of common gas scrubbers and impingers.

that necessary for the midget impinger. With highly soluble or reactive combinations of absorbent and absorbate, at moderate contaminant concentrations, the collection efficiency of both types of units approaches 100%.

3. *Packed Columns*

A number of homemade devices of this type have been described in the literature, in which glass beads or plastic saddles are used in the scrubber to break up the bubbles and increase the efficiency of absorption.

4. *Countercurrent Scrubbers*

Collection devices of this type are used in a number of recording instruments. The contactor usually consists of a long column containing a concentric helix or obstacles in the wall of the column which obstruct the flow of air and reagent. The reagent flows down the column in a thin layer and is brought into intimate contact with the turbulent flow of air coming in the opposite direction.

5. *Atomizing Scrubbers*

In collection devices of this type, the reagent is sprayed through the flowing column of sampled air. A fine spray is used; the reagent is collected in the bottom of the vessel and recirculated to the spray head. In general, drops of liquid falling through a gas provide a less efficient absorption medium than do bubbles of the gas rising through the liquid. One device of this type is modeled after the venturi scrubber used in air cleaning (*33*).

D. Freezeout

This method is used where it is desirable to obtain a gross sample of all of the polluting constituents in the air. The technique involves drawing a sample of air through a series of containers which are held at progressively lower temperatures. The coolants which might be used in a typical series are ice and water (0°C.), ice and salt (—21°C.), dry ice (—79°C.), liquid air (—147°C.), and liquid nitrogen (—196°C.). Liquid nitrogen is preferable to liquid oxygen (—183°C.) because of the safety factor, but it has the disadvantage of condensing oxygen from the air. The coolant should be contained in Dewar flasks. The common sampling rate for this technique is 1 cu. dm./min. The containers used are usually double-walled flasks immersed in the coolant. Both Shepherd (*34*) and Barnebey (*35*) traps have been used with success. Air flow takes place through the thin space between the walls. The Shepherd traps have been reputed to offer more severe icing problems with subsequent clogging.

One of the problems which must be met is that of handling the large quantities of water which may condense out and freeze in the early stages. This water may contain some of the pollutants of interest and should thus be analyzed. A water-cooled condenser preceding the low-temperature train may help solve the problem. A filter flask can serve as the receiver.

After collection, the samples must be sealed or held at the low temperature until ready for analysis. Analysis may require absorption after gasification, or some technique which permits analysis in the gaseous state. Examples of the latter are mass spectrometry, infrared spectrophotometry for organic materials, and gas chromatography.

E. Grab Sampling Techniques

In a number of instances it may be desirable to collect grab samples of polluted air. Several techniques are presently available for obtaining large and small grab samples. These include several types of evacuated bottles or flasks and several types of plastic envelopes or balloons. Also under investigation but not yet in use is a technique for compressing large volumes of air into cylinders.

In its most common form, the evacuated bottle consists of a flask which contains some reactive solution. A vacuum is drawn on the flask and the flask sealed. The volume of air which can be collected by this method may be calculated from the conditions of evacuation (*36*). In use, the flask is taken to the point of sampling, the seal broken, and the reactive solution shaken to absorb the maximum amount of impurities. The efficiency of this method approaches 100%. The solution containing the absorbed materials may then be analyzed by the usual chemical techniques. The major disadvantage of this procedure is the small amount of sample which can be collected. There is also a possibility of contaminating the sample if a greased stopcock is used as the seal.

Stainless steel evacuated flasks, either with or without plastic inserts, have been successfully used in grab sampling. Samples may usually thus be obtained that are larger than those obtained with the use of glass containers. The flask may be evacuated and filled, as previously mentioned.

Another collection device is the plastic bag or balloon which, when inflated, will hold 5 to 10 cu. ft. This may be made of many types of satisfactory plastics including polyethylene, polychlorotrifluoroethylene, polytetrafluoroethylene, or polyethyleneterephthalate. In use, the bag is inflated by using a vacuum cleaner or some similar pressure device. Because the air must first pass through the pressure device, there is a possibility of alteration or contamination of the sample. The collected sample is returned to the laboratory and the desired constituent absorbed, or some technique is used which can perform analysis directly on the gas sample (*16*).

A loose plastic liner may be filled by evacuating the container around it. The container may be made of any material which will permit evacuation of air between it and the liner. Liquid displacement methods are suitable for all of the devices mentioned.

Another very handy sampling technique involves the use of impregnated granular adsorbents or papers. These devices are generally hand-operated and are available for a wide variety of gases and vapors. In most of them, a color change or length of stain is a measure of the concentration. Most of the units are proprietary devices.

IV. Simplified Techniques

An approach which is satisfactory for many purposes is to obtain cumulative indications over a period of time by simplified techniques (*37*). No quantitative measure of the concentration of polluting material per unit volume of air may be obtained by such methods, but satisfactory information for many purposes may be secured. The unit cost of such techniques is practically insignificant when compared with more elaborate procedures and equipment. These techniques depend for their activity on having the natural movement of the air bring the pollutant in contact with the appropriate reagent. Results of most of these procedures are dependent upon wind velocity, atmospheric moisture, and air temperature. Although in some instances attempts have been made to refine and to elaborate upon the basic techniques, much of the benefit may thus be lost. Generally, results obtained by simplified techniques correlate quite well with results obtained by other procedures. Simplified techniques may help to provide preliminary information on which to base decisions concerning a more elaborate sampling program, or they may be an end in themselves. Such techniques are available for sulfur dioxide, gaseous fluorides, hydrogen sulfide, ozone, and others. Undoubtedly, other reactants described in the literature could be applied in simplified techniques. More are needed for a variety of contaminants.

A. Sulfur Dioxide

The earliest of the dosimeter methods is applicable to one of the most common air pollutants. This is the lead peroxide candle method for estimating sulfur dioxide. The procedure was developed by Wilsdon and McConnell (*38*) for work done in England during the early 1930's. It is a cumulative method which determines the rate of sulfate formation by exposing lead peroxide paste to sulfur dioxide. The candle which is used consists of a porcelain form about 10 cm. in circumference. A 10×10 cm. piece of cotton gauze is wrapped around the porcelain form as reinforcement, and the active reagent applied. The active reagent is applied in the form of a paste consisting of 8 gm. of lead peroxide in about 5 ml. of gum mucilage. The mucilage is prepared by soaking 2 gm. of gum tragacanth in 10 ml. of absolute alcohol, and then dissolving with 190 ml. of distilled water.

A modification of the procedure, developed at the University of Florida, has proved quite satisfactory and laborsaving. A glass specimen jar, 4.4 cm. in diameter and 15 cm. in length, is used as the form. These jars have Bakelite screw caps and are commonly known as "Olive jars, 5 oz."

It is essential that preparation and storage of the materials take place in a location which is not exposed to sulfur dioxide or sulfates. Each jar should be numbered near the cap end with a scriber, preferably with the number of a sampling station. Each jar should be marked with a scriber at a distance from the closed end such that the total area below the mark, including the bottom surface, is equal to 100 sq. cm. For the jars recommended, this distance is 6.1 cm. Cut pieces of 2.5-cm. (flattened diameter) tubular gauze about 20 cm. in length, and staple through the gauze perpendicular to the long axis about 0.5 cm. from one end. Turn gauze inside out and slip smoothly over the closed end of the jar. The top edge should be even with the scribed mark.

Prepare mucilage by dispersing 2 gm. of gum tragacanth in 10 ml. of absolute ethanol and adding, with one action while stirring, 190 ml. of distilled water. Prepare a thin smooth paste by mixing the lead salt and mucilage in the ratio of about 7 gm. of lead dioxide to 5 ml. of mucilage. Mix thoroughly at frequent intervals during use. If the mixture becomes too thick during use, additional 5% ethanol in distilled water may be added to balance the solvent losses. The prepared forms are dipped to the scribed mark, with the gauze serving as a reinforcement. After dipping, they are allowed to drain for a few seconds and the surface is smoothed with a 1-inch brush. Dry the cylinder slowly in the air. A completed cylinder should have a reactive surface of 100 sq. cm. The coating should be thick enough to hide the texture of the gauze but thin enough to dry without crazing. The consistency of the paste and method of application may be varied to produce the desired result by experience. At least one prepared cylinder should be stored in an airtight jar for use as a control when the analysis is run. All cylinders to be exposed simultaneously should be prepared at the same time. Exposure takes place in a standard shelter which protects the reactive surface from rain. After exposure for one month or longer, the candle is removed from the shelter and the area of the reactive surface measured. The coated fabric is stripped from the form by slitting with a razor, and the amount of sulfate determined. A similar candle containing the gauze reinforcement, but which has not been exposed, is used as a control. The results of observations are reported as milligrams of sulfate per day per 100 sq. cm. of lead peroxide.

Wilsdon and McConnell indicate that the rate of sulfate formation is proportional to the concentration of SO_2 in the atmosphere, at least up to 15% conversion of the reactive material. From experiments in a wind tunnel, the rate of reaction was found to vary inversely as the fourth root of the wind velocity. An increase in temperature of 1°C. will increase the reaction rate about 0.4%. The reaction rate was also found to be increased considerably when the surface was wet. Conversion to lead sulfate was also found to be a function of the lead peroxide particle size.

B. Gaseous Fluorides

One procedure, reported by MacIntire (*39*) and his co-workers in Tennessee and by Wander (*40*) in Florida, involves the use of the epiphyte, *Tillandsia usneoides,* which is commonly known as Spanish moss. This plant is not a parasite in that it obtains all of its nutritional requirements from the air. It does, however, need some support and is usually found on oak and other trees, although in some instances it may be found attached to power lines and fence posts. The plant is a cumulative sorbant for volatile fluorides. MacIntire exposed batches of the moss at various locations in an area suspected of being polluted by fluorides. Exposures were made at inside and outside locations for 3 months and showed substantial uptakes of fluoride, of as much as six times the blank fluoride content. He concluded that the concentrations were indicative of the proximity to the source of suspected fluoride emission. The moss used in this study was brought into the area from nonfluoride areas.

Wander determined the fluoride content of native Spanish moss in the vicinity of a manufacturing plant producing triple superphosphate. The variation of fluoride content with distance from the plant is given in Table VII.

He concluded that the source of fluoride emission could be pinpointed in this fashion. The deviation from the general trend of fluoride reduction with distance can be attributed to meteorological and topographical factors. For both cases, fluorides were determined by standard methods for vegetation.

In most areas of the United States, Spanish moss cannot be grown except, perhaps, in the summertime. In areas where it can be grown, however, it serves as a useful indicator of the dispersion of gaseous fluorides.

A similar technique, using limed filter papers in place of the epiphyte, was reported by Miller (*41*) and co-workers in Washington. They used Whatman No. 1 filter paper soaked in a lime suspension consisting of 28 gm. of low-fluoride lime per liter of water. The papers were dried and exposed in groups of six in shelters which permitted adequate air movement but protected the papers from the weather. Six treated papers were mounted in a rack in a vertical position, spaced 25 mm. apart. In the work reported, a 4-week exposure was used. In some instances, several sets of paper were exposed in various positions within the shelter; very little difference was found in the fluoride content. Following exposure, the papers were ashed and distilled. The results were reported in p.p.m. fluoride, presumably on a dry weight basis. The results were found to correlate reasonably well with the fluoride content in adjacent gladiolus leaves and forage. Since the work originally done by Miller, additional work has been done on the treated papers by Adams (*42*) and later by Robinson (*43*). Adams found that fluoride pickup by papers in duplicate shelters had a standard deviation of 5.2%. He further reported that there was a curvilinear relationship between the average monthly fluoride levels in the limed paper and the fluoride accumulated in herbage. Robinson compared fluoride collected by filter papers with local atmospheric fluoride concentration as determined by conventional air sampling. It was concluded that filter papers should not normally be expected to give a quantitative picture of fluoride concentration comparable with that obtained by quantitative sampling.

TABLE VII

FLUORIDE CONCENTRATION VARIATION WITH PLANT DISTANCE

Distance from plant (mi.)	F^- content (p.p.m.)
0.2	9400
1.5	688
2.5	688
3.5	888
4.0	132
5.0	110
6.0	60
7.0	100
20.0	100

Work done at the University of Florida (*44*) indicates that activated silica prepared by adding sodium bicarbonate to a solution of sodium silicate, forming a colloidal precipitate of silicon dioxide, makes a more satisfactory dipping solution. The deposited material does not tend to flake off as does the lime coating. Activated silica was about 12.5% more effective in collecting HF than the lime treatment. It has also been found more satisfactory to express the results in milligrams of fluoride per square centimeter of filter paper exposed.

C. Hydrogen Sulfide

Sewage treatment plant workers are responsible for another procedure which is useful in air pollution sampling (*45*). This involves hydrogen sulfide estimation by the use of lead acetate-impregnated papers or tiles. The latter is preferred. A lead acetate solution is prepared containing 500 ml. of distilled water, 100 ml. of glacial acetic acid, 450 gm. of lead acetate, and 350 ml. of glycerine. Unglazed white porcelain tiles of some convenient size are dipped in this solution, allowed to dry, and exposed in a place where they will be protected from rain. After exposure, the concentration of hydrogen sulfide can be estimated by comparing the shade of the exposed tiles with standards prepared by exposing units to known concentrations of hydrogen sulfide. Here again, no quantitative estimate can be made, but the relative exposure of various localities to hydrogen sulfide can be determined.

D. Ozone

Probably the most recent simplified technique in the field of air pollution is the use of rubber strips for the determination of ozone. A number of workers have recognized the effect of ozone on rubber and proposed it as an analytical tool. Bradley and Haagen-Smit (*46*) claim that rubber is a fairly specific reagent for ozone, except that nitrogen dioxide and sunlight in air produce similar cracks. This may be due to the catalytic effect of nitrogen dioxide in producing ozone. They indicate that the action of ozone on rubber is influenced by (1) degree of stress; (2) nature of rubber compounds; (3) concentration of ozone; (4) time of exposure; and (5) temperature. These workers used a standard rubber compound which was well vulcanized and air dried for a few days. In their original work, the rubber was cut into strips $50 \times 8 \times 2$ mm., folded into a loop, and bound at the open end. Thus, the elongation in the rubber varies from 0 to 100%. The folded rubber unit was positioned in a tube and exposed to an air flow conducted past it at a known rate. The time of initial cracking—that is, when both edges and body exhibit cracking—was determined.

For use in routine field sampling, it is rather difficult to determine the exact time of initial cracking. The latest procedure, therefore, involves a measurement of the total crack depth after exposure to ozone. Rugg (*47*) first proposed the use of crack depth as an indication of ozone exposure. His proposal was based on a conclusion by Powell and Gough (*48*). Rugg exposed stretched pieces of rubber to atmospheric ozone and measured the crack depth in a fresh section cut perpendicular to the cracks. The deepest cracks were assumed to be the active ones. The deepest crack and those within 10% were measured under a microscope and averaged to get reported values. He investigated the effect of ozone concentration, temperature, exposure time, and elongation, among other factors. He did not, however, apply the observations to air pollution measurements.

Haagen-Smit and Fox (*49*) applied the concept of total crack depth as a measure of ozone exposure. They used the sum of the depth of all visible cracks. They followed their previous procedure of using bent strips, with the rubber being exhaustively extracted in carbon tetrachloride and dried. The prepared rubber strips were bent, tied, and exposed. After exposure, an examination was made on a newly cut surface, 1 mm. from the edge and perpendicular to the cracks. Under 100$\times$ magnification, the sum of the depths of all cracks was taken as the significant value. For a 10-hour exposure, 1.0 mm. total crack depth corresponds to 3 p.p.m. of ozone.

A more refined device, called an Ozonometer, was developed by Beaty and June (*50*). This simple device utilized the principle of creep in tension at constant stress due to rubber cracking. They found the rate of deflection was proportional to the ozone concentration, with a reproducibility of $\pm 5\%$.

Some of the techniques described have been used in air pollution research projects at the University of Florida for such purposes as defining the geographical limits of a polluted area, confirming selected locations for volumetric samplers in a network, and estimating vertical concentration in conjunction with a volumetric sampler at ground level. They have been found quite satisfactory for these purposes and should be useful for many applications where dosimeter-type measurements are needed.

References

1. Committee D-22, "Methods of Atmospheric Sampling and Analysis." American Society for Testing Materials, Philadelphia, 1959.
2. L. Silverman, *Air Conditioning, Heating and Ventilating,* No. 8, **52,** 88 (1955).
3. R. O. McCaldin and E. R. Hendrickson, *Am. Ind. Hyg. Assoc. J.* **20,** 509 (1959).
4. G. S. Raynor, *J. Air Pollution Control Assoc.* **7,** 122 (1957).

5. F. W. Gilcreas and E. R. Hendrickson, *Eng. Progr. Univ. Florida* **10,** 21 (1956).
6. E. R. Hendrickson, *Eng. Progr. Univ. Florida* **10,** 17 (1956).
7. F. P. Terraglio, J. P. Sheehy, and R. M. Manganelli, *J. Air Pollution Control Assoc.* **8,** 220 (1958).
8. Committee on Air Pollution Controls, "Instruments for the Study of Atmospheric Pollution," 3rd ed. American Society of Mechanical Engineers, New York, 1959.
9. "Encyclopedia of Instrumentation for Industrial Hygiene" (C. D. Yaffe, D. H. Byers, and A. D. Hosey, eds.). Univ. of Michigan, Ann Arbor, 1956.
10. C. A. Gosline (ed.), "Air Pollution Abatement Manual." Manufacturing Chemists Association, Washington, D. C., 1952.
11. A. C. Schmidt and L. L. Wiltshire, *Am. Ind. Hyg. Assoc. Quart.* **16,** 134 (1955).
12. W. K. Harrison, Jr., J. S. Nader, and F. S. Fugman, *Am. Ind. Hyg. Assoc. J.* **21,** 115 (1960).
13. "Fluid Meters," 5th ed. American Society of Mechanical Engineers, New York, 1959.
14. Committee D-3, *ASTM Standards,* Part 5, p. 1137 (1955).
15. K. W. Wilson and H. Buchberg, *Ind. Eng. Chem.* **50,** 1705 (1958).
16. R. A. Baker and R. C. Doerr, *Intern. J. Air Pollution* **2,** 142 (1959).
17. W. J. Smith and N. F. Surprenant, *Proc. Am. Soc. Testing Materials* **53,** 1122 (1954).
18. M. B. Jacobs, "Analytical Chemistry of Poisons, Hazards, and Solvents." Interscience, New York, 1941.
19. A. Goetz, *Am. J. Public Health* **43,** 150 (1953).
20. M. W. First and L. Silverman, *A.M.A. Arch. Ind. Health* **7,** 1 (1953).
21. S. H. Katz *et al., U. S. Public Health Bull. No.* **144,** (1925).
22. T. Hatch, H. Warren, and P. Drinker, *J. Ind. Hyg. Toxicol.* **14,** 301 (1932).
23. K. R. May, *J. Sci. Instr.* **22,** 187 (1945).
24. L. S. Sonkin, *J. Ind. Hyg. Toxicol.* **28,** 269 (1946).
25. J. S. Nader, *J. Air Pollution Control Assoc.* **8,** 35 (1958).
26. Committee TR-2, *J. Air Pollution Control Assoc.* **5,** 176 (1955).
27. Committee D-22, American Society for Testing Materials, Philadelphia, in press.
28. E. C. Barnes, *in* "Air Pollution," Proc. 1st U.S. Tech. Conf. (L. C. McCabe, ed.), p. 547. McGraw-Hill, New York, 1952.
29. T. W. Kethley, M. T. Gordon, and C. Orr, *Science* **116,** 368 (1952).
30. A. Goetz, *Geofis. pura e appl.* **36,** 49 (1957).
31. A. Turk, *Ann. N. Y. Acad. Sci.* **58,** 193 (1954).
31a. S. Calvert and W. Workman, *Anal. Chem.* in press (1961).
31b. S. Calvert and W. Workman, *Talanta* **4,** 89 (1960).
32. L. R. Roberts and H. C. McKee, *J. Air Pollution Control Assoc.* **9,** 51 (1959).
33. P. L. Magill, M. Rolston, J. A. MacLeod, and R. D. Cadle, *Anal. Chem.* **22,** 1174 (1950).
34. M. Shepherd, S. M. Rock, R. Howard, and J. Stormes, *Anal. Chem.* **23,** 1431 (1951).
35. H. L. Barnebey and W. L. Davis, *J. Air Pollution Control Assoc.* **7,** 86 (1957).
36. Committee D-22, *ASTM Standards* Part 10, p. 1328 (1958).
37. E. R. Hendrickson, *Proc. Am. Soc. Civil Eng.* **84,** Paper No. 1776 (1958).
38. B. H. Wilsdon and F. J. McConnell, *J. Soc. Chem. Ind. (London)* **53,** 385T (1934).

39. W. H. MacIntire, L. J. Hardin, and W. Hester, *Ind. Eng. Chem.* **44,** 1365 (1952).
40. I. W. Wander, *Eng. Progr. Univ. Florida* **10,** 14 (1956).
41. V. L. Miller, D. F. Allmendinger, F. Johnson, and D. Polley, *J. Agr. Food Chem.* **1,** 526 (1953).
42. D. F. Adams, *J. Air Pollution Control Assoc.* **7,** 88 (1957).
43. E. Robinson, *Am. Ind. Hyg. Assoc. Quart.* **18,** 145 (1957).
44. C. I. Harding, Masters Thesis, University of Florida (1959).
45. G. Chanin, J. R. Elwood, and E. H. Chow, *Sewage Ind. Wastes* **26,** 1217 (1954).
46. C. E. Bradley and A. J. Haagen-Smit, *Rubber Chem. Technol.* **24,** 750 (1951).
47. J. S. Rugg, *Anal. Chem.* **24,** 818 (1952).
48. E. F. Powell and V. E. Gough, *Trans. Inst. Rubber Ind.* **21,** 102 (1945).
49. A. J. Haagen-Smit and M. M. Fox, *Ind. Eng. Chem.* **48,** 1484 (1956).
50. J. R. Beatty and A. E. June, *Rubber World* **131,** 232 (1954).

CHAPTER 12

Source Testing and Monitoring

BERNARD D. BLOOMFIELD

Division of Occupational Health, Michigan Department of Health, Lansing, Michigan

I. Introduction

A. BASIC CONSIDERATIONS

The evaluation of an industrial plant or a group of plants, or even of an entire city, with respect to air pollution resolves itself into a study of specific pollution sources. The exhaust stack, the continuous roof monitor, or the open window thus become important, because it is here that the investigators can determine the composition and quantity of the material being emitted. Source-testing techniques are also used before and after a piece of collection equipment, to establish its "collection efficiency."

The basic difference between source testing and monitoring is that the former implies a relatively elaborate and complete set of measurements to establish a starting or final condition, whereas the latter implies simpler and less complete measurements at regular intervals of a property which increases or decreases in proportion to others. Monitoring of an effluent source involves the use of smoke density meters, closed circuit TV systems, mirrors, continuous recording analytical equipment, and equipment for periodic grab sampling and analysis over long periods of time.

Source testing is usually done where there is acknowledged or suspected pollution or where it is desired to measure the efficiency of collection equipment. In some instances an apparently innocuous individual source is sampled to acquire data on the cumulative effect of many thousand such sources or to determine the effect of process changes on the effluent from the process. Regardless of the study purpose, the sampling procedure utilized should enable a reasonably accurate evaluation of the source expressed in terms of the rate of emission of specific pollutants. Even the simplest stack study requires the determination of gas flow, temperature, and humidity in the stack and, in some instances, will indicate process imbalance by virtue of such conditions as unusually high stack temperatures, low moisture levels, or erratic gas flow rates.

B. Planning the Study

Testing and monitoring require a considerable amount of planning of equipment and procedures for sampling and subsequent analysis of samples in the laboratory. Timing must also be planned both because the industrial processes involved frequently undergo cyclic changes and because actual sampling time is but a small fraction of the total time involved in assembling equipment, calibration, and travel. Such details as power supply, scaffolding, and access to the sampling source must be arranged for in advance.

The amount of sample required for suitable laboratory analysis dictates the sampling procedure to be employed. For example, in sampling ammonium chloride in a stack, a membrane filter may plug within a few seconds. Such a sample would be too light to weigh and insufficient for other laboratory procedures. Despite the wide range of equipment available, it sometimes appears ironic that what should be a simple stack-sampling procedure often requires a detailed literature search and the development of specialized sampling equipment. Complete familiarity with the process involved is therefore necessary before undertaking a source-sampling study. Operations directly related to the source should be carefully reviewed to determine the peculiarities of the processing equipment used, the time cycles involved, and the peak loading which might cause effluent and temperature variations. A review of this type can uncover a wide variety of significant process idiosyncrasies which, if not known, could completely invalidate results. Errors can result because peak loading periods were missed, an insufficient number of samples were taken, or temperature variations and composition changes were not accounted for, so that the results are not representative of the process. For example, for a few minutes in every hour the gas flow characteristics and the particulate loading may double in the electric furnace melting of brass scrap where scrap containing large amounts of oil are loaded into the furnace, thereby producing high stack gas temperatures and the emission of incompletely burned oil. Similarly, in both the grey iron cupola and the open hearth, stack loading varies depending upon the charging, melting, and pouring cycle. The sampling procedure must account for these variations.

Gases are usually collected by absorption, adsorption, freeze-out, or grab sampling. Particulate material sampling is more difficult than gas sampling because of particle size, mass agglomeration, charge, and shape. A satisfactory sample is one which is representative of the flow pattern in the duct or stack, is free of contamination, and has undergone no chemical or physical change.

II. Source Testing and Monitoring Procedures

A. Measurement of Gas Flow Rate

The first step in source sampling is always the measurement of the rate of flow of gas or air through the duct, stack, roof monitor, window, or other cross section at which pollutant concentration is to be sampled. In particulate sampling, the approximate range of stack or duct velocity must be known before sampling starts, to enable the use of most isokinetic sampling procedures, i.e., sampling in which the flow of gas into the sampling device has the same velocity and direction as the ambient atmosphere being sampled. A wide variety of instruments for measuring air velocity are available for this purpose (*1–3*). The standard Pitot tube combination with a differential pressure gage is the most widely used and most satisfactory velocity-measuring instrument. As shown in Fig. 1, the Pitot tube consists of two concentric tubes, one serving to measure impact pressure and the other to measure static pressure. Since both taps are connected across a differential manometer the pressure reading indicates velocity pressure. Velocity can be determined by referring to a velocity pressure table or by calculating with the use of the following:

$$V = 1096.5\sqrt{\frac{p_v}{S}} \quad (1)$$

$$= 4005\sqrt{p_v} \text{ for air at 70°F. and 29.92 in. Hg} \quad (2)$$

$$= 953\sqrt{p_v \cdot \frac{1}{G} \cdot \frac{T}{P}} \quad (3)$$

where V = velocity, feet per minute at duct conditions
p_v = velocity pressure, inches of water
S = gas density at duct conditions, pounds per cubic foot
G = specific gravity of gas (air = 1)
T = absolute temperature of gas in duct, °R.
P = absolute static pressure of gas in duct, inches of mercury

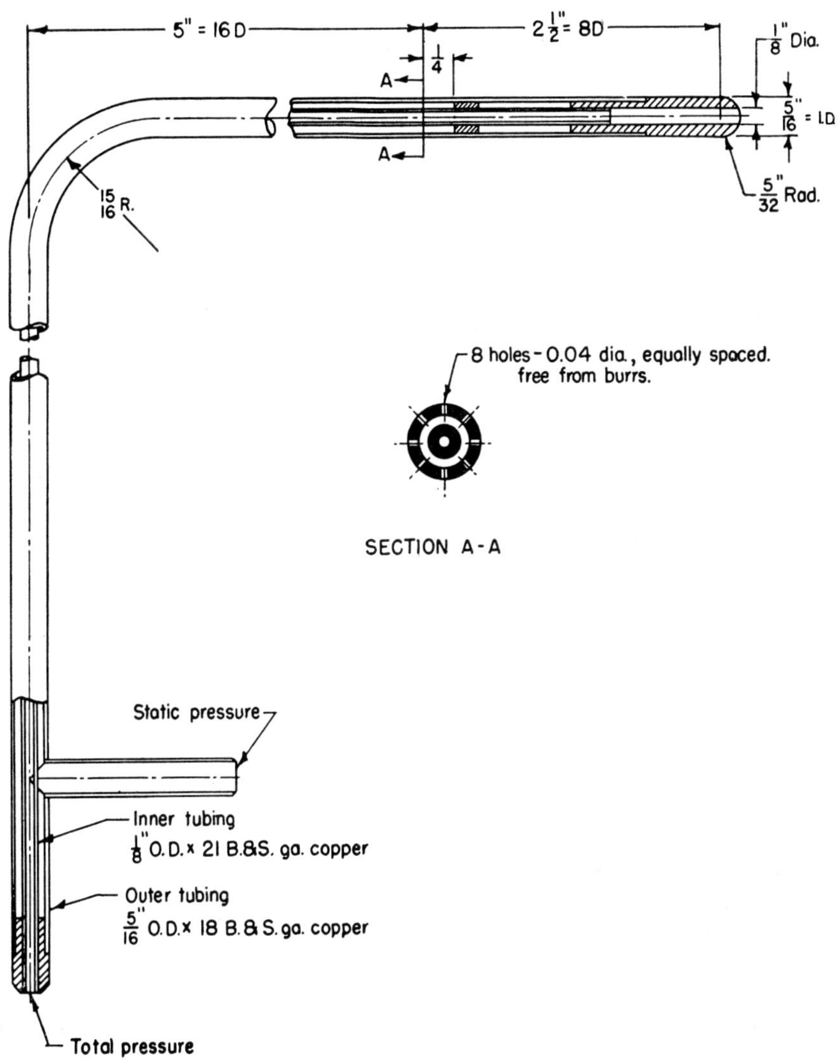

FIG. 1. Standard Pitot tube. From Am. Soc. of Heating, Refrigeration and Air Conditioning Engrs. (*5*).

Figure 2 illustrates a type of double Pitot tube which consists of two opposing openings, one made to face upstream and the other facing downstream during velocity measurement. The instrument design serves to minimize the difficulties of plugging of the fine static pressure holes of the standard Pitot tube when used in dirty gas streams and, by virtue of design, gives a higher manometer reading than the standard Pitot tube. The main disadvantages are greater sensitivity to nonparallelism with flow and a variable calibration coefficient depending upon flow

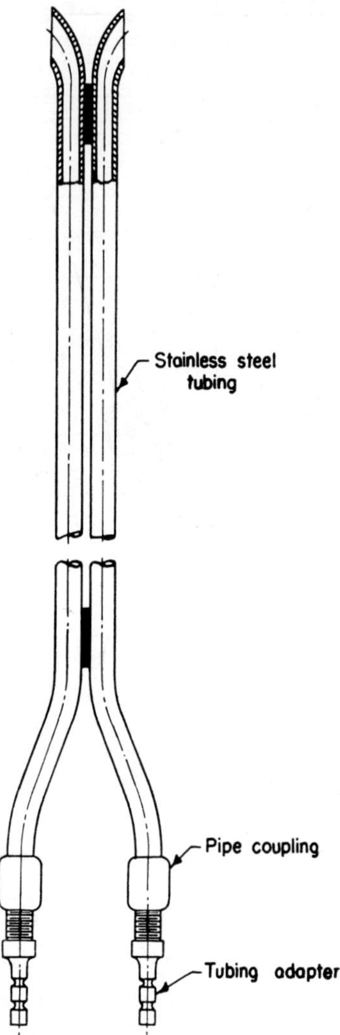

FIG. 2. Double Pitot tube. Courtesy Western Precipitation Corp.

conditions. It is necessary that double Pitot tubes and similar, specially designed instruments be calibrated under flow conditions which are substantially similar to those at test locations.

The Pitot tube traverse for determining the average gas velocity in a duct is made whenever possible at a section 5 to 10 diameters downstream from any major gas stream disturbance such as an elbow or branch entry, 3 to 5 diameters upstream from similar turbulent conditions, and in circular ducts should consist of two sets of readings, 90°

apart. Each set of readings should be spaced so as to be at the center of annular rings of equal area in a circular duct, and at the centers of a minimum of 9 hypothetical squares on at least 3 lines in a rectangular duct (Fig. 3). For approximate results in circular ducts, a center-line reading can be used provided the measurement location is preceded by at least 10 diameters of straight duct. It is necessary that the center-line velocity pressure be multiplied by 0.81 or the center-line velocity by 0.90 to obtain average duct velocity. Since accessible duct cross sections

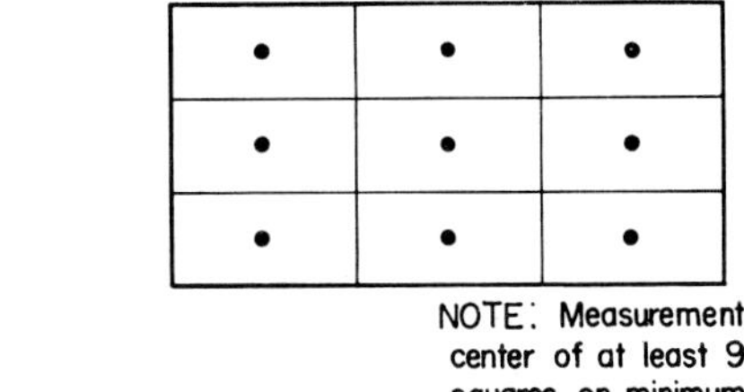

NOTE: Measurements made at center of at least 9 hypothetical squares on minimum of 3 lines.
RECTANGULAR DUCT

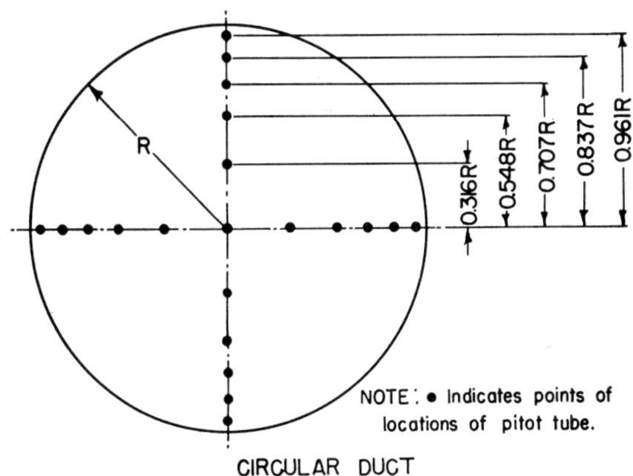

NOTE: • Indicates points of locations of pitot tube.

FIG. 3. Location of Pitot traverse points.

preceded by 7½ diameters of duct are frequently not available (Fig. 4), it is generally necessary to select a measuring cross section which is a compromise between accessibility and aerodynamic conditions optimum for measurement. Further, since the ideal sampling location is often nonexistent, a series of Pitot traverses are required to "feel out" the most suitable sampling location. Where necessary in excessively turbulent ducts, the number of Pitot traverse points should be increased. Conditions of flow also serve to govern the number of sampling points and stack samples, to obtain representative results. Pitot traverse points are usually also used as sampling points. The differential manometer used with the Pitot tube limits the minimum velocity measurement to about 800 ft./min. (equivalent to about 0.04 in. of water). The Whalen gage (*4*) is more sensitive than the inclined manometer and can be used for measuring velocities as low as 200 ft./min. The gage utilizes two

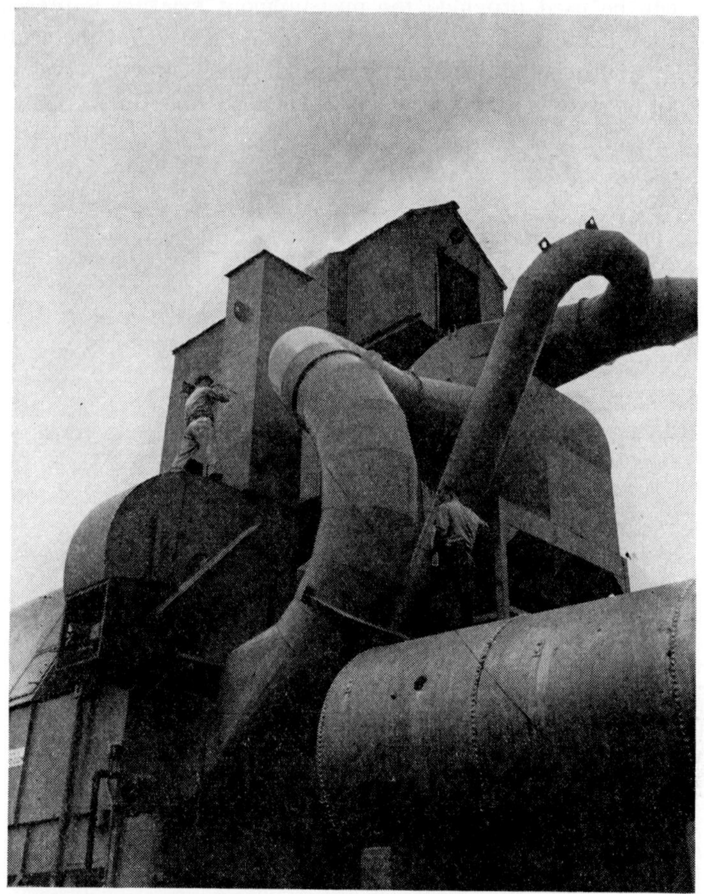

Fig. 4. Ideal Pitot traverse locations are seldom available.

liquids of different specific gravities and is a null method instrument which must be carefully leveled and handled. Its delicate nature does not suit it to the usual field study.

In using the Pitot tube, it is important to recognize the fact that variations in temperature, pressure, and humidity affect density and, accordingly, enter into the determination of velocity pressure. The procedure for determining the flow rate of gas with a Pitot tube traverse consists essentially of measuring the velocity pressure readings where required, converting them to equivalent velocities, averaging these velocity values (one does not average the velocity pressures) and, finally, multiplying average velocity by the cross sectional area of the duct. This procedure will give the actual flow in cubic feet of gas per minute at the temperature, pressure, and humidity of the gas being measured.

Instruments such as the rotating vane anemometer, the swinging vane anemometer, the heated thermometer anemometer, and the thermal anemometer are also used for measuring velocity but are not well suited to stack-sampling procedures. They do find use in measuring gas flow through roof monitors, windows, and other building openings.

B. Collection of Samples from Stack

1. *Stack Sampling Equipment*

A series of stack sampling system components is illustrated in Fig. 5, which also indicates those points where temperature and pressure measurements are to be made. Depending upon stack conditions and the sampling system, relative humidity, where required, can be determined either by measuring dry and wet bulb temperature at the sampling location or by measuring the total condensate. As is apparent, relative humidity may significantly affect the gas density calculation and the flow meter correction factor. Methods for determining relative humidity and specific gravity of gases are discussed in detail elsewhere (*3, 5*). Figure 6 illustrates a procedure for measuring the dry and wet bulb temperatures of a gas at a temperature above 212°F.

The stack-sampling components illustrated in Fig. 5 are indicative of the wide variety of sampling systems that can be used in a stack study, depending upon the source to be sampled, the contaminants involved, and the data desired. All incorporate combinations of probes to go into the stack and collection devices (Table I) for removing the contaminants being measured from the gas that is being sampled through the probe. Much of the probe equipment shown is not commercially available, so that this type of equipment must be constructed as needed. The major disadvantage in using probe type (a), in Fig. 5, is the length of pipe between the nozzle and the collecting device, in which material deposition can occur. Such probes are frequently jacketed and heated in order to prevent condensation. The error introduced by deposition of materials in the probe is eliminated with the use of nozzle assemblies (b) and (c), Fig. 5, which are placed directly in the gas stream and which, by attaining gas stream temperature, also eliminate the condensation problem. One variation of nozzle assembly type (b), Fig. 5, is described

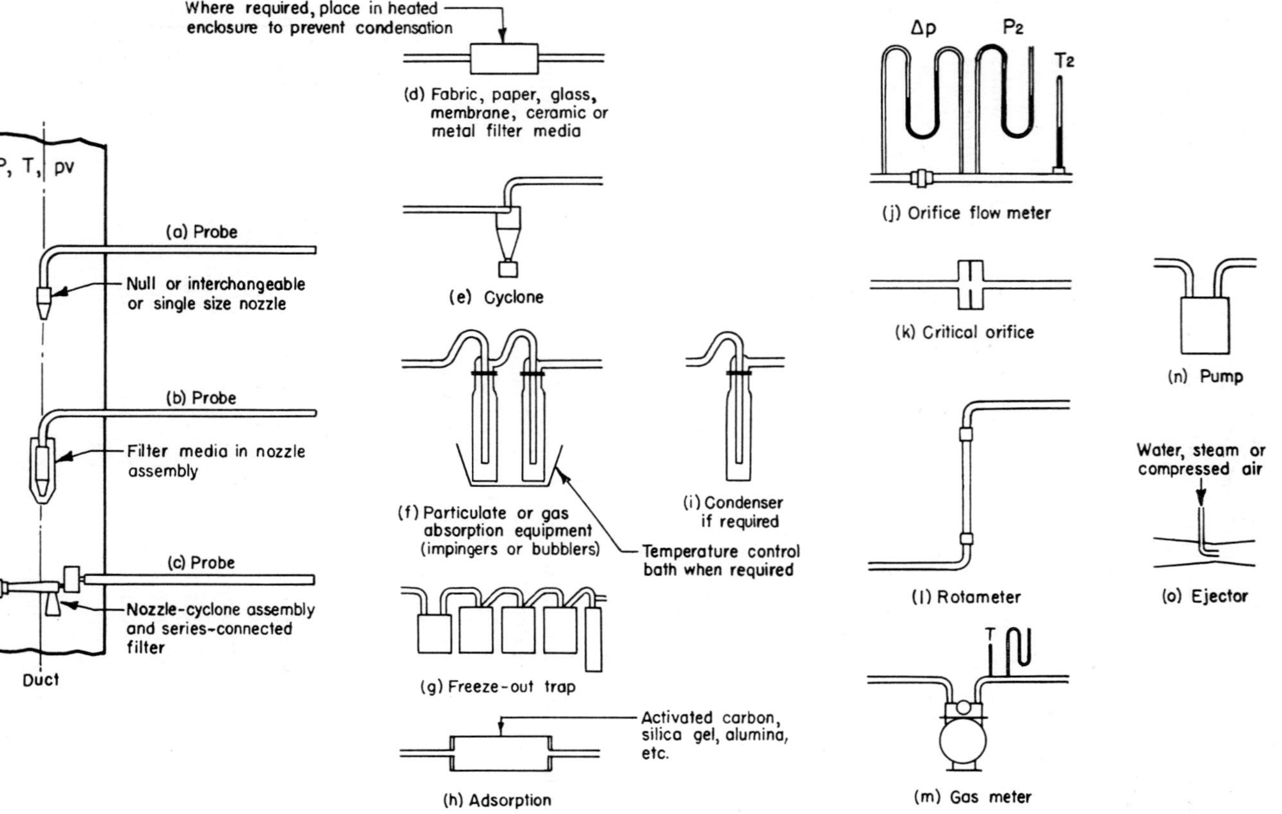

Fig. 5. Sampling system components.

TABLE I
COLLECTION DEVICES USED IN SOURCE SAMPLING

Principle	Instrument or media	Pressure drop[a]	Remarks
Filtration	Alundum thimbles		
	RA 84	2.2 in. Hg at 0.25 c.f.m. to 6.9 in. Hg at 0.75 c.f.m.	Suitable for high temperature (1000°F.) use. Sampling holders commercially available. Utility improved by lining with glass fiber mat.
	RA 360	0.8 in. Hg at 0.25 c.f.m. to 3.2 in. Hg at 1 c.f.m.	
Filtration	Paper thimble (Whatman)	0.4 in. Hg at 0.75 c.f.m. to 1.2 in. at 2 c.f.m.	95–99% efficiency (count) for particles $\geq 1\ \mu$. For low temp. use (180°F. max.).
Filtration	Glass paper (Mine Safety Appliance Co. #1106 and 1106-B)	4.4 in. H_2O at 28 f.p.m.	DOP[b] efficiency of 99.93% and 99.97% at 28 f.p.m. #1106 suitable for high (600°F.) temperature gas streams.
Filtration	Fiberfrax refractory fiber sheet stock	3.1 in. H_2O at 28 f.p.m.	DOP efficiency 99% at 28 f.p.m.
Filtration	Membrane	See Tables II and III and Fig. 9 in Chapter 11	For low temperature use (180°F. max.).
Filtration	Chemical filter paper (Whatman)	See Tables II and III and Fig. 9 in Chapter 11	For low temperature use (180°F. max.).
Filtration	Fabrics		
	Cotton (Wellington)	$\frac{1}{2}$ in. H_2O at 20 f.p.m.	Max. temp. 180°F. } 95–99% eff. (count) for particles $\geq 1\ \mu$.
	Wool, white (Albany)	$\frac{1}{2}$ in. H_2O at 185 f.p.m.	Max. temp. 215°F. } (same as above)
	Nylon (Stevens)	$\frac{1}{2}$ in. H_2O at 7.5 f.p.m.	Max. temp. 225°F. } 95–99% eff. (count) for particles $\geq 1\ \mu$.
	Asbestos (US Rubber)	$\frac{1}{2}$ in. H_2O at 50 f.p.m.	Max. temp. 275°F. } (same as above)
	Orlon (Stevens)	$\frac{1}{2}$ in. H_2O at 42 f.p.m.	Max. temp. 275°F. } (same as above)
Centrifugal action	Cyclone	Varies with cyclone design. Typical range: 3–36 in. H_2O	Suitable for high temperature (1500°F.) if constructed of stainless steel. Can be designed for efficient collection of particles $\geq 10\ \mu$ in size. Constant pressure drop devices.

[a] Pressure data based on new filtration media.

[b] Using 0.3 μ dioctyl phthalate test aerosol.

TABLE I (*Continued*)

Principle	Instrument or media	Pressure drop[a]	Remarks
Impingement	Impinger (Greenburg-Smith)	2.9–3.2 in. Hg at 1 c.f.m.	Constant pressure drop device utilizing various collection liquids and exhibiting collection efficiency range of 90–99% (count) for particles $\geq 1\ \mu$. Temperature control required with hot gases.
Absorption	Fritted bubbler (medium frit.) stem in impinger flask	2.4 in. Hg at 0.25 c.f.m. to 5.8 in. Hg at 1 c.f.m.	Constant pressure drop device utilizing various collection liquids with high efficiency range for absorbable materials. Temperature control required with hot gases.
Adsorption	Cartridge or tube containing activated carbon, silica gel, or alumina	Varies with type of material and method of use	Efficiency of collection (activity and retention) varies with sorbate. Generally with carbon, any gas or vapor whose molecular structure contains fewer than 3 atoms, independent of hydrogen, is not practically adsorbable. The use of carbon is limited to gas temperatures of 120°F. or less depending upon boiling point.

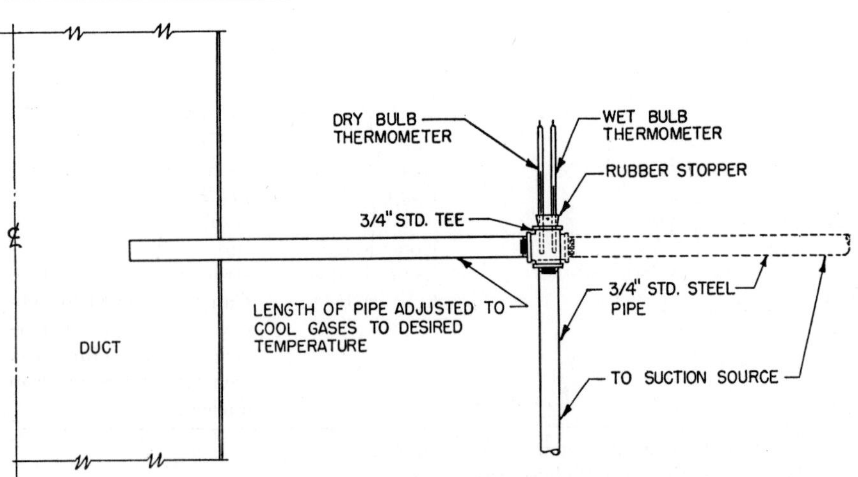

FIG. 6. Gas cooler for reading dry and wet bulb temperatures.

by Dennis, Samples, Anderson and Silverman (*6*) and is illustrated in detail in Fig. 7. Nozzle assembly type (c), Fig. 5, includes a miniature cyclone and, when required, a fabric filter system in series, all placed directly in the duct as shown. This arrangement has been developed by Hawksley, Badzioch, and Blackett (*7*). The assembly is shown in detail in Figs. 8a and b.

Although ceramic or paper thimbles, Figs. 5 (d) and 9a, b, c, are most commonly used for sampling, a wide variety of other filter media, in-

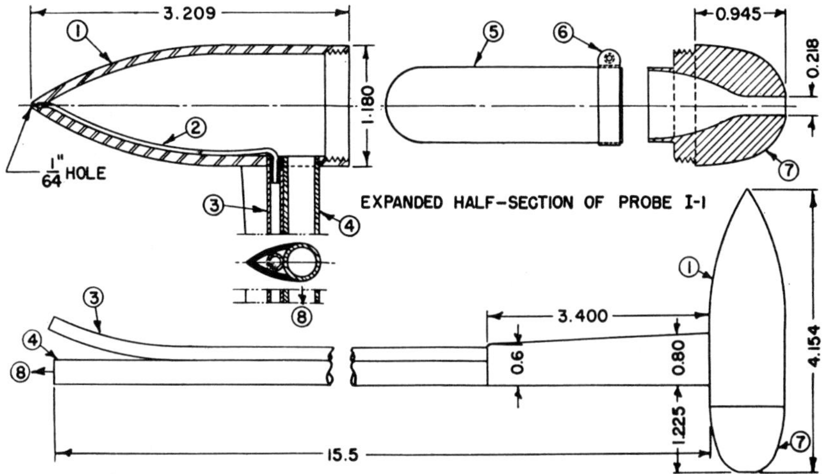

FIG. 7. Null-type stack-sampling nozzle. Courtesy of *Ind. Eng. Chem.* (*6*)

cluding the membrane filter (*8, 9*), can be utilized. Sampling time of filtration type devices is limited by increased resistance resulting from the build-up of collected material. Where an external dry cyclone, Fig. 5 (e), (*7, 10*), or a wet scrubber such as the impinger, Figs. 5 (f) and 10, is used as the collection device, resistance build-up does not commonly occur, since these are essentially constant pressure drop devices. Their use both obviates the necessity of frequent pump adjustment for maintaining a constant sampling volume and enables longer sampling periods. The freeze-out trap, Fig. 5 (g), which is illustrated in detail in Fig. 11, is used for condensing gases at flow rates of 0.1 to 0.2 cu. ft./min. (c.f.m.). Different cooling systems are used, and the number of components is a function of the number of cooling systems, desiccants, and adsorbents utilized.

The collection devices to be used for the great many aerosols of interest are dependent upon the physical and chemical properties of the materials to be collected and, in many instances, are selected as the result of detailed study of the contaminant characteristics. For example, sulfuric acid mist in the fine droplet form may or may not be satisfac-

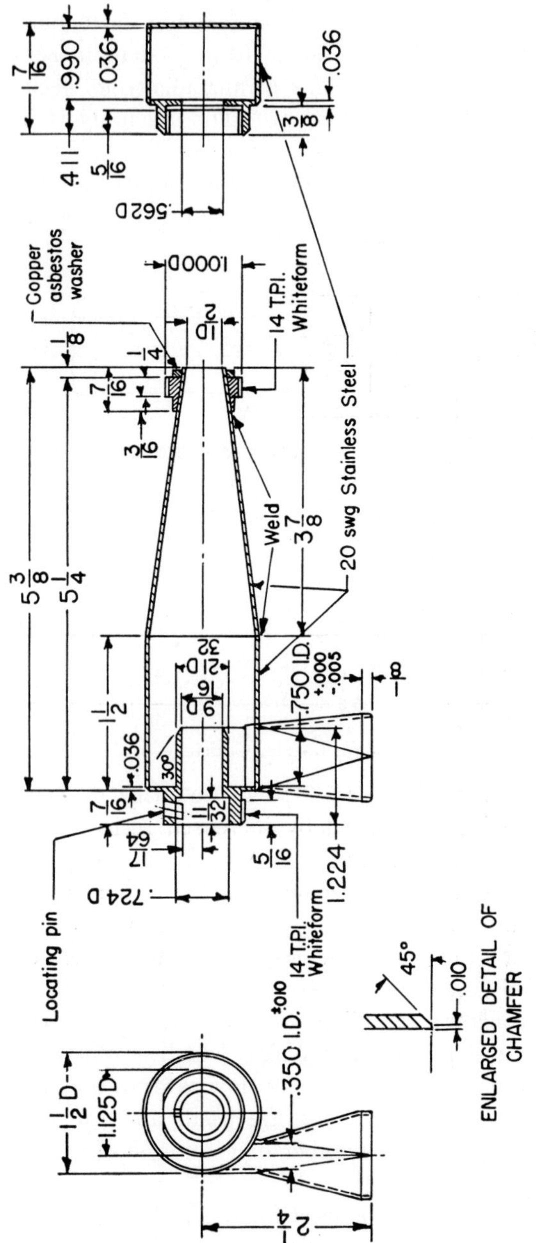

FIG. 8a. Dimensions of cyclone-type stack sampling-nozzle. Courtesy of *J. Inst. Fuel* (7).

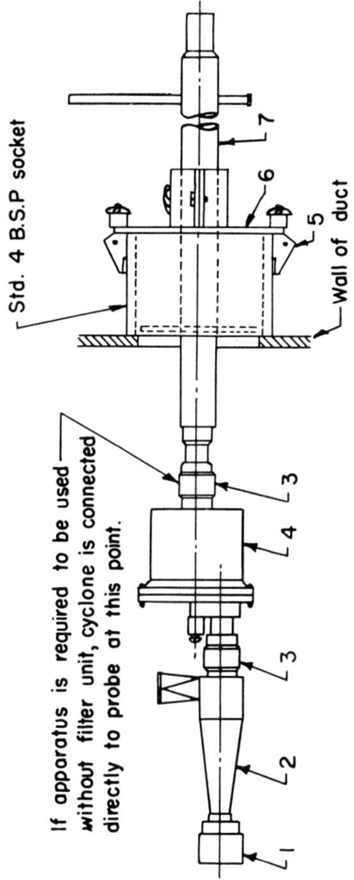

FIG. 8b. General arrangement of cyclone-filter probe. Courtesy of *J. Inst. Fuel* (7).

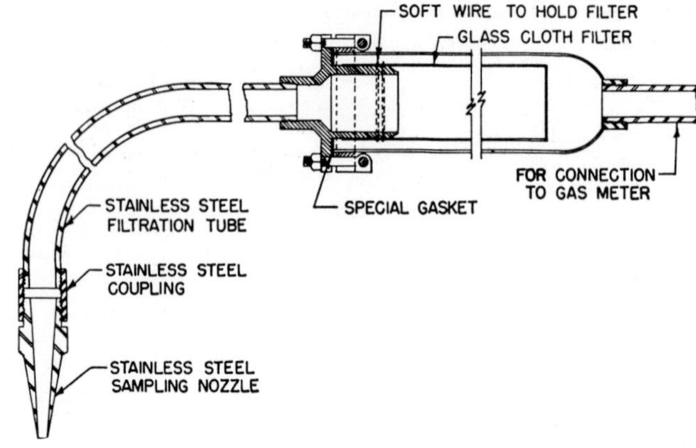

FIG. 9a. Nozzle, short probe, and collector device assembly. Courtesy Western Precipitation Corp., Los Angeles.

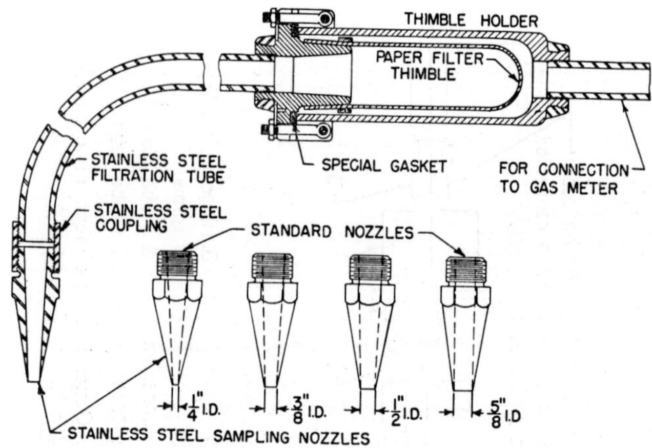

FIG. 9b. Nozzle, short probe, and collector device assembly. Courtesy Western Precipitation Corp., Los Angeles.

torily collected in a bubbler or an impinger using water, depending upon the droplet size. Ammonium chloride, which is soluble in water, is not successfully collected with conventional wet collection devices when present in the submicron size range. The latter is best handled with a fabric filtration type device.

A condenser, Fig. 5 (i), may be required in the sampling system, depending upon the humidity of the stack gas being sampled, its purpose being to enable calculation of the humidity of the stack gas and/or to

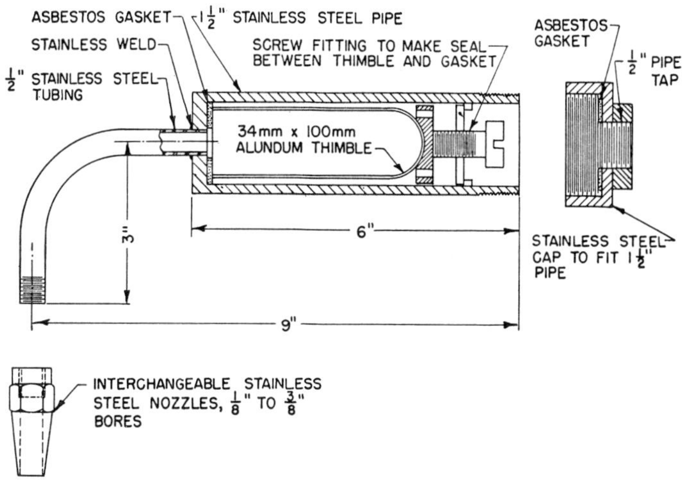

FIG. 9c. Nozzle, short probe, and collector device assembly. Courtesy Western Precipitation Corp., Los Angeles.

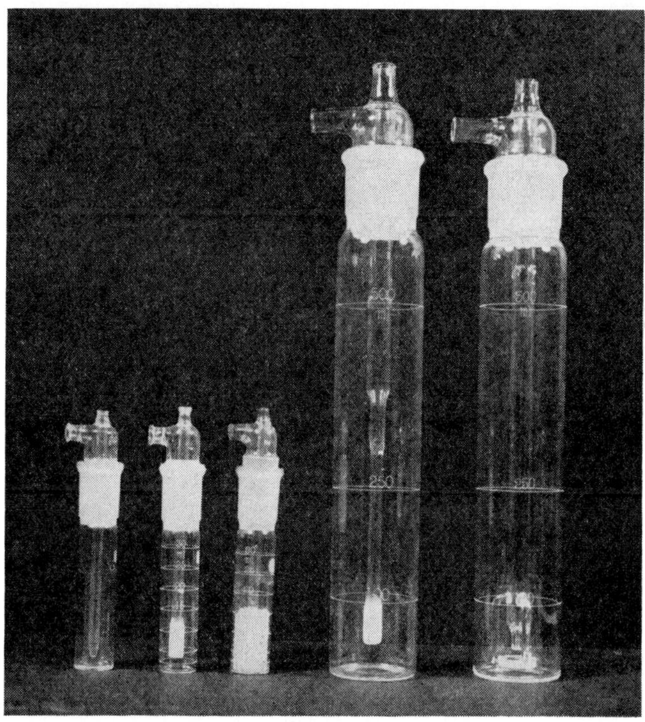

FIG. 10. Wet scrubbing equipment.

condense the moisture in the sampling system before it enters the flow meter and suction equipment. The orifice, Fig. 5 (j), is an excellent means of measuring flow rate by virtue of its size and operating characteristics. The critical orifice, Fig. 5 (k), is sometimes used as a metering device, depending upon the sampling system and the flow rate desired; it requires a suction source sufficient to create critical orifice

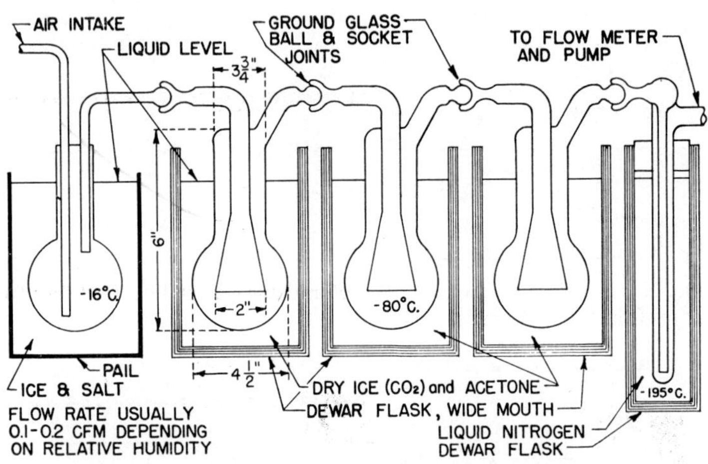

FIG. 11. Freeze-out trap for collecting gaseous contaminants. Courtesy of the U. S. Public Health Service.

conditions. The rotameter, Fig. 5 (l), usually constructed of glass, and the gas meter, Fig. 5 (m), are generally less desirable than the orifice meter because of their fragility, weight, and size. A pump, Fig. 5 (n), is the usual choice of equipment for providing the required suction, although in some instances an ejector, Fig. 5 (o), utilizing steam, compressed air, or water is used.

2. *Isokinetic Sampling for Particulates*

Particulate matter, especially in the range of **3** μ or greater, presents a problem, in that the inertial effect on the particles can result in selective or erroneous samples if the sampling velocity (velocity in the nozzle) is not the same as the velocity of the gas stream at the sampling point. As illustrated in Fig. 12, when the velocity of the gas within the sampling nozzle is less than the gas velocity in the duct, portions of the gas stream approaching at a higher velocity are deflected. The result is that the light particles in the low micron size range follow the deflected gas stream and do not enter the probe. The heavier particles, by virtue of their inertia, continue into the probe, with the result that a nonrepresentative high concentration of coarse particles is collected and the sample weight is in error on the high side. Conversely, when the velocity within the probe is higher than that of the gas stream being sampled, a convergent air stream will develop at the nozzle face, with an excessive amount of lighter particles entering the probe. The result is a sample

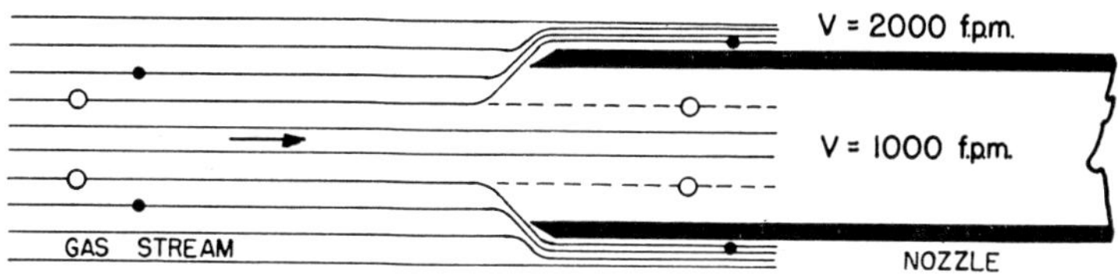

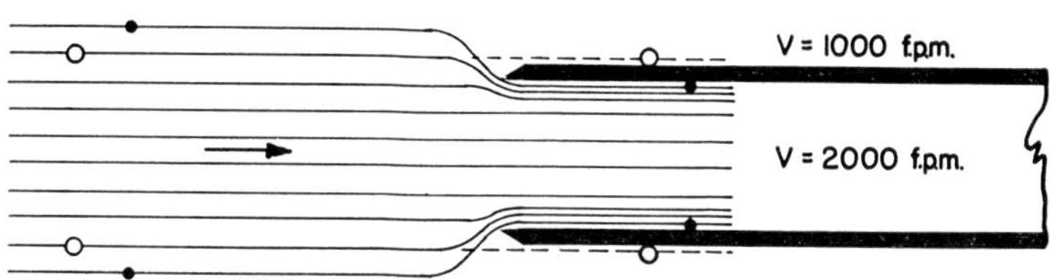

FIG. 12. Selective sampling due to non-isokinetic conditions.

indicating an excessively high concentration of light particles and a sample weight that is in error on the low side. The latter condition is also due to the inertial effect on the heavier particles which, instead of converging into the nozzle's face with the gas stream, travel past the edge of the nozzle and are not collected.

Watson (*11*) developed the following equation as an expression of the relationship of sample validity to nozzle and duct flow conditions:

$$\frac{C}{C_0} = \frac{U_0}{U}\left\{1 + f(p)\left[\left(\frac{U}{U_0}\right)^{1/2} - 1\right]\right\}^2 \tag{4}$$

where C = concentration measured

C_0 = true concentration

U_0 = stream velocity

U = mean air velocity at sampling orifice

$p = \dfrac{\mu^2 \rho U_0}{18\eta D}$

D = diameter of orifice

ρ = specific gravity of particles

μ = diameter of particles

η = viscosity of liquid carrying the aerosol

Figure 13 illustrates the relationship of $f(p)$ and p based on wind tunnel data. Watson conducted experiments in a wind tunnel of low turbulence, utilizing spherical spore particles of two basic varieties, one 32 μ in diameter and the other 4 μ in diameter, in order to determine $f(p)$. In his experimental runs, the wind tunnel velocity was maintained

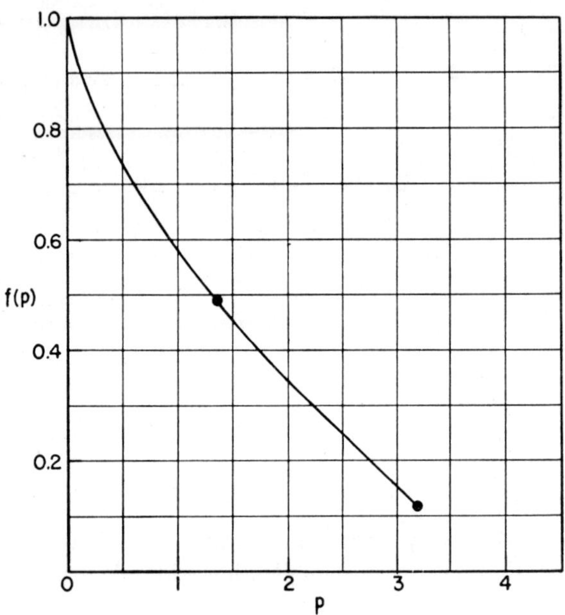

FIG. 13. Relationship between $f(p)$ and p. Courtesy of the American Industrial Hygiene Association (*11*).

at about 900 ft./min., which is on the low side in terms of actual processing equipment or pollution sources. The effect of the velocity at which tests of this phenomenon are conducted is illustrated in Fig. 14, derived from data by Hemeon and Haines (*12*). Dennis, Samples, Anderson and Silverman (*6*) investigated the aerodynamic characteristics of five specially designed probes in gas streams having velocities ranging from 1000 to 6000 ft./min. Their laboratory work verified the findings of these and other investigators.

The conclusions to be reached from these several studies are that for precise work the correction chart for deviations from isokinesis must be determined experimentally for each combination of dust sizes, dust densities, and gas velocity that may be met in practice, but that, where precision does not demand or time does not allow such experimental determination, the following rules of thumb may be used: (1) Isokinetic

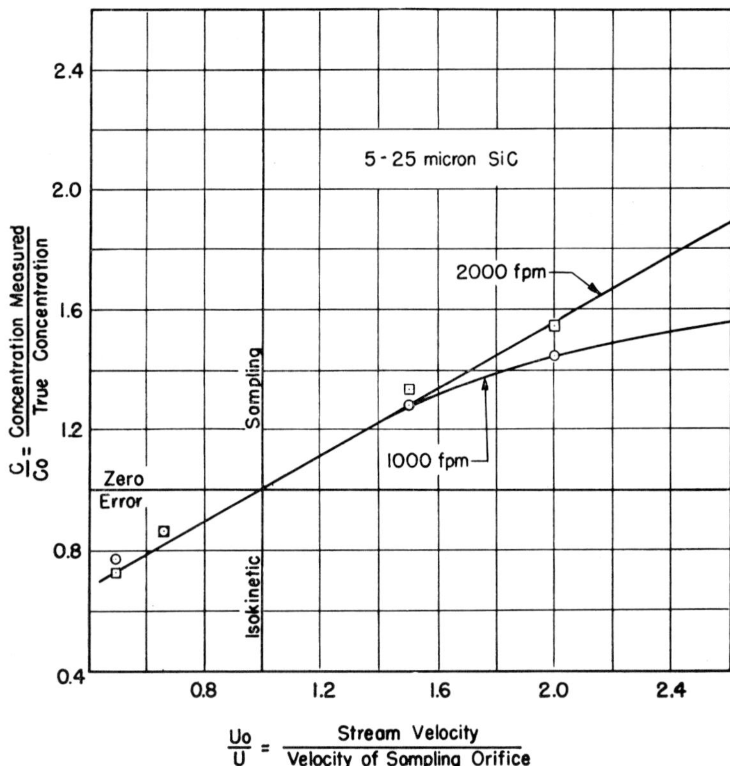

FIG. 14. Errors due to departure from isokinetic sampling. Based on data of Hemeon and Haines (*12*).

sampling is unnecessary for smoke and fumes which are not admixed with particulate matter of over 5 μ in size. (2) For the size distribution of dusts encountered in practice, Table II may be used.

In the absence of specific data pertaining to the size distribution of

TABLE II

$\frac{U_o}{U}$	$\frac{C}{C_o}$ Range	$\frac{C}{C_o}$ Typical value
0.6	0.75–0.90	0.85
0.8	0.85–0.95	0.90
1.2	1.05–1.20	1.10
1.4	1.10–1.40	1.20
1.6	1.15–1.60	1.30
1.8	1.20–1.80	1.40

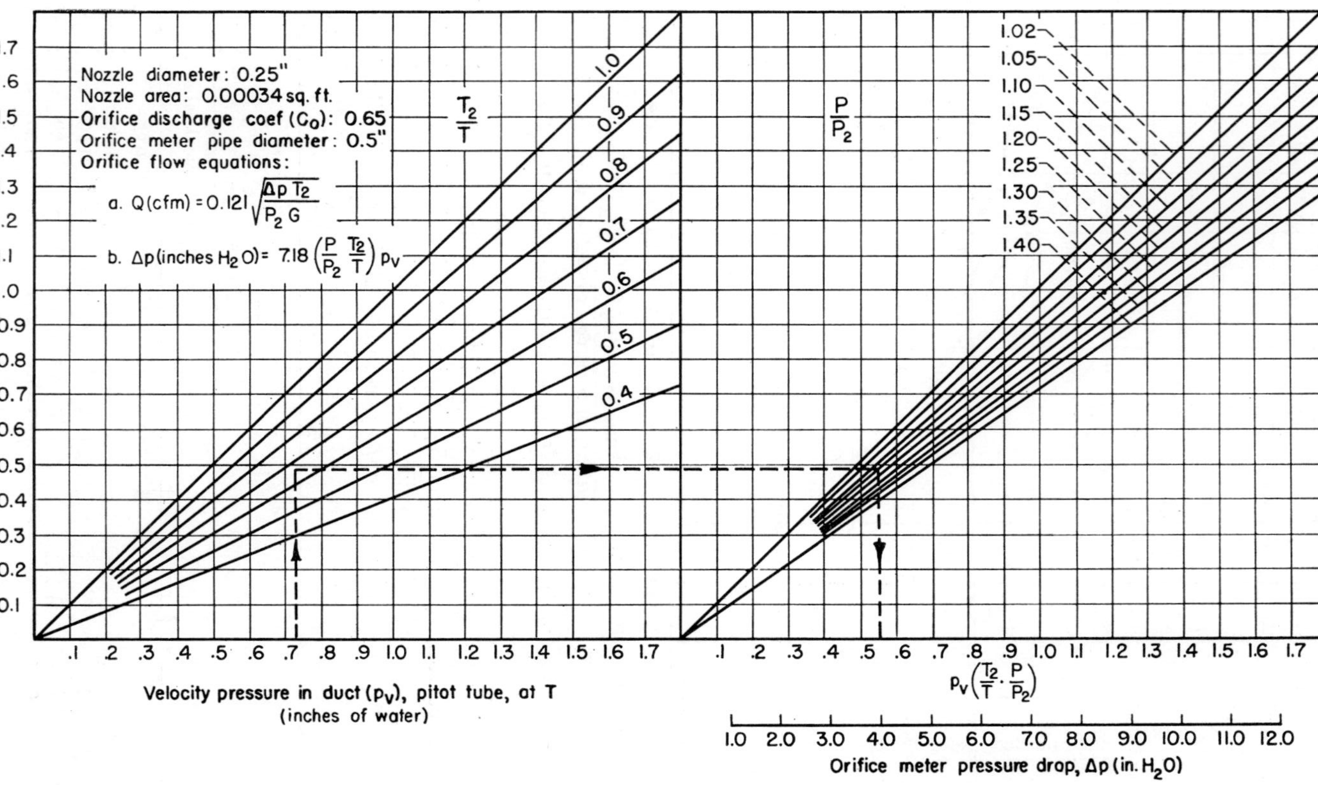

FIG. 15. Graphic calculations for differential pressure across orifice. Based on graphic procedure described by Gallaer (*14*).

the material to be sampled, it is necessary that isokinetic sampling procedures be used to assure sampling reliability. However, once systematic sampling has proved the particulate matter all to be below the size (approximately 5 μ) for which such sampling procedure is necessary, future sampling need not be isokinetic. Hemeon and Haines (*12*) investigated the effect of nozzle size on the collection of both coarse and fine particulate material and found that with particles in the 5 to 25 μ range there was little deviation in sample weights collected, with each of three nozzles, ⅛, ¼, and ⅜ in. diameter. Where the particle size ranged from 420 to 500 μ, a condition atypical of stack sampling, it was found that use of the small diameter nozzle resulted in a lower weight of sample being collected.

The American Society of Mechanical Engineers Power Test Code #27 (1957) for Determining Dust Concentration in a Gas Stream (*13*) mentions the importance of a thin-edge nozzle of not less than ¼ in. diameter in which "the tapering, if any, shall be on the outside, not on the inside." There is an advantage in using nozzles larger than ¼ in. because they enable the sampling of a proportionately greater volume and the obtaining of a larger sample.

It is possible to accomplish isokinetic sampling of a number of sampling points with constant nozzle diameter by varying the flow rate at each sampling point so that the velocity in the nozzle is equal to the velocity at the sampling point. This can be accomplished by computing from the velocity profile the nozzle flow necessary at each sampling point and by adjusting flow to that value as the nozzle is moved from point to point. Since rapid on-the-spot computations are necessary, it is desirable to prepare graphic aids to computation wherever possible. Figure 15 illustrates a graphic aid for conversion of Pitot and temperature readings to the orifice flow meter setting required. Derivation of the graphical chart is as follows for given chart values and 3⁄16 in. diameter orifice:

$$Q_0 \text{ (orifice c.f.m.)} = \left(\frac{\pi (D'_2)^2}{4}\right) \frac{C_0}{\sqrt{1-\beta^4}} \sqrt{2gh} = 5.21 \frac{C_0 D_2^2}{\sqrt{1-\beta^4}} \sqrt{\frac{\Delta p T_2}{P_2 G}}$$

$$= 0.121 \sqrt{\frac{\Delta p T_2}{P_2 G}} \text{ (for orifice meter specified)}$$

$$Q_n \text{ (nozzle c.f.m.)} = A_n \times 953 \sqrt{\frac{p_v T}{GP}}$$

Since $Q_n = Q_0$,

$$A_n \times 953 \sqrt{\frac{p_v T}{GP}} = 0.121 \sqrt{\frac{\Delta p T_2}{GP_2}} \times \left(\frac{TP_2}{T_2 P}\right)$$

$$\Delta p = \left(\frac{953 \times A_n}{0.121}\right)^2 \left(\frac{P}{P_2}\frac{T_2}{T}\right) p_v = 7.18 \left(\frac{P}{P_2}\frac{T_2}{T}\right) p_v$$

where

D_2' = orifice diameter, feet
D_2 = orifice diameter, inches
C_0 = orifice coefficient, dimensionless
β = ratio of orifice diameter to pipe diameter, dimensionless
g = acceleration due to gravity, 32.17 feet per second per second
h = orifice pressure differential in feet of fluid flowing at orifice outlet conditions
Δp = differential pressure across orifice, inches of water
P_2 = absolute static pressure at orifice outlet, inches of Hg
T_2 = absolute temperature at orifice outlet, °F.
G = specific gravity (air = 1), dimensionless
A_n = nozzle area, square feet
P = absolute static pressure in duct, inches of Hg
T = absolute temperature in duct, °F.
p_v = velocity pressure, inches of water

Pressure and temperature corrections are made automatically and in cases where moisture condensation is to be corrected for, it is simply a matter of applying a new abscissa scale to the chart, or correcting the Δp value to be held on the orifice manometer by multiplying by the moisture correction factor squared.

Figures 5 and 15 and the above derivation of the graphical chart indicate temperature and pressure measurements made at the flow meter outlet. Some investigators take measurements at the flow meter inlet and either location is satisfactory just so long as one is consistent on the matter of meter calibration and the mathematics involved.

Isokinesis can also be attained with the use of a "null" type nozzle. The null type of nozzle (several variations of which are shown in Figs. 16a, b, c, d) incorporates hollow chambers surrounding the nozzle and uses static pressure tubes which are connected to both the interior and exterior sides of the sampling nozzle, thereby indicating static pressure in the main gas stream as well as in the sampling nozzle itself. Each static pressure tap is connected to one of the two legs of a manometer. In operation, flow through the sampling tube is adjusted to continuously maintain no pressure differential across the manometer, i.e., a null condition. Figure 17 illustrates the sampling errors due to departure from null condition and the lack of reliability when using the null nozzle in low velocity (1000 ft./min.) gas streams.

The reason that the null method does not guarantee isokinetic sampling conditions is that the static balance between pressures measured on the outer and inner probe walls is not necessarily indicative of a matched velocity condition. Thus, although the null condition is indicated by the differential manometer, the isokinetic condition may not actually exist, because of deviations caused by differences in turbulence for duct and probe flow, the shape of the entry nozzle, its degree of surface roughness, and the location of the static holes in the interior and exterior of the nozzles.

The alternate procedure for maintaining isokinetic conditions requires the use of a series of nozzles of different diameters, as shown in Fig. 18. The sampling rate is kept constant, and the nozzle is selected on the

TABLE III
NOZZLE SERIES FOR ISOKINETIC SOURCE SAMPLING

	Nozzle Size			
Nozzle number	Letter or number of drill	Diameter (inches)	Area (sq. ft.)	Velocity (ft./min. at 1 c.f.m.)
1	27	0.1440	0.00011	8853
2	25	0.1495	0.00012	8144
3	22	0.1570	0.00013	7450
4	20	0.1610	0.00014	7030
5	18	0.1695	0.00016	6390
6	16	0.1770	0.00017	5830
7	14	0.1820	0.00018	5540
8	12	0.1890	0.00019	5140
9	10	0.1935	0.00020	4900
10	8	0.1990	0.00021	4640
11	6	0.2040	0.00023	4420
12	4	0.2090	0.00024	4210
13	3	0.2130	0.00025	4040
14	2	0.2210	0.00027	3760
15	1	0.2280	0.00028	3530
16	B	0.2380	0.00031	3240
17	D	0.2460	0.00033	3030
18	F	0.2570	0.00036	2780
19	H	0.2660	0.00039	2590
20	J	0.2770	0.00042	2390
21	L	0.2900	0.00046	2180
22	N	0.3020	0.00050	2010
23	P	0.3230	0.00057	1760
24	R	0.3390	0.00062	1600
25	T	0.3580	0.00070	1430
26	V	0.3770	0.00078	1290
27	X	0.3970	0.00086	1160
28	—	0.4375	0.00104	960

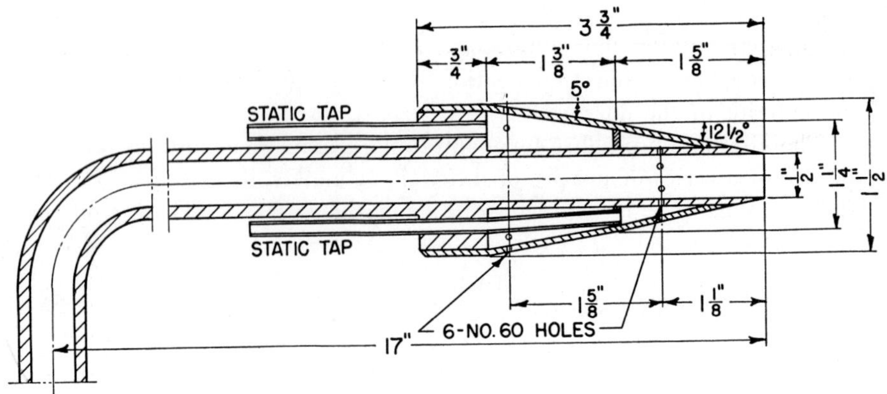

FIG. 16a. Null-type stack-sampling nozzle. Courtesy of Western Precipitation Corp., Los Angeles (*6*).

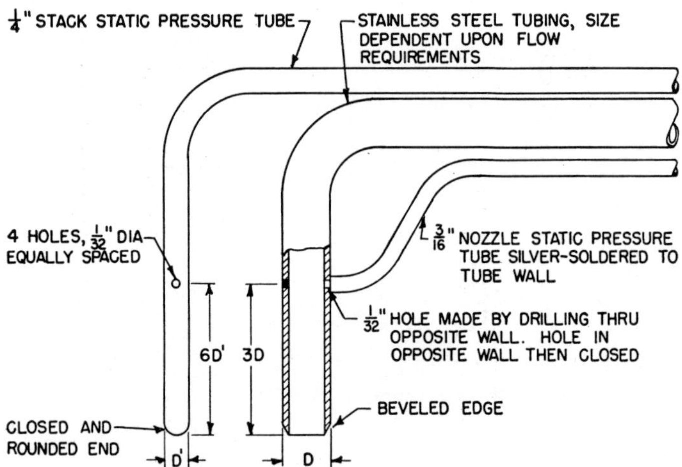

FIG. 16b. Null-type stack-sampling nozzle. Courtesy of *J. Air Pollution Control Assoc.* (*12*).

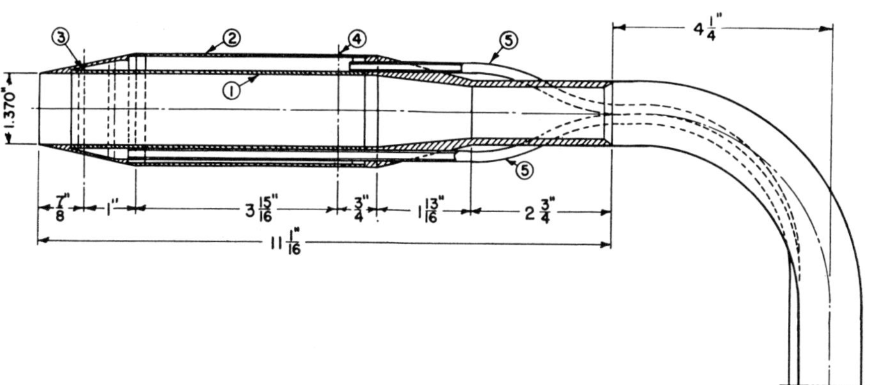

FIG. 16c. Null-type stack-sampling nozzle. Courtesy of Bethlehem Steel Co. Sampler designed by Buell Engineering Co. (*6*).

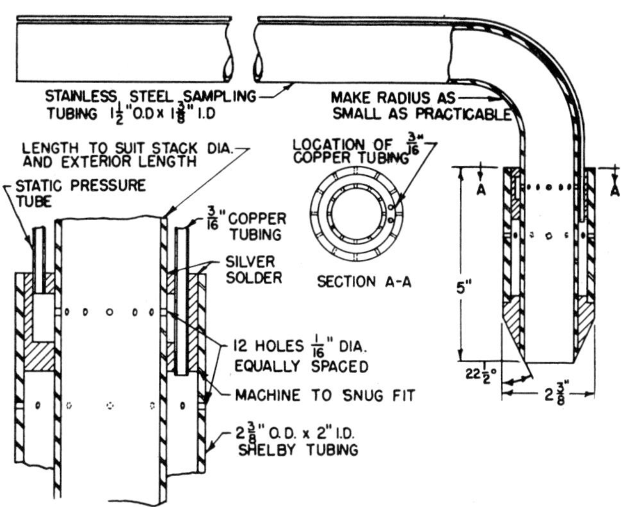

FIG. 16d. Null-type stack-sampling nozzle. Courtesy of *J. Air Pollution Control Assoc.* (*12*).

basis of its inlet diameter, so as to match the duct velocity. This technique is particularly advantageous when the collection device exhibits a constant pressure drop, such as the impinger or the cyclone (without after-filter) and when only one pump calibration point, predetermined

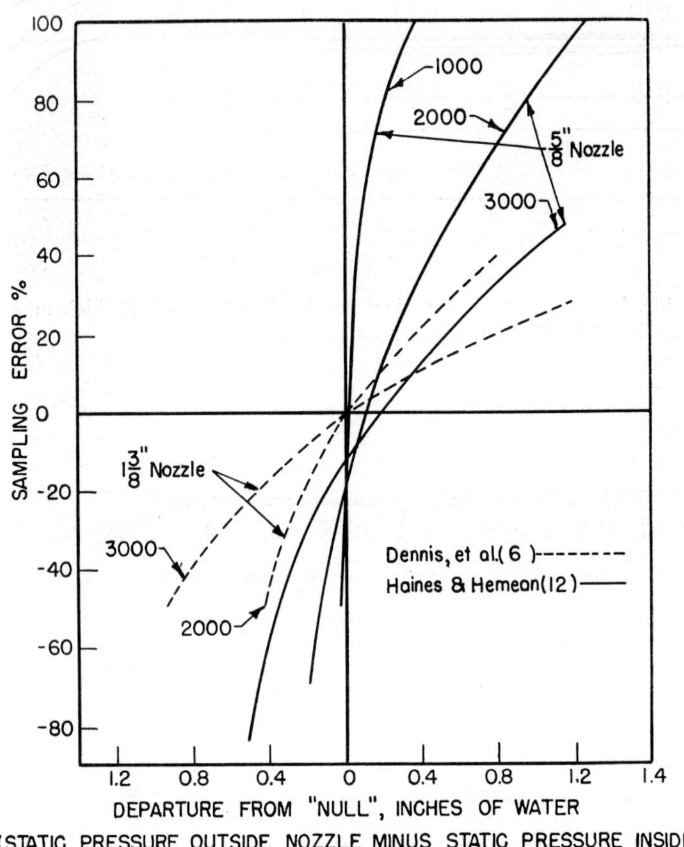

FIG. 17. Sampling error caused by departure from null conditions when using null-type probes.

in the laboratory, is used in the field for maintaining a constant flow rate. The nozzles are changed to suit the velocity at the sampling point, nozzle size being a function of gas densities in the stack and at the flow-metering device. Therefore, a means for rapid choice of nozzle diameter in the field should be provided in the form of a chart or nomograph usable at the sampling site. Table III lists a nozzle series.

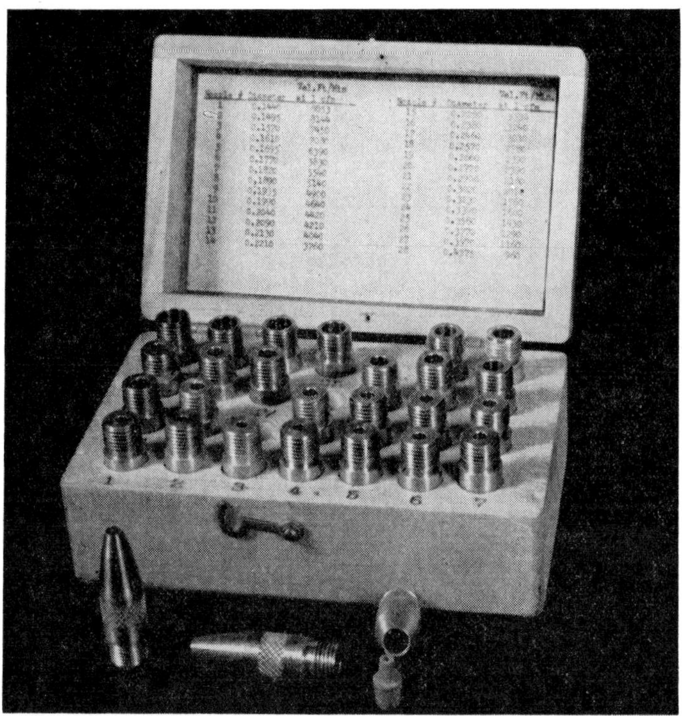

FIG. 18. Nozzle series for isokinetic sampling. Courtesy of Michigan Dept. of Health.

3. *Typical Calculations for Isokinetic Sampling of an Air Stream Containing Particulate Matter*

a. Sampling System. Nozzle-probe apparatus, Fiberglas filter media, condenser, orifice meter, and suction pump in series. Single nozzle size, adjustable suction source to achieve isokinetic sampling conditions.

b. Sampling Conditions

Item	Symbol	Units	Value
(1) Barometric pressure	Pb	in. Hg	29.80
(2) Duct diameter	D	in.	40
(3) Duct temperature	t	°F.	350
(4) Duct static pressure	p	in. H_2O	3
(5) Cooled gas temperature, dry bulb	t_d	°F.	190
Cooled gas temperature, wet bulb	t_w	°F.	120

b. Sampling Conditions (cont.)

Item	Symbol	Units	Value
(6) Meter temperature	t_2	°F.	80
(7) Meter pressure at outlet	P_2	in. of Hg	3.5
(8) Pitot traverse data			

Reading number	Velocity pressure in duct, p_v (in. H_2O)	Velocity pressure adjusted to $t_{std.}$ and $p_{std.}$ (70°F. and 29.92 in. Hg,) allowing use of Eq. 2)	Velocity in duct, V (ft./min.)
(1)	0.66	1.02	4045
(2)	0.68	1.05	4103
(3)	0.68	1.05	4103
(4)	0.75	1.16	4314
(5)	0.78	1.20	4386
(6)	0.83	1.28	4531
(7)	0.73	1.12	4238
(8)	0.71	1.09	4181
(9)	0.70	1.08	4162
(10)	0.70	1.08	4162

Item	Symbol	Units	Value
(9) Velocity in duct (average)	V	ft./min.	4223
(10) Sampling nozzle, I.D.	d	in.	1/4
(11) Sampling nozzle area	A_n	sq. ft.	0.00034
(12) Sampling rate at nozzle	Q_n	cu. ft./min.	1.44

$$Q_n = VA_n = 4223 \times 0.00034 = 1.44 \text{ cu. ft./min.}$$

Item	Symbol	Units	Value
(13) Moisture content of air in duct	H	lb./lb. dry gas	0.0635[a]
(14) Moisture content of air in meter outlet	H_2	lb./lb. dry gas	0.0223[b]
(15) Moisture not measured by meter	H_3	lb./lb. dry gas	0.0412

$$H_3 = H - H_2 = 0.0635 - 0.0223 = 0.0412$$

Item	Symbol	Units	Value
(16) Specific volume of water vapor condensed at meter outlet conditions	W	cu. ft./lb. dry gas	1.02

[a] From psychrometric chart using t_d, t_w.
[b] From psychrometric chart, t_2 saturated.

b. Sampling Conditions (cont.)

Item	Symbol	Units	Value

$$W = \frac{H_3(t_2 + 460)}{P_b - P_2} \times \frac{p_{\text{std.}}}{(t_{\text{std.}} + 460)} \times \frac{(\text{cu. ft. gas/mole at } p_{\text{std.}} \text{ and } t_{\text{std.}})}{\text{molecular wgt. of water}}$$

$$= \frac{0.0412(80 + 460)}{(29.80 - 3.50)} \times \frac{29.92}{(70 + 460)} \times \frac{387}{18} = 1.02$$

Item	Symbol	Units	Value
(17) Specific volume of gas at meter outlet conditions	W_g	cu. ft./lb. dry gas	16.0

$$W_g = \left(\frac{387}{29} + \frac{H_2\,387}{18}\right)\left(\frac{29.92}{530}\right)\left(\frac{t_2 + 460}{P_b - P_2}\right)$$

$$= (0.75 + 1.21H_2)\,\frac{540}{26.30} = 16.0$$

Item	Symbol	Units	Value
(18) Sample flow rate at meter	Q_m	cu. ft./min.	1.02

$$Q_m = Q_n \times \frac{W_g}{(W_g + W)} \times \frac{(t_2 + 460)}{(t_d + 460)} \times \frac{(P_b - P)}{(P_b - P_2)}$$

$$= 1.44 \times \frac{16}{17.02} \times \frac{540}{810} \times \frac{29.57}{26.30} = 1.44 \times 0.94 \times 0.67 \times 1.12 = 1.02$$

Item	Symbol	Units	Value
(19) Sampling time	s	min.	10
(20) Sample volume at nozzle	M	cu. ft.	14.4

$$M = Q_n s = 1.44 \times 10 = 14.4$$

Item	Symbol	Units	Value
(21) Sample weight	Y	gm.	1.4
(22) Stack loading	Z	gr./cu. ft.	1.50

$$Z = \frac{Y}{M} \times \frac{15.43 \text{ gr.}}{\text{gm.}} = \frac{1.4}{14.4} \times 15.43 = 1.50$$

Item	Symbol	Units	Value
(23) Duct area	A	sq. ft.	8.73
(24) Flow rate in duct at duct conditions	Q	cu. ft./min.	36,867

$$Q = VA = 4223 \times 8.73 = 36{,}867$$

Item	Symbol	Units	Value
(25) Duct loading	E	lb./hr.	474

$$E = \frac{Z \times Q \times 60}{7000 \text{ gr./lb.}} = \frac{1.50 \times 36{,}867 \times 60}{7000} = 474$$

4. *Sampling for Gases and Vapors*

The procedure used for sampling a gas or mixture of gases in a duct or stack differs little from that employed in the sampling of particulate matter insofar as basic routine is concerned. Isokinetic sampling procedures are not required. There is nevertheless the problem of selecting the proper collecting device which will enable reliable qualitative and quantitative analysis. Table IV lists typical sampling procedures for various contaminants. Obviously, since different gases, mists, and vapors all exhibit a wide variety of physical and chemical characteristics, no all-purpose collection device exists. For example, in the sampling of gasoline vapors, activated carbon serves as an effective adsorption medium, whereas its collection efficiency falls off sharply for butane or propane and it is totally unsatisfactory for methane.

Absorption, in which the gas sample is bubbled or drawn through an absorbing liquid, is the most common collecting procedure. A wide variety of equipment designed for gas-washing purposes has been described and used (*14a*). The Greenburg-Smith impinger (Fig. 10), which is commonly used at a sampling rate of 1 cu. ft./min., is an effective absorption device for certain gases and can be effectively used in a series train to increase efficiency of absorption. The gas sample is forced through a single orifice submerged beneath the absorbing medium. Various types of bubblers (Fig. 10) for absorption have been used; they are commonly of the type having a submerged sintered tip through which the gas sample is dispersed in a collecting liquid in fine bubble form or they may be made simply of a glass container having a glass inlet tube submerged in glass beads and filled with the collecting medium. Another variety of absorption apparatus is the nebulizer or atomizer through which a stream of gas is drawn. A typical example is a venturi shape in which a fine spray is formed in the venturi throat, the gas and droplets make contact, absorption takes place, and the fine droplets are separated from the gas stream by impaction in a cyclone or similar separator. The absorbing liquid thus collects and is recycled for a predetermined time. Basically, absorption efficiency is inversely proportional to bubble or droplet size and is thereby a direct function of surface contact area. It is important, when sampling for any gas, that collection efficiency of the equipment be known for the contaminant concerned.

Adsorption is another commonly used procedure for collecting a specific gas or combination of gases. Usually, a container is filled with an adsorbent such as activated carbon, alumina, or silica gel through which the gas stream is passed. The contaminant gases are bound by molecular forces to the adsorbent surfaces and, if condensation in the adsorbent does not occur, the gases remain physically and chemically unchanged. A varicty of other adsorbents are available for specific gases. Following collection, the contaminant gases are removed either by heat or eluted by an inert carrier gas.

Freeze-out or condensation consists essentially of a trap immersed in a low temperature bath, such as dry ice and acetone or liquid nitrogen, through which the gas sample is drawn and condensable contaminants collected. Bath temperature is necessarily selectively controlled according to the contaminant to be collected. Atmospheric water collects easily. Various combinations of freeze-out traps, desiccants, and adsorbents have been used for collecting specific materials. The efficiency of collection of a gaseous contaminant with a freeze-out trap is, of course, dependent upon the concentration of the contaminant and the equipment arrangement. Figure 11 illustrates a five-component freeze-out train utilizing three different cooling systems connected so as to progressively cool the gas sample. The first trap contains ice and salt at a temperature of —80°C. and the fifth and final trap contains liquid nitrogen at a temperature of —195°C. Flow rate is a function of relative humidity, ranging from 0.1 to 0.2 cu. ft./min.

Where analytical equipment of extreme sensitivity, such as the mass spectrometer, is available, it is sometimes possible to take a grab sample from the stack into an evacuated bottle without any attempt to concentrate the contaminant in an absorbent, adsorbent, or freeze-out trap. A technique for collection of a sample of this type at a sampling rate controlled to proportionately sample a cyclic process so that one integrated sample represents the contaminant discharged to the atmosphere over a long period of time, has been described by Brief and Drinker (*15*).

5. *Flow Rate Control in Sampling*

Flow rate control is best accomplished with the use of a simple bypass arrangement around the suction device and either a calibrated orifice meter or, where a constant pressure drop collection device is used, calibration of the pressure drop across the device in terms of flow. Volume meters of the wet or dry type, although used by some investigators, are more suited to the laboratory than to the field by virtue of weight, size, recording lag, and lack of ruggedness. Rotameters are also excellent flow rate meters more suited to laboratory use than to metering flow in the field where dirt, moisture, positioning, and fragility present difficulties. Where rotameters or wet or dry meters are used for calibrating equipment, consideration should be given to manufacturers' use instructions, to pressure drop through the metering instruments, and to

TABLE IV
SAMPLING PROCEDURE OUTLINE FOR SOME SPECIFIC CONTAMINANTS*

Pollutant	Collecting device	Collecting medium	Sampling rate (cu. ft./min.)	Minimum sampling volume[a] (cu. ft.)
Acetates	Fritted bubbler	Alcohol	0.05	2.2
Acetone	Fritted bubbler	Water or aq. alkali	0.1	1
	Combustible gas indicator			
Acid vapors and mists	Impinger or fritted bubbler	Aq. alkali	Up to 1	Sulfuric acid—60 Nitric acid—0.1 Hydrochloric acid—5
Aldehydes	Fritted bubbler	$NaHSO_3$ sol.	0.1	1
Alkali mists	Impinger or fritted bubbler	Water	Up to 1	20
	Impinger or fritted bubbler	Dil. H_2SO_4	Up to 1	20
Ammonia	Fritted bubbler	Dil. H_2SO_4	Up to 1	1
Ammonium picrate	Impinger or fritted bubbler	Water	0.1	5
Ammonium salts	Impinger	Water	Up to 1	1
Amyl acetate	Fritted bubbler	Alcohol	0.05	2
Aniline	Fritted bubbler	Dil. H_2SO_4	0.05	1
Antimony	Impinger	Water	1	10
	Membrane filter	None	3	10
Arsenic	Impinger	Water	3	3
	Membrane filter	None	3	3
Arsine	Fritted bubbler	$AgNO_3$ sol.	0.1	3
Benzene (benzol)	Fritted bubbler	Isoöctane	0.25	3
Beryllium	Impinger	Water	1	10
	Membrane filter	None	3	10
Cadmium	Impinger	Water	1	10
Carbon dioxide	Fritted bubbler	Barium hydroxide	0.2	3

Carbon disulfide	Fritted bubbler	Alcoholic KOH	0.05	0.1
	Fritted bubbler	Diethylamine–Cu acetate	0.05	0.1
Cellosolve	Fritted bubbler	Water	0.1	1
	Fritted bubbler	$H_2SO_4 + K_2CrO_7$	0.1	1
Chlorinated hydrocarbons	Combustion tube with fritted bubbler	Na_2CO_3 + arsenite reagent	0.1	1
Chromates	Impinger	Water or aq. alkali	Up to 1	[a]
			Sample until yellow color is detected	
Chromic acid	Impinger	Water or aq. alkali	Up to 1	[a]
			Sample until yellow color is detected	
Cobalt	Impinger	Water	1	15
	Membrane filter	None	3	15
Copper	Impinger	Water	1	15
	Membrane filter	None	3	15
Cresol	Fritted bubbler	Aq. alkali	0.05	1
Cyanides[b]	Fritted bubbler	Aq. alkali	0.1	2.5
Dimethylaniline	Fritted bubbler	Alcohol	0.1	1
Dinitrotoluene	Fritted bubbler	Alcohol	0.1	5
Diphenylamine	Fritted bubbler	Dil. H_2SO_4	0.1	1
Esters	Fritted bubbler	Alcohol	0.05	Same as acetates
Ethyl alcohol	Fritted bubbler	$H_2SO_4 + K_2CrO_7$	0.05	0.5
Fluorides	Impinger	Water	Up to 1	15
	Fritted bubbler	Aq. alkali	Up to 1	15
	Membrane filter	None	3	15
Halogenated compounds (see Chlorinated hydrocarbons)				
Hydrogen cyanide	Fritted bubbler	Aq. alkali	0.1	2.5

* Courtesy of Michigan Department of Health.

[a] Based on analytical procedure.

[b] Samples must be sent into the laboratory the same day they are taken. Care must be taken so that sampling solution is not exposed to temperatures below 60°F. or extreme changes in temperature.

TABLE IV (*Continued*)

Pollutant	Collecting device	Collecting medium	Sampling rate (cu. ft./min.)	Minimum sampling volume[a] (cu. ft.)
Hydrogen sulfide	Two bubblers in series	Ammoniacal $CdCl_2$	0.05	Until yellow precipitate appears
Lead	Impinger	Dil. HNO_3	1	10
	Millipore membrane filter	None	3	10
Lead tetraethyl	Fritted bubbler	Isoöctane or gasoline (lead free)	0.1	10
Manganese	Impinger	Water	1	10
	Millipore membrane filter	None	3	10
Mercury	Impinger	Dil. HNO_3	1	10
	Millipore membrane filter	None	3	10
Methanol	Fritted bubbler	Water	0.05	1
Nitrates	Impinger	Water	Up to 1	0.5
Nitrobenzene	Grab sample flask	Nitrating acid	—	(500 ml.–1 liter)
Nitrogen oxides	Grab sample flask	—	—	(500 ml.–1 liter)
Nitroglycerine	Fritted bubbler	Propylene glycol	0.1	3
Nitroparaffins	Fritted bubbler	Isopropyl alcohol	0.1	1
Nitropropane	Fritted bubbler	Isopropyl alcohol	0.1	1
Nitrotoluene	Grab sample flask	Nitrating acid	—	(500 ml.–1 liter)
Nitroxylene	Grab sample flask	Nitrating acid	—	(500 ml.–1 liter)
Ozone	Fritted bubbler	NaOH + KI solution	0.4	4
Phenols	Fritted bubbler	Aq. alkali	0.1	1
Phosgene	Fritted bubbler	Aniline + diphenylurea	0.1	1
Phosphates	Impinger or fritted bubbler	Water	Up to 1	10
Phosphoric acid	Impinger or fritted bubbler	Aq. alkali	Up to 1	10
Phosphorus oxides	Impinger or fritted bubbler	Water	Up to 1	10
Selenium	Impinger	Water	1	10
	Fritted bubbler	HBr–Br_2	0.1	1

Sodium oxalate	Impinger	Water	1	15
Stibine	Bubbler	$HgCl_2+HCl$	0.1	10
Sulfur dioxide	Fritted bubbler	2% glycerol in 0.05 *N* NaOH	0.2	2
Sulfur trioxide	Fritted bubbler	Aq. alkali	0.1	60
Tellurium	Impinger	Water	1	20
	Membrane filter	None	3	20
Thiocyanates	Fritted bubbler	Aq. alkali	0.1	3
Turpentine	Two fritted bubblers in series	Alcohol	0.1	3
Zinc	Impinger	Water	1	15

periodic calibration with a primary air displacement device such as a spirometer. The critical pressure (constant flow rate) type of orifice meter (*16, 17*) has some use in source sampling where the temperature and pressure ranges and the resistance range of the sampling system are known and where the suction source can produce critical pressure conditions across the orifice.

6. *Manipulation of Sampling Equipment*

It is good practice to insert the probe, turn on the suction device, and carefully keep the probe at the exact sampling point for the predetermined time period. If reverse flow through the suction device is possible and the duct is under suction, the open air end of the suction device should be plugged at the time it is shut off in order to eliminate the possibility of reverse flow through the sampling system. Where the probe is to be washed free of settled matter and condensate, it should be handled with extreme care, so as to enable collection and subsequent evaluation of the washed material, which may be appreciable in terms of sample weight.

7. *Sampling Duration*

For any stack study the equipment selection and sampling time will depend upon accuracy of results required. Where such results determine the acceptance or rejection of air-cleaning equipment involving large capital outlays or the payment of performance penalties or bonuses, precise sampling procedures are necessary and accurate results are required. On this basis a large number of points must be sampled for an extended period of time at several cross sections of duct. The total sampling period will be lengthy. For example, in a rectangular 5 ft. x 5 ft. duct, precise sampling procedures call for a velocity profile determined at 25 center-line points, with subsequent sampling for equal time periods at each of these points. Where particulates are involved the procedures must be isokinetic and the metering of gas flow accurate. Assuming the use of Alundum thimbles with a ten-minute sampling period per point, the minimum sampling time would be 250 min. Allowing time for relocating the probe and changing thimbles, a minimum sampling period of about 5 hr. per cross section will be required. Two or more sampling systems may be used simultaneously to minimize the over-all sampling time requirement. Sampling time is not necessarily the most significant time factor, since the setting up of equipment, preliminary testing, and the tearing down of equipment, as well as travel time frequently far exceed this. A complete test involving duplicate runs and cross sections before and after a collector can thus easily require from three days to a week and a crew of two to four men.

For other than equipment acceptance testing, precision is usually sacrificed in the interest of shortening the test duration and decreasing the number of people required to run a test. Where tests are to be routinely conducted by plant personnel, several days spent in initially establishing iso-dust-concentration contours, by taking individual samples at each sample point for various flow rates by the precise methods discussed above, will allow the selection of either a single sampling point or a traverse line, the use of which can cut subsequent routine sampling time down to a minimum. Where a single or traverse line sampling point is chosen for routine sampling, a relatively high flow rate sampling device (50 cu. ft./min.) such as a miniature cyclone or a cyclone-filter system can be used. Correction factors accounting for deviation from 100% collection efficiency and from isokinetic sampling can be applied, and a differential manometer connected across the cyclone can be used as the metering device. Calibration curves can be prepared in advance on the basis of gas temperature and density, eliminating the need for any additional flow metering equipment. Under these conditions, the sampling procedure is reduced to (1) making the Pitot tube traverse and determining duct temperature and pressure, (2) selecting a sampling nozzle diameter to conform to the above criteria, and (3) traversing the duct through one or more sampling holes with a probe-cyclone-fan combination with neither flow meter nor flow regulator. At 50 cu. ft./min. flow rate a cyclone or cyclone-filter combination will collect as much sample in 30 sec. as an Alundum thimble will collect in 50 min. The entire sampling operation using such devices can be made independent of laboratory facilities because the large sample to tare ratio will minimize the weighing error and enable the use of a portable field balance in place of a laboratory type of balance. Stern (*10*) describes the combination of this technique with the use of a two-stage electrostatic precipitator, the latter to sample an aliquot of the cyclone outlet gas, to allow computation of the cyclone efficiency correction factor during the test.

Where a sampling device of less than 100% collection efficiency is used without application of an efficiency correction factor to test for compliance for air pollution control regulations, the net effect is to apply a less stringent standard, as much less stringent as is the amount of deviation of the collection efficiency of the sample device from 100%.

The British Standard Institute has drafted a set of standards (*11a*) for the simplified measurement of dust emission from chimneys. Five different apparatus assemblies were considered and judged suitable to their specified sampling requirements. An accuracy of ±25% satisfies the simplified technique and it is further stipulated that "the apparatus used shall be such that the whole operation of sampling can be completed within one hour by not more than two operators, who need not be necessarily skilled technicians but who shall be familiar with the handling and reading of instruments such as manometers and chemical balances."

8. *Roof Monitor and Vent Sampling*

Sampling of roof monitors and general purpose, natural draft vents is frequently necessary and often difficult. The roof monitor is used for the low velocity displacement of large air masses and accessibility is usually difficult. Since high contaminant dilution is typical, the sample volumes required may be large.

The air flow rate through a continuous roof monitor can be estimated on the basis of manufacturers' design data, indoor and outdoor temperatures, and meteorological conditions. A more suitable procedure is actual measurement of the exhaust flow rate at the monitor opening. Zoning of roof monitor sections for both air flow measurement and sampling may be advantageous, depending upon building use, plant layout, and indoor contaminant sources.

Building vents, either of the natural draft or mechanical type, present no special problems not already discussed in previous portions of this chapter. Low velocities are common to natural draft vents, whereas any range of discharge velocities can be encountered where mechanically driven equipment is used. The stack-sampling procedures already discussed are applicable. However, it is frequently necessary to have a duct type of outlet installed at the vent exhaust points so that relatively uniform and measurable flow patterns can be obtained and representative samples collected.

Smoke bombs of the 2-minute or 5-minute duration type are sometimes helpful in establishing air flow patterns in buildings where roof monitors and vents are used. Industrial buildings are frequently under negative pressure and the skillful use of smoke bombs can quickly demonstrate the effect of an unbalanced supply and exhaust condition and indicate areas of difficulty as related to air pollution sampling.

9. *Tracer Techniques*

Tracer techniques have been successfully used to distinguish the airborne effluents of a particular stack, to evaluate plume dispersion and travel, and to determine the pollutant contribution of one area to another. All of the tracer techniques involve the use of a specifically added foreign material or an easily differentiated stack effluent which is emitted in known concentrations and subsequently collected and quantitated. The use of radioactive and fluorescent particulates and fluorescent dye aerosols has been studied and described.

Haines, Hemeon and Cember (*18*) describe a method of dispersing antimony oxide from a stack, collecting air samples on Whatman No. 4 filter tape, irradiating the samples in an atomic pile, and determining the level of beta activity and thereby the tracer concentration per sample. Antimony oxide was selected because it is not normally present in the atmosphere in significant concentrations, because of its high neutron activation cross section, and because of the energetic radiation level of antimony-122, its principal radioisotope. The antimony oxide method permits the measurement of less than 0.01 μg., as compared with the stack emission rate of 10^5 $\mu\mu$g./sec.

Braham, Seely and Crozier (*19*) and others (*20–22*) have described the use of fluorescent pigments as tracer materials for tagging and tracing mass air movement and for determining concentration distribution in aerosol plumes. Three of the tracers used are synthetic crystalline zinc sulfide, zinc cadmium sulfide, and zinc silicate, all of which fluoresce under ultraviolet light, range in size from 0.5 to 5 μ, are practically inert and relatively nonhygroscopic, and are not significantly affected by sunlight or temperature.

Effective dispersion of the tracer materials is critical. The instrument that releases the aerosol cloud must produce minimum agglomeration and uniform distribution in the conveying air stream. A centrifugal blower fed by a hopper and rotating gear mechanism has been used by the Stanford Research Institute for powder dispersion, as has a procedure based on the erosion of solid pellets of tracer material with compressed air jets.

Air sampling has been done with a single-stage impaction device or a membrane filter, and subsequent particle counting has been done under low power magnification (100$\times$) using an ultraviolet light source. Drum-type impaction sampling devices, utilizing filter tapes and a sequential timing and sampling system, have been used and enable an effective determination of concentration variation with time.

A water-soluble fluorescent dye aerosol has been successfully used as a tracer by Stanford Research Institute investigators (*23*). It is dispersed from a water solution by atomization; droplets quickly evaporate to dry aerosols. The membrane filters used for sampling are subsequently leached with water, and the total sample fluorescence, representative of the mass of dye received, is determined with a fluorescence photometer. The main advantages of this tracer medium are the extremely small amounts that may be quantitated, the simple and quick laboratory procedure, and the relatively easy dispersal procedure.

In a recent study (*24*) of air pollution in the New York metropolitan area, zinc cadmium sulfide dust was used as a tracer to investigate the transport of pollutants in both directions across the common boundary of New York and New Jersey.

III. Monitoring

A mirror mounted so that it reflects the stack effluent to an observer in the plant is often used as a monitoring device, with obvious disadvantages. Also in use are closed circuit TV systems.

Staining of filter media and analysis by light transmittance or reflectance are the principles of an automatic smoke sampler used to give

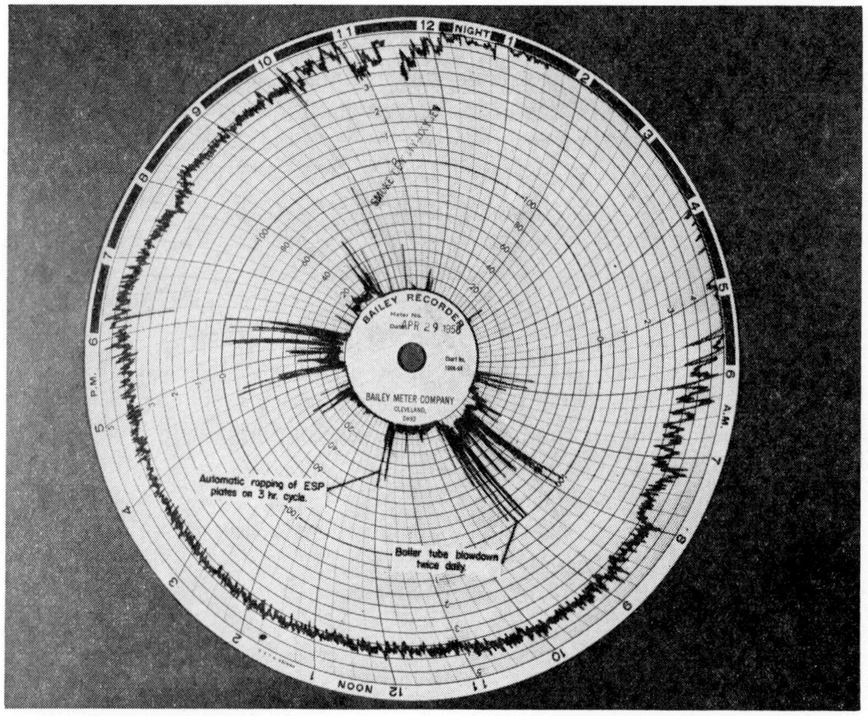

FIG. 19. Photoelectric cell smoke density chart.

a continuous integrated record of smoke concentration in a stack. The sample, together with a controlled volume of clean dilution air, is aspirated through a slowly moving roll of filter paper tape.

A simple and commonly used stack-monitoring device for particulate material consists of a source of light focused through the gas stream onto a photoelectric cell which in turn is wired to automatic recording equipment. As the stack loading increases and light transmittance decreases the index value increases. Automatic smoke density instruments also utilize thermopiles which absorb light as heat and transmit it as electric current.

Figure 19 is a 24-hour photoelectric cell meter record of a power plant exhaust stack. It indicates maximum, or 100%, readings during the two periods when the boiler tubes are blown down, thus liberating a large amount of particulate matter which passes through electrostatic precipitation equipment because of overloading. The 3-hour precipitator rapping cycle is also clearly indicated. Since all of the power plant charts are constantly observed in the control room, any excessive stack loading, indicating poor combustion or defective dust collection, can be immediately determined and corrected.

References

1. American Conference of Governmental Industrial Hygienists, "Industrial Ventilation," 6th ed. P. O. Box 453, Lansing, Michigan, 1960.
2. K. J. Caplan, *in* "Encyclopedia of Instrumentation for Industrial Hygiene" (C. D. Yaffe, D. H. Byers, and A. D. Hosey, eds.). Univ. of Michigan, Ann Arbor, 1956.
3. Methods for Determination of Velocity, Volume, Dust and Mist Content of Gases, Bull. WP-50, Western Precipitation Corp., Los Angeles, California, 1956.
4. A. C. Willard, A. P. Kratz, and V. S. Day, *Univ. Illinois Eng. Expt. Sta. Bull.* **120** (1921).
5. "Heating, Ventilating, Air Conditioning Guide" (Annual), Am. Soc. Heating, Refrigeration and Air Conditioning Engrs., New York, 1958.
6. R. Dennis, W. R. Samples, D. M. Anderson, and L. Silverman, *Ind. Eng. Chem.* **49,** 294 (1957).
7. P. G. W. Hawksley, S. Badzioch, and J. H. Blackett, *J. Inst. Fuel* 147 (1958).
8. M. W. First and L. Silverman, *A.M.A. Arch. Ind. Hyg. Occupational Med.* **7,** 1 (1953).
9. A. Goetz, *Am. J. Public Health* **43,** 150 (1953).
10. A. C. Stern, *Combustion* **4–5,** 35 (1933).
11. H. H. Watson, *Am. Ind. Hyg. Assoc. Quart.* **15,** 21 (1954).

11a. Simplified Methods for Measurement of Grit and Dust Emission from Chimneys, Technical Committee SFE/28, British Standards Institution (1959).

12. W. C. L. Hemeon and G. F. Haines, Jr., *J. Air Pollution Control Assoc.* **4** (1954).
13. Determining Dust Concentration in a Gas Stream, Power Test Code #27 (1957) and Test Code for Dust Separating Apparatus, Power Test Code #21 (1941), Am. Soc. Mech. Engrs., New York.
14. C. A. Gallaer, *Power* **101,** 88 (1957).

14a. A.S.T.M. Standards on Methods of Atmospheric Sampling and Analysis, Committee D-22, American Society for Testing Materials, 1959.

15. R. S. Brief and P. A. Drinker, *A.M.A. Arch. Ind. Health* **17,** 1 (1958).
16. T. Merriman and T. H. Wiggin, "American Civil Engineers Handbook," 5th ed., Wiley, New York, 1944.
17. J. H. Perry, "Chemical Engineers' Handbook," 3rd ed. McGraw-Hill, New York, 1950.
18. G. F. Haines, Jr., W. L. C. Hemeon, and H. Cember, *J. Air Pollution Control Assoc.* **7,** 262 (1958).
19. R. R. Braham, B. K. Seely, and W. D. Crozier, *Trans. Am. Geophys. Union* **33,** 825 (1952).
20. W. D. Crozier and B. K. Seely, *Trans. Am. Geophys. Union* **36,** 42 (1955).
21. W. A. Perkins, P. A. Leighton, S. W. Grinell, and F. X. Webster, *Air Pollution Symposium. 2nd Symposium, Pasadena, Calif.* (1952).
22. F. R. Holden, F. W. Dresch, and R. D. Cadle, *A.M.A. Arch. Ind. Hyg. Occupational Med.* **9,** 291 (1954).
23. E. Robinson, J. A. MacLeod, and C. E. Lapple, *J. Meteorol.* **16,** No. 63–67 No. 1 (1959).
24. Interstate Sanitation Commission Report (New York, New Jersey, Connecticut), Smoke and Air Pollution, February (1958).

CHAPTER 13

Air Analysis

MORRIS B. JACOBS

Division of Occupational Medicine, School of Public Health and Administrative Medicine, Columbia University, New York, New York

I. Introduction

In general, the methods of analysis used in air pollution work fall into the field of microchemistry and, in particular, the methods employed for the determination of gaseous contaminants fall into the field of ultramicrochemistry. In industrial hygiene chemistry, where micro-techniques for the determination of inside air pollutants have been well developed, the order of magnitude of results of analyses is of parts per million (p.p.m.) or of milligrams or hundreds of micrograms per cubic meter. In analyses of outside air, the order of magnitude is much smaller. Here we are concerned with tenths of a part per million, parts per hundred million, and even parts per billion, and with micrograms per cubic meter.

II. Sootfall and Dustfall Analysis

A. Gravimetric Methods

Gravimetric means are used to determine the amount of material that falls into a vessel exposed for a given period of time (usually a month) and which may or may not contain water, rain water, antifreeze, or a fungicide. After the material is collected, the container is carefully covered and is returned to the laboratory for analysis. The usual components determined by macro methods are insoluble solids, soluble solids, insoluble ash, and soluble ash, and from these, by computation, total solids and total ash. Generally, these measurements are reported in terms of tons per square mile per month, but other units of expression are used, such as pounds or ounces per thousand square feet. There has been some attempt to report such measurements in metric units, but virtually no communities in the English-speaking countries have adopted the metric convention.

B. Chemical Methods

In the jar method described by Jacobs (*1*), in addition to the aforementioned gravimetric determinations, various chemical determinations are made on the sootfall. The volume of the collection fluid is measured; the amount of tar, actually chloroform extract, in the insoluble matter is determined; and the following estimations are made: free carbon by the method of McCarthy and Moore (*2*), chlorides turbidimetrically, sulfates turbidimetrically, phosphates by a variation of the molybdenum blue method, and nitrates by the xylenol method (*1, 3*). Acidity is determined titrimetrically, and the pH with a pH meter or with the aid of indicator papers. Sodium, potassium, and calcium are estimated by flame photometry.

In the Los Angeles variation (*4*), the volume of the collection fluid, the acidity to both phenolphthalein and methyl orange, and chlorides are determined, in addition to the usual gravimetric determinations.

In the British method (*5*), some stress is laid on the determination of calcium in the sootfall. This is done by a variation of the oxalate method (*1*). The Toronto method (*6*) follows the British procedure. The APCA (*7*) and ASTM (*8*) variations do not include chemical methods.

C. Spectrographic Methods

Emission spectrographic methods can be used on the sootfall ash to obtain semiquantitative and quantitative results on about 20 metallic constituents, the principal ones (*9*) being manganese, lead, tin, iron, aluminum, copper, and silver. Flame spectrographic determinations can be made on the soluble portion for sodium, potassium, calcium, magnesium, manganese, iron, and strontium (*10*). Cholak, Schafer, and Hoffer (*11*) discussed such methods in connection with a report on their study of sootfall in urban atmospheres.

III. Suspended Particulate Matter

Most collection methods depend on filtration for the collection of the sample, but some use electrostatic (*11*) and thermal precipitation (*12*).

A. Gravimetric Methods

To obtain the total amount of suspended particulate matter in an atmosphere, the filter is dried and weighed; it is placed in its holder or sampler and a known volume of air is drawn through it (at a known rate for a known time); then the filter is removed from its holder or sampler, redried, and weighed. If the filter is ashless or if a membrane filter paper is used, it is now ignited in a tared crucible and the weight of the ash is obtained. If a membrane filter is used, the filter can be dissolved in acetone or in an analogous solvent and the resuspended particles can be counted under a microscope or used for additional analysis.

B. Chemical Methods

When Schleicher and Schuell Fast Flo acid-washed filter paper is used, sampling is generally carried on for an hour or two. This type of filter lends itself not only to the quantitative determination of total solids and ash but also to the determination, by wet chemical methods, of lead, copper, and zinc, by a variation of the dithizone method (*1*).

Glass fiber web and accordion-pleated filters do not lend themselves readily to inorganic analysis after ashing. The glass fiber web is virtually all ash (approximately 4 gm. per 8×10-in. sheet). Extracts of the material filtered out of the air can, however, be made from it for subsequent analysis.

1. *Inorganic Matter*

Sulfates, nitrates, and chlorides can be determined on a water-soluble extract (*13*) of the glass fiber filter. Clayton (*14*) details methods for the extraction of the accordion-pleated cellulose filter and the subsequent determination of chlorides, fluorides, and sulfur. Some of these methods are analogous to those mentioned in the section on the analysis of sootfall.

2. *Organic Matter*

Several schemes have been devised for the determination of a number of components or groups of components in benzene or acetone extracts of the fiber glass filter web. The benzene extract provides the crude organic portion of the material (*15*) filtered out of the air. This can be separated into compounds having basic organic groups, acidic groups, or neutral organic compounds. The latter can be additionally separated into an aliphatic fraction, an aromatic fraction, and an oxygenated neutral fraction. In some schemes, the protein content is determined (*16*).

C. Spectrographic Methods

Emission spectrographic analysis can be made on the entire ash of Fast Flo filter paper samples. This will yield information similar to that mentioned in the section on sootfall. Membrane filters can be analyzed in a similar fashion. Clayton (*14*) obtained data on 24 elements by the spectrographic analysis of the material trapped by accordion-pleated filters.

In the case of glass filter webs, a portion of the filter is used for the spectrographic analysis and information is obtained, usually, on barium, beryllium, bismuth, cadmium, cobalt, copper, chromium, antimony, lead, manganese, iron, molybdenum, nickel, tin, vanadium, and zinc (*17*).

Water-soluble extracts can be analyzed by flame spectrographic methods for sodium, potassium, calcium, magnesium, and a few other metals.

D. Smoke Density and Smoke Shade Methods

The methods used for the determination of smoke density fall into two principal categories, namely, those designed to determine (1) the concentration of smoke in a stack or issuing from a stack and (2) the blackness of a deposit on a filter paper through which the general air is filtered. The first group of determinations can conveniently be termed methods for the measurement of smoke density, and the second can be designated methods for the measurement of smoke shade.

1. *Smoke Density*

Smoke density may be defined as the degree of blackness of a smoke expressed in terms of an arbitrary scale. Ettinger, Braverman, and Jacobs (*18*) utilized the von Brand smoke recorder (*19*) for the evaluation of smoke abatement devices both in the laboratory and in the field.

2. *Smoke Shade*

Smoke shade may be defined as the degree of blackness of a spot or trace produced by filtering a known volume of air through a known area of filter paper. Some prefer to call such measurements "dirt shade" since there is a high degree of correlation between the blackness of a stain and the amount of soiling of curtains, clothes, etc.

Since most of the devices used for sampling air for smoke shade are automatic instruments, they are a type of monitoring instrument. The spots can be used not only for smoke shade measurements but also, in some instances, for chemical analysis by ultramicro methods (*1*).

The principal instruments used for the measurement of smoke shade are the American Iron and Steel Institute (A.I.S.I.) filter paper sampler (*20*) and the von Brand instrument (*18, 19*). Nader (*21*) described the use of a membrane filter tape which could be used for various determinations in the laboratory, particularly with radiochemical techniques. Mention should be made of the Owens automatic air filter (*5, 22, 23*), which was the progenitor of such devices. Many other samplers have been devised and a number of these are noted by Jacobs (*1*).

There are two major methods for measuring the stain produced. Transmission measurements, calculated in terms of COH's are preferred by Hemeon (*24*), whereas reflectance measurements, expressed in Ruds, are preferred by Gruber and Alpaugh (*25*).

Hemeon defined a COH unit as that quantity of light-scattering solids producing an optical density of 0.01 when measured by light transmission. Thus, a spot giving a light transmission value of 50%, based on the light transmission of the filter paper tape taken as 100%, has an optical density of 0.301; converted to COH units it has a value of 30.1. The smoke concentration is considered the number of COH units per 1000 linear ft. of air drawn through the filter paper.

Gruber and Alpaugh used a cumulative value for a 6-hr. period to calculate "Reflectance Units of Dirt Shade," or Ruds, as a measure of a soiling index, and preferred to base this on 10,000 linear ft. In practice, the percentage reflectance of clean filter paper is set at 100 on a Photovolt Reflectance Meter. Hence a smoke shade of 0 is "absolutely" clean, and a smoke shade of 100 is "absolutely" black.

IV. Gaseous Pollutants

In some respects, the aforementioned methods are the most important in air pollution control work, for they are probably performed more commonly than any other methods. Measurements of air pollution based solely on the determination of the amount and the character of the particulate matter that falls out of the air or that is filtered out of the air are inadequate.

To obtain a true and proper evaluation of the air pollution in any given community or region, it is necessary to analyze the air for certain gaseous pollutants. Among the more significant of such gaseous air contaminants are sulfur dioxide, sulfur trioxide, hydrogen sulfide, oxidants and ozone, nitrogen dioxide and other nitrogen oxides, and ammonia.

A. Sulfur Dioxide

The methods used for the determination of sulfur dioxide may be grouped as (a) gravimetric and turbidimetric or sulfate determination (*23, 26, 27*), (b) titrimetric or total acidity methods (*27*), (c) colorimetric such as the fuchsin or rosaniline method (*27–32*) and the disulfitomercurate method of West and Gaeke (*33*), (d) iodometric (*27, 34*), and (e) cumulative such as the lead peroxide method (*1, 5*).

Very likely the method of choice for regular sampling and analysis using sequence samplers or manual methods is the titrimetric variation known as the peroxide method (*1, 26, 27, 35*). In this method, the sulfur dioxide in the air is trapped with the aid of a macro impinger containing a neutral solution of hydrogen peroxide. The sulfur dioxide trapped is oxidized to sulfuric acid, and the concentration of the latter is determined by titration with standard alkali.

Hydrogen Peroxide Method Procedure. Add 3 drops of mixed indicator solution, consisting of 0.6 gm. bromocresol green and 0.4 gm. methyl red dissolved in 1 l. of methyl alcohol, to 75 ml. of an aqueous solution of hydrogen peroxide, which is prepared by dissolving 17 ml. of 3% hydrogen peroxide in sufficient distilled water to make 1 l. of solution, in a macro impinger. Neutralize the absorbing solution with 0.002 N sodium hydroxide solution. Pass air through the absorbing solution at a rate of 1 cu. ft./min. for 30 min. Titrate the contents of the impinger with 0.002 N sodium hydroxide solution. Calculate the parts of sulfur dioxide per million parts of air, using the following formula:

$$\text{p.p.m. } SO_2 = \frac{\text{ml. NaOH} \times 0.002 \times (273 + {}^\circ\text{C.}) \times 1.45}{\text{vol. of air sampled in cu. ft.}}$$

The disulfitomercurate method (*33*) may be used where it is desired to obtain information specifically for sulfur dioxide concentration as contrasted with total acidity, which is the result obtained with the hydrogen peroxide titrimetric method.

Disulfitomercurate Method Procedure. Pass 1.35 cu. ft. of air through 10.0 ml. sodium tetrachloromercurate (II) absorbing solution, which is prepared by dissolving 27.2 gm. mercuric chloride and 11.7 gm. sodium chloride in water and diluting to 1 l. Add 1.0 ml. of acidified pararosaniline solution; this is made by mixing 4 ml. of 1% pararosaniline solution with 6 ml. concentrated hydrochloric acid and diluting to 100 ml. Add 1.0 ml. of formaldehyde solution, prepared by diluting 5 ml. of 40% formalin solution to 1 l. with distilled water. Use 10 ml. of the sodium tetrachloromercurate (II) absorbing solution as a blank, and treat it the same way. Allow the mixtures to stand for 20 to 30 min. for full color development. Determine the absorbance at 560 mμ and obtain the sulfur dioxide concentration from a standard curve. If a sample of 1.35 cu. ft. of air was taken, then each microgram of sulfur dioxide is equivalent to 0.01 p.p.m. of sulfur dioxide in the air sampled.

B. Sulfur Trioxide

Two principal methods are used for the determination of sulfur trioxide in air. One is the barium sulfate method (*23, 26, 27*), in which the sulfate trapped is precipitated as barium sulfate, which is then estimated gravimetrically, turbidimetrically, or nephelometrically; and the other is the filter paper method of Mader, Hamming, and Bellin (*36*), in which the sulfuric acid aerosol is trapped on specially prepared filter papers with subsequent determination of the acidity. In the latter method sulfur dioxide gas does not interfere.

Filter Paper Disc Method Procedure. Place two 1-in. washed filter paper discs of known pH into a holder; Whatman No. 4 filter paper or membrane filters such as Millipore filters may be used. Draw air through the filters at a rate of 50 to 60 cu. ft./hr., recording the pressure drop through the filter, and the air temperature. Remove the filter discs after 1 hr. and macerate them in 20 ml. of water. Measure the pH and titrate with 0.002 N sodium hydroxide solution. Use a pH meter for determining the end point, which must be taken as that of carbon dioxide-free water corrected for filter paper batch acidity or alkalinity. Calculate the parts of sulfuric acid per million parts of air by the equation

$$\text{p.p.m.} = \frac{\text{ml. NaOH} \times 0.002 \times 0.049 \times 22.41 \times 10^6}{98 \times 28.32 \times \text{cu. ft. air (S.T.P.)*}}$$

C. Hydrogen Sulfide

A number of methods have been devised for the detection and determination of hydrogen sulfide in industrial atmospheres for industrial hygiene purposes as, for instance, lead acetate test papers (*27*) and the hydrogen sulfide detector (*37, 38*). These methods, however, are not sufficiently sensitive for air pollution control work. Among the methods

* S.T.P. = Standard temperature and pressure.

that have found some application in the determination of hydrogen sulfide as an air pollutant are the cadmium sulfide method (*39–41*), the methylene blue method (*4, 27, 41–44*), and the impregnated ceramic tile method (*45*).

In the methylene blue variation of Jacobs, Braverman, and Hochheiser (*41*), which these investigators consider best for air pollution control work, the air is bubbled through an absorption mixture of an alkaline suspension of cadmium hydroxide contained in a macro impinger, at rates as high as 1 cu. ft./min., and the trapped sulfide is reacted with a mixture of *p*-aminodimethylaniline, ferric ion, and chloride ion to yield methylene blue.

Methylene Blue Method Procedure. Make up an acid-amine stock solution by adding 30 ml. of water to 50 ml. of concentrated sulfuric acid and cooling. Add 12 gm. of *N,N*-dimethyl-*p*-phenylenediamine to the mixture and stir until solution is complete. Dilute 25 ml. of this stock solution to 1 l. with 1:1 sulfuric acid. To prepare the absorption mixture, dissolve 4.3 gm. of cadmium sulfate, $CdSO_4 \cdot 8H_2O$ in distilled water. Dissolve 0.3 gm. of sodium hydroxide in distilled water and add to the cadmium sulfate solution and dilute to 1 l. with distilled water. This mixture must be stirred before using.

Transfer 50 ml. of the stirred absorption mixture into a macro impinger and pass air through the mixture for 30 min. at 1 cu. ft./min. Add 0.6 ml. of the diluted amine reagent and 1 drop of a ferric chloride solution, made by dissolving 100 gm. of $FeCl_3 \cdot 6H_2O$ in distilled water and diluting to 100 ml. Agitate after the addition of the reagents. Transfer to a 50-ml. volumetric flask, make up to volume with distilled water, and allow to stand for 30 min. Prepare a reference blank by transferring 45 ml. of the absorption mixture to a 50-ml. volumetric flask, add the same quantities of reagents, stir after adding each reagent, allow to stand for 30 min., insert in spectrophotometer or colorimeter and set the zero. Read the optical density of the test solution. Determine the concentration of hydrogen sulfide from the standard curve and calculate the parts of hydrogen sulfide per billion parts of air by use of the equation:

$$\text{p.p.b. } H_2S = \frac{\mu g.\ H_2S \times 719}{\text{vol. of sample in l.}}$$

D. Sulfur Compounds Mixtures

The analysis of mixtures of sulfur compounds has been considered in detail (*26, 27, 35*). In air pollution work, tests are made for each individual compound.

E. Carbon Monoxide

The methods of analysis for carbon monoxide have been described in considerable detail by Jacobs (*27*), as these are applied in industrial hygiene work. In air pollution control work, two chemical methods have been commonly used.

The principal chemical method is that employing the National Bureau of Standards indicator tube, the manufacture of which has been detailed by Shepherd (*46*). Highly purified silica gel is impregnated with ammonium molybdate solution and a solution of palladium or palladium oxide, and digested in sulfuric acid to form a palladium silicomolybdate. If this gel is exposed to an atmosphere containing carbon monoxide, a molybdenum blue is formed, the depth of color varying from faint green to a blue in proportion to the amount of carbon monoxide present in the air being sampled. Such tubes are available commercially and are used with aspirator bulbs, hand pumps, or small motor-powered pumps.

Although the iodine pentoxide method (*47*) is not sufficiently sensitive for concentrations routinely found in the general atmosphere, it can be used on occasion for the estimation of higher concentrations of carbon monoxide in flue gases and exhaust gases. The variation of the American Gas Association Laboratories (*1, 48*) is to be preferred. In this method the atmosphere or exhaust gas to be analyzed is passed through a U tube containing iodine pentoxide heated to 302°F. If carbon monoxide is present, free iodine is liberated. This is absorbed in potassium iodide solution and is estimated titrimetrically.

F. Carbon Dioxide

In incinerator flue gases, other flue gases, and motor vehicle exhaust gases, volumetric methods employing Orsat gas analysis equipment or more elaborate equipment (*49*) can be used. These are generally not useful for the estimation of the amount of carbon dioxide in the general atmosphere. In such types of analysis, gravimetric methods, in which the carbon dioxide is precipitated as barium carbonate (*27*), or adsorbed on a tared tube containing an adsorbent, or titrimetric methods, in which the carbon dioxide is determined by a double or single titration, are used. In the variation of Mack (*49a*), the atmosphere containing the carbon dioxide is passed through a standard solution of barium hydroxide containing barium chloride, and the excess barium hydroxide is determined with standard oxalic acid.

G. Hydrogen Cyanide

Hydrogen cyanide and other cyanides are generally not air contaminants, but on occasion it is necessary to determine the amount present in an atmosphere. The Gettler and Goldbaum (*50*) test paper method can be used for this purpose. These investigators found that the sensitivity of the Prussian blue test could be enhanced by trapping the hydrogen cyanide or cyanides in bubblers, regenerating the hydrogen cyanide, and then leading the gas stream through a small piece of impregnated filter paper held in a holder so that the gas passed through a small area.

H. Halogens

Mention has already been made of the determination of chlorides and fluorides in samples of suspended particulate matter. Normally, chlorine gas is not found as an air contaminant. In those instances in which it must be determined, two principal methods can be used, namely, the *o*-tolidine method (*1, 27, 51–53*) and the iodide-thiosulfate method (*1, 27*).

A really satisfactory method for the determination of microgram amounts of fluoride in air was not available in 1961. This was also true for the determination of fluoride in water (*54*). There are disadvantages in using the Willard and Winter (*55*) perchloric acid distillation separation technique. The eriochrome cyanine R colorimetric method of Megregian (*56*) is probably most widely used. There has been some development of fluorimetric methods (*57*), and Nielsen and Dangerfield (*58, 59*) have proposed ion exchange separation of fluoride with subsequent determination by the colorimetric procedure of Megregian.

I. Nitrogen Compounds

1. *Nitrogen Oxides*

The oxides of nitrogen are among the more important air contaminants. The methods for the determination of these gaseous pollutants fall into two main categories, namely, those in which the nitrogen oxides are estimated as nitrite and those in which they are determined as nitrate.

The literature concerning the determination of nitrogen dioxide in air has been covered thoroughly by Jacobs (*1, 27, 60–62*) and would be out of place here. It is the opinion of the author that the best method available is that of Jacobs and Hochheiser which is a nitrite method (*62*). This can be used for grab samples or with sequence samplers. Air is aspirated through a fritted-glass bubbler containing 0.1 *N* sodium hydroxide solution containing a little butyl alcohol. The trapped nitrogen dioxide-nitrogen tetroxide is estimated colorimetrically as the azo dye by using the gas to diazotize sulfanilamide in phosphoric acid and then coupling it with *N*-(1-naphthyl)ethylenediamine dihydrochloride. Nitrogen dioxide in the order of parts per hundred million can be readily determined.

Jacobs and Hochheiser Method Procedure. Aspirate air at 1 l./min. through 30 to 35 ml. of 0.1 *N* sodium hydroxide solution, containing 2 ml. butyl alcohol/l., in a bubbler equipped with a coarse fritted-glass disperser. Transfer the sample to a 50-ml. Nessler tube, add 1 drop of 1% hydrogen peroxide solution and mix. Add 10 ml. diazotizing solution, prepared by dissolving 20 gm. of sulfanilamide in 1 l. of water containing 50 ml. of phosphoric acid and, subsequently, 1 ml. of 0.1% *N*-(1-naphthyl)ethylenediamine dihydrochloride coupling reagent. Dilute to 50 ml. and mix. Allow to stand for 30 min. and determine the absorbance in the spectrophotometer at 550 mμ using a reagent blank as the reference. Obtain the concentration of nitrogen dioxide from a standard curve and express as parts of nitrogen dioxide per hundred million parts of air. For a 52-l. air sample at 760 mm. and 25°C., 1 μg. of nitrogen dioxide is equivalent to 1 p.p.h.m.

The official British method (*63*) for the detection and determination of "nitrous fumes" (as the British and the older literature refer to the mixture of nitrogen dioxide-nitrogen tetroxide and nitric oxide, etc.) comprises direct absorption of the nitrogen oxides in a mixed reagent of a solution of sulfanilic acid, α-naphthylamine, and acetic acid. The color produced is compared against standards. The D-22 Committee of the ASTM (*64*) adopted a variation of the British method, in which *N*-(1-naphthyl)ethylenediamine dihydrochloride is substituted for α-naphthylamine as the coupling agent (*65, 66*).

Thomas and co-workers (*67*) passed the air to be analyzed through an ozone stream so that any nitric oxide present would be oxidized to nitrogen dioxide, the total nitrogen dioxide then being determined by use of the sulfanilic acid-naphthylethylenediamine acetic acid reagent. By determining the amount of nitrogen dioxide before and after oxidation of the air stream, the amount of nitric oxide could be found by difference.

The determination of total nitrogen oxides as nitrate by the phenoldisulfonic acid method was also adopted by the ASTM (*68*). This method is applicable to the higher concentrations of nitrogen oxides found in motor vehicle exhaust gases (*1*). An alternative method for the determination of total nitrogen oxides as nitrate is the xylenol method

(*1, 3, 69, 70*), which has already been mentioned in connection with its use in the estimation of nitrate in suspended particulate matter.

2. *Ammonia*

In general, variations of the Nessler method (*27, 34*) are used for ammonia determination. Under some circumstances, it may become necessary to distill the sample before making the nesslerization step, but in most air pollution control analyses this is not required. Cloudy solutions that are formed after the additions of Nessler reagent can be clarified by use of an alkaline Rochelle salt solution (*1*).

Ammonia Method Procedure. Aspirate air at 1 cu. ft./min. for 30 min. through 50 ml. of acid absorbing solution, made by adding 1 ml. of concentrated sulfuric acid to 10 l. of distilled water, in a macro impinger. Transfer the test solution to a 50-ml. glass-stoppered Nessler tube or a 50-ml. volumetric flask. Place 46 ml. of absorbing solution in a second Nessler tube or flask to serve as a blank. Add 4 ml. of Nessler reagent to each tube or flask and mix thoroughly. Transfer to 50-ml. glass colorimeter cells and read exactly 10 min. later in a Klett-Summerson photoelectric colorimeter, using the green or No. 54 filter. Use the reagent blank as the reference. Convert the Klett-Summerson reading to micrograms of ammonia by reference to a standard curve. To express parts of ammonia per million parts of air for a 30-cu. ft. sample, without temperature correction, divide the Klett-Summerson reading by 400.

J. Ozone and Oxidants

In 1961 no available method for the determination of oxidant was free from criticism. This was due principally to the fact that no means was available for preparing known micro concentrations of ozone, so that it was not possible to establish the accuracy of any method (*71*).

The principal methods used are the alkaline iodide method of Smith and Diamond (*72, 73*), the ASTM variation of this method (*71*), the neutral iodide method (*71, 74*), titrimetric methods (*75–78*), the phenolphthalin method (*79*), the rubber-cracking method (*80*), and the ferrous thiocyanate method (*81*).

The phenolphthalin method has the marked disadvantages that it is readily affected by substances other than oxidants and that the reagent is not stable on standing; the rubber-cracking method has the disadvantages that it is difficult to standardize and that other substances, such as organic free radicals, crack the test rubber (*82*); and although ferrous thiocyanate is more sensitive to hydrocarbon peroxides than to ozone, it may be affected by ferric salts in the air.

The various modifications of the alkaline iodide method are based on the absorption of oxidant, mainly ozone, from the air in an alkaline solution of potassium iodide. The absorption solution is oxidized with hydrogen peroxide to free it from interference of sulfur dioxide, and the pH is adjusted to 3.8 to overcome the interference of nitrogen dioxide. On acidification, the iodine is liberated from the hypoiodite formed on absorption of the oxidant, and the amount of triiodide subsequently produced is estimated with the aid of a spectrophotometer.

Oxidant Method Procedure. Transfer 30 ml. of absorption solution —prepared by dissolving 10 gm. potassium iodide and 4 gm. sodium hydroxide in distilled water and diluting to 1 l.—to a fritted bubbler and dilute to 75 ml. Aspirate air through the absorbing solution at 5 l./min. Transfer a 15-ml. aliquot to a small beaker, add 2 drops of 1% hydrogen peroxide solution, and boil the solution to expel excess peroxide. Cool, transfer to a 25-ml. glass-stoppered graduated cylinder and add enough 3 *N* acetic acid to obtain a pH of 3.8. Adjust the final volume to 25 ml. Two minutes after the addition of the acetic acid, read the absorbance at 352 mμ. Use water as the reference. The standard curve may be made with potassium iodate and the absorbing solution. One microgram of iodine is equivalent to 0.19 μg. of ozone.

In another variation of this method, sulfamic acid is used to react with the nitrogen dioxide to form nitrogen, so that this source of interference is avoided (*70, 83, 84*). The effect of sulfamic acid in the determination of ozone and oxidants has been studied by Altshuller, Schwab, and Bare (*84*).

V. Organic Pollutants

Many organic compounds are found as air contaminants. The more important are hydrocarbons (as a group), phenols, and aldehydes. Methods for the determination of solid organic substances that are components of the suspended particulate matter were mentioned earlier in this chapter.

A. Hydrocarbons

The amount of hydrocarbons in the air is usually determined by physical chemical methods such as mass spectrometry, vapor phase chromatography, and infrared spectroscopy, chiefly on freeze-out condensates.

Few specific chemical methods have been developed for hydrocarbons with respect to their use in air pollution work. Particular mention should, however, be made of the butanone method for benzene (*85, 86*), especially the Dolin modification (*87*), and the work of Sawicki (*88*) on the detection of polycyclic compounds. Sawicki (*88*) describes a color test for the detection of pyrene and benzo(a)pyrene using quinone as a reagent. A brilliant dark blue color is produced.

Sawicki (*88*) modified the benzal chloride test of Lippmann and Pollak (*89*) by substituting trifluoroacetic acid for the sulfuric acid in the test. In another method for polynuclear hydrocarbons, Sawicki, Miller, and Stanley (*90*) employ piperonal chloride. One factor of importance in these tests is that benzene gives a "negative" reaction.

One may also mention the sulfuric acid-formaldehyde test for benzene (actually a test for aromatic hydrocarbons) such as the bubbler method of the British (*91*) and the silica gel-tube method of Hubbard and Silverman (*92*). These tests are not as sensitive as some of those mentioned above.

Though it is known that the olefin hydrocarbons are serious air pollutants, particularly from a plant damage point of view, there are few adequate tests for these substances in the minute concentrations in which they ordinarily occur in air. Kitagawa describes a tube containing an impregnated gel that can be used for the detection of very low concentrations of ethylene (*93*).

Hughes and Gorden (*94*) adapted the Ilosvay (*95, 96*) copper acetylide reaction for the determination of acetylene in air in concentration of about 10 p.p.b. to 10 p.p.m.

B. Phenol

The most commonly used reagents for phenol are the Gibbs' reagent (*97*) and the Folin and Ciocalteu reagent (*98*). Jacobs and his coworkers (*99*) prefer the use of aminodimethylaniline. In this method, which is sensitive to parts per 10 billion, the air is aspirated at a rate of 1 cu. ft./min. through 0.5% sodium bicarbonate solution in a fritted bubbler. The amine reagent is added, and the dye base formed is oxidized by hypochlorite. The dye is shaken out with chloroform and its concentration is compared to that of a standard.

Ultramicro Procedure. Draw air at 1 cu. ft./min. through 45 ml. of 0.5% sodium bicarbonate solution in a fritted bubbler. Transfer the absorption solution to a 125-ml. separatory funnel. Add 4 drops of amine test reagent and then add 0.1% calcium hypochlorite solution drop by drop until the pink color changes to blue or colorless. Allow to stand for 5 min. and extract with 10 ml. of chloroform. Filter the chloroform phase through a pledget of cotton into a small test tube. Stopper the tube and allow to stand for 30 min. Read the optical density at 600 mμ. Obtain the concentration of phenol from a standard curve.

To prepare the amine test solution, first make a stock solution by mixing 30 ml. of water and 50 ml. of concentrated sulfuric acid, and cooling. Add 30 gm. of *N,N*-dimethyl-*p*-phenylenediamine (*p*-aminodimethylaniline), stir until dissolved, and make up to 100 ml. with additional distilled water. To prepare the test reagent, dilute 5 ml. of the stock solution to 100 ml. with distilled water.

C. Aldehydes

The method of choice for the determination of aldehydes in air is the Goldman and Yagoda (*100*) variation of the sulfoxylate method. Aldehydes react with aqueous solutions of sodium bisulfite to form nonvolatile aldehyde-bisulfite complexes. These complexes are stable in slightly acid and neutral solutions but decompose when the solution is made alkaline. The excess bisulfite is destroyed with iodine solution at a pH of 6 to 7, and the sulfite combined as the sulfoxylate is liberated subsequently by the proper adjustment of the hydrogen ion concentration.

Goldman-Yagoda Method Procedure. Aspirate air at 1 cu. ft./min. through 75 ml. of an absorbing solution, prepared by dissolving 9 gm. of sodium metabisulfite and 1 ml. of concentrated sulfuric acid in distilled water and diluting to 1 l. in a macro impinger for 30 min. Place the impinger in an ice bath and hold for 20 min. Add 1 ml. of starch indicator solution and titrate to a blue color with 8% iodine solution. Record the volume used; this is done to check for a 5% excess of bisulfite. Discharge the blue color by adding sodium thiosulfate solution drop by drop and then readjust to a faint blue with 0.001 *N* iodine solution. Replace the impinger in the ice bath and chill thoroughly. Add 50 ml. of a cold buffer solution, prepared by dissolving 80 gm. of sodium carbonate and 20 ml. of glacial acetic acid in distilled water and diluting to 1 l., and keep in the ice bath for 10 min. Titrate again with 0.001 *N* iodine solution to a faint blue end point. For customary work without correction for temperature and pressure, the parts of aldehyde, expressed as formaldehyde, per million parts of air are:

$$\text{p.p.m. aldehydes} = \text{ml. } 0.001\ N\ I_2 \times 0.013 \text{ (at } 0°\text{C. and 760 mm.)}$$

Rounds and Pearsall (*101*) used Schryver's method (*102, 103*) to distinguish between total aldehydes on the one hand and formaldehyde on the other.

D. Total Organic Compounds

Freeze-out or adsorption techniques may be used to determine gaseous, vapor, and liquid organic compounds that would not be trapped by filtration methods. The procedures used by Turk (*104*) for the analysis of odorants in air may be adapted to the estimation of total organic compounds in air. After separation of such compounds (*105*) they may be isolated and identified by the methods customarily used for the identification of organic compounds in general and of solvents in particular (*106*). See also the review by Sawicki (*107*).

References

1. M. B. Jacobs, "Chemical Analysis of Air Pollutants." Interscience, New York, 1960.
2. R. McCarthy and C. E. Moore, *Anal. Chem.* **24,** 411 (1952).
3. H. Yagoda and F. H. Goldman, *J. Ind. Hyg. Toxicol.* **25,** 440 (1943).

3a. "Laboratory Methods." *Air Pollution Control Dist., Co. of Los Angeles, Calif.,* 1958.

4. "Test Procedures and Methods in Air Pollution Control." *Air Pollution Control Dist., Co. of Los Angeles, Calif.,* 1952.
5. The Investigation of Atmospheric Pollution, *Gt. Brit. Dept. Sci. Ind. Research, Fuel Research* (1952).
6. A. F. Fisher, *J. Air Pollution Control Assoc.* **7,** No. 1, 47 (1957).
7. Recommended Standard Method for Continuing Dustfall Survey, APM 1-a, *J. Air Pollution Control Assoc.* **5,** 177 (1955).
8. "Proposed ASTM Tentative Method for Collection and Preliminary Analysis of Dust Fall." Am. Soc. Testing Materials, Philadelphia, 1958.
9. J. Cholak and R. V. Story, *J. Opt. Soc. Am.* **31,** 730 (1941).
10. J. Cholak and D. M. Hubbard, *Ind. Eng. Chem., Anal. Ed.* **16,** 728 (1944).
11. J. Cholak, L. J. Schafer, and R. F. Hoffer, *A.M.A. Arch. Ind. Hyg. Occupational Med.* **2,** 443 (1950).
12. M. T. Gordon and C. Orr, *Air Repair* **4,** 1 (1954).
13. E. C. Tabor and W. V. Warren, *A.M.A. Arch. Ind. Health* **17,** 145 (1958).
14. G. D. Clayton, "Determination of Atmospheric Contaminants." Am. Gas Assoc., New York, 1953.
15. E. C. Tabor, T. E. Hauser, J. P. Lodge, Jr., and R. H. Burtschell, *A.M.A. Arch. Ind. Health* **17,** 58 (1958).
16. L. A. Chambers, E. C. Tabor, and M. J. Foter, "Protein Content of the Atmosphere," Tech. Rept. A58-9, U. S. Public Health Service, Sanitary Engineering Center, Cincinnati, Ohio, 1958.
17. Air Pollution Measurements of the National Air Sampling Network, *U. S. Public Health Serv. Publ. No.* **637** (1958).
18. I. Ettinger, M. M. Braverman, and M. B. Jacobs, *J. Air Pollution Control Assoc.* **8,** 120 (1958).
19. E. K. von Brand, *Mech. Eng.* **72,** 479 (1950).
20. W. C. L. Hemeon, *Proc. Air Pollution Smoke Prevention Assoc.* p. 115 (1951).
21. J. S. Nader, High Flow Millipore Tape Sampler, *Proc. 51st Ann. Meeting Air Pollution Control Assoc., Philadelphia, 1958.*
22. N. Shaw and J. S. Owens, "The Smoke Problem of Great Cities." Constable, London, 1925.
23. J. E. Ives, R. H. Britten, D. W. Armstrong, W. A. Gill, and F. H. Goldman, *U. S. Public Health Service Bull.* **224** (1936).
24. W. C. L. Hemeon, G. F. Haines, Jr., H. M. Ide, *Air Repair* **3,** 22 (1953).
25. C. W. Gruber and E. L. Alpaugh, *Air Repair* **4,** No. 3, 143 (1954).
26. M. B. Jacobs, Techniques for measurement of hydrogen sulfide and sulfur oxide. *Symposium on Atmospheric Chemistry of Chlorine and Sulfur Com-*

pounds, Cincinnati, Ohio, 1957; Am. Geophys. Union, *Natl. Acad. Sci.-Natl. Research Council, Geophys. Monograph* No. 3, 24–34 (1959).
27. M. B. Jacobs, "Analytical Chemistry of Industrial Poisons, Hazards, and Solvents," 2nd ed. Interscience, New York, 1949.
28. W. M. Grant, *Anal. Chem.* **19,** 345 (1947).
29. A. Steigmann, *Anal. Chem.* **22,** 492 (1950).
30. S. Atkin, *Anal. Chem.* **22,** 947 (1950).
31. A. M. Stang, J. E. Zatek, and C. D. Robson, *Am. Ind. Hyg. Assoc. Quart.* **12,** 5 (1951).
32. P. F. Urone and W. E. Boggs, *Anal. Chem.* **23,** 1517 (1951).
33. P. W. West and G. C. Gaeke, *Anal. Chem.* **28,** 1816 (1956).
34. F. H. Goldman and M. B. Jacobs, "Chemical Methods in Industrial Hygiene." Interscience, New York, 1953.
35. M. B. Jacobs, *in* "Air Pollution," *Proc. 1st U. S. Tech. Conf.* (L. C. McCabe, ed.). McGraw-Hill, New York, 1952.
36. P. P. Mader, W. J. Hamming, and A. Bellin, *Anal. Chem.* **22,** 1181 (1950).
37. J. B. Littlefield, W. P. Yant, and L. B. Berger, *U. S. Bur. Mines, Rept. Invest. No.* **3276** (1935).
38. J. J. Forbes and G. W. Grove, *U. S. Bur. Mines, Miners' Circ.* **33** (1938).
39. E. D. Gardner, S. P. Howell, and G. W. Jones, *U. S. Bur. Mines, Bull. No.* **287** (1927).
40. S. Moskowitz, J. Siegel, and W. J. Burke, *N. Y. State Ind. Bull.* **19,** 33 (1940).
41. M. B. Jacobs, M. M. Braverman, and S. Hochheiser, *Anal. Chem.* **29,** 1349 (1957).
42. W. Mecklenburg and F. Rosenkranzer, *Z. anorg. Chem.* **86,** 143 (1914).
43. L. H. Almy, *J. Am. Chem. Soc.* **47,** 1381 (1925).
44. S. E. Sheppard and J. H. Hudson, *Ind. Eng. Chem., Anal. Ed.* **3,** 73 (1930).
45. G. Chanin, J. R. Elwood, and E. H. Chow, *Sewage and Ind. Wastes* **26,** 1217 (1954).
46. M. Shepherd, *Anal. Chem.* **19,** 77 (1947).
47. M. C. Teague, *Ind. Eng. Chem.* **12,** 964 (1920); *U. S. Bur. Mines, Monograph* **1,** 51 (1927).
48. "Iodine Pentoxide Method." Am. Gas. Assoc. Labs., Cleveland, Ohio.
49. P. W. Mueller, "Modern Gas Analysis." Interscience, New York, 1955.
49a. W. B. Mack, *Plant Physiol.* **5,** 1 (1930).
50. A. O. Gettler and L. Goldbaum, *Anal. Chem.* **19,** 270 (1947).
51. "Standard Methods for the Examination of Water, Sewage, and Industrial Wastes," 10th ed. Am. Public Health Assoc., New York, 1955.
52. *Gt. Brit. Dept. Sci. Ind. Research,* Leaflet **10** (1939).
53. L. E. Porter, *Ind. Eng. Chem.* **18,** 730 (1926).
54. "Analytical Reference Service—Report on Sample Type III." U. S. Public Health Service, Sanitary Engineering Center, Cincinnati, Ohio, 1958.
55. H. H. Willard and O. B. Winter, *Ind. Eng. Chem., Anal. Ed.* **5,** 7 (1933).
56. S. Megregian, *Anal. Chem.* **26,** 1161 (1954).
57. W. A. Powell and J. H. Saylor, *Anal. Chem.* **25,** 960 (1953).
58. J. P. Nielsen and A. D. Dangerfield, *A.M.A. Arch. Ind. Health* **11,** 61 (1955).
59. J. P. Nielsen, *Anal. Chem.* **30,** 1009 (1958).
60. M. B. Jacobs, "War Gases." Interscience, New York, 1942.
61. M. B. Jacobs, "The Chemical Analysis of Foods and Food Products," 3rd ed. Van Nostrand, Princeton, New Jersey, 1958.
62. M. B. Jacobs and S. Hochheiser, *Anal. Chem.* **30,** 426 (1958).

63. *Gt. Brit., Dept. Sci. Ind. Research,* Leaflet **5** (1939).
64. *ASTM Standards* Designation: D1607–58T.
65. A. C. Bratton and E. K. Marshall, *J. Biol. Chem.* **128,** 537 (1939).
66. B. E. Saltzman, *Anal. Chem.* **26,** 1949 (1954).
67. M. D. Thomas, J. A. MacLeod, R. C. Robbins, R. C. Goettelman, and R. W. Eldridge and L. H. Rogers, *Anal. Chem.* **28,** 1810 (1956).
68. *ASTM Standards* Designation: D1608–58T.
69. H. A. Barnes, *Analyst* **75,** 388 (1950).
70. "Analysis of Atmospheric Pollutants—Course Manual—Air Pollution Training," U. S. Public Health Service, Cincinnati, Ohio, 1958.
71. "Tentative Method of Test for Oxidant (Ozone) Content of the Atmosphere." Am. Soc. Testing Materials, Philadelphia, 1958.
72. R. G. Smith and P. Diamond, *Am. Ind. Hyg. Assoc. Quart.* **13,** 235 (1952).
73. R. G. Smith, "Determination of Ozone in Air." Bur. Ind. Hyg., Detroit Dept. Health, Detroit, 1953.
74. J. Cholak, L. J. Schafer, W. J. Younker, and D. Yeager, *A.M.A. Arch. Ind. Health* **11,** 280 (1955); **15,** 198 (1957).
75. C. E. Thorp, *Ind. Eng. Chem., Anal. Ed.* **12,** 209 (1940).
76. J. Crabtree and A. R. Kemp, *Ind. Eng. Chem., Anal. Ed.* **18,** 769 (1946).
77. A. Ehmert, *J. Atmospheric and Terrest. Phys.* **2,** 189 (1952).
78. C. W. Wadelin, *Anal. Chem.* **29,** 441 (1957).
79. L. C. McCabe, *Ind. Eng. Chem.* **45,** No. 9, 111A (1953).
80. C. E. Bradley and A. J. Haagen-Smit, *Rubber Chem. and Technol.* **24,** No. 4, 750 (1951).
81. G. W. Todd, *Anal. Chem.* **27,** 1490 (1955).
82. J. Crabtree and B. X. Biggs, *J. Polymer Sci.* **11,** 280 (1953).
83. R. H. McQuain, J. M. Leavitt, R. C. Wanta, and W. W. Frisbie, Urban air sampling by helicopter, *Proc. 51st Ann. Meeting Air Pollution Control Assoc., Philadelphia, 1958.*
84. A. P. Altshuller, C. M. Schwab, and M. Bare, "The Reactivity of Oxidizing Agents with Potassium Iodide Reagent." *Anal. Chem.* **31,** 1987 (1959).
85. H. H. Schrenk, S. J. Pearce, and W. P. Yant, *U. S. Bur. Mines, Rept. Invest. No.* **3287** (1935); *No.* **3302** (1936).
86. R. Fabre, R. Truhaut, and M. Peron, *Ann. pharm. franc.* **8,** 613 (1950).
87. B. H. Dolin, *Ind. Eng. Chem., Anal. Ed.* **15,** 242 (1943); *N. Y. State Ind. Bull.* **25,** No. 7 (1946).
88. E. Sawicki, *Chemist Analyst* **46,** 67 (1957).
89. E. Lippmann and I. Pollak, *Monatsh. Chem.* **23,** 670 (1902).
90. E. Sawicki, R. Miller, T. Stanley, and T. R. Hauser, "Detection of Polynuclear Hydrocarbons and Phenols with Benzal and Piperonal Chlorides." *Anal. Chem.* **30,** 1130 (1958).
91. *Gt. Brit., Dept. Sci. Ind. Research,* Leaflet **4** (1939).
92. B. R. Hubbard and L. Silverman, *A.M.A. Arch. Ind. Hyg. Occupational Med.* **2,** 49 (1950).
93. T. Kitagawa, Komyo Chemical Industrial Co., Meguro, Tokyo, Japan.
94. E. E. Hughes and R. Gorden, Jr., *Anal. Chem.* **31,** 94 (1959).
95. L. I. Ilosvay, *Ber. deut. chem. Ges.* **32,** 2698 (1899).
96. T. A. Geisman, S. Kaufman, and D. Y. Dollman, *Anal. Chem.* **19,** 919 (1947).
97. H. D. Gibbs, *J. Biol. Chem.* **72,** 649 (1927).

98. O. Folin and V. Ciocalteu, *J. Biol. Chem.* **73,** 627 (1927).
99. M. M. Braverman, S. Hochheiser, and M. B. Jacobs, *Am. Ind. Hyg. Assoc. Quart.* **18,** *No. 2,* 132 (1957).
100. F. H. Goldman and H. Yagoda, *Ind. Eng. Chem., Anal. Ed.* **15,** 377 (1943).
101. F. G. Rounds and H. W. Pearsall, Diesel Exhaust Odor, *SAE Natl. Diesel Engine Meeting, Chicago, 1956.*
102. R. W. Kersey, J. R. Maddocks, and T. E. Johnson, *Analyst* **65,** 203 (1940).
103. E. C. Barnes and H. W. Speicher, *J. Ind. Hyg. Toxicol.* **24,** 10 (1942).
104. A. Turk, *Ann. N. Y. Acad. Sci.* **58,** 193 (1954).
105. *ASTM Standards* Designation: D 1354-55 T.
106. M. B. Jacobs and L. Scheflan, "Chemical Analysis of Industrial Solvents." Interscience, New York, 1953.
107. E. Sawicki, "Organic Spectrophotometric Analysis—A Review," U. S. Public Health Service, Sanitary Engineering Center, Cincinnati, Ohio, 1961.

CHAPTER 14

Production of Controlled Test Atmospheres

JAMES P. LODGE, JR.*

Chemical Research and Development Section, Division of Air Pollution, United States Public Health Service, Robert A. Taft Sanitary Engineering Center, Cincinnati, Ohio

I. Introduction

Since air pollution research impinges on nearly all fields of science, its research techniques are, in the main, those of the basic sciences. However, in addition to these, certain techniques have been developed which are peculiar to the field. They generally derive from the extremely low concentrations of substances in air with which air pollution research must deal. One of these, and one of the least fully understood, is the production of controlled atmospheres of known composition.

Controlled atmospheres may be used as primary standards for the calibration of analytical techniques, or as simulated environments for the study of biological responses or of the resistance of materials. Each use has its own inherent problems, and no one system exists which is optimum for all applications.

A. BASIC CONSIDERATIONS

It is always preferable that the concentration of substances in the test atmosphere be established by calculation from established physical constants and the parameters of the system. However, such calibration

* Present address: National Center for Atmospheric Research, Boulder, Colorado.

from first principles is frequently impossible, especially where the introduction of aerosols is involved, and it becomes necessary instead to analyze the controlled atmosphere by chemical or physical means. In order to avoid the pitfall of circular reasoning, these means must be independent of the purpose for which the controlled atmosphere is being prepared. It should be recognized that any inherent errors of the analytical method will be perpetuated in all subsequent uses of the system.

When a controlled atmosphere is to be used to test a field analytical method, it should precisely duplicate the pertinent features of the air qualities to be measured in the field. In practice this is impossible, since it presupposes a degree of knowledge of field conditions which would make further field measurements superfluous. At the moment, there are very few cases in which we can specify with certainty the features of the atmosphere which are pertinent. Instead, we must first work with simplified systems in order to isolate the effects of pure pollutants or simple mixtures, then work our way by successive approximations toward true controlled models of the complex mixture which is our urban atmosphere. The degree to which the same considerations apply to atmospheres in animal studies and the like will depend, of course, on the design of the experiment. Recent work on the effect of aerosols on the toxicity of certain gases toward animals (*1*) suggests that our view of the pertinent features of atmospheres for toxicity studies has also been far too simplified.

B. Components of the System

The first requirement of a controlled atmosphere is a source of "pure air." This ideally consists of oxygen, nitrogen, the noble gases, carbon dioxide, and a controlled amount of water vapor. Such air may be produced only at considerable expense and trouble. It is both customary and generally valid simply to remove from the air those substances most likely to confound the effects under study. Where a really high degree of air purity is required, it can be substantially achieved by a system consisting of several filters of increasing efficiency, a charcoal bed for removal of organic matter and polar gases, a furnace for combustion of the last traces of organics, an air conditioner for controlling temperature and humidity and, perhaps, still another filter to remove any particulate matter introduced by the conditioner or the furnace. Depending on the precise requirements of the study under way, more or fewer of the stages of purification may be omitted, or specific chemical methods may be substituted. For example, it is claimed that the specific removal of unsaturated hydrocarbons may be accomplished by means of a bromine-impregnated charcoal (*2*). Small amounts of acidic gases may be removed, together with carbon dioxide, by soda lime or an equivalent solid alkali. It appears that hydrogen fluoride can be removed on a charcoal impregnated with sodium silicate (*3*). The other components of the controlled atmosphere system are: a source of the test substance or substances; a container, duct, or other boundary for the system; and devices to limit, define, or measure the flux or amounts of air and test substances. The type and configuration of the components determines the class of the system.

II. System Types

Whether simple or complex, controlled atmospheres may be classified by their method of production and their use as static or dynamic. It is also convenient to distinguish two intermediate types, which will be referred to here as quasi-static and quasi-dynamic. All these types are widely used. Each has its advantages and disadvantages; each has certain purposes for which it is superior and certain ways in which it is totally inadequate.

A. Static Systems

In a true static system, appropriate quantities of the test substances are added to a fixed and isolated volume of air. All tests are conducted within this fixed volume. Depending upon the size and geometry of the volume, and the nature of the test substances, some sort of stirring may be provided.

1. *Rigid Systems*

Small static chambers are not infrequently glass flasks, bottles, or carboys. A round flask is a good choice, since it may be evacuated to permit filling with the test atmosphere. In such an apparatus the flask is pumped to a residual pressure of, at most, a few millimeters of mercury, the test substance is added, and the flask is then filled to atmospheric pressure with purified air. Gases, vapors, and liquids are generally added by means of a hypodermic syringe; for higher concentrations, the amounts added may be determined by the measurement of pressure changes. Alternatively, a flask, bottle, or carboy may merely be flushed with large volumes of purified air, then the gases or vapors added at atmospheric pressure. In this case, it is more important to provide for adequate mixing. Where this must be rapid, a fan or magnetic stirrer may be used; for many purposes it is sufficient to shake or roll the container. One example of the entirely proper use of a fully static system is in gas phase infrared spectrophotometry. For example, Altshuller and Wartburg (*4*) studied the effect of atmospheric pressure on the calibration of infrared hydrocarbon analyzers, using the gas cell as their entire system. Both syringe and manometric techniques were used for sample introduction. Since no chemical reaction was involved, wall adsorption (small, in this case) was the only cause of deviation from computed concentrations.

2. *Flexible Systems*

Larger chambers may be made from plastic bags. These have the advantage that they may be squeezed flat to expel all air, then filled with purified air and the desired pollutants. Polyethylene is simple to handle, and has been used on occasion (*5*), but many pollutants either

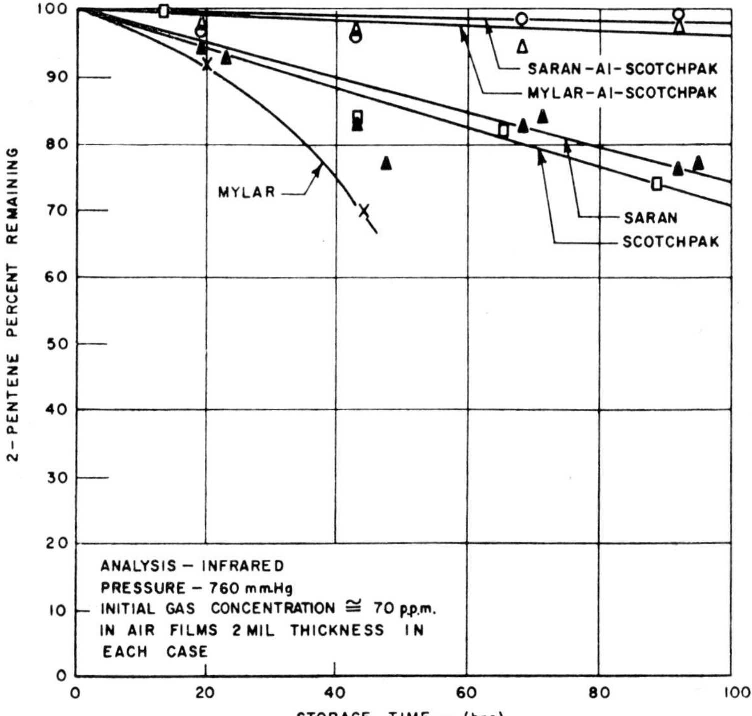

FIG. 1. Evaluation of polymeric films for 2-pentene storage. From R. A. Baker and R. C. Doerr, *Intern. J. Air Pollution* **2,** 149 (1959).

diffuse through it or are sorbed on it. Mylar is better, but it cannot be heat sealed in the laboratory. Aluminized Mylar is still better; apparently, the aluminizing seals the pores in the plastic film. Mylar has the advantage that it is almost totally inelastic. A Mylar bag, filled to a constant pressure of perhaps one-half inch of water (gauge), has the properties of a sort of gaseous volumetric flask. Tests made in the author's laboratory have shown that it is possible to duplicate volumes in this way with an accuracy of better than 2%. However, for simply storing a gas mixture unchanged, certain laminates have been found to be far better than any single plastic film. Of the substances tested so far, aluminized Scotchpak 20A20 (Minnesota Mining and Manufacturing Company) has been found to be best (*6*). Figure 1 shows the results of prolonged storage of pollutants in a variety of plastic bags.

3. *Limitations*

The truly static system suffers from one enormous drawback. All experiments must, by definition, be performed within the system. Most experiments involve the reaction of the test substances with some reagent, plant, animal, or other substance. The chamber walls may also remove the test substances, especially in small chambers. Hence the concentration of pollutant within the chamber is likely to decrease with time; the concentration will only briefly approximate that calculated from the amount of pollutant introduced. This makes it necessary to measure continually the concentrations in the chamber. If the measuring system is chemical, it will further contribute to the decrease in concentration. A partial solution is afforded by using very large chambers; however, it is in most cases preferable to use other systems, except in cases where the rate of concentration decrease is itself the problem under study.

B. Quasi-static Systems

If the limitation that all tests must be performed within the test volume is removed, the system takes on a slightly dynamic character. Such a system will be referred to here as *quasi-static*. In such a system, dilution and mixing are acomplished as in a static system, within a fixed volume. The mixture is now withdrawn from the fixed volume, to be brought into dynamic contact with the experimental system.

1. *Rigid Systems*

Rigid containers such as carboys and flasks have been used for this purpose, and have the advantage that their volume may be measured accurately. However, it is necessary to introduce pure air in order to displace the sample from such a fixed volume. This means that the concentration of pollutant will decrease exponentially with the volume withdrawn. Probably the best use of the carboy method is in the calibration of analytical techniques, in which the important factor is the passage of an accurately known total mass of pollutant through the analytical system at a reasonably realistic concentration. For other purposes, the use of large chambers permits the effect of the air dilution to be minimized. McCaldin (*7*) has ably reviewed the literature of such methods, and has explored the use of such a chamber, including the effects of the walls, leakage, and other typical problems inherent in the systems.

Another very practical approach to the problem of maintaining known concentrations in a quasi-static system has been discussed at length by Setterlind (*8*). In this method, a number of flasks or carboys of identical size, filled with the test substance at known concentration, are connected in series by means of suitable glass or plastic tubing. The sample is withdrawn from the end flask of the line. A compensating volume of fresh air enters the first flask and mixes with the test mixture there; it is this mixture which moves to the second flask. In this way, the effect of the added pure air decreases with the number of flasks. Setterlind showed that, assuming perfect mixing, for a system of five flasks, almost two and one-half times the volume of any individual flask could be withdrawn from the fifth flask before its residual concentration of added material decreased to 90% of its initial value. By way of contrast, only 10% of the first flask could be withdrawn before this decrease had taken place. Since these relationships are independent of flask size, it may be seen that almost five times as much usable sample can be withdrawn from the five-flask system as from an equal volume of air in a single container. For the general case of a series of n flasks connected in this fashion, Setterlind showed that the residual concentration in the nth flask is given by the equation

$$C_n = C_0 \exp(-V/V_0)\left[1 + \frac{1}{1!}\left(\frac{V}{V_0}\right) + \frac{1}{2!}\left(\frac{V}{V_0}\right)^2 + \ldots + \frac{1}{(n-1)!}\left(\frac{V}{V_0}\right)^{n-1}\right]$$

where C_0 = initial concentration
C_n = residual concentration in the nth flask
V_0 = the volume of the flask
V = volume withdrawn

It will be recognized that the expression in brackets is a well-known series expansion for $\exp(V/V_0)$. Thus, for an infinite number of flasks, it yields $C_n = C_0$ as in fact it should.

Setterlind also discusses at length methods of initial production of known concentrations in the flasks.

2. *Flexible Systems*

Plastic bags are ideally suited to the construction of quasi-static systems. In addition to the advantages cited above, they collapse as the sample is withdrawn, so that it is unnecessary to add air to compensate for the volume withdrawn. The work of Baker, cited above, was actually done entirely on a quasi-static system. The author's group makes extensive use of such bags, not only for the preparation of test atmospheres, but also for the transportation of gaseous samples from the test site to the laboratory.

3. *Limitations*

All of the above systems, however, suffer from one inherent shortcoming. Since the test mixture is made up in a static system, there is some limit, fixed by the physical parameters of the system, to the amount of air which can be withdrawn from the system with accurate knowledge of its composition. Where larger volumes are needed, a more fully dynamic system is imperative.

C. Quasi-dynamic Systems

It is convenient to distinguish two types of dynamic system. For many purposes it is desirable to produce the test mixture dynamically, and then to flow it into a test volume of sufficient size that its residence time in the test volume is very long compared with its transit time through the balance of the system. The familiar animal test chambers, and many other pieces of apparatus, fall into this class. Such systems will be referred to as quasi-dynamic. On the other hand, systems for instrument calibration and the like not infrequently have nearly constant linear gas velocity throughout. These we shall call dynamic systems.

The quasi-dynamic system shares certain shortcomings with static systems. Because of the long residence time of the test mixture in the test volume, wall effects and other processes which tend to remove pollutant can cause important deviations from ideality in the concentration. The quasi-dynamic system is, however, frequently the method of choice for studies of slow chemical processes in the atmosphere, and it is almost invariably the choice for the classic type of inhalation toxicity tests in animals.

Silver (*9*) gave the earliest consideration to the mathematical principles of gassing chambers. Chambers for animal testing have more recently been extensively reviewed by Fraser *et al.* (*10*). Their monograph discusses the engineering of such chambers, techniques of introduction of vapors, gases and dusts, and techniques for the determination of chamber concentration. The animals in the chamber provide a very fine sink for the materials under test, so that it is invariably necessary to monitor the air within the chamber. The best that can be said for calculated concentrations is that they probably represent the upper limit of concentration. It should also be noted that both Silver and Fraser operate their chambers at concentrations much higher than those generally encountered in air pollution research.

An excellent discussion of the theoretical aspects of quasi-dynamic chambers for the study of atmospheric reactions is given by Rose and Brandt (*11*). A very large chamber for the study of photochemical reactions of automotive exhaust was designed and constructed. Mathematical models were devised for the system, acting as a classic, perfectly-stirred reactor, and for several possible deviations from ideality. Subsequent testing of the chamber with nonreactive materials such as carbon dioxide showed that the stirred reactor model agreed with the experimental data to within less than 2%.

D. Dynamic Systems

Aside from considerations of the test volume, however, quasi-dynamic and fully dynamic systems are identical. The problem is still that of producing an accurately known, extremely constant flow of the test substance into an equally constant flow of purified air. It is not even completely unknown for a dynamic system to be used to fill a carboy or plastic bag for subsequent use in a static or quasi-static system. Brief and Church (*12*) have described a chamber said to be readily convertible from static to dynamic operation, and vice versa.

III. Introduction of Gases and Vapors

The entire question of introduction of known quantities of pollutant into the system, whatever its type, has been discussed only briefly to date. The introduction technique must be compatible with the balance of the system; batch methods may be used with static types, while dynamic systems require some sort of continuous feed.

A. Batch Methods

Syringe and manometric methods have been referred to previously, and are suitable for the introduction of gases and vapors. The work of Setterlind (*8*), previously cited, includes detailed discussion of ampoule methods. Here, a tared quantity of liquid is introduced into the test volume, which must be static or quasi-static, by means of a very thin-walled, sealed glass container which is subsequently broken to release the vapor. There is also a very practical discussion of the syringe method. It should be noted in this connection that there are now available syringes of far smaller volume than were available to Setterlind.

B. Equilibrium Methods

Still another technique used occasionally involves equilibration of the diluting air with the vapor of the test substance at a known temperature. If total equilibration can be achieved, as it can in a static system, quite accurate control of concentrations may be achieved by adequate temperature control. Birstein (*13*) used cryoscopic methods to produce concentrations of a few parts per million of water vapor in studies of ice nucleation. Work of this sort has been greatly facilitated by an extensive review of the available literature on very low vapor pressures (*14*). Equilibration with a dilute aqueous solution has been used to produce extremely low concentrations of hydrogen fluoride for plant fumigations and the like (*15*). Dubrovskaya has produced controlled sulfur dioxide concentrations in a dynamic system by a similar technique (*16*).

C. Continuous Methods

1. *Diffusion*

A system which may be thought of as an extension of the vapor pressure method was first proposed by McKelvey and Hoelscher (*17*). Instead of attempting to reach equilibrium, they permitted the vapor from an excess of liquid to diffuse through a capillary tube. Purified air passing the other end of the tube picked up the vapor as it emerged, and mixed with it. In theory, the resulting concentration should have been calculable from the temperature, vapor pressure of the liquid, the coefficient of diffusion of the vapor, and the physical dimensions of the diffusion tube. In practice, it was found that their particular apparatus did not conform with the theory. Altshuller and Cohen (*18*) have subsequently studied a similar device, the performance of which accords very well with theory. It can form the basis of an excellent small-capacity dynamic or quasi-dynamic system. However, it is limited by the characteristics of air flow over the top of the diffusion tube to a capacity of about 1 liter per minute of air.

2. *Direct Displacement*

It is more usual to displace the test substance into a dynamic air stream by some positive means, such as metering pumps or pistons. In general, the exact choice of displacement mechanism is likely to depend upon the size of the system, i.e., upon the air flow to be handled. There is a distinct separation of types of systems based on size.

a. Small systems. In what may be called the micro range—that is, in systems having at most a capacity of a few liters per minute of test mixture—there is a strong tendency toward the use of motor-driven syringes. For example, Smith and Grant (*19*) used a motorized microburette of the Gilmont type with suitable modifications to make it gas tight and to permit easy flushing and filling with gas. This system produced approximately one liter per minute of gas mixture having a concentration of the order of 100 p.p.m. Attempts in the author's laboratory to adapt this system to still lower concentrations have not been completely successful.

A rather obvious technique on the micro scale is the use of dynamic serial dilution. In such a system, a small flow of the test gas is metered into a larger flow of air. After mixing, an aliquot of this mixture is metered into a still larger flow of air. In theory, the process may be repeated a number of times to produce very low concentrations, the excess mixture at each stage of dilution being discarded. Several such systems have been constructed, but no information has ever been published on any of them, so far as can be discovered. General experience seems to repeat the findings of the author's laboratory, namely, that such systems are prey to a variety of resonances, instabilities, and ambiguous corrections, which make them extremely hard to control. However, the principle has considerable merit, and it is to be hoped that a successful system can be developed and made commercially available. It has potentially the greatest dynamic range of any system for producing low concentrations.

b. Large Systems. On the other hand, the situation is almost exactly reversed in the case of the macro system, handling a substantial number of cubic feet per minute. In this case, motor-driven syringes of even the largest sort have insufficient capacity for supplying the test gas for more than a short time, although Holl and Muehleisen (*20*) have approached this in the adaptation of a large spirometer to meter hydrogen chloride into a rather large air stream. It is more customary, however, to meter the test gas through a simple device such as an orifice or a rotameter under the pressure of a pump, or from a tank of compressed gas. In many such cases, extreme constancy of composition is not of great importance, so long as a known mean level is maintained. Plants and many other types of receptors have themselves a tendency to average out the effects of fluctuations over a considerable range of variation and to respond only to the mean level.

At substantial flow rates, serial dilution also becomes more feasible. Rose and Brandt (*11*) have described a highly successful two-stage dilution system for use with their quasi-dynamic, auto exhaust photolysis chamber. This permitted variation of the dilution factor from 600:1 to 3600:1, to dilute raw automotive exhaust rapidly to atmospheric concentrations. The system was so designed that it was not necessary at any time to pump the exhaust gas. The entire system was driven by a combination of venturi action and ram air pressure from the primary air mover, a high capacity fan.

IV. Introduction of Aerosols

Complex as may be the problem of maintaining a constant known concentration of a gas or a vapor in air, the problem of maintaining constancy in an aerosol system is far more complex. In most test atmospheres containing aerosols, there are three independent variables which must be maintained constant: the mass concentration, the mean effective particle size, and the dispersion of particle size about this mean. The exact design of the experiment will define the constancy of these parameters which is needed; the degree of control possible may well be dictated by the particular dust or aerosol which one desires to introduce into the test gas. Thus, for example, the experiment may call for the suspension of a particular commercial silica dust in the air. Since this dust already has a defined mean particle size and particle size distribution, only number (or mass) concentration need be kept constant.

It appears virtually impossible to design a system for the introduction of aerosols into a test atmosphere, which permits calculation of the resulting concentration from first principles. In general, the best that may be hoped for is constancy of feed rate. The resulting concentration must be determined by actual measurement. Even if it is possible to determine the mass rate of feed of the dust or aerosol, losses by settling, aggregation, and wall collision are of sufficient magnitude to make it necessary to determine concentrations at the point where the experimentation is being done. The monograph by Fraser *et al.* (*10*), previously cited, lists or references a large number of devices for the production of substantial quantities of dust or aerosol suspensions. The only obvious omission is the Dautrebande generator (*21*), which is particularly adapted to the production of quite uniform submicron aerosols. For problems in which the calibration of equipment for the determination of particle size is involved, use can be made of the extremely uniform spheres of polystyrene latex in sizes graded from a few hundredths of a micron up to slightly over one micron, available from Dow Chemical Company, Midland, Michigan. These can be dispersed from a dilute aqueous suspension by means of a nebulizer. Farlow (*22*) has discussed an ingenious use of these uniform spheres for the determination of droplet sizes from atomizers. Uniform glass beads are available in somewhat larger sizes (*23*); biological particles such as spores, pollen grains, and intact bacteria have also been used.

Ingenious use has been made of a rotating drum chamber, which keeps aerosols suspended for far greater lengths of time than a stationary one (*24*). It was reported that 6 μ particles had a half-life of the order of 9 hr. in this system.

V. Complex Systems

Attempts to produce simultaneously controlled concentrations of both gases and particulate matter have not been numerous. They consist generally of two separate feed systems, one for gases and the other for particles, entering into the same manifold or chamber. This technique was used, for example, in the work of LaBelle *et al.* (*25*) and of Amdur (*1*) on the potentiation of gas toxicity by particulate matter. The most elaborate system evolved to date has been that of a static chamber designed by the Stanford Research Institute (*26*) in an attempt to generate a "mean urban atmosphere." A more or less representative concentration had been selected, through an extensive literature search (*27*), for all substances identified in urban atmospheres. Gas and vapor concentrations were to be provided by a combination of ampoule methods, positive displacement, and (in the case of ozone) *in situ* generation. Particulates were introduced by the ingenious method of encapsulating them and firing them into the chamber from an air rifle. The shock of breaking the capsule dispersed the material in the air of the chamber. The system does not seem to have been entirely successful. Aside from the obvious problems, previously discussed in connection with the static chamber, the "mean urban air" contained species that are mutually incompatible, even in the range of a few parts per million. However, the apparatus demonstrated graphically both the capabilities and the limitations of the static system in such a complex problem.

References

1. M. O. Amdur, *Intern. J. Air Pollution* **1,** 170 (1959).
2. H. Sleik and A. Turk, "Air Conservation Engineering," 2nd ed., p. 9. Connor Engineering Corp., Danbury, Connecticut, 1953.
3. A. Turk, Paper presented at 3rd Air Pollution Research Seminar, New Orleans, Louisiana, March 22–24, 1960.
4. A. P. Altshuller and A. F. Wartburg, *Appl. Spectroscopy* **15,** 67 (1961).
5. K. W. Wilson and H. Buchberg, *Ind. Eng. Chem.* **50,** 1705 (1958).
6. R. A. Baker and R. C. Doerr, *Intern. J. Air Pollution* **2,** 142 (1959).
7. R. O. McCaldin, Controlled Atmospheres for Air Pollution Studies, Doctoral Thesis, Univ. of Florida, Miami, Florida, 1958; R. O. McCaldin and E. R. Hendrickson, *Am. Ind. Hyg. Assoc. J.* **20,** 509 (1959).
8. A. N. Setterlind, *Am. Ind. Hyg. Assoc. Quart.* **14,** 113 (1953).
9. S. D. Silver, *J. Lab. Clin. Med.* **31,** 1153 (1946).
10. D. A. Fraser, R. E. Bales, M. Lippmann, and H. E. Stokinger, *U. S. Public Health Monograph No.* **57** (1959).

11. A. H. Rose, Jr., and C. S. Brandt, *J. Air Pollution Control Assoc.* **10,** 331 (1960).
12. R. S. Brief and F. W. Church, *Am. Ind. Hyg. Assoc. J.* **21,** 239 (1960).
13. S. J. Birstein, *in* "Physics of Precipitation" (H. Weickman, ed.), Geophysical Monograph No. 5, p. 247. American Geophysical Union, Washington, D. C., 1960.
14. E. E. Hughes and S. G. Lias, *Natl. Bur. Standards (U. S.) Rept. No.* **6435** (1959).
15. A. C. Hill, L. G. Transtrum, M. R. Pack, and W. S. Winters, *Agron. J.* **50,** 562 (1958).
16. V. A. Ryazanov, K. A. Bushtueva, and Yu. V. Novikov, *in* "Limits of Allowable Concentrations of Atmospheric Pollutants" (V. A. Ryazanov, ed.), Book 3, p. 97 (B. S. Levine, translator). Office of Technical Services Document 59-21175, U. S. Dept. of Commerce, Washington, D. C. (1959).
17. J. M. McKelvey and H. E. Hoelscher, *Anal. Chem.* **29,** 123 (1957).
18. A. P. Altshuller and I. R. Cohen, *Anal. Chem.* **32,** 802 (1960).
19. S. B. Smith and R. J. Grant, Technical Report A59–3, Robert A. Taft Sanitary Engineering Center, Cincinnati, Ohio, 1959.
20. W. Holl and R. Muhleisen, *Geofis. pura e. appl.* **31,** No. 2, 21 (1955).
21. L. Dautreband, *Aerosol-Forschung* **2,** 585 (1953).
22. N. H. Farlow and F. A. French, *J. Colloid Sci.* **11,** 177 (1956).
23. R. D. Cadle and W. Thuman, Symposium on Particle Size Measurement, *Am. Soc. Testing Materials Spec. Tech. Publ. No.* **234,** 296 (1959).
24. L. J. Goldberg, H. M. S. Watkins, E. E. Boerke, and M. A. Chatigny, *Am. J. Hyg.* **68,** 85 (1958).
25. C. W. LaBelle, J. E. Long, and E. E. Christofano, *A.M.A. Arch. Ind. Health* **11,** 297 (1955).
26. W. C. Thuman, Development of Technology for Production, Sampling and Assay of Simulated Atmospheres in Closed Chambers, Final Report, Stanford Research Institute Project No. SU-2285, Stanford Research Institute, Menlo Park, California, 1959.
27. H. C. Wohlers and G. B. Bell, Literature Review of Metropolitan Air Pollutant Concentrations—Preparation, Sampling, and Assay of Synthetic Atmospheres, Final Report, Contract No. DA18-064-404-CML-123. Stanford Research Institute, Menlo Park, California, 1956.

CHAPTER 15

Odor and Its Measurement

ELMER R. KAISER

College of Engineering, New York University, New York, New York

Part of the air pollution problem of all sizable communities is the presence of gases and vapors in the atmosphere that offend the sense of smell. Despite the fact that such contaminants or malodors are usually present in small quantities, ranging from 1 part to 1000 parts per billion, they are annoying and have adverse effects on personal comfort and property values. Some odorants are more than a nuisance since they cause nausea, loss of appetite, and sleeplessness. The study of odorants, odor perception, and the effect of mixtures of odors in the atmosphere on their combined stimulus to the olfactory organ is today the subject of increasing investigation.

Those who wish to gain a more thorough grounding in the state of odor art than is possible from one chapter will do well to read the books, "The Chemical Senses" by Moncrieff (*1*) and "Odors—Physiology and Control" by McCord and Witheridge (*2*).

I. Stimulation of the Olfactory Receptor

The human olfactory organ occupies an area of about 6 sq. cm. in the membrane of the upper nasal cavity and has a yellow-brown appearance. Nerve cell fibers connecting to the brain project from the surface and are overspread with an aqueous mucus. Volatile particles inhaled with air are presumably dissolved in the mucus and initiate chemical reactions which cause sensory impulses. While only a minor part of the air breathed normally reaches the olfactory receptors, the act of sniffing increases air impingement on the organ (*3*). The amazing sensitivity of olfactory reception is apparent from the fact that a sniff of 50 cc. of air containing only 2×10^{-9} mg. of mercaptan serves as an adequate odor stimulus (*4*). The keenness of odor perception varies widely among persons, a few having no sense of smell (anosmic), while others are deficient because of advanced age or other causes. Physical condition, especially respiratory, is an important factor, as are skill and experience in odor detection.

In addition to noting intensity of odor, qualities can be identified in such terms as flowery, fruity, putrid, spicy, burnt, and resinous. These six qualities have been classified (H. Henning) as primary, with other qualities being combinations of them. Pervasiveness and acceptability are other attributes of odors which can be measured (*5*).

Much careful work is still needed to determine the true mechanism of olfactory stimulation, as there are several theories, such as infrared radiation and catalysis, which are as yet unproven.

II. Measurement of Odor Concentration

Numerous attempts have been made to design odor meters which are free of the limitations of the human nose. Although meters have been and will be devised for specific odorants or classes of compounds, human odor perception still remains the principal means of odor measurement.

A. Odor Scales

The first requirement for measurement is a definable and reliable yardstick. Because it is based on subjective response, the odor scale must necessarily be simple. The generally accepted scale is presented in Table I.

Nader (*6*) has defined "individual perception threshold (IPT)" as "the lowest concentration of a particular odor at which a subject gave both an initial positive response and a repeated response when the same stimulus was given a second time." As people vary in their ability to sense faint odors, the "population perception threshold (PPT50)" for a particular odor was defined, therefore, as "that concentration below which 50% of the people who have a capable sense of smell are able to detect an odor."

At the perception threshold concentration one is barely certain that an odor is detected, but it is too faint to identify further. The "recognition threshold" is the lowest concentration at which a skilled observer can identify and describe the odor, or at least compare its quality with another odor. Above the threshold levels, increasing concentration of

TABLE I
SENSORY SCALE FOR EVALUATING INTENSITY LEVELS

Degree of odor intensity	Description
0	Odorless
½	Threshold (perception)
1	Threshold (recognition)
2	Definite
3	Strong
4	Overpowering

odorant in air causes sensations that have been found useful for measurement but at reduced accuracy. Skilled observers may interpolate between degrees, as 1½ or 2½. For evaluation of cigarette smoke, Yaglou (*7*) devised a 5-point scale with somewhat more descriptive terms and including the factor of irritation to the eyes, nose, or throat.

B. Organoleptic Panel Technique

As the concentrations at perception may vary from 30 to 50% for individual observers on any given day (*2, 8*), and more on different days, it is necessary to increase the number of observers and to average the results where greater measurement accuracy is desired.

A group of three, five, or more trained observers, each with at least an average keenness of smell, and who will follow prescribed rules, can make valuable odor determinations (*9*). The individuals can be selected by their abilities to select a bottle of odor-free air from three bottles, two of which contain faint odors. For example, 10 cc. of a 1% solution of vanillin or ionone in odorless ethylene glycol will provide a faint odor in two bottles, while ethylene glycol alone may be used for the blank. The recommended practice is to have the group or panel in the charge of a person who submits coded odor samples for individual evaluation. Statistical methods are then applied to determine the odor intensities and qualities which a larger number of persons or the general population would have perceived.

In preparation for a determination, 30 min. or more should have elapsed since smoking or eating. Washing with unscented soap, the wearing of clean clothes, and no use of cosmetics are among the requirements. The panelists should rest in an odor-free room, preferably one in which the air has been treated with activated carbon to remove trace odors.

The observer is then ready to enter a room or booth in which the air has been treated with odorant, or a stream of odorized air may be sprayed into a nostril, or special hoods may be used to direct the odorant to the nasal area. The determination of odor intensity and/or quality is made on the basis of the first one or two sniffs only, for reasons that will be explained later.

C. Sampling of Odorized Air or Gas

Where an ample supply of odorous gas is available, as from the flue of an incinerator, industrial ventilator, or outdoors near a sewage plant, a sample can be collected in a large, clean glass bottle by flushing several volumes of the air or gas through the bottle and sealing it with a glass stopper or metal foil. An exhaust pump connected to a small tube inserted through the neck and extending to near the bottom of the bottle is a simple means of drawing in volumes of air or gas through the remaining area of the bottle opening. The sample can then be taken to an odor laboratory for appraisal.

Some success has also been reported (*10*) in collecting odorants from effluent gas by bubbling the gas through water in a Greenburg-Smith impinger. Samples of gas have also been collected over mercury and evaluated for odor concentration (*11*).

Turk (*12*) suggests the use of activated carbon to adsorb and concentrate the odorants from a known quantity of gas or air. In the laboratory the adsorbed gases and vapors may then be desorbed from the activated carbon by superheated steam or by vacuum. The desorbed material may be trapped by condensation in glass cold traps, which are connected in series and immersed in baths of ice-salt, solid CO_2 in acetone, and liquid nitrogen, respectively. Mass and infrared spectrometry may be used to identify the compounds collected.

D. Apparatus for Measurement of Odor Concentration

1. *ASTM Odor Syringe Apparatus*

The most satisfactory determination of odor concentration is by the dilution of a sample with odor-free air until the perception threshold is reached. The Standard Method for Measurement of Odor in Atmospheres (Dilution Method) D 1391-56 of the American Society for Testing Materials (*8*) outlines a simple dilution procedure. As shown in Fig. 1, a few graduated 100-ml. and 2-ml. syringes and hypodermic needles constitute the equipment. Individual observers or panels can use the method. Only a small sample of odorous gas is required. Measured quantities of this gas and odor-free air are mixed in a syringe, and injected into the nostril during suspension of breathing. The procedure is

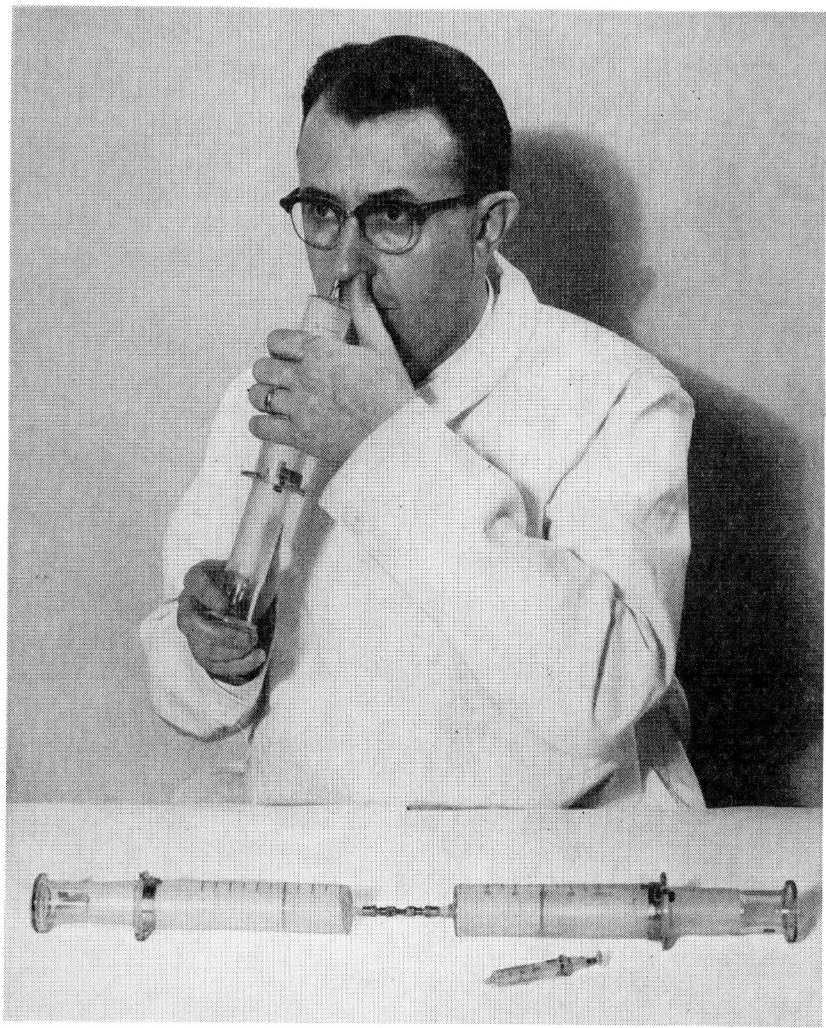

FIG. 1. ASTM odor syringe apparatus. Odorized air and odor-free air are blended in measured parts by syringes, followed by sniff test.

repeated in a random series of concentrations until a barely perceptible mixture has been proved.

The odor concentration $C = 100/V_s$ in which C = odor concentration, which is the number of cubic feet that 1 cu. ft. of sample will occupy when diluted to the odor threshold; V_s = milliliters of the original sample present in the most dilute sample in which odor is perceptible, and 100 = milliliters of diluted sample. A value C = 10, for example, indicates that the original odor would have to be diluted with at least ten times its volume of odor-free air to diminish the odor to below the perception threshold of the observer. Where greater accuracy is desired, a number of observers should be used and their results averaged, but a single observer should be able to attain results that are reproducible within ±50% on a given day.

As an odor unit (ASTM) is 1 cu. ft. of air at the odor threshold, the number of odor units emitted from a stack per unit of time is the product of the odor concentration and the cubic feet of gas flowing from the stack in the same time.

2. *Nader Odor-Evaluation Apparatus*

An odor-evaluation apparatus for field and laboratory use has been devised by Nader (*6*), which utilizes the perception principle with con-

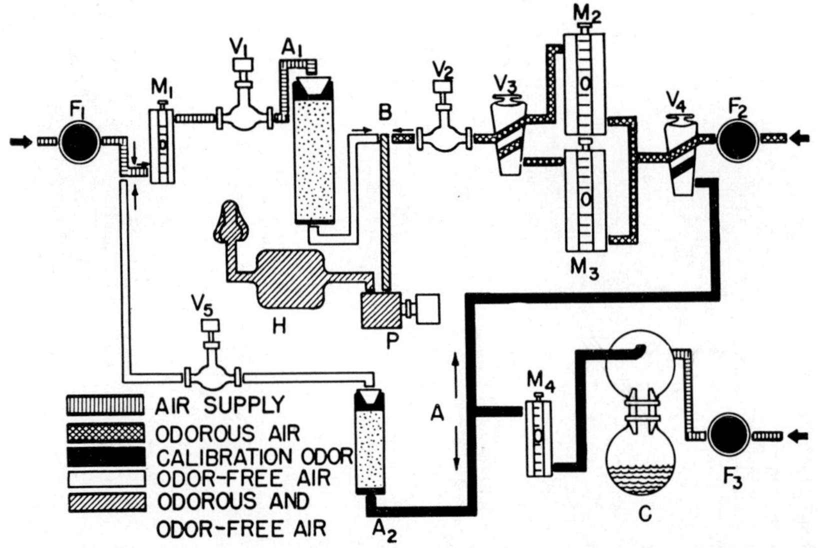

FIG. 2. Nader odor-evaluation apparatus. F_1, F_2, F_3: glass-wool filters; M_1: air flow meter, 30 l./min.; M_2: air flow meter, 1.5–40 cc./min.; M_3: air flow meter, 15–425 cc./min.; M_4: air flow meter, 9–900 cc./min.; V_1, V_2, V_5: needle values; and V_3, V_4: two-way valves. A_1: activated charcoal absorber column: 2¼ in. × 15 in. length, ⅛ in. wall; A_2: activated charcoal absorber column, 1 in. o.d. × 12 in. length, ⅛ in. wall; P: carbon-vane oilless air pump, approximately 25 l./min. free air flow; H: Teflon hood with glass viewing window; C: odorant diffusion cell, approximately 4.0 mm. diam. and 10 cm. capillary. Glass or Teflon is used for all connecting tubing. (Courtesy of J. S. Nader.)

tinuously proportioned streams of odorous air and odor-free air (Fig. 2). The observer wears a hood into which the mixtures are flowed. The source of the odor can be an odorous gas or air stream or it can be a liquid known proportions of which are evaporated into a controlled air stream. Odor-free air is produced by passing ambient air through activated carbon. The apparatus can therefore be used near the source of the odor, even when the surrounding atmosphere has been contaminated, as is often the case.

To prevent bias, the individual subject is unaware of the concentration of the sample or whether it is a blank sample.

A simple portable "Scentometer" for measuring odor strength has been developed by Gruber *et al.* (*12a*). The user breathes mixtures of odorous and purified air as proportioned by orifices until the threshold stimulus is reached. Other olfactometers, both simple and complex, have been devised over the years and have areas of usefulness. An interested student of olfactometry will do well to consult the references for further details (*1, 2, 13*).

III. Factors Affecting Odor Perception

A. Concentration of Odorant in Air

The relationship of odor concentration in air to the sensation of odor has long been thought to follow the Fechner-Weber law: "the sensation increases as the logarithm of the stimulus." In other words, the stimulus (odor concentration) must be increased geometrically for the sensation (odor intensity) to increase arithmetically. For example, Kerka and Humphreys (*14*) recently reported that they had confirmed the Fechner-Weber law by the results shown in Fig. 3 with four odorants. Modern

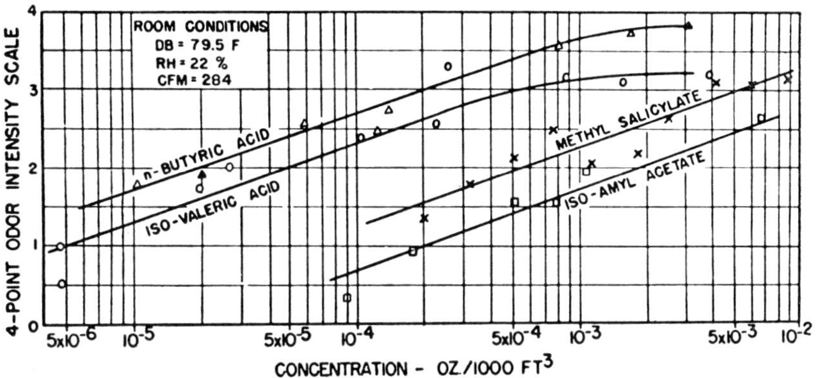

FIG. 3. Odor intensity versus concentration. [From *Trans. Am. Soc. Heat. & Air Cond. Engrs.* **62,** No. 1587 (1956).]

psychophysics (*14a*) has established that all subjective response (sensation) grows as the stimulus magnitude raised to a power n ($n = 0.55$ for coffee odor and 0.6 for heptane odor). The odor scale normally used is not a linear relationship of intensity of odor, which largely explains why the Fechner-Weber law seems to apply, whereas the "Law" has been repealed in psychophysical circles.

B. Odor Fatigue or Adaptation

It is a common experience to notice a faint odor when one is first exposed to it, as when entering a building or motoring from open country into an industrial area. On prolonged exposure the odor is no longer apparent. The olfactory sense has become dulled to the odor.

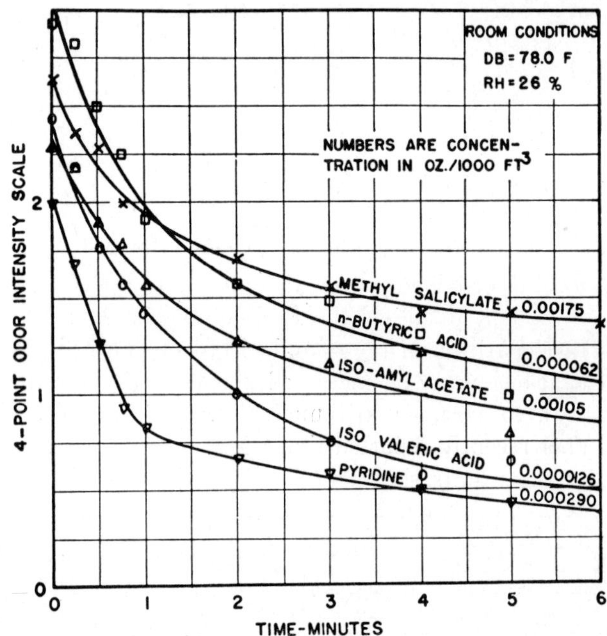

FIG. 4. Adaptation to pure-vapor odors. [From *Trans. Am. Soc. Heat. & Air Cond. Engrs.* **62,** No. 1587 (1956).]

Figure 4 illustrates the rapid decrease in odor sensation during the first minute, and a more gradual decrease thereafter (*14*). Within the first minute the odor sensation decreased one point on the odor intensity scale. As odor adaptation or fatigue apparently begins with the first inhalation, determinations of odor intensity should be made promptly, preferably on the first or second inhalation. The sense of smell should then be restored to full potential by breathing odor-free air.

C. Effect of Humidity and Temperature

The humidity and temperature of ambient air vary widely, but the human nose is an air conditioner, adding more or less heat and humidity to bring air to a nearly constant condition by the time it reaches the olfactory receptors. To accomplish this result, the flow of water from the mucous membranes of the upper respiratory tract, and the flow of blood to supply heat to that region, also vary. The over-all result is a decrease in odor stimulus or intensity as the specific humidity of the air increases.

For example, in air at 70°F. containing a constant concentration of odorant, observers will class the odor intensity "definite" at 50 grains of moisture per pound dry air, but only "threshold" at twice that humidity (*14*). This effect is not to be confused with the increase in odor production of some materials during humid weather.

The effect of air temperature on odor perception is not very pronounced in the range of 40 to 100°F.; a general tendency toward a slight decline in odor intensity with increasing temperature has been observed (*14*).

Humidity and temperature should therefore be controlled where possible in odor investigations.

IV. Malodors and their Sources

Malodors are the cause of many complaints made to local air pollution control agencies. In a recent survey made by the Air Pollution Control Association (*15*) the most frequent complaints have been tabulated in Table II.

TABLE II

Odors Most Frequently Reported to Air Pollution Control Agencies

Source or type of odor	No. of times reported
Animal	
Meat-packing and rendering plants	12
Fish-oil odors from manufacturing plants	5
Poultry ranches and processing	4
Combustion processes	
Gasoline and diesel engine exhaust	10
Coke-oven and coal-gas odors (steel mills)	8
Maladjusted heating systems	3

TABLE II (*Continued*)

Odors Most Frequently Reported to Air Pollution Control Agencies

Source or type of odor	No. of times reported
Food processes	
Coffee roasting	8
Restaurant odors	4
Bakeries	3
Paint and related industries	
Manufacture of paint, lacquer, and varnish	8
Paint spraying	4
Commercial solvents	3
General chemical	
Hydrogen sulfide	7
Sulphur dioxide	4
Ammonia	3
General industrial	
Burning rubber from smelting and debonding	5
Dry-cleaning shops	5
Fertilizer plants	4
Asphalt: roofing and street paving	4
Asphalt: manufacturing	3
Plastics manufacturing	3
Foundry	
Core-oven odors	4
Heat treating, oil quenching, and pickling	3
Smelting	2
Combustible waste	
Home incinerators and back yard trash fire	4
City incinerators burning garbage	3
Open-dump fire	2
Refinery	
Mercaptans	3
Crude oils and gasolines	3
Sulfur	1
Decomposition of waste	
Putrefaction and oxidation: organic acids[a]	3
Organic nitrogen compounds: decomposition of protein[a]	2
Decomposition of lignin (plant cells)	1
Sewage	
City sewers carrying industrial waste	3
Sewage treatment plants	2

[a] Odors are probably related to meat-processing plants.

Even the most pleasant food odors are cause for serious complaint when they persist day after day. Many of the odors normally encountered are mixtures of compounds, often so complex as to defy detailed identifications except by tedious research by odor specialists.

Table III is a partial list of odorants, their character, and the minimum concentrations for perception. The list was compiled from several sources (*2, 14, 16*). The concentration for a faint odor was given when the perception concentration was not known. The odor values for a compound are subject to variation, depending on the techniques used and the purity of the compound.

The volume of gaseous odorant at 25°C. (77°F.) per million volumes of air is given, as are the equivalent milligrams of odorant per liter of air. The relationship between them is expressed by the equations:

$$\text{p.p.m.} = \frac{\text{mg./l.}}{\text{mol. wt.}} \times 24450$$

$$\text{mg./l.} = \frac{\text{p.p.m.} \times \text{mol. wt.}}{24450}$$

Fortunately, mg./l. and oz./1000 cu. ft. of air are equal.

The concentrations necessary for increased intensity of odor are obtained by multiplying the concentration for perception, C_p, by the dilution factor, F, raised to the appropriate power, as follows:

Concentration for:

Faint (weak, readily perceptible odor) $= C_pF$

Easily noticeable (moderate odor) $= C_pF^2$

Strong (forcible odor) $= C_pF^3$

Very strong (intense effect) $= C_pF^4$

Many odorants may be dissolved in water, at least in the low concentrations of interest in odor studies, but most offensive industrial odors are generally not readily soluble in water. The intensity of odor of the solution is a function of the proportion of odorant. Meuly and Tremaine (*17*) have suggested the terms "scent value (SV)" and "gram scent value (GSV)" to aid in the appraisal of odorants collected in water:

"If a camphor solution, diluted to 3 p.p.m. in water, contains the concentration of odorant which causes the stimulus of 1 scent unit (recognition threshold), then camphor itself contains the reciprocal number of scent units or $0.33 \times 10^6 = 330{,}000$ scent units. Thus the odor content of an odorant may be expressed by the number of scent units which it contains and this value we call the *scent content value* or scent value (SV). The SV of camphor is 330,000. . . . A bottle with 20 grams camphor thus contains locked up a GSV of $20 \times 330{,}000$ or 6,600,000."

TABLE III

MINIMUM CONCENTRATION OF ODORANTS (C_p) IN AIR FOR POSITIVE PERCEPTION

Name	Formula	Mol. wt.	Volumes per million of air (p.p.m.)	Mg./liter and oz./1000 cu. ft.	Dilution factor (F)	Character of odor
Acetaldehyde	CH_3CHO	44.05	0.066	0.00012	33	Pungent
Acrolein	$CH_2:CH\ CHO$	56.06	1.8	0.0041	9.4	Acrid odor of burning fat
"Akrol"	Mixed terpenes			0.00013	26	Acrid pine-tar odor; irritating
Allyl alcohol	$CH_2:CH\ CH_2OH$	58.08	1.4	0.0033	5.0	Alcoholic; not unpleasant
Allylamine	$CH_2:CH\ CH_2NH_2$	57.09	6.2	0.014	4.7	Similar to ammonia
Allyl disulfide	$(CH_2:CHCH_2)_2S_2$	146.26	0.0012	0.0000072	14	Garlic; decomposes
Allyl isocyanide	$CH_2:CH\ CH_2NC$	67.09	0.018	0.000049	8.9	Sweet but repulsive
Allyl mercaptan	$CH_2:CH\ CH_2SH$	74.14	0.0015	0.0000045	3.2	Very disagreeable; garlic
Allyl sulfide	$(CH_2:CH\ CH_2)_2S$	114.20	0.00014	0.00000065	71	Garlic
Allyl thiocyanate (iso)	$CH_2:CH\ CH_2NCS$	99.1	0.15	0.00061	2.8	Mustard oil; disagreeable
Ammonia	NH_3	17.03		0.037 faint		Sharp, pungent
Amylene (mixed isomers)	C_5H_{10}	70.13	19	0.00054	12	Nauseating in high concentrations
Amylene acetate (iso)	$CH_3COO(CH_2)_4CH_3$	130.2	0.0033	0.000018	34	Banana
Amyl isovalerate (iso)	$C_4H_9COO\ C_5H_{11}$	172.2	0.0066	0.000046	17	Very disagreeable
Amyl mercaptan (iso)	$(CH_3)_2CH(CH_2)_2SH$	104.21	0.00043	0.0000018	19	Unpleasant
Amyl sulfide (iso)	$[(CH_3)_2CH(CH_2)_2]_2S$	174.34	0.0030	0.000021	14	Strong and unpleasant
Artificial musk (2,4,6-trinitro-*tert*-butylxylene)	$(NO_2)_3C_6(CH_3)_2C_4H_9$	297.26	0.0000065	0.000000075	22	Pleasant
Benzaldehyde	C_6H_5CHO	106.12	0.042	0.00018	17	Bitter almonds
Benzyl chloride	$C_6H_5CH_2Cl$	126.58	0.040	0.00021	8.1	Lacrimator; aromatic
Benzyl mercaptan	$C_6H_5CH_2SH$	124.19	0.0026	0.000013	15	Unpleasant
Benzyl sulfide	$(C_6H_5CH_2)_2S$	214.31	0.0060	0.000053	12	Unpleasant
Bis-α-dichloroethyl sulfide	$(CHCl\ CH_3)_2S$	159.07	0.0023	0.000015	11	Unpleasant
Bromacetone	$Br \cdot CH_2CO \cdot CH_2$	135.98		0.0005 faint		Pungent and stifling

Bromacetophenone	$C_6H_4CO \cdot CH_3 \cdot Br$	199.05	0.015	0.00012	5.5	Lacrimator; odor like bromine
α-Butylene	$CH_3CH_2CH:CH_2$	56.10	0.92	0.0021	15	Gashouse
β-Butylene	$CH_3CH:CH \cdot CH_3$	56.10	2.1	0.0048	12	Gashouse
γ-Butylene	$CH_2:C(CH_3)CH_3$	56.10	1.3	0.0030	17	Gashouse
n-Butyl mercaptan	$(CH_3)_2CH \cdot CH_2SH$	90.2	0.0010	0.0000037	22	Strong, unpleasant
n-Butyl sulfide	$(CH_3CH_2CH_2CH_2)_2S$	146.29	0.015	0.000090	13	Unpleasant
Butyric acid	$CH_3(CH_2)_2COOH$	88.1	0.00056	0.000002	8	Very disagreeable
Carbon disulfide	CS_2	76.12		0.0026 faint		Aromatic, slightly pungent
Chloracetophenone	$C_6H_4 \cdot CO \cdot CH_3Cl$	154.59	0.016	0.00010	3.6	Apple blossom; strong lacrimator
Chlorvinyldichlorarsine	$ClCH:CH\ AsCl_2$	207.27		0.014 faint		Geraniums (lewisite)
Chlorine	Cl_2	70.91		0.010 faint		Pungent and irritating
o-Chlorphenol	ClC_6H_4OH	128.56	0.0036	0.000019	9.1	Medicinal; phenolic
Chloropicrin	Cl_3CNO_2	164.39		0.0073 faint		Flypaper
Coumarin	$C_6H_4CH:CH\ CO\ O$	146.14	0.0033	0.000020	17	Vanilla; pleasant
Crotonaldehyde	$CH_3 \cdot CH:CHCHO$	70.09	0.062	0.00018	6.2	Eye and nose irritant
Crotyl mercaptan	$CH_3 \cdot CH:CHCH_2SH$	88.16	0.00012	0.00000643	40	Skunk
Cyanogen chloride	$CNCl$	61.48		0.0025 faint		Bitter almonds
Dichlordiethyl sulfide	$(ClC_2H_5)_2S$	161.08		0.0013 faint		Garlic or horseradish
Dichloroethylene (*trans*)	$C_2H_2Cl_2$	96.95		0.0043 faint		Ethereal odor
Dimethyl trithiocarbonate	$CH_3S \cdot CS \cdot SCH_3$	138.26	0.0058	0.000033	6.9	Foul and disagreeable
Diphenylchlorarsine	$(C_6H_5)_2AsCl$	264.57		0.0003 faint		Shoe polish
Diphenylcyanarsine	$(C_6H_5)_2AsCN$	255.13		0.003 faint		Bitter almonds and garlic
Diphenyl ether	$(C_6H_5)_2O$	170.20	0.0010	0.0000070	10	Geranium; pleasant
Diphenyl sulfide	$(C_6H_5)_2S$	186.26	0.00034	0.0000026	19	Ethereal but unpleasant
Diphosgene	$ClCO\ OCCl_3$	197.85		0.0088 faint		Suffocating, disagreeable
Dithioethylene glycol	$CH_2SH \cdot CH_2SH$	94.19	0.031	0.00012	13	Disagreeable, garliclike
Ethylene dichloride	CH_2ClCH_2Cl	98.97		0.025 faint		Aromatic, ethereal
Ethyldichlorarsine	$C_2H_5AsCl_2$	162.87		0.001 faint		Irritating, biting
Ethyl isothiocyanate	CH_3CH_2NCS	87.14	1.7	0.0061	6.3	Mustard oil; irritating
Ethyl mercaptan	CH_3CH_2SH	62.13	0.00026	0.00000066	43	Decayed cabbage
Ethyl selenide	$(C_2H_5)_2Se$	137.08	0.0012	0.0000067	9.6	Garlic; putrid and nauseating
Ethyl selenomercaptan	CH_3CH_2SeH	109.03	0.00030	0.00000013	13	Very foul and disagreeable
Ethyl sulfide	$(C_2H_5)_2S$	90.18	0.0028	0.000010	25	Garliclike, foul, nauseating

TABLE III (*Continued*)
MINIMUM CONCENTRATION OF ODORANTS (C_p) IN AIR FOR POSITIVE PERCEPTION

Name	Formula	Mol. wt.	Volumes per million of air (p.p.m.)	Mg./liter and oz./1000 cu. ft.	Dilution factor (F)	Character of odor
Ethyl thioether	$(CH_3 \cdot CH_2)_2S$	90.2	3	0.012 faint		Very disagreeable
Hydrogen cyanide	HCN	27.03		0.001 faint		Bitter almonds
Hydrogen sulfide	H_2S	34.08	0.13	0.00018	5.9	Rotten eggs; nauseating
Methyl anthranylate	$NH_2 \cdot C_6H_4 \cdot CO \cdot OCH_3$	151.16	0.0094	0.000058	6.3	Floral essence; fruity
Methyldichlorarsine	CH_3AsCl_2	160.86		0.0008 faint		Slight; irritating
Methyl mercaptan	CH_3SH	48.10	0.041	0.000081	14	Decayed cabbage or onions
Methyl salicylate	$HO\ C_6H_4COOCH_3$	152.14	0.096	0.00006	8	Oil of wintergreen; pleasant
Methyl sulfide	$(CH_3)_2S$	62.13	0.0037	0.0000094	23	Decayed vegetables
Methyl thiocyanate	CH_3SCN	73.11	0.25	0.00075	13	Almonds; unpleasant
Nitrobenzene	$C_6H_5NO_2$	123.1	1.9	0.0096	3.1	Almonds; pleasant
Ozone	O_3	48.00		0.001 faint		Slightly pungent, irritating
Phenyl isocyanide	$C_6H_5N \cdot C$	103.1	0.0010	0.0000042	10	Repulsive, nauseating
Phenyl isothiocyanate	C_6H_5NCS	135.18	0.094	0.00052	4.7	Cinnamon; pleasant
Phosgene	$COCl_2$	98.92		0.0044 faint		Ensilage or fresh-cut hay
Propargyl aldehyde	$CH:CCHO$	54.05	0.16	0.00035	6.5	Acrid, irritating
n-Propyl mercaptan	$CH_3(CH_2)_2SH$	76.1	0.0016	0.0000050	16	Unpleasant
n-Propyl sulfide	$(C_3H_7)_2S$	118.23	0.011	0.000053	15	Foul, nauseating
Pyridine	C_5H_5N	79.10	0.23	0.00074	9.0	Disagreeable, irritating
Skatole	C_9H_9N	131.17	0.019	0.00010	12	Fecal, nauseating
Sulfur dioxide	SO_2	64.07		0.009 faint		Pungent, irritating
p-Thiocresol	$CH_3C_6H_4SH$	124.19	0.0027	0.000014	7.6	Rancid, skunklike
Thiophenol	C_6H_5SH	110.17	0.00026	0.0000012	52	Putrid, nauseating
Valeric acid (iso)	$CH_3(CH_2)_3COOH$	102.13	0.0012	0.000005	8	Very disagreeable

Solutions follow Henry's law: the odor concentration in air is proportional to the concentration in water.

V. Odor Control

To control an odor nuisance, consideration should, of course, first be given to the prevention of odorants being produced, such as by better plant housekeeping, enclosure of odor-producing processes, sealing of leaks, change of chemical processing, etc. Odorants can also be trapped at or near the source so as not to be released to the atmosphere.

Where it is impractical to prevent odor, or to remove odorants from enormous volumes of air or flue gas, the malodor nuisance can often be ameliorated or mitigated by the addition to the air of certain volatile compounds that reduce the sensation of malodor. In practice, such treatment is known as masking, counteracting, reodorizing, or cancellation.

A few cautions must be observed for reasons of safety. The treatment should never be used to cover toxic concentrations of odorants, nor should the treating agent anesthetize the smell organ, thereby depriving the exposed population of the warning value of odor recognition.

A. Masking

Odor masking is the process of eliminating the perception of one odor or a group of odors by superimposing another odor or group of odors, to create a new odor sensation, preferably pleasant (*18*). The masking agent must be sprayed, or otherwise vaporized in proper proportion, into the air to be treated. The agent does not alter the composition of the pre-existing odor.

Organic odor-masking chemicals are numerous and must be selected and compounded to suit the particular masking or odorization problem. Examples of masking chemicals are vanillin, methyl ionones, eugenols, benzyl acetate, alcohol, heliotropin, and essential oils.

The systematic selection and compounding of materials for each type of application requires osmic research and much technical knowledge of aromatic chemicals. The experience includes trade secrets held by a limited number of companies and specialists. Complete formulation must include a determination of maximum odor strength, optimum quality of the mask-and-odor mixture, chemical stability, volatility, lasting power, etc. (*17*).

Industrial odor masks are generally liquids which can be sprayed into the air or stack gases to be treated, sometimes as a dilute solution in water (Fig. 5). For certain processes, such as digester operation in the kraft (paper) sulfate process, or cooking of meat scraps and bones in rendering plants, the odor-masking compounds are added directly to the "cook." They are thus vaporized with the odorants from the process. Concentrations may range from 10 to 50 p.p.m. based on the weight of the process charge under treatment.

Solvents, fuels, rubbers, plastics, and textiles all have been treated by odor maskers in commercial practice (*19*).

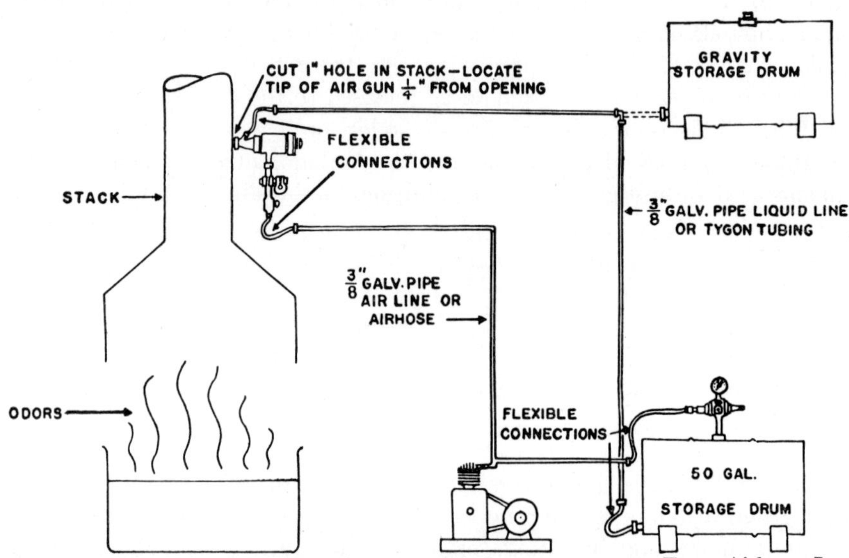

FIG. 5. Injection of odor-treating materials into gas streams. From Airkem, Inc.

B. Counteraction

Counteraction is the diminution of the total odor intensity by the addition of another odorant. The effect is not olfactory anesthesia, as individuals can immediately smell other odorants when exposed to new atmospheres. Zwaardemaker (*20*), an early Flemish odor researcher, demonstrated the reduction in odor intensity when certain pairs of odorants are sniffed together. He cited, among others, paraffin and rubber, and cedarwood and rubber. Von Bergen states that "in the group benzene, toluene, xylene, pseudocumene, and durene, combinations in the correct proportions from this group can be produced which are almost odorless" (*18*). Ammonia can be countered by ionone (*21*). The principle of counteraction is thus distinctly different from masking.

The selection and compounding of odor counteractants is best done by those experienced in such delicate work and familiar with the compounds available. Suitable materials can usually be selected and compounded by laboratory tests with samples of the offending odor. Effectiveness of a counteractant can only be determined by actual odor perception. There is no universal odor counteractant. The formulas are designed for specific groups of odors.

For maximum effectiveness and economy, odor counteractants should be vaporized or sprayed into the effluent gases from a stack or process in a constant proportion to the offending odor. Atomization by compressed air (2–3 cu. ft./min.) is a typical method. Spray treatment of the air over open dumps and lagoons and inside industrial plants is also practiced.

C. Cost of Masking and Counteracting Malodors

Before an odor treatment can be specified and the cost of treatment determined, the following procedure is advisable:

(1) Determine the emissions of particulate matter and gases from the odor source, and identify the pollutants as to quantity and type. Are these quantities within legal limits?

(2) Determine the temperature and rate of flow in cu. ft./min. of the odorous exhaust gases.

(3) Arrange for an odor appraisal by a specialist. Experimentation with selected odorants and rates of application will probably be necessary.

(4) Arrange for a 30-day trial of the odor-control medium with evaluation by a competent jury over the area affected.

The cost of treating malodorous air and exhaust gases includes the initial cost of application equipment and recurring cost of quantities of the control medium. Such costs will obviously increase with the size of the installation and the severity of the problem. For example, a small food-processing operation reported a cost of $1.60 a day for the medium; a cement plant has a comparable cost of $4000 a year. A sewage plant treating 4.5 million gallons a day has a daily cost of $12 for the odor-control agent.

The spray equipment for each stack may be purchased for about $200, piping and installation being extra. Equipment is a negligible expense where the control chemical is merely poured into the process, as into a rendering-plant cooker or paper-pulp digester.

The type and quantity of control liquid to be used in a specific application, and the costs per gallon, will vary widely. A median cost (1961) is about $8 a gallon. The cost of treatment per ton of processed product ranges between 25 and 50 cents for rendering plants, and 15 to 30 cents for paper pulp manufacture.

The amounts vaporized into industrial exhaust systems range, generally, between 3 to 8 pt./8 hr. for each 10,000 cu. ft./min. or 0.010 to 0.027 oz./1000 cu. ft. Assuming $8 a gallon ($1 a pint) for the medium, treatment would cost between $3 and $8 a day for an 8-hr. flow of 10,000 cu. ft./min., or a total of 4.8 million cu. ft. These figures are given only for general consideration. Wide variations from these costs, particularly downward, are possible in specific cases. Air treatment by counteractants and masks is relatively low in cost compared with other methods when low concentrations of malodors are present in large quantities of air.

VI. Summary

The science of odor measurement and of the effect of odorant concentration on olfactory sensation is well advanced and is becoming more widely understood. The interaction of two or more odorants on the olfactory sense is less well recognized. Fundamental data are needed on the numerous combinations and proportions of such materials.

Odor control begins with measures to reduce the quantity of malodor liberated into the atmosphere. There is no substitute for good plant housekeeping. When the remaining odor is present in relatively low concentrations in large quantities of air, and is nontoxic in these proportions, treatment with odor counteractants and masking agents is a low-cost and practical method of control.

References

1. R. W. Moncrieff, "The Chemical Senses," 2nd ed. Leonard Hill Ltd., London, 1951.
2. C. P. McCord and W. N. Witheridge, "Odors—Physiology and Control," 1st ed. McGraw-Hill, New York, 1949.
3. *Encyclopedia Britannica* **20,** 819–20 (1957).
4. C. P. McCord and W. N. Witheridge, "Odors—Physiology and Control," 1st ed., p. 29. McGraw-Hill, New York, 1949.
5. A. Turk, *Air. Poll. Control Assoc. 4th Air Sanitation Conf., Philadelphia,* pp. 33–42 (1956).
6. J. S. Nader, *Am. Ind. Hyg. Assoc. J.* **19,** 1–7 (1958).
7. C. P. Yaglou, *Trans. Am. Soc. Heat. & Air-Cond. Engrs.* **61,** 25 (1955).
8. Anonymous, Standard Method for Measurement of Odor in Atmospheres (Dilution Method)," Rept. D 1391–57. Am. Soc. Testing Materials, Philadelphia, 1959.
9. L. C. Cartwright, C. T. Snell, and P. H. Kelley, *Anal. Chem.* **24,** 503 (1952).
10. R. Pantaleoni, *J. Air Poll. Control. Assoc.* **5,** 213–15 (1956).
11. E. R. Kaiser, J. Halitsky, M. B. Jacobs, and L. C. McCabe, *J. Air Poll. Control Assoc.* **9,** 85–91 (1959).
12. A. Turk, *Air Repair* 55–58 (1954).
12a. N. A. Huey, L. C. Broering, G. A. Jutze, and C. W. Gruber, *J. Air. Poll. Control Assoc.* **10,** 441–6 (1960).
13. J. F. Mateson, *J. Air Poll. Control Assoc.* **5,** 167 (1955).
14. W. F. Kerka and C. M. Humphreys, *Trans. Am. Soc. Heat. & Air-Cond. Engrs.* **62,** 531–52 (1956).
14a. S. S. Stevens, *Science* **133,** 80–86 (1961).

15. W. F. Kerka and E. R. Kaiser, *J. Air Poll. Control Assoc.* **7,** 297–301 (1958).
16. S. H. Katz and E. J. Talbert, *U. S. Bur. Mines, Tech. Paper* **480,** 14–15, 20–21 (1930).
17. W. C. Meuly and B. K. Tremaine, *TAPPI* **36,** 154–61 (1953).
18. J. von Bergen, *Chem. Eng.* **64,** 239–50 (1957); *J. Air Poll. Control Assoc.* **8,** 101–11 (1958).
19. A. Turk, *Am. Soc. Testing Materials Spec. Tech. Publ.* **164,** 78 (1954).
20. H. Zwaardemaker, "Die Physiologie des Geruchs." Engelmann, Leipzig, 1895.
21. Airkem, Inc., *Chem. Week* **79,** 58, 60, 62 (1957).

CHAPTER 16

Meteorological Measurements

E. WENDELL HEWSON

Department of Engineering Mechanics, The University of Michigan, Ann Arbor, Michigan

I. Introduction

Measurements of the significant characteristics of the atmosphere are an essential part of most investigations of air pollution. These characteristics govern many aspects of the problem after a contaminant is released to the atmosphere. The nature of the pollution problem, in relation to meteorology in its various phases, is set forth in Chapter 5, and the ways of using meteorological data are given either explicitly or by implication.

There are a number of primary sources of information on meteorological measurements (*1–4a*). These give more comprehensive coverage of the subject than is possible in the present chapter, and should be consulted for information not provided here. A valuable assessment of meteorological instrumentation for air pollution surveys is available (*4b*).

II. Primary Meteorological Measurements

The primary measurements are those which have proved to be essential for an estimate of the distribution of contaminants from one or more sources. These are measurements of wind direction, wind speed, and wind turbulence (*4c*).

A. Wind Direction

The measurement of wind direction will be discussed under two main headings: surface wind direction, and wind direction aloft.

1. *Surface Wind Direction*

The instrument almost universally used is the wind vane, of which there are four main types (*1, 4, 5*).

a. Flat Plate Vane. In the flat plate vane, the sensor which governs the azimuth angle of a vertical shaft denoting the wind direction is a vertical plate mounted at one end of a horizontal rod. There is a counterweight at the other end of the horizontal rod and the latter is attached near its mid-point to the vertical shaft. Wind pressure acting on the flat plate keeps the counterweight heading into the wind.

Fig. 1. A flat plate wind vane (*left*) and a cup anemometer driving a d.c. generator giving instantaneous wind speeds (*right*). (Courtesy of Belfort Instrument Company, Baltimore, Maryland.)

A flat plate vane is shown at the left in Fig. 1. The vane is coupled directly to the shaft of a synchro generator, which is wired to a synchro receiver in the recorder that is used to position the direction pen (*5*).

b. Splayed Vane. A vane which follows small changes in wind direction somewhat better than the flat plate vane is the splayed type. In this, two flat plates joined at a small angle at one end of a horizontal rod act as the wind direction sensor.

c. Airfoil Vane. In this type, the wind sensor has an airfoil cross section, with the span often being three or four times the chord. The airfoil vane may be designed to give excellent response characteristics.

d. Multiple Element Vane. This vane may consist of two or more plates or airfoil sections arranged in various combinations. These vanes are sometimes used when very rapid response to wind direction changes is required.

e. Analysis of Vane Action. Electrical circuitry is the preferred technique for indicating or recording wind direction (*3, 5*). Sensitivity in the response of a wind vane is increased by reducing the moment of inertia of the system. The stability, speed of response, and damping action of various types of wind vanes have been analyzed in detail (*3, 6*).

2. *Wind Direction Aloft*

It is sometimes desirable to have direct measurements of wind direction well above the ground, e.g., at the height of the plume from a stack. Several methods are available (*3, 4, 4a*). Each involves considerable expense and time of personnel.

a. Pilot Balloons. The direction of the wind aloft may be determined by tracking the motion of a small balloon inflated with hydrogen or helium by means of one or more theodolites (*7*). The average wind direction in successive height intervals is obtained by triangulation techniques. The method is of limited value with low cloud, fog, or smoke, in which the balloon may be quickly lost.

b. Kite Balloons. A kite balloon is an elongated captive balloon with fins at one end; it is tethered in such a way that it behaves as an ordinary captive spherical balloon in light winds and as a kite in stronger winds, and thus maintains altitude under both conditions. The wind direction at the height of the balloon may be determined continuously or at intervals by suitable measurements at the ground of the azimuth angle of the horizontal projection of the tethering cable. The balloon cannot be left untended for long periods since it must be refilled at intervals to replace the inflating gas lost by slow leakage; another danger is that a sudden wind squall may carry the kite balloon away before it can be reeled in to safety.

c. Radio and Radar. Wind directions aloft may be obtained in low cloud, fog, or smoke by the use of radio or radar theodolites (*4, 7a*). With the former, a small radio transmitter is carried aloft by a freely rising balloon and is tracked. With the latter system, pulses of electrical energy emitted by the radar are reflected from a target carried by the free balloon back to the radar; the system measures distance to the target as well as azimuth and elevation angles and is thus inherently more accurate than the radio direction finder. Operation and maintenance costs for both radio and radar theodolites are so high that their use in air pollution investigations is not justified except in most unusual circumstances.

B. Wind Speed

Wind speed measurements may be required both near the ground and aloft.

1. *Surface Wind Speed*

There are a number of instruments for measuring surface wind speeds, of which the rotation anemometers are, in general, the most satisfactory for air pollution studies (*1, 3, 4, 4a*).

a. Rotation Anemometers. The windmill anemometer consists essentially of a circular array of blades attached to a horizontal shaft, mounted in bearings, which is free to rotate in response to wind forces acting on the blades. The housing containing the bearings is mounted at the top of a freely rotating vertical shaft. The blade assembly is kept heading into the wind by a wind vane at the opposite end of the housing. The rate of rotation of the blades and horizontal shaft is proportional to the wind speed. In one well-established design the blades and shaft drive a d.c. generator which produces a voltage directly proportional to wind speed (*8*). Such an instrument may be used to measure wind direction as well as wind speed, both of which may be indicated on dial instruments or a suitable recorder.

The cup anemometer is the second type of rotation anemometer. The cup anemometer in its modern form consists of three conical cups attached, by horizontal arms 120° apart, to a freely rotating vertical shaft mounted in bearings (*9, 9a*). The cups rotate in a horizontal plane at a rate which is proportional to the wind speed. In one type, shown at the right in Fig. 1, the vertical shaft drives a d.c. generator whose output is indicated on a dial instrument or on a chart-type recorder, to give instantaneous wind speeds. A second kind of cup anemometer is the totalizing type in which the passage of each $\frac{1}{10}$ or $\frac{1}{60}$ mile of wind and each 1 mile of wind past the instrument is counted, either by a counter that must be read at intervals or by a recording counter. A detailed

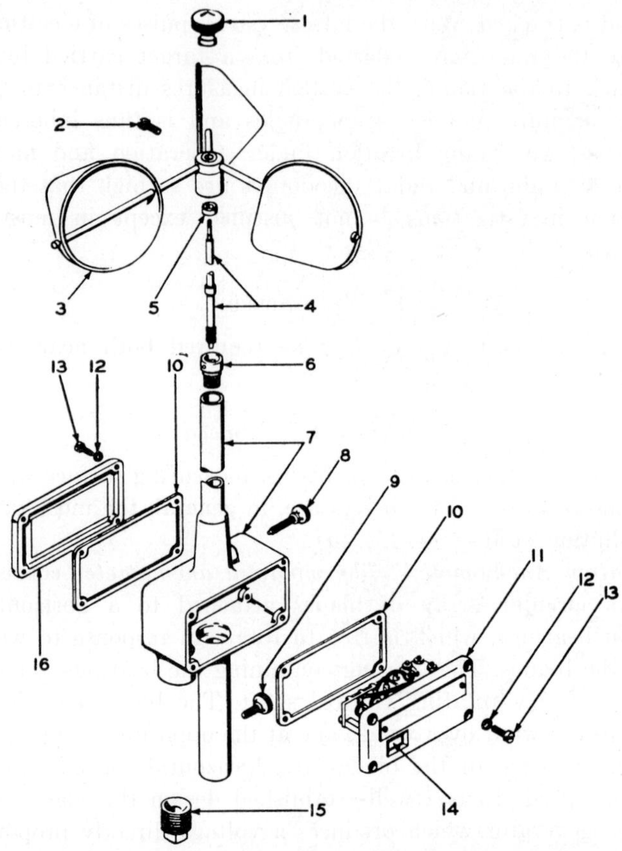

FIG. 2. An exploded view of a totalizing cup anemometer showing the component parts: (1) rotor retaining nut; (2) hub setscrew; (3) rotor assembly; (4) spindle; (5) upper ball bearing; (6) ball bearing housing; (7) anemometer case; (8) spindle retaining screw; (9) pintle thumb screw; (10) gasket; (11) movement plate; (12) lockwasher; (13) plate screw; (14) odometer dial; (15) ¾-in. pipe plug; (16) rear cover plate. (Courtesy of Friez Instrument Division, The Bendix Corporation, Baltimore, Maryland.)

sketch of a totalizing cup anemometer is presented in Fig. 2. The average wind speed during any period is obtained by dividing the difference in counter readings at the end and beginning of the period by the time elapsed. Since in air pollution studies the average wind speed is most often required, the totalizing cup anemometer is generally preferred.

Both types of rotation anemometers may be adversely affected by freezing rain forming a layer of ice on the blades or cups. Severe freezing rain may stop the rotation altogether, but this rarely occurs. Other types of anemometers are equally or more affected by precipitation.

b. Pressure-Tube Anemometers. This instrument consists essentially of a horizontal Pitot tube which is kept heading into the wind by a vane. A static tube surrounds the upper part of the vertical shaft that supports the Pitot tube and vane. Pipes from the Pitot and static heads serve to transmit pressure differentials to the recorder, which linearizes the response of the sensor either by a float of special design or by a system of springs (*1, 3, 4*). A pressure-tube anemometer was used effectively in the air pollution investigation in the Columbia River valley near Trail, British Columbia (*10*).

Freezing rain and snow may obstruct the entrances to the Pitot and static heads. Heating equipment may be installed to prevent ice and snow accumulation if necessary. If subfreezing temperatures are anticipated, an antifreeze solution of the correct specific gravity must be used in the float chamber. The main advantage of this instrument is the fact that an electrical power supply is not required, since the recording pen is actuated by air pressure differentials; the rotating drum holding the chart is usually driven by clockwork.

c. Pressure-Plate Anemometers. In this type of anemometer, illustrated in Fig. 3, a hinged plate is kept normal to the wind by a vane (*11*). The small movements of the hinged plate are transmitted to an armature which in turn moves in the field of an electromagnet. The coil of this electromagnet forms one arm of an a.c. bridge. The alternating current flowing when the bridge is out of balance is rectified and filtered, and recorded on a suitable oscillograph.

The use of this instrument is most appropriate in air pollution investigations where accurate measurements of wind turbulence are required, as well as measurements of wind direction and speed.

d. Hot-Wire Anemometers. In this instrument the temperature of an electrically heated element which is cooled by the passing wind is recorded by suitable means. Several types have been developed for use in the atmosphere (*1, 11a,b*).

The principle of the compensated heated thermocouple type of hot-wire anemometer (*12*), as used in the Hastings Air Meter, is illustrated in Fig. 4. Alternating current heats the fine thermocouple wires extending between and supported by studs A, D, and B, but not those between

D and C. The butt-welded thermojunctions halfway between AD, BD, and CD are supported only by fine wires, 0.08 mm. in diameter, which meet to form each thermojunction. Since the electrical resistance of the wire between A and D and that between B and D are equal, and since the secondary of the transformer is center-tapped, only the thermoelectric direct current passes through the millivoltmeter G. The thermocouples

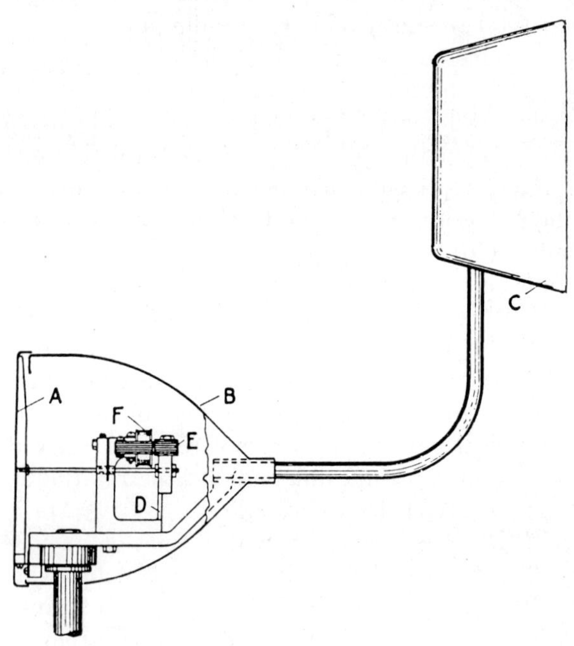

Fig. 3. Sectional view of pressure-plate anemometer of Sherlock and Stout, showing the component parts: A, pressure plate; B, housing; C, vane; D, spring; E, armature; F, electromagnet. (From W. E. K. Middleton and A. F. Spilhaus, "Meteorological Instruments," University of Toronto Press, Toronto, Ontario, Canada.)

between A and D and between B and D are in parallel with reference to meter G, which therefore registers the thermoelectric voltage appropriate for a single thermocouple. A third but unheated thermocouple between C and D in the meter circuit eliminates the influence of temperature fluctuations in the wind: by wiring this thermocouple as a source of bucking voltage, any fluctuations in the thermoelectric output of the heated wires caused by fluctuating air temperatures are exactly canceled out by the counterelectromotive forces developed in this unheated thermocouple. Laboratory tests have shown perfect compensation even for temperature fluctuations with an amplitude as great as 27°C. The time constants range from 0.22 to 0.08 sec. for wind speeds of from 1 to 8 m./sec.

The fine-wire sensor must be carefully handled and the whole apparatus requires considerable attention while in use. The instrument is not suitable for foggy conditions when small water droplets may impinge

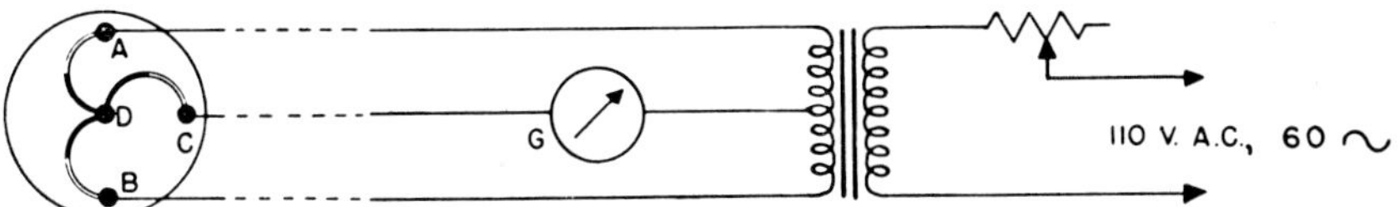

FIG. 4. Circuit diagram illustrating the principle of the compensated heated thermocouple type of hot-wire anemometer used in the Hastings Air Meter. Heated thermojunctions are located between supports A and D and between supports B and D; the unheated compensating thermojunction is suspended between supports C and D. Millivoltmeter G measures the direct thermoelectric force and hence the wind speed. (After G. C. Gill.)

on the fine hot wire. In heavily polluted atmospheres enough particulate matter may collect on the sensing hot wire to change significantly its response to passing wind. Such an instrument should be employed in air pollution studies only if the other types mentioned above have been proved inadequate for one reason or another.

2. *Wind Speed Aloft*

The wind speed at higher levels may be determined by tracking a freely rising balloon by means of one or more ordinary theodolites (*7*) or by a radio or radar theodolite (*3, 4, 4a*), using the techniques mentioned in the section on wind direction measurements.

C. WIND TURBULENCE

Turbulence in the atmosphere is the highly irregular motion of the wind—irregular both in speed and direction—and is the primary agency by which diffusion of air contaminants occurs. Since turbulent flow with a pronounced vertical component is so effective in promoting the upward diffusion of air contaminants from their surface sources, it is often desirable to measure this vertical component as well as one or both of the horizontal components. In some circumstances, however, it is sufficient to measure one horizontal component.

Since the vertical component of wind turbulence is mainly governed by the vertical stability or instability of the air, the vertical component may often be estimated with satisfactory accuracy from measurements of the existing temperature lapse rate—the rate of decrease of temperature with height—which determines the degree of stability or instability present. Instruments for making direct measurements of wind turbulence will be described first.

1. *Direct Measurements of Wind Turbulence*

The instruments which may be used for direct measurements of wind turbulence are those capable of measuring accurately the rapid fluctuations of either wind direction or wind speed. Many sensitive wind vanes or anemometers meet these requirements. Some of the methods by which the records made by such instruments may be analyzed to yield meaningful turbulence parameters are set forth elsewhere (*1*).

a. Wind Vanes. Several types of rapid-response recording wind vanes are suitable for use in measuring the horizontal crosswind component of turbulence, such as that shown in Fig. 5 (*13*). A low moment of inertia

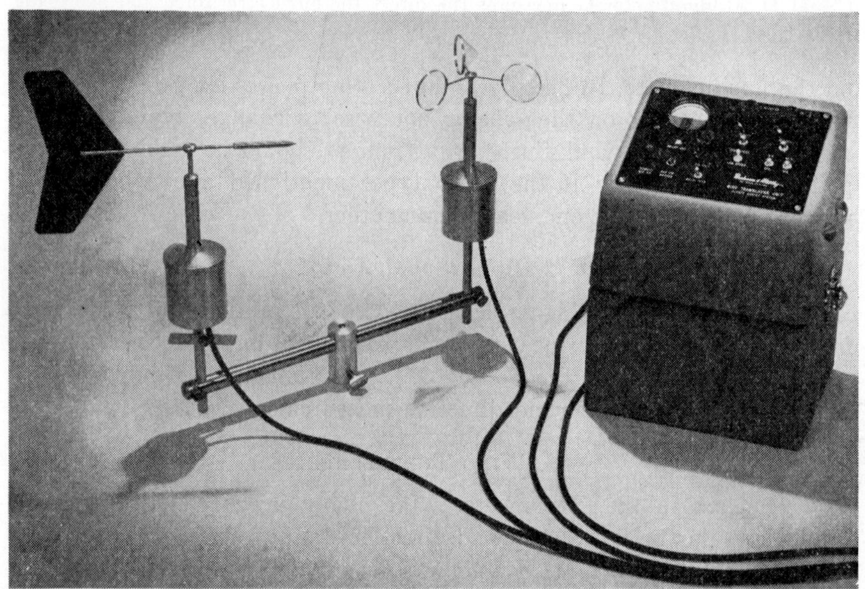

FIG. 5. Rapid response assembly of: *left,* wind direction transducer; *center,* wind speed transducer; *right,* translator unit. (Courtesy of Beckman & Whitley, Inc., San Carlos, California.)

favors rapid response. At the same time the dynamics of the system should be such as to permit the vane to follow, without overshooting, the turbulent elements which are of primary importance in diffusing air pollutants (*3*). A wind vane especially designed for turbulence measurements in air pollution investigations has proved satisfactory in extensive field use (*10*).

b. Bivanes. A bivane is a special type of wind vane which is designed to measure wind direction fluctuations in vertical planes as well as those in horizontal planes. Synchro generators rotate with the vertical and horizontal mounting shafts of the instrument. The synchro

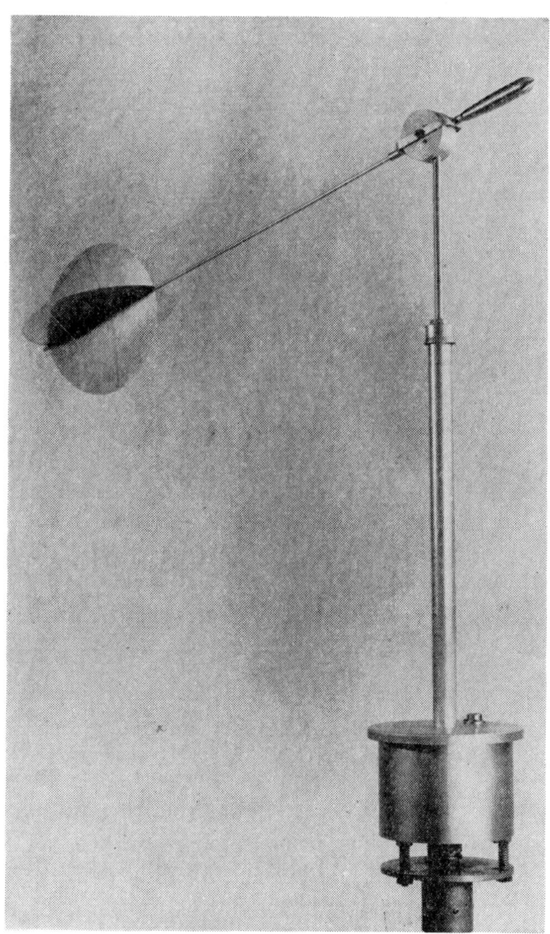

FIG. 6. All-weather rapid response bivane. (After G. C. Gill.)

receivers actuate recording instruments which give by separate traces the azimuth and elevation angles of the fluctuating wind velocity vector (*14*). A rapid response bivane of novel design uses microtorque potentiometers instead of synchro generators and receivers (*15*); an all-weather version of this bivane is shown in Figs. 6 and 7. Both microtorque potentiometers are located in the cylindrical housing at the base of the instrument, as indicated in Fig. 7. Changes in azimuth angle of the bivane are transmitted to one potentiometer by gearing. Changes of elevation angle are transmitted to the other potentiometer by a bead chain which passes over a pulley in the upper cylindrical housing, shown in Fig. 6, and under an equal pulley in the lower housing, in the manner shown in Fig. 7. The elevation angle potentiometer is located behind the pulley and on the same horizontal shaft with it.

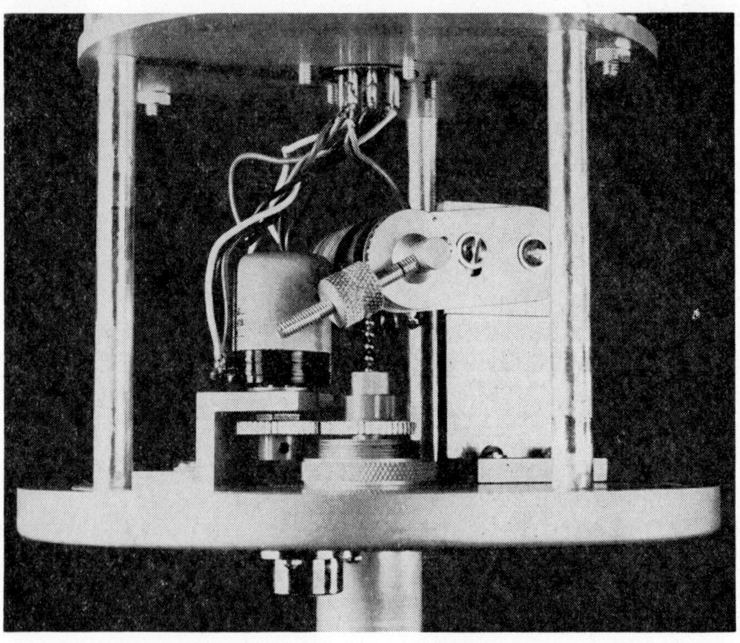

Fig. 7. Base of all-weather rapid response bivane showing location and operation of microtorque potentiometers. (After G. C. Gill.)

Another type of bivane uses a simple counting mechanism to indicate turbulence, which makes it especially suitable for air pollution investigations (*16, 17*). Both the horizontal and vertical shafts of rotation of the bivane have ratchet mechanisms attached to them. A light gear train is driven, using a gentle friction clutch, by the shaft bearing the two vanes and counterweight, as the downwind portion of the shaft descends. As the latter ascends, the ratchet mechanism prevents a corresponding opposite rotation of the gear train. When the vertical shaft rotates in response to changes in the horizontal component of wind direction, a similar clutch and ratchet device permits movement of the gear train in one direction but prevents its movement in the opposite direction. Contacts are made with each 1000° or submultiple of motion in one direction. The number of changes in direction of the bivane may also be recorded if desired. Turbulence data are recorded as "pips" on a strip chart. A bivane of this type has given satisfactory service for a number of years at the plants of the American Smelting and Refining Company near Salt Lake City, Utah.

c. Anemometers. Turbulent winds are characterized by fluctuations in wind speed, and their horizontal components of turbulence may thus be evaluated by means of a suitable recording anemometer. The recording anemometers described earlier in the section on surface wind speed are suitable for this purpose; the only exception is the totalizing cup anemometer which, because it counts cup rotations rather than gives instantaneous wind speeds, records only the long period wind fluctuations caused by very large eddies, and makes no record of the short period fluctuations which are due to the passage of smaller eddies.

The rotation anemometers are, with the exception noted above, generally satisfactory for turbulence measurements in most air pollution investigations. The heavier rotation anemometers, with a large moment of inertia, accelerate more rapidly in an increasing wind than they decelerate in a decreasing wind. Errors of this type have been analyzed in detail (*3, 18, 19*). Precision cup anemometers with low friction and a small moment of inertia, in which such errors are negligibly small, are available (*13, 20–22*).

A precision cup anemometer is shown in Fig. 5. In the cylindrical housing at the base of the cup anemometer there is a photocell and light source with a shutter or chopper to introduce a number of pulses per revolution of the cups (*22*). In the translation unit the electrical pulses from the wind speed transducer are fed into the grid of a subminiature amplifier tube. An electromechanical relay operates in the plate circuit of this tube. With each pulse this relay causes capacitors to charge and discharge through an R–C circuit into the recorder, tending to smooth out the pulses. Two sets of capacitors are provided in the translator to give two speed ranges with a given transducer. Precision instruments of this type are very suitable for wind turbulence measurements.

A rapid response hot-wire anemometer has been designed to provide accurate measurements of the vertical components of wind turbulence (*23*). The temperature changes of the hot wires caused by the changes of the wind speed are detected by a thermometric bridge and, by means of a circuit with feedback control, an electrical signal is constructed which is linearly related to the velocity. Two such anemometers properly positioned will give a continuous record of both upward and downward components of wind turbulence. The time constants vary from about 0.3 to 0.1 sec. for wind speeds of from ½ to 10 m./sec. An instrument of this type will be especially valuable if accurate knowledge of the vertical diffusion of air pollution is required. The same precautions in the use of such an instrument, mentioned earlier, must be observed.

Special investigations may require the use of anemometers of the pressure-tube, pressure-plate, or hot-wire type for turbulence measure-

FIG. 8. Gust accelerometer for direct measurements of horizontal component of turbulence. (After E. W. Hewson and G. C. Gill.)

ments. The requirements should be analyzed carefully, however, to make certain that one of the relatively simple rotation anemometers will not be adequate for the study.

d. Gust Accelerometers. As its name implies, the gust accelerometer is an instrument which gives a direct recording of turbulent wind acceleration, positive and negative, for any specified time interval. The sensor is a horizontal aluminum wheel around whose periphery are equally spaced, vertical curved blades, each of the same size and shape; as illustrated in Fig. 8, this wheel is attached to the top of a vertical shaft mounted in bearings (*1, 10*). The rotation of this shaft in response to wind forces is bridled and linearized by sets of steel springs, shown in Fig. 9. As a result of this constraint the wheel does not turn freely like a cup anemometer, but rotates in one direction as the wind speed

FIG. 9. Gust accelerometer detail showing bridling and linearizing systems of springs and counting disc and mercury switch. (After E. W. Hewson and G. C. Gill.)

increases and in the opposite direction as the wind speed decreases. Maximum rotation of the blades is limited by stops to one complete revolution.

The instrument indicates or records directly the average gust acceleration during any time interval. A circular disc having a series of uniformly spaced, small permanent magnets around its periphery is concentrically mounted near the base of the vertical shaft, as illustrated in Fig. 9. As this disc rotates back and forth, the magnets pass in succession close to a small mercury switch, and actuate it. Each opening and closing of the switch may be counted directly by a suitable counter, or each may be recorded by the deflection of a recording pen trace on a moving chart, which may then be totaled for any chosen period. Horizontal gust acceleration is given directly. For example, if there is one make or one break for each change of wind speed of 2 mi./hr., then the total number of makes and breaks in an hour is numerically equal to one-half the horizontal turbulent acceleration in miles per hour per hour. Hence 400 recording pen deflections in an hour denote an average turbulent acceleration of 800 mi./hr.[2]

A prime advantage of this instrument is that it gives directly a numerical measure of turbulence. The gust accelerometer was adopted as a standard instrument for turbulence measurements by the Trail Smelter Arbitral Tribunal, in drawing up its code of regulations for the maximum permissible emission of SO_2 from the plant of the Consolidated Mining & Smelting Company of Canada, Ltd., at Trail, British Columbia (*10*). A gust accelerometer has operated for years with a minimum of maintenance at Sudbury, Ontario, near the Copper Cliff plants of the International Nickel Company.

e. Kite Balloons. A convenient method of obtaining for limited periods of time an estimate of the turbulence at some height above the surface, e.g., at the height of a smoke plume, is by the use of a kite balloon. The captive balloon is flown at the specified height, and the varying tension on the cable is measured as an indicator of the fluctuating wind forces acting on the balloon (*10*). The wind forces acting on the fine-wire tethering cable are negligible in comparison with those acting on the kite balloon.

A simple but effective device is the use of a spring balance with a linear commutator attached to the spring. One end of the balance is attached to some fixed object and the other end is attached to the balloon cable. Varying wind forces on the balloon cause the spring to extend or contract and the commutator to make and break contacts in proportion to the changing tension in the cable. The makes and breaks may be counted or recorded to give a measure of the turbulence at the height of the balloon.

The chief drawback of the method is that the balloon must be refilled at intervals and the anticipated weather followed carefully, so that the balloon may be reeled in if high and squally winds threaten.

2. *Indirect Measurements of Wind Turbulence*

Indirect measurements are those which permit an estimate of the degree of vertical stability or instability of the atmosphere. One indicator of such stability or instability is the measured rate of change of temperature with height.

a. Temperature Lapse Rate. The rate of temperature *decrease* with increasing height is known as the temperature lapse rate. When the temperature of unsaturated air drops off rapidly with height, at a rate greater than 1°C./100 m., the air is unstable, and turbulence and mixing are pronounced. When the rate of decrease is less than 1°C./100 m. the air is relatively stable, and turbulence and mixing are less but still appreciable. Finally, if the temperature increases with height—a condition known as an *inversion*—the air is very stable and turbulence and mixing are very small in the vertical but still substantial in the horizontal. For saturated air the limiting lapse rate between instability and stability is less, ranging from about 0.4°C./100 m. for very warm air to about 0.9°C./100 m. for very cold air.

The most satisfactory method of measuring temperature lapse rates for air pollution studies is the use of a series of temperature sensors mounted on a tower. Since the temperature differences are often small over the height of the tower, it is sometimes necessary to use differential sensors, such as differential thermocouples, to achieve acceptable accuracy, although carefully calibrated and maintained resistance thermometers or thermistors may be adequate. If differential thermocouples are installed at several heights on the tower, a stepping switch may be used to take the output from each pair of thermocouples in succession to a sensitive recording potentiometer. The lapse rate installation on the 30-m. tower at the site of the Enrico Fermi Nuclear Power Plant, at the west end of Lake Erie a few miles to the northeast of Monroe, Michigan, is of this type. The iron-constantan thermojunctions have an output of 50 μv./°C. and a time constant of 1 min. Using a Bristol High-Speed Dynamaster Recorder with zero input at the center of the chart and a range of $\pm$500 μv., the system records temperature differences of $\pm$10°C. with an accuracy of $\pm$0.1°C. for those atmospheric layers in succession at 1-min. intervals (*24*).

Temperature lapse rate observations to heights of 500 m. may be made by an instrument known as a *wiresonde,* in which the sensor is carried aloft by a kite balloon. In one type the sensor is a ceramic rod whose electrical resistance varies with temperature (*25*). Another type uses a thermistor (*26*). Soundings are taken by allowing the kite balloon to ascend to a specified height and then measuring the electrical resistance of the sensor, and hence its temperature, by means of a Wheatstone bridge on the ground. The balloon then ascends to the next height and a reading is made, and so on. Heights are computed by multiplying the footage of cable paid out by the sine of the elevation angle of the balloon. Neglecting the curvature of the cable results in an error of less than 2% under ordinary operating conditions. Use of a wiresonde is indicated when a relatively small number of lapse rate measurements is required, or when measurements are required at a number of locations. A wiresonde will be very expensive to operate for a long series of measurements.

A method of obtaining lapse rates up to 1 km. is provided by the cold propellant *rocketsonde* (*26a*). This is a recoverable radio telemetering instrument designed to be carried aloft by a cold propellant rocket which rises to heights of 1 km. Transmission of pressure, temperature, and relative humidity data occurs as the instrument is lowered at 3 m./sec. by means of a self contained parachute. The complete unit including batteries, but without the propellant, weighs 0.9 kg. Over heavily forested terrain, for example, where the probability of recovery is low in comparison with that over open country, the convenience of this instrument tends to be offset by the cost of replacements.

Lapse rates at still greater heights may be measured by an assembly of pressure, temperature, and humidity sensors carried aloft by a freely rising balloon. The data are transmitted by radio from the assembly to a ground receiver. Such measuring equipment is known as a *radiosonde* (*4*). If this equipment is combined with radio or radar theodolites for upper wind determinations, the apparatus is called a *rawinsonde* (*7a*).

b. Radiation. In some circumstances the existing lapse rate may be related to the net radiational gain or loss of heat at the ground. After sunrise on a clear morning the incoming solar radiation absorbed by the ground exceeds the loss of heat from the ground by outward terrestrial radiation, so that the ground warms and the air above is in turn heated by the ground below. If the incoming radiation is strong and the wind light, the lapse rate of temperature soon exceeds 1°C./100 m., and an unstable layer of air with marked turbulence develops upward from the ground. On a night with clear skies and light winds the ground cools by terrestrial radiation and the air above is in turn cooled, leading to the development of an upward-growing inversion layer from the ground, in which vertical turbulence and diffusion are very small.

A convenient instrument for measuring the net radiational heat gain or loss is the thermal radiometer (*27–30*). Such an instrument consists essentially of a radiation sensor in the form of a thin horizontal plate, usually square and 130 $cm.^2$ or less in area, a blower, and a nozzle for directing a steady flow of air over the upper and lower surfaces of the plate and thus eliminating the variable cooling effect of changes in the natural wind. The sensor consists of a thermopile made up of a series of thermocouples which are so located that one set of thermojunctions is in a plane adjacent and parallel to the upper surface of the plate and the other set of thermojunctions is in a plane adjacent and parallel to the lower surface of the plate. The plate is of a sandwich type of construction, with the thermopile located between sheets of an electrical insulating material such as Bakelite or glass, and covered above and below with sheet aluminum, the outer surfaces of which have been blackened. Fig. 10 is a cross sectional sketch of a typical plate assembly.

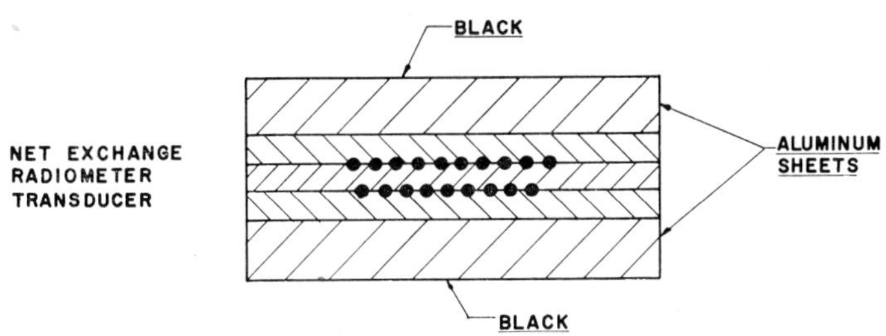

FIG. 10. Cross section of typical radiometer sensing element.

Differential radiational heating or cooling of the upper and lower blackened surfaces establishes a vertical temperature gradient whose magnitude is proportional to the output of the thermopile, which may be taken directly to a recording potentiometer.

The radiometer will not operate satisfactorily if rain, snow, fog, dew, or frost is deposited on the sensor. Exposure to heavy rain or hail or to atmospheres heavily polluted with particulates make reblackening and recalibration necessary. Light rain will not change the calibration and may help to maintain accuracy by washing away deposits of soot and dust. During one 6-month period of continuous operation the calibration constants did not vary by more than $\pm 5\%$.

Radiometer measurements are a less reliable indicator of turbulence than are temperature lapse rate measurements. Near large bodies of water and during seasons when the temperature of rapidly moving air masses is markedly greater or less than that of the underlying surface, radiometer measurements will have little or no relation to wind turbulence.

c. Smoke Plume Photography. Another indirect method of estimating wind turbulence is by determining photographically the rate of growth, both vertically and horizontally, of a smoke plume (*30a–d*). The technique is particularly appropriate for air pollution studies, since it utilizes the diffusion resulting from wind turbulence. The ratios of plume dimensions only, not absolute magnitudes, are required; this minimizes difficulties which might arise when photographing the plume against backgrounds affording limited contrast. Time exposures are desirable to give the average dimensions of the plume. The method has a number of advantages, but fails when the visibility is low owing to fog or low cloud or to contaminants from other sources.

III. Secondary Meteorological Measurements

There are a number of meteorological elements which are significant in air pollution processes and evaluation but which, in general, tend to be of secondary importance. In particular situations, however, one or more of these may be of primary significance.

A. Visibility

Visibility is defined as the greatest horizontal distance at which an object of specified characteristics can be seen and identified in any particular circumstances or, in the case of night observations, could be seen and identified if the general illumination were raised to the normal daylight level. Visibility is a quantity that may give some indication of air pollution by particulate matter, but the use of visibility observations for such a purpose presents a number of problems (*31–33a*).

1. *Systems of Markers*

Around any observing station a number of visibility marks, such as dark objects which appear against the horizon sky, are chosen, and the distance to each from the point of observation determined. For daylight observations, the marks are prominent objects on the skyline. For night observations, the marks are specified lights in the area. The visibility of the lights is converted into daylight visibility by a comparison of the visibility before and after sundown in the same meteorological situation. The observer then makes his estimate of the visibility by noting the farthest visibility mark that he is able to distinguish clearly, and then noting whether the visibility in other directions is about the same.

The visibility in a single direction, or the prevailing visibility based on all directions, may be specified. Observations should be made with reference to a plane 6 ft. above the ground or as close as possible to this plane. Standard practice, adopted by the Weather Bureau, Air Force, and Navy (WBAN) of the United States for joint use (*34*), calls for visibility to be reported at land stations in statute miles, to the nearest value given in Table I. When the visibility is halfway between two reportable values, the lower value should be selected. For more detailed instructions, one of the manuals on standard observing practice should be consulted (*2, 34*).

TABLE I
REPORTABLE VISIBILITY VALUES

Increments of separation (miles)							
$\frac{1}{16}$	$\frac{1}{8}$		$\frac{1}{4}$	$\frac{1}{2}$	1		5
Reportable visibility values (miles)							
0	$\frac{3}{8}$	$1\frac{1}{4}$	2	$2\frac{1}{2}$	3	10	15[a]
$\frac{1}{16}$	$\frac{1}{2}$	$1\frac{3}{8}$	$2\frac{1}{4}$	3	4	11	20
$\frac{1}{8}$	$\frac{5}{8}$	$1\frac{1}{2}$	$2\frac{1}{2}$	—	5	12	25
$\frac{3}{16}$	$\frac{3}{4}$	$1\frac{5}{8}$	—	—	6	13	30
$\frac{1}{4}$	$\frac{7}{8}$	$1\frac{3}{4}$	—	—	7	14	35
$\frac{5}{16}$	1	$1\frac{7}{8}$	—	—	8	15[a]	40
$\frac{3}{8}$	$1\frac{1}{8}$	2	—	—	9	—	etc.

[a] "15+" is recorded when the visibility is estimated to be greater than 15 miles and suitable markers beyond 15 miles are not available.

2. *Transmissometers*

As the name implies, a transmissometer measures the transmission of light by a portion of the atmosphere. The instrument consists essen-

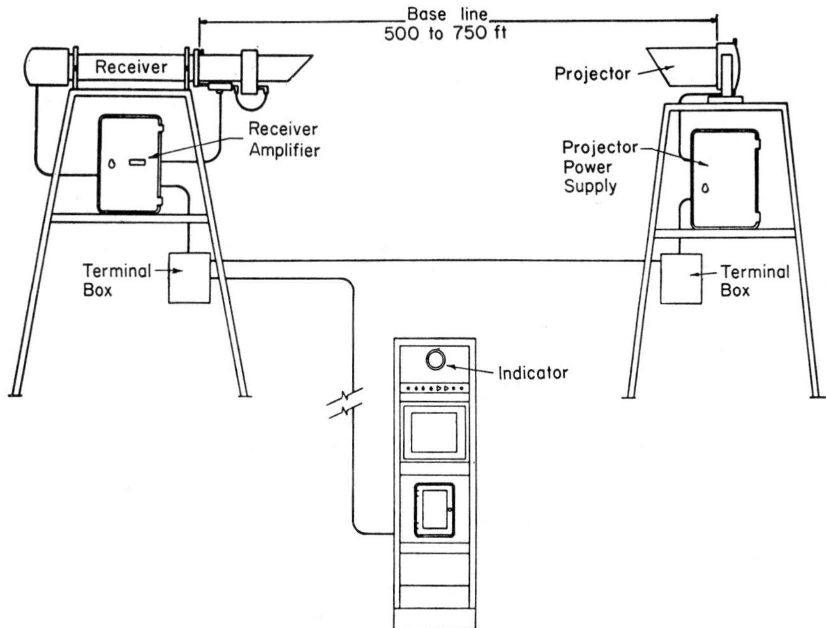

FIG. 11. Schematic diagram of a typical transmissometer installation. (Courtesy of United States Weather Bureau.)

tially of an intense source of carefully focused light and, at an appropriate distance—500 ft. is sometimes chosen—a photocell receiver, on which the light from the source is focused, as illustrated in Fig. 11 (*34a*). If necessary, the indicating and recording apparatus may be located as far as 10 mi. from the sensing equipment (*35*). The output of the photocell varies with the amount and size of obscuring particulate matter between source and receiver.

The greatest usefulness of a transmissometer is in giving a continuous record of the absence or presence in significant amounts of particulate contaminants along a specified path, e.g., between a possible source of pollution and a sensitive area such as a residential district. The general utility of the transmissometer is limited by the fact that, unlike a human observer, it can estimate the visibility in one direction only.

3. *Telephotometers*

The telephotometer utilizes the principle that a perfectly black target viewed from a distance appears gray or white due to light scattered by the haze between the observer and the target. One convenient model operates as follows (*36*). A photometer or photocell and amplifiier alternatively views the target and the horizon sky by means of a long focus lens. A motor-driven diaphragm with two different apertures produces successive images of the target and the horizon sky on the photocell, the output of which is taken to a recorder.

A telephotometer operates satisfactorily with a much shorter light path than a transmissometer, which may be advantageous in certain circumstances. On the other hand, the telephotometer requires a clear view of the horizon sky, which the transmissometer does not require. In heavily built-up areas where the horizon sky is not visible, the transmissometer is therefore the preferred instrument, provided that a sufficiently long unobstructed light path is available.

A variety of other instruments have been devised for measuring the optical properties of the atmosphere (*3, 32, 36a,b*), but in general their use has been limited.

B. Humidity

Of the various means by which atmospheric humidity may be expressed, the relative humidity is the most frequently used in air pollution studies. The degree of corrosion by SO_2, for example, is closely related to the relative humidity. The relative humidity of the atmosphere will also have an important bearing on the length of the visible plume from a stack whose effluent is warm and has a high water vapor content: as the plume cools by mixing with the ambient atmosphere, some of this water vapor will condense and become visible as small droplets which persist much longer in an atmosphere with high relative humidity than in one with a low relative humidity.

Three humidity-measuring devices will be described briefly: the wet and dry bulb hygrometer, or psychrometer; the hair hygrometer; and the infrared hygrometer.

1. *Wet and Dry Bulb Hygrometer*

This instrument consists essentially of two thermometers, one with its temperature-sensing element covered with a piece of muslin which is moistened by a suitable means, and the other identical except for the moistened muslin. In saturated air the two thermometers give the same reading. In unsaturated air, evaporation from the wet bulb occurs, lowering its temperature (*37*). The relative humidity is then obtained from tables. An alternate name for this instrument is the psychrometer.

The muslin covering the wet bulb must be wet. In one type of psychrometer water is carried from a container along a wick to the muslin, thus keeping it wet; a motor-driven fan causes a steady flow of air past the wet bulb which is necessary to ensure a steady-state, accurate reading (*38*). The sling psychrometer consists of two thermometers mounted side by side on a frame which is attached by a swivel connector to a handle; the bulb of one is covered by tubular gauze. The gauze-covered bulb is dipped in water, and the framework and two thermometeters are whirled steadily (*38*). The instrument must be whirled until a steady rate of evaporational cooling leads to a wet bulb reading which is constant with time. If the whirling continues too long, all the water in the muslin will evaporate and the indicated reading will rise to that of the dry bulb thermometer. A hand-aspirated psychrometer employing a rubber hand pump for ventilation of the wet bulb is also available (*38*).

2. *Hair Hygrometer*

The sensor in the hair hygrometer is a group of human hairs kept extended to their full length by light tension applied to one end of the group. Human hair elongates slightly as the relative humidity increases and shortens slightly as it decreases. These changes in length with varying humidity are magnified and read directly in the indicating instrument or recorded by a pen making a trace on a moving chart (*38*). For temperatures between 0 and 30°C., and for relative humidities between 20 and 80%, a good hair hygrometer will, if subjected to an abrupt change in relative humidity, register 90% of the true change in about 3 min. At lower temperatures the rate of response is much slower. Full descriptions of the operational characteristics, maintenance requirements, etc., for both psychrometers and hair hygrometers are available (*1–4*).

3. *Infrared Hygrometer*

A more accurate and also more complex instrument known as an infrared hygrometer gives mass of water vapor per unit volume of air by comparing the relative absorption of infrared radiation over a 1-m. path or less by the 1.37 μ water vapor absorption band with that by a 1.24 μ reference band, the absorption at the latter wave length being effectively zero. The details of the instrument are shown schematically in Fig. 12. The beam from an infrared lamp is chopped by a sector wheel driven at 900 r.p.m. and consisting of four 1.37 μ filters and four 1.24 μ filters each 45° and positioned alternately in the wheel. Detection of the chopped infrared beam is made by a lead sulfide photocell and amplifier operating a self-balancing null system whereby the energy in the absorption band is kept equal at all times to the energy in the reference band. Balance is maintained by automatically varying the temperature of the lamp supplying the infrared energy, and the temperature of the lamp is a measure of the water vapor in the sensing path. An index of the lamp temperature is obtained by a monitor photocell which drives a remote self-balancing recording potentiometer (*38, 39*).

The prime advantage of the method is that no phase change or absorption of water vapor is involved and, consequently, there are no complications at subfreezing temperatures: there is no decrease in sensitivity at low temperature and low vapor concentrations. Smoke in small or medium concentrations has no appreciable influence on the readings, but at very high concentrations errors are caused by differential scattering effects. Polluted atmospheres containing gaseous contaminants having absorption bands at 1.24 or 1.37 μ or both may produce erroneous readings.

Other types of hygrometers are also available (*3, 4, 4a*).

C. Precipitation

Rain may be significant by virtue of its ability to wash out water-soluble contaminant gases and particulate matter having dimensions greater than 1 μ. The washout by precipitation of airborne radioactive wastes is a matter of particular concern. For discussions of special problems such as accuracy, aerodynamic effects, measurement of snowfall, etc., see (*2–4*).

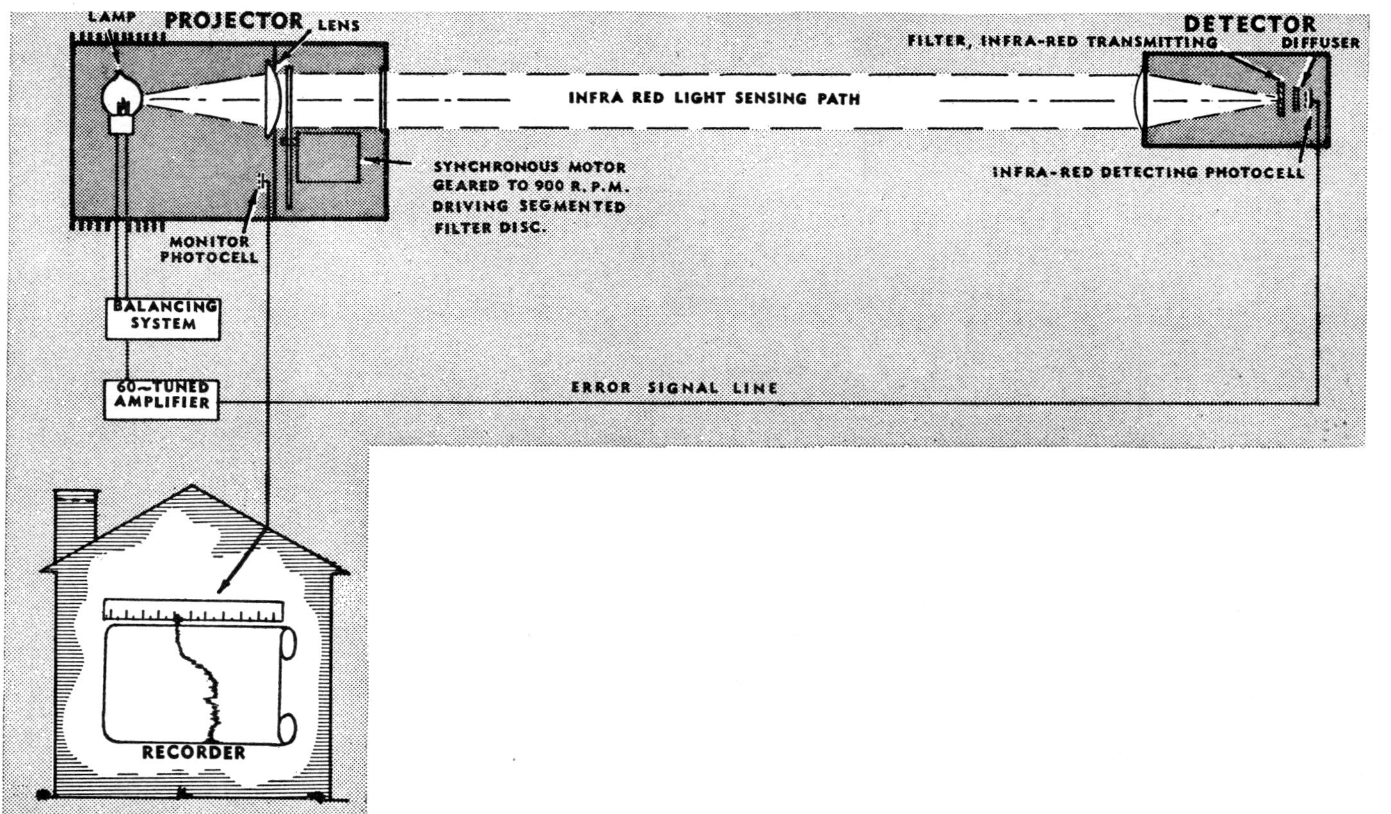

FIG. 12. Schematic diagram illustrating principle of operation of the infrared hygrometer. (Courtesy of United States Weather Bureau.)

1. *Simple Rain Gage*

The simple rain gage consists essentially of a funnel supported with its mouth horizontal and with a collecting vessel located below. To prevent rain from splashing in and out, the top of the funnel should consist of a cylinder with its axis vertical, and the slope of the funnel should be steep, at least 45°. The outlet of the funnel should be small, to minimize evaporational losses.

To permit accurate measurement of precipitation amounts, the inside cross sectional area of the collector is often $\frac{1}{10}$th of that of the mouth of the funnel, giving a magnification of 10 in measuring the depth of the collected water. The collector may be a glass vessel with suitable units of depth or volume engraved on it for direct readings, or it may be of metal, and a dip stick may be used to measure the amount of precipitation.

2. *Weighing Rain Gage*

The simplest of the recording gages weighs the rain, hail, sleet, or snow which is funneled into a bucket having a 12-in. rainfall capacity. The weighing mechanism converts the weight of precipitation to its equivalent in inches and actuates a pen arm which traces a record on a moving 6-in. chart. This instrument is particularly appropriate for use in climatic regions having cold winters, when the funnel is removed to allow free entry of snow into the bucket, and a salt antifreeze solution is placed in the bucket to prevent damage by freezing and to permit rapid emptying. Fresh antifreeze must be added after each emptying. For subtropical regions and areas with low rainfall another type of weighing instrument has been developed (*39a*).

3. *Tipping Bucket Rain Gage*

In this instrument, the rain leaving the funnel runs into a container divided into two equal compartments by a partition (Fig. 13). The container when empty, is designed to balance in unstable equilibrium about a horizontal axis, and in its normal position is tilted, as shown, with one side or the other resting against a stop. When a specified small amount of rain, usually 0.01 in., has drained from the funnel into the upper compartment, the bucket tilts the opposite way, so that the compartment containing the rain comes to rest against the stop on the opposite side, the rain empties out, and the other compartment commences to fill. The amount and intensity of the rain are given by the number and rate of bucket movements (*2–4*).

Since this gage does not measure snowfall, it is unsuitable for cold winter use; electrical heating will melt the snow but will also increase evaporation to an undesirable degree.

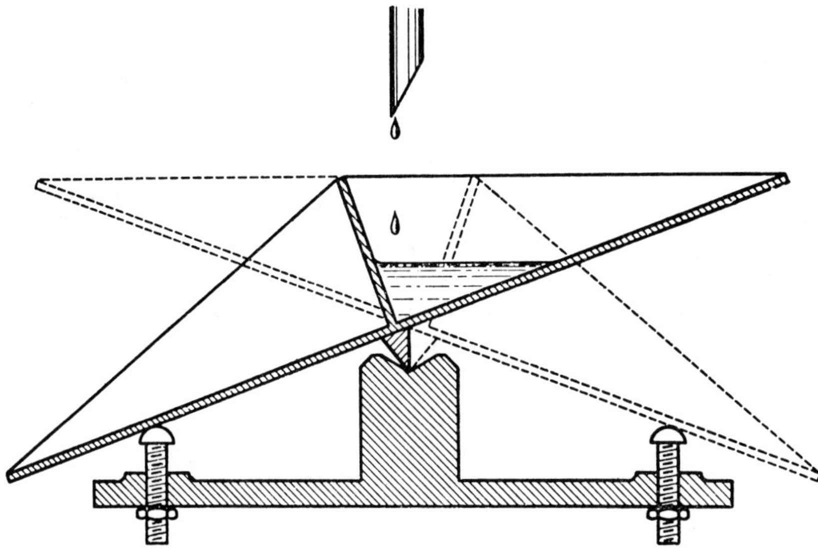

FIG. 13. Principle of tipping bucket rain gage. (Reproduced from Fig. 90 in M.O.577 "Handbook of Meteorological Instruments Part I" by permission of the Controller of Her Britannic Majesty's Stationery Office.)

4. *Radar Measurements*

Radar has proved to be a powerful tool in the analysis of precipitation patterns and of precipitating clouds (*40*). A mobile weather radar, which can be taken to practically any area of interest for precipitation studies is shown in Fig. 14; Fig. 15 is a photograph taken with this radar. The technique of evaluation of radar precipitation patterns has advanced to such a stage that these will give information on the precipitation amounts over a large area, equivalent to that to be gained from a network of one rain gage per 100 sq. mi.

There is little doubt that weather radar technology will be used increasingly in air pollution studies in which washout by rain is an important factor. Weather radar will be particularly valuable for precipitation washout studies over areas where it is difficult if not impossible to maintain regular rain gages, such as over the Great Lakes.

D. SOLAR RADIATION

In an earlier section the thermal radiometer was mentioned as an appropriate instrument for assisting in making a rough indirect estimate

FIG. 14. Mobile weather radar for precipitation studies.

of turbulence and diffusion. Solar radiation is important in another way: it has been shown to cause highly significant photochemical reactions in smogs (*41, 42*). It may therefore be necessary in some air pollution investigations to make direct measurements of the amount of solar radiation.

The various instruments which may be used to measure the radiant energy received from the sun are known as actinometers. In one of the simpler types of actinometers, two bimetallic strips lie side by side under a glass dome. The blackened strip is heated more by the sun than the reflecting strip, leading to a differential bending of the strips which actuates the arm holding the recording pen.

A more accurate instrument of the actinometer family is the Eppley pyrheliometer, in which the sensor consists of two concentric silver rings, the inner one covered with lampblack and the outer one with magnesium oxide. The temperature difference between the two rings is indicated by the output of a thermopile of either 10 or 50 junctions, which may be carried to a millivolt recorder. The thermopile sensor is mounted at the center of a 3-in. sealed glass bulb containing dry air.

More complete descriptions of various actinometers, with instructions for maintenance, etc. are available (*1–4, 43*).

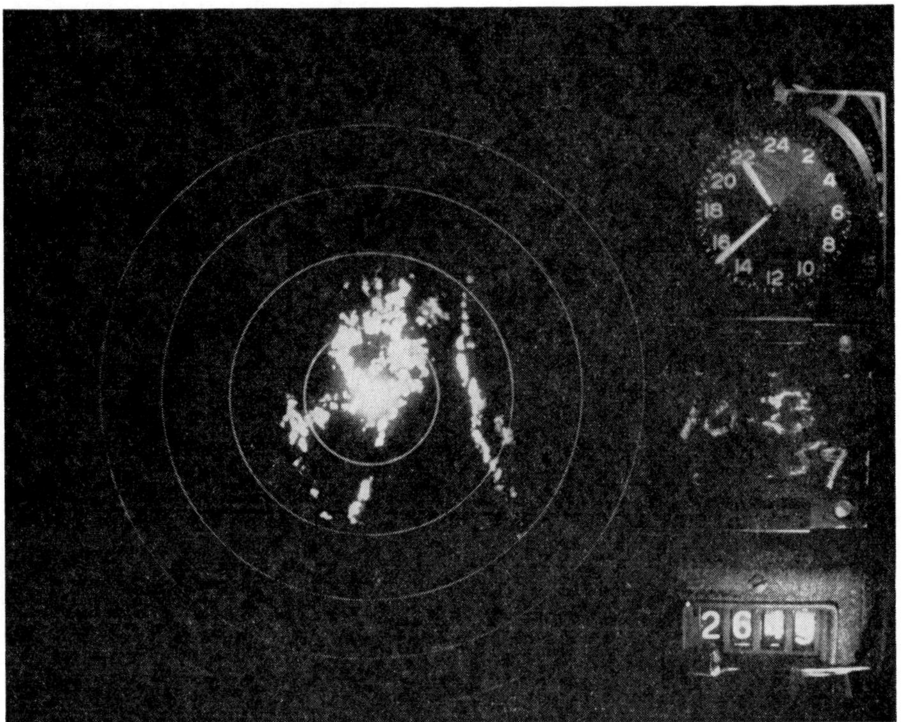

FIG. 15. Photograph taken by the mobile weather radar of a precipitating cold frontal line squall near Ann Arbor, Michigan. Concentric circles are horizontal range markers whose radii are 20, 40, 60, 80, and 100 nautical miles. Time: 9:38 P.M., November 23, 1959.

IV. Instrument Siting, Mounting, and Protection

The proper placing of instruments is necessary if representative values of the various meteorological elements are to be obtained and if trouble-free operation is to be achieved.

A. PRINCIPLES OF INSTRUMENT SITING

The cardinal principle of instrument siting is that the sensor should be located in such a position and in such a manner that it yields values of the variable which are representative of the atmosphere for the area of interest. The application of this principle to the various instruments will be illustrated in the sections below.

B. FIXED INSTRUMENTS

The discussion of fixed instruments will be divided into two sections; one on fixed instruments near the surface; and the other on fixed instruments aloft.

1. *Fixed Instruments near the Surface*

The most important group of meteorological instruments for air pollution surveys consists of the various wind instruments. Since the same criteria apply in the proper siting of instruments for measuring wind direction, wind speed, and wind turbulence, no differentiation will be made.

a. Wind Instruments. The standard exposure of wind instruments over level, open terrain is 10 m. above the ground. Open terrain is defined as an area where the distance between the anemometer and any obstruction is at least ten times the height of the obstruction. Where a standard exposure is not available, the wind instruments are often mounted at some height that is greater than 10 m. by an amount depending on the extent, height, and distance of the obstructions; the wind at this height should represent as closely as possible that which would occur at 10 m. in the absence of such obstructions. The concept of an "effective height" of the instruments in such situations has been introduced; effective height is the height over open level terrain in the vicinity of the wind sensor which, it is estimated, would have the same mean wind characteristics as those actually recorded by the existing sensor with its various obstructions (*3*). Thus the effective height above a given point on the ground might be different for wind vanes, anemometers, and bivanes, and might be a function of wind direction and wind speed as well. Unfortunately, the concept gives no firm guidance in determining the effective height, which in the final analysis is a matter of individual judgment.

The difficult problem of the exposure of wind instruments is discussed in greater detail in other publications (*2–4*).

b. Radiation Instruments. Two essentials for correct exposure of these are (1) that the site should provide an uninterrupted view of the sun at all times of the year, throughout the whole period when it is above the horizon; and (2) that the recorder should be firmly fixed to a rigid support. It may be advantageous to install the instrument on the roof of a building. For more complete discussions, see (*3*), (*4*).

c. Visibility Instruments. Since most visibility data used in air pollution analyses have been visual observations of systems of markers, and since very few specially planned and designed programs of instrumental observations for air pollution surveys have been undertaken, there is little experience available on which to base sound advice on the siting of visibility instruments. As mentioned earlier, in built-up areas the transmissometer has advantages over the telephotometer when a long enough, unobstructed light path between source and receiver is available.

Another obvious guiding principle is that the visibility should be measured in areas and directions and at heights of primary concern for the particular air pollution problem under consideration.

d. Humidity Instruments. Hygrometers without artificial ventilation are usually located about 4 to 5 ft. above the ground in instrument shelters with louvered sides which insure a free flow of air past the sensor and at the same time provide protection from heating by solar radiation. With artificial ventilation, which should be at the rate of at least 4 m./sec., shielding from radiation must be provided. Instruments should also be located away from buildings and other objects which may have temperatures appreciably higher or lower than that of the air at the same height over open ground. A roof location should be avoided in favor of an open ground site if the latter is available.

e. Precipitation Instruments. The optimum location of rain gages presents a difficult problem because the catch tends to be related to the local structure of the wind. Local eddies induced by the gage itself usually decrease the amount of water collected. On the other hand,

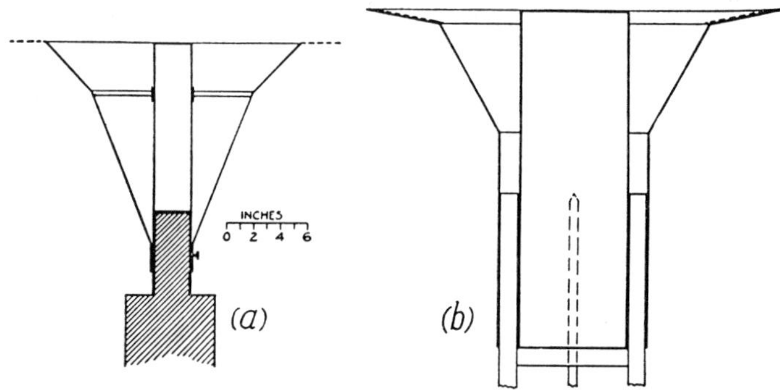

FIG. 16. Typical wind shields for precipitation gages: (*a*) original Nipher shield; (*b*) shield recommended by Brooks (*44*). (From W. E. K. Middleton and A. F. Spilhaus, "Meteorological Instruments," University of Toronto Press, Toronto, Ontario, Canada.)

eddies caused by the local topography and nearby objects may either increase or decrease the catch, depending on particular circumstances. Wherever possible, the rain gage should be exposed with its mouth horizontal over level ground, and surrounding objects should not be closer than a distance equal to four times their height. Subject to this limitation, however, a site that is sheltered from the full force of the wind should be chosen.

Slope and roof sites are generally unsatisfactory. The mouth of the gage should be high enough to prevent rain from splashing in, but no higher. Another method of minimizing wind errors is to provide a wind shield for the gage; many types of shields have been proposed (*2–4, 44*). (Fig. 16.)

2. *Fixed Instruments Mounted on Towers*

The two important categories of instruments to be considered here are those for measuring wind and those for measuring temperature lapse rate.

a. Wind Instruments. Wind instruments on towers are preferably mounted at the end of horizontal booms extending outward a minimum distance equal to the maximum horizontal dimension of the tower at that height. The resulting errors when this rule is not observed have been analyzed (*44a*). A logarithmic spacing in the vertical is often advantageous, e.g., at 10, 20, 40, and 80 m. Provision for bringing the instruments near the tower for servicing, as by using a telescoping boom, must be made. For various methods of mounting wind instruments, see (*45*).

Wind instruments have also been mounted on horizontal booms extending horizontally from a stack, at distances as specified above. Because of the disturbance of the wind field by the stack, however, such instruments will give accurate measurements for wind directions from half the compass only. For example, instruments on a boom extending southward will give reliable results only for winds from the east, south, and west and intermediate directions. If winds from all directions must be analyzed, a second instrumented boom extending in the opposite direction, e.g., northward, must be installed and used for winds with a northerly component.

b. Temperature Lapse Rate Measurements. The temperature sensors should be mounted on horizontal booms, as in the case of the wind instruments, in order to avoid measuring the temperature of air locally heated or cooled by the tower structure. The same vertical spacing may also be used.

The sensors must also be shielded from radiational heating or cooling and from precipitation. In one type of shield, protection is afforded by one or more horizontal plates with special thermal characteristics located above and below the sensor (*46*). The wind provides natural air flow and ventilation of the air temperature sensing element. In a second type, artificial ventilation is provided by drawing air by an exhaust fan through the downward facing open end of a pipe and past the sensor near its entrance; the portion of the pipe around the sensor is made up of two concentric cylindrical linen-reinforced Bakelite tubes, the outer surface of the larger one being covered with gold leaf to minimize the absorption of solar and terrestrial radiation (*24, 47*).

Mounting temperature sensors on booms attached to a stack is unwise: even small differential errors due to the proximity to a warm stack may lead to serious errors in temperature lapse rate.

C. Movable Instruments

Movable instruments may be either surface-based or airborne.

1. *Movable Surface Instruments*

Mobile meteorological stations have been built and used in air pollution surveys, usually in conjunction with sampling programs also conducted from the mobile station (*48*).

a. Design of Mobile Meteorological Station. Many of the mobile meteorological stations consist of a truck chassis with a body of the delivery van type. When in use, all meteorological instruments must be located so as to be independent of disturbing influences caused by the presence of the truck itself. In particular, if wind instruments are mounted on the truck when in use, they should be at a minimum height above the ground, which is twice the height of the highest part of the truck, and preferably higher. The most satisfactory height is the standard height of 10 m. above the ground.

The interior layout of a rather complete mobile meteorological station mounted on a truck chassis is shown in Fig. 17. Tower sections are carried. When observations are to be made, these are assembled and erected nearby to form a guyed tower, of any specified height from 12 ft. to 75 ft. or even higher if required. Such a tower provides an excellent mounting base for instruments for measuring wind, radiation, vertical wind profile, and vertical temperature profile, i.e., temperature lapse rate. The recording equipment for these is located in the working area of the truck, as shown in Fig. 17. Radio facsimile equipment permits reception of the latest analyzed weather maps, to allow assessment of current meteorological trends of interest. There is also provision for meteorological measurements aloft by pilot balloon, wiresonde, and radiosonde.

Another type is the automatic weather station which transmits weather data at prescribed times by radio. Such automatic stations may be parachuted from aircraft into inaccessible territory or transported to a chosen site by more conventional means. Full descriptions of these have been published (*4, 49*).

b. Use of Mobile Meteorological Station. Meteorological stations of

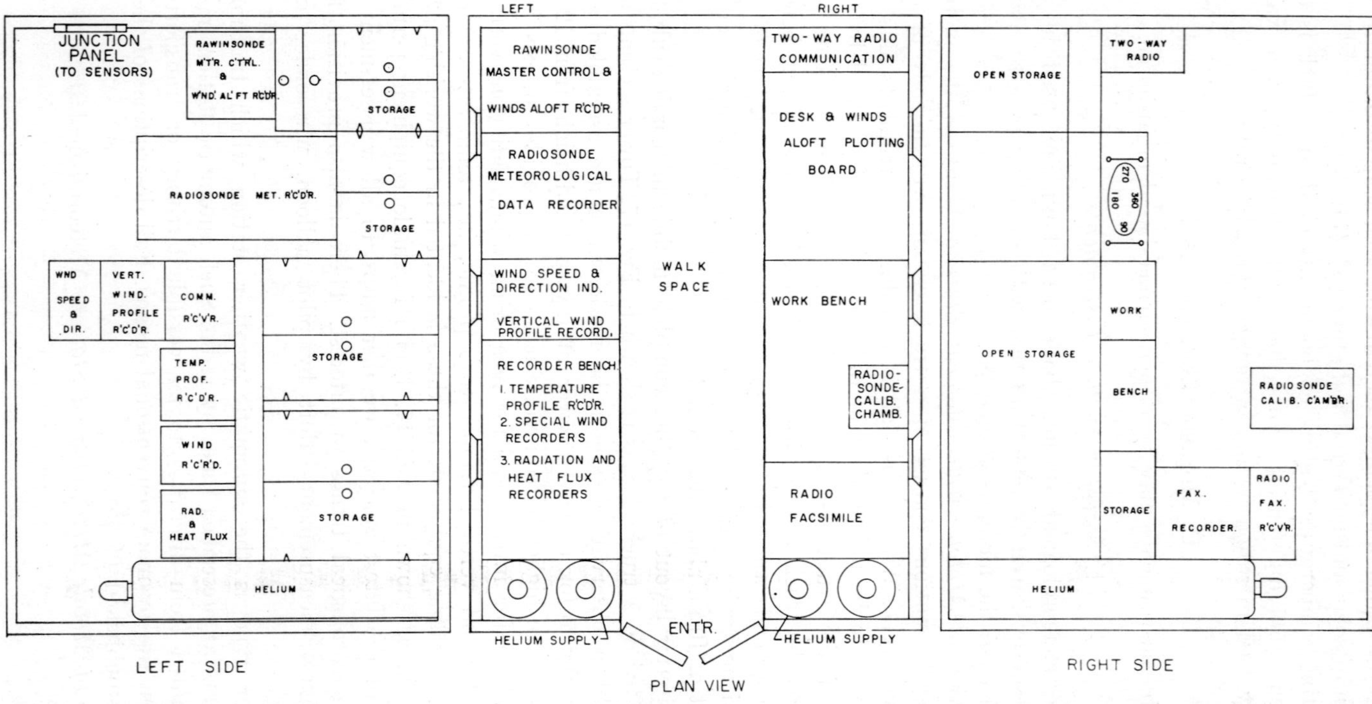

FIG. 17. Interior layout of the mobile meteorological station based at the Willow Run Field Station of the Meteorological Laboratories, The University of Michigan, Ann Arbor, Michigan.

this type are especially useful for air pollution surveys of an area where there is sufficient local difference in topography to make observations at a single fixed station unrepresentative; they are also useful for brief surveys of a number of areas. Care must be exercised, however, to be certain that the atmospheric characteristics being measured are the primary ones required. For example, the mobile station should not be set up in a pronounced hollow unless the limited air movement and stability conditions in the hollow are believed to have particular significance for the air pollution problem being studied. A site more exposed to unobstructed winds may be more appropriate. In general, the exposure criteria given earlier for fixed instruments should be met with equal care.

2. *Movable Airborne Instruments*

a. Rawinsonde. The site for radio or radar wind equipment should be on high ground with the horizon as free from obstructions as possible. A symmetrical hill with lower ground nearby and surrounded at greater distances by hills rising gently, at a slope of 1° to 2°, affords a good site; it eliminates ground echoes beyond short range (*2*).

b. Wiresonde. There are restrictions on the use of wiresondes. A wiresonde should not be operated near power lines because of the hazard both to personnel and equipment. Government regulations prohibit the flying of kite balloons and associated equipment at heights where they may be dangerous to low flying aircraft, unless special authorization has been given.* Such authorization is, generally, for limited geographical areas and for limited periods of time. Application should be made well before the planned time of wiresonde use, to permit completion of the necessary formalities.

c. Airplane, Airship, and Helicopter. These aircraft have been used primarily for atmospheric sampling of contaminants (*50–52*), but measurements of lapse rate have on occasion been made simultaneously with the sampling (*10*). A detailed discussion of instruments mounted on airplanes and their proper exposure is available (*4, 4a*). Airships have had very limited use in air pollution surveys, presumably because of their high cost of operation. As in the case of wiresondes, it is generally necessary to obtain authorization for such special flights.

V. Instrument Requirements

Instrument requirements may be classified as follows: minimum, intermediate, and maximum. Wherever possible, sampling for atmos-

* For detailed information on restrictions in the United States and procedures for applying for authorization, contact Regional Air Space Subcommittee, c/o Federal Aviation Agency, Washington 25, D. C.

pheric contaminants should be conducted simultaneously with a program of meteorological measurements; such a combined program is virtually a necessity even in a minimum investigation.

A. Minimum Instrumentation

The minimum requirement will depend on the type of source and on the topography.

1. *Single Source*

a. Level and Uniform Terrain. The minimum here is a recording wind vane and a totalizing cup anemometer at a height of 10 m., with a turbulence indicator such as a recording wind vane or a gust accelerometer at a greater height, perhaps 30 m. The lower instruments are provided to permit comparison with long period records from instruments in the area at the standard height that may be available. The higher instruments should be located at a height as nearly as possible equal to the average height of the plume. In general, a small tower is required to mount the instruments at these heights.

b. Complex Terrain. In complex terrain, more than one of the level terrain installations may be required. In a valley, instruments on the valley slopes may be needed (*10*). At a shore line location, there should be an installation of the level terrain type as near the shore line as possible (*24*). If there is a small low flat island within a mile or so of shore, a similar installation on it would be most helpful, since meteorological conditions there may be very different from those at the shore line for offshore or alongshore winds. Such differences will be especially important for a deep lake with several population centers on its shores.

2. *Multiple or Area Source*

An industrial city represents a multiple, or area, source.

a. Level or Uniform Terrain. If buildings are high in the business section, direct measurements of turbulence and wind speed, as by a gust accelerometer attached to a cable between buildings and well above street level, would be valuable. A tower instrumented, as for a single source over level terrain, should be used on a relatively unobstructed site in a neighborhood with low buildings.

b. Complex Terrain. With irregular topography, the level terrain minima above should be met, with valley-side instrumentation in addition for a city in a valley. A shore line city should have additional wind instruments at a height of 10 m., and at several distances from the shore, to determine the distance of penetration of sea or lake breezes in the late spring, summer, and early autumn.

B. Intermediate Instrumentation

The instrumentation requirements will depend, to a degree, on whether pollution from a single source or from a multiple, or area, source is being analyzed.

1. *Single Source*

In the great majority of cases, the single source of pollution will be an industrial stack. The key facility required for a program of meteorological measurements is an adequate tower on which to mount instruments. If the industrial plant is situated on a level plain and if a television tower happens to be located on the same plain, even a number of miles away, the tower would serve as an excellent mount and the atmospheric conditions at the tower could safely be taken as representative of those at the plant except, perhaps, in the amounts of shower precipitation. Such meteorological measurements have been and are being made on TV towers. Television stations in the United States have an obligation to provide a certain amount of public service without cost. Some of such stations have served the public by permitting their towers to be used for meteorological measurements needed to assess and control air pollution problems, and a wider use of more TV towers in the future may confidently be anticipated. Since only the topmost radiating antenna is electrically charged, the lower portion of the tower structure is as safe to use as a tower designed and erected for meteorological purposes.

If there is no television tower nearby, the height of the tower to be erected must be related to the average height of the plume from the stack. If possible, the top of the tower should extend to that height. For purposes of illustration, however, we may think of a tower 80 m. high, with wind vanes and totalizing cup anemometers at 10, 20, 40, and 80 m., shielded temperature sensors at 2, 20, 40, and 80 m., and a single gust accelerometer or bivane at the top. Alternatively, the wind instruments may be mounted on the stack itself, in the manner described earlier; since lapse rate measurements near a stack are not likely to be reliable, the direct turbulence measurements at the top of the stack would be relied upon for information on diffusion conditions, or additional direct turbulence indicators could be installed at lower levels if necessary.

A rain gage should be installed and perhaps a hygrometer as well. If significant photochemical reactions are suspected in a stack effluent containing hydrocarbons, a pyrheliometer should also be installed. With a valley or shore line plant location, additional wind instruments may be set up on the valley sides or near the shore, and wiresonde lapse rate measurements may be made using a kite balloon at places and times of particular interest.

2. *Multiple, or Area, Source*

The same considerations hold for a multiple, or area, source such as an industrial city. If available, one or more TV towers should be used, the number depending on the location of major sources of pollution in relation to local topographic features. Unless the terrain is very flat and uniform, a study of air pollution meteorology for a city requires a wider horizontal deployment of sensors than does a point source study. Complicated systems of valley or shore line winds or both may exist and may need detailed investigation. Wiresonde studies of the prevalence of low level inversions may be indicated.

It should be emphasized again that a full sampling program for atmospheric contaminants must be conducted simultaneously with the meteorological measurements. Either set of data is difficult to interpret without the other. In the past, the sampling programs for air quality have received greater emphasis than adequate meteorological studies, but the situation is improving in this respect, and atmospheric conditions are receiving more attention. In difficult situations, it is becoming more customary to introduce artificial tracer materials into the air and to follow their movements by air trajectory studies and sampling programs, in order to chart diffusion patterns more accurately.

If investigations of the above scope are contemplated, the services of one or more experienced air pollution meteorologists should be obtained, to insure that maximum results are achieved for the substantial investment required.

C. Maximum Instrumentation

It is impossible to make very specific recommendations for a problem so complex and so serious as to require maximum meteorological instrumentation. The range of possible combinations of atmospheric conditions, local topography, and location of sources is so great that it would be fruitless to attempt to classify them. Virtually all the instrumental resources described earlier in this chapter may be required, including wiresondes, rocketsondes, rawinsondes, aircraft observations, mobile meteorological stations, and extensive sampling, both of indigenous contaminants and of artificial tracers.

Finally, the whole meteorological program should be under the immediate direction of individuals with the highest competence in air pollution meteorology and closely coordinated with the other phases of the total investigation.

References

1. E. W. Hewson, *in* "Encyclopedia of Instrumentation for Industrial Hygiene" (C. D. Yaffe, D. H. Byers, and A. D. Hosey, eds.), p. 521. University of Michigan Institute of Industrial Health, Ann Arbor, Michigan, 1956.
2. "Guide to International Meteorological Instrument and Observing Practice," WMO—No. 8. TP. 3. World Meteorological Organization, Geneva, 1954.
3. "Handbook of Meteorological Instruments, Part I: Instruments for Surface Observations," M.O. 577. Her Majesty's Stationery Office, London, 1956.
4. W. E. K. Middleton and A. F. Spilhaus, "Meteorological Instruments," 3rd ed. University of Toronto Press, Toronto, 1953.

4a. "Handbook of Geophysics," rev. ed., Chapter 20. Macmillan, New York, 1960.

4b. G. C. Gill, H. Moses, and M. E. Smith, *J. Air Pollution Control Assoc.* **11,** 77 (1961).

4c. R. A. McCormick, *Bull. Am. Meteorol. Soc.* **41,** 175 (1960).

5. "Encyclopedia of Instrumentation for Industrial Hygiene" (C. D. Yaffe, D. H. Byers, and A. D. Hosey, eds.), pp. 567, 569, 579, 583, 608, 617, 634, and 669. University of Michigan Institute of Industrial Health, Ann Arbor, Michigan, 1956.
6. M. A. Garbell, *J. Meteorol.* **4,** 82 (1947).
7. "Encyclopedia of Instrumentation for Industrial Hygiene" (C. D. Yaffe, D. H. Byers, and A. D. Hosey, eds.), p. 607. University of Michigan Institute of Industrial Health, Ann Arbor, Michigan, 1956.

7a. T. O. Haig and V. E. Lally, *Bull. Am. Meteorol. Soc.* **39,** 401 (1958).

8. "Encyclopedia of Instrumentation for Industrial Hygiene" (C. D. Yaffe, D. H. Byers, and A. D. Hosey, eds.), pp. 579 and 583. University of Michigan Institute of Industrial Health, Ann Arbor, Michigan, 1956.
9. "Encyclopedia of Instrumentation for Industrial Hygiene" (C. D. Yaffe, D. H. Byers, and A. D. Hosey, eds.), pp. 569, 608, 617, 634, 669. University of Michigan Institute of Industrial Health, Ann Arbor, Michigan, 1956.

9a. I. Karmin, *Bull. Am. Meteorol. Soc.* **40,** 473 (1959).

10. E. W. Hewson and G. C. Gill, *in* Report Submitted to the Trail Smelter Arbitral Tribunal, by R. S. Dean and R. E. Swain. *U. S. Bur. Mines Bull.* **453,** 23 (1944).
11. R. H. Sherlock and M. B. Stout, *Univ. Mich. Eng. Research Inst. Eng. Research Bull. No.* **20,** 1931.

11a. L. J. Anderson, *Bull. Am. Meteorol. Soc.* **40,** 49 (1959).

11b. L. J. Fritschen and R. H. Shaw, *Bull. Am. Meteorol. Soc.* **42,** 42 (1961).

12. G. C. Gill, *Bull. Am. Meteorol. Soc.* **35,** 69 (1954).
13. G. West, *Electronics* **25,** No. 6, 136 (1952).
14. D. A. Mazzarella, *Bull. Am. Meteorol. Soc.* **33,** 60 (1952).
15. G. C. Gill, *in* "Encyclopedia of Instrumentation for Industrial Hygiene" (C. D. Yaffe, D. H. Byers, and A. D. Hosey, eds.), p. 627. University of Michigan Institute of Industrial Health, Ann Arbor, Michigan, 1956.
16. M. D. Thomas, *Proc. Natl. Air Pollution Symposium. 2nd Symposium, Pasadena, Calif.*, p. 16 (1952).
17. M. D. Thomas and J. O. Ivie, *J. Air Pollution Control Assoc.* **3,** 41 (1953).
18. S. P. Fergusson, *Harvard Meteorol. Studies No.* **4,** (1939).
19. G. E. W. Hartley, *Proc. Inst. Elec. Eng.* **98,** *Pt. II,* No. 64, pp. 430, 456 (1951).
20. P. A. Sheppard, *J. Sci. Instr.* **17,** 218 (1940).

21. E. L. Deacon, *J. Sci. Instr.* **25,** 44, 283 (1948).
22. "Encyclopedia of Instrumentation for Industrial Hygiene" (C. D. Yaffe, D. H. Byers, and A. D. Hosey, eds.), p. 569. University of Michigan Institute of Industrial Health, Ann Arbor, Michigan, 1956.
23. R. J. Taylor, *J. Sci. Instr.* **35,** No. 2, 47 (1958).
24. E. W. Hewson and G. C. Gill, Meteorological Installation and Analysis, p. 5. *Univ. Mich. Eng. Research Inst. Rept. No. 2515-1-P* (1957).
25. L. J. Anderson, *Bull. Am. Meteorol. Soc.* **28,** 356 (1947).
26. "Encyclopedia of Instrumentation for Industrial Hygiene" (C. D. Yaffe, D. H. Byers, and A. D. Hosey, eds.), p. 636. University of Michigan Institute of Industrial Health, Ann Arbor, Michigan, 1956.
26a. "Cricketsonde Meteorological Rocket." Baltimore, Maryland, Friez Instrument Division, The Bendix Corporation Publication EIR-392, 6 pp. (1961).
27. J. T. Gier and R. V. Dunkle, *Trans. Am. Inst. Elec. Engrs.* **70,** 339 (1951).
28. V. E. Suomi, M. Franssila, and N. F. Islitzer, *J. Meteorol.* **11,** 276 (1954).
29. J. MacDowall, *Meteorol. Mag.* **84,** 65 (1955).
30. "Encyclopedia of Instrumentation for Industrial Hygiene" (C. D. Yaffe, D. H. Byers, and A. D. Hosey, eds.), p. 565. University of Michigan Institute of Industrial Health, Ann Arbor, Michigan, 1956.
30a. A. B. Kazanskii and A. S. Monin, *Izvest. Akad. Nauk S.S.S.R., Ser. Geofiz. No.* **8,** 1020 (1957) (English translation).
30b. F. Gifford, Jr., *Intern. J. Air Pollution* **2,** 42 (1959).
30c. N. E. Bowne, *Bull. Am. Meteorol. Soc.* **42,** 101 (1961).
30d. A. R. Orban, J. D. Hummell, and G. G. Cocks, *J. Air Pollution Control Assoc.* **11,** 103 (1961).
31. E. W. Hewson, *in* "Compendium of Meteorology" (T. F. Malone, ed.), p. 1140. American Meteorological Society, Boston, Massachusetts, 1951.
32. C. Steffens, *in* "Air Pollution Handbook" (P. L. Magill, F. R. Holden, and C. Ackley, eds.), Section 6. McGraw-Hill, New York, 1956.
33. H. L. Green and W. R. Lane, "Particulate Clouds: Dusts, Smokes and Mists." E. & F. Spon, London, 1957.
33a. E. W. Burt, *Am. Ind. Hyg. Assoc. J.* **22,** 102 (1961).
34. "Manual of Surface Observations (WBAN)" Circular N, 7th ed., revised. Government Printing Office, Washington, D. C. (1957).
34a. V. D. Rockney, *Bull. Am. Meteorol. Soc.* **40,** 554 (1959).
35. C. A. Douglas and L. L. Young, Development of a Transmissometer for Determining Visual Range, *Civil Aeronautics Administration, Tech. Div. Rept.* **47,** (1945).
36. "Encyclopedia of Instrumentation for Industrial Hygiene" (C. D. Yaffe, D. H. Byers, and A. D. Hosey, eds.), p. 572. University of Michigan Institute of Industrial Health, Ann Arbor, Michigan, 1956.
36a. W. E. K. Middleton, "Vision Through the Atmosphere." University of Toronto Press, Toronto, 1952.
36b. J. S. Nader, G. C. Ortman, and M. T. Massey, *Am. Ind. Hyg. Assoc. J.* **22,** 42 (1961).
37. E. W. Hewson and R. W. Longley, "Meteorology Theoretical and Applied," p. 59. Wiley, New York, 1944.
38. "Encyclopedia of Instrumentation for Industrial Hygiene" (C. D. Yaffe, D. H. Byers, and A. D. Hosey, eds.), pp. 593, 594, 611, and 657; 583, 587, 602, and 614; 649. University of Michigan Institute of Industrial Health, Ann Arbor, Michigan, 1954.

39. L. W. Foskett *et al.*, *Monthly Weather Rev.* **81,** 267 (1953).
39a. E. Nothmann, *Bull. Am. Meteorol. Soc.* **39,** 273 (1958).
40. L. J. Battan, "Radar Meteorology." Univ. Chicago Press, Chicago, Illinois, 1959.
41. A. J. Haagen-Smit, *Science* **128,** 869 (1958).
42. N. A. Renzetti and G. J. Doyle, *J. Air Pollution Control Assoc.* **8,** 293 (1959).
43. "Glossary of Meteorology" (R. E. Huschke, ed.). American Meteorological Society, Boston, Massachusetts, 1959.
44. C. F. Brooks, *Intern. Assoc. Hydrology Bull., Riga, No.* **23** (1938).
44a. H. Moses and H. G. Daubek, *Bull. Am. Meteorol. Soc.* **42,** 190 (1961).
45. "Exploring the Atmosphere's First Mile" (H. H. Lettau and B. Davidson, eds.), Vol. I. Pergamon Press, New York, 1957.
46. D. J. Portman, *in* "Exploring the Atmosphere's First Mile," (H. H. Lettau and B. Davidson, eds.), Vol. I, p. 159. Pergamon Press, New York, 1957.
47. H. E. Cramer, G. C. Gill, and F. A. Record, *in* "Exploring the Atmosphere's First Mile," (H. H. Lettau and B. Davidson, eds.), Vol. I, p. 172. Pergamon Press, New York, 1957.
48. "Encyclopedia of Instrumentation for Industrial Hygiene" (C. D. Yaffe, D. H. Byers, and A. D. Hosey, eds.), pp. 671, 672, 674, and 676. University of Michigan Institute of Industrial Health, Ann Arbor, Michigan, 1956.
49. P. D. Lowell and W. Hakkarinen, *Natl. Bur. Standards (U. S.) Tech. News Bull.* **35,** 61 (1951).
50. F. E. Gartrell and S. B. Carpenter, *J. Meteorol.* **12,** 215 (1955).
51. R. H. McQuain, J. M. Leavitt, R. C. Wanta, and W. W. Frisbie, Urban Air Sampling by Helicopter. *Proc. Ann. Meeting Air Pollution Control Assoc.* pp. 27-1 thru 27-24, May 25–29 (1958).
52. Joint District, Federal and State Project for the Evaluation of Refinery Emissions. *Air Pollution Control Dist., Co. of Los Angeles, Calif. No.* **1,**— Interim Progress Report. 84 pp. (July 1956).

CHAPTER 17

Automatic Instrumentation

N. A. RENZETTI*

California Institute of Technology, Pasadena, California

I. Introduction

The application of automatic devices for recording the concentration of air pollutants in the open atmosphere is a rapidly expanding field. The forces responsible for this trend are:

(1) The need to protect the public health from exposure to toxic concentrations of injurious materials.

(2) The need to provide continuous measurements of atmospheric pollutants in order to assess a community air pollution problem and to establish trends.

* Formerly Chief Physicist, Air Pollution Foundation.

(3) The need to elucidate the nature of atmospheric reactions in order to ascertain the materials responsible for such air pollution manifestations as eye irritation, crop damage, odor, soiling of surfaces, reduction in visibility, etc.

The instruments to be discussed herein are principally those which sample, analyze, and record, all automatically, the concentration of the particular pollutant. Many devices perform any one of the three functions automatically, but require manual operations to carry out the remaining functions. For most gases the concentrations of concern are in the range from 0 to 1 p.p.m. (by volume); however, for some the upper limit may go as high as 5 p.p.m. or as low as 50 parts per billion. An exception is carbon monoxide, which reaches 100 p.p.m. in polluted atmospheres. The devices for particulate matter involve the range from 1 to 1000 μg./cu. m.

II. Principles of Sampling: Gaseous Phase

Three general methods that may be used with automatic instruments for sampling gas phase pollutants are the continuous, batch, and dosimetric. These methods have evolved from considerations of the type of data required as the end product of the analysis, as well as of the technique of analysis itself. For each of these procedures the pollutant is made available to the analysis by adsorption on a solid surface; by adsorption in a suitable liquid medium; or directly to radiation, as in absorption spectrometry.

A. Continuous

Obviously, the continuous technique is used when a continuous record of concentration versus time is desired. This situation arises most often when concentrations vary rapidly for the following reasons.

(1) Highly variable emissions from one or more sources.

(2) Meteorological factors, such as appreciable wind speed or atmospheric instability.

(3) Rapid chemical reactions.

B. Batch

Batch-type sampling is used for periodic measurements, such as every half-hour, hour, or longer; and for obtaining an average concentration over a specified increment of time, when the sampling time is small compared with the expected rate of change of pollutant concentration.

C. Dosimetric

The dosimetric principle involves sampling the pollutant continuously, accumulating it, and retaining it, usually in solution, until a predetermined level is reached. The varying time spans necessary to accumulate equivalent pollutant concentrations are then recorded. This technique of sampling is employed for either of the following reasons:

(1) With both the continuous and batch techniques extensive recorder chart paper may accumulate, a great deal of which will have little or no pollutant concentration indicated. Thus, great lengths of chart must be inspected in order to discover short-term periods of significant pollution.

(2) The other reason arises when one wants only to know the product of time and concentration of a certain pollutant to which a community has been exposed, because a physiological response is governed by this factor.

III. Principles of Sampling: Particulate Phase

The continuous and batch methods of sampling the particulate matter in the atmosphere have been used with automatic instruments. These methods evolved primarily from the demands of the analytical technique subsequently employed.

Continuously sampling is usually required for the class of instruments involving analysis by light scattering, attenuation, or transmission. In these cases the air stream containing the particulate matter passes through the light beam essentially unaltered. In batch sampling, the particulate is normally filtered out on a substrate of highly viscous or solid material and then is subject to analysis.

IV. Principles of Analyses: Gaseous Phase

Those methods of analysis which are, or possibly will be, made susceptible to automation as part of an instrument system will be discussed in this section. In essence, these techniques are such that the end point of the analysis is an electric current or potential which is proportional to the concentration of the analyte. For each case, one automatic instrument that typifies the technique will be described, and note made of other similar devices.

A. Electrolytic Conductivity

The analyte, or the gaseous material whose concentration is to be analyzed, is absorbed from the air sample in a liquid medium. The resultant change in conductivity of the solution is detected by a conductivity cell and is recorded directly in parts per million (by volume) of air on a continuous strip chart recorder.

The Thomas autometer is the classic example of this type of

instrumentation (*1*). This device measures the concentration of sulfur dioxide in the range of 0–5 p.p.m. The air containing the analyte flows counter to hydrogen peroxide-sulfuric acid solution flow in an absorbing column in which the SO_2 is absorbed and oxidized to the sulfate ion. The solution then passes into the conductivity cell where the resultant change in electrolytic conductivity is detected. A conventional a.c. Wheatstone bridge provides the measuring electric current circuitry for continuous recording (*2*).

B. Electrolytic Titrimetry

The analyte is absorbed from the air sample in a liquid medium and reacts with a suitable reagent. A product of the reaction is produced simultaneously by a separate electrolytic process, and the concentration of the analyte is derived from suitable comparison circuitry.

The atmospheric ozone recorder of Regener demonstrates this principle in practice (*3, 4*). The chemical reaction is of the well-known iodide-iodine type; the ozone quantitatively produces iodine from the potassium iodide solution. The addition of sodium thiosulfate to the potassium iodide solution prevents volatilization of the iodine and allows an accurate amperometric detection of the end point by means of a pair of sensing electrodes.

The quantity of sodium thiosulfate in each chamber is titrated by a coulometric production of iodine from the iodide solution. This iodine is produced by a current which passes through a separate pair of production electrodes. This method of determining sodium thiosulfate has been used for some time in a manual method for ozone determinations.

Both the sensing and the production electrodes are mounted in a separate tube through which the solution flows at a fast rate owing to the pumping action of the air stream which passes through the reaction chamber.

In order to render this process automatic, the current that flows through the sensing electrodes owing to the appearance of iodine is used to control the concentration of iodine by means of a servo system. This servo system adjusts the current through the production electrodes in such a manner as to keep the concentration of iodine always at a fixed, very low level. The instrument, for reasons to be described, consists of two reaction chambers served by splitting the original sample stream. In each line there is an oven to heat the sample to about 300°C., which effectively removes the ozone.

Each of the two chambers has its own servo system. The iodine-producting current is thus for each chamber a measure of the amount of sodium thiosulfate which enters per unit time and which has not reacted with iodine from other sources. If now both ovens are in operation, the air flowing through the two chambers is the same in every respect and the two iodine-producing currents are equal. However, when one of the ovens is turned off, one chamber is supplied with ozone which produces iodine from the iodide. The difference in the two production currents that now develops is a direct and absolute measure of the amount of ozone reacting per unit time in that chamber which is supplied with ozone. It is this difference in the two production currents which is recorded on a strip chart recorder.

The described differential method of measuring ozone, apart from being highly specific to ozone, has the added convenience that the indication of the instrument does not depend on the strength of the solution. It is well known that a dilute solution of sodium thiosulfate does not stay constant over a period of several days unless special precautions are taken.

An instrument for measuring hydrogen sulfide, sulfur dioxide, or mercaptans also uses this principle. The Titrilog (*1*) operates on the principle of generating bromine in the titration cell for measuring the concentration of bromine-reactable compounds. Bromine is generated continuously by electrolysis in a titration cell through which the sample gas bubbles at a regulated rate. Control of the bromine-generating current is effected by the use of a feedback type of electronic amplifier as the source of generating current. This current flows through the cell electrolyte from a bromine electrode located in the titration compartment of the cell to a hydrogen-generating electrode in the external part of the cell.

A second pair of electrodes supplies the input voltage to the feedback amplifier. The reference electrode of this pair is a mercury-mercurous bromide electrode located in the outer cell, and the sensing electrode is a platinum foil electrode responsive to bromine, located in the titration compartment. Opposing the voltage of this electrode pair is an adjustable bias voltage supplied from a dry cell. The difference voltage of this input circuit is the input to the amplifier. This signal to the amplifier is so connected that the amplifier response is positive, thus supplying bromine-generating current when no bromine is present in the cell. Bromine concentration thus increases in the cell until the sensing voltage equals the bias voltage, which is set to correspond to the desired "end point" concentration of bromine. When no bromine-reactable compounds are present, the bromine-generating current is only sufficient to make up for bromine carried out of the cell in the gas stream. This is the "zero level" of the instrument. When reactable compounds enter the titration cell, bromine is reduced. The amplifier responds to the increased input signal and generates sufficient bromine to react with the compounds in the sample and to maintain the "zero level" concentration.

The net current above the "zero level" current is a linear measure of the concentration of reactable compounds in the gas stream. Analysis of gas samples for specific compounds is made by connecting a selective filter in the sample line to the cell, thus removing the compounds of interest. The difference in the bromine-generating current from the total current is a measure of the concentration of the absorbed compounds. Bromine-generating current is recorded on a recording milliammeter. This instrument, with 0.5 to 1 l./min. flow, gives a lag time of 20 sec., a sensitivity at full scale of 10 p.p.m., and a 0.1 p.p.m. minimum detectable limit.

Austin (*5*) has developed an instrument for measuring the concentration of olefinic hydrocarbons. It is based upon the principle that olefins will react in the gas phase at elevated temperature with bromine and that the concentration of residual bromine can be determined by means of a potentiometric measurement of the voltage from a pair of electrodes, one of which is sensitive to bromine concentration.

In the instrument which has been in development, bromine is generated by electrolysis in a separate cell through which is bubbled a stream of air. This air sweeps out the generated bromine and carries it into the inlet sample line. The mixture of sampled gas and bromine is then passed through a bed of granulated Pyrex (temperature, about 400°C.), where reaction takes place. From the reaction bed the sampled gas is bubbled through a solution of sulfuric acid and potassium bromide. The concentration of bromine in this solution will be proportional to the concentration of residual bromine in the sampled gas stream.

The voltage of a platinum electrode, compared with that of a mercury-mercurous bromide or other stable electrode, will therefore vary with the log of the bromine concentration. This voltage is recorded by means of a standard electrolytic recording millivolt meter. It will be noted that the scale of the instrument should be logarithmic.

In practice it has been found that the reaction of bromine with the olefin is not quantitative, but rather is responsive to the bromine concentration, so that the actual recorded voltage approaches a linear relationship to the concentration of olefin in the gas, and the actual calibration of the instrument must be made experimentally. This instrument has a response time of 20 to 40 sec. with flow rates of 0.5 to 1 l./min. It operates in the range of 0 to 5 p.p.m. with a limit of sensitivity of 0.05 p.p.m.

C. Electrolytic Galvanimetry

The analyte is absorbed from the air sample in an electrolytic solution. The latter passes into a galvanic cell system in which the two electrodes are immersed. The amount of electric current flow between the electrodes is a function of the concentration of the ionic level produced by the original trace gas in the solution. A recording milliammeter serves to present the data.

Weber (*6*) has applied this principle to a fluoride instrument. Aluminum and platinum wires, immersed in a dilute acetic acid solution, are connected externally through a microammeter. Electric current, produced by galvanic action at the expense of the aluminum electrodes, flows and temporarily decreases to a low value. If a microgram quantity of soluble fluoride is added, the current increases in proportion to the equilibrium value characteristic of the added fluoride concentration.

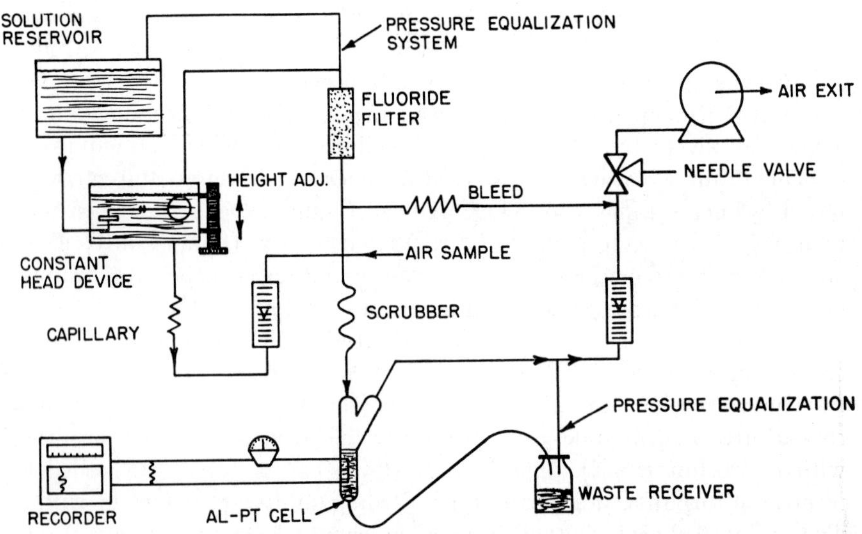

Fig. 1. Continuous analyzer for gaseous fluorides.

If the fluoride is removed, the current returns again to the previous low value. A typical response of the system to 2 μg. of hydrogen fluoride per liter of air was 75% of the maximum response in 3 min. and, in the return to zero concentration, 75% of the decrease is achieved in 4 min. and 95% in 10 min. Full deflection for the 2 μg. amounted to 80 μamp. Calibration curves derived at air flow rate of 2 l./min. and solution at 0.5 ml./min. are not linear but appear to be reproducible. Figure 1 shows a line flow diagram of a system which could be applied to atmospheric concentration in the range of 0–100 parts per billion (p.p.b.). Background data from the present model suggests that one may expect a sensitivity of ± 5 p.p.b.

Strange (*7*) has used the galvanic cell in a somewhat different manner in his hydrogen sulfide and hydrogen cyanide recorder. The electrolytic solution, buffered with sodium carbonate, scrubs the analyte from the gas stream. The cell has silver and saturated calomel electrodes, and the sulfide and cyanide ions influence the silver ion concentration; this in turn affects the silver half-cell potential. Thus, the cell millivolts (100–600) are related to the concentration of the original gases and are presented in a potentiometric strip chart recorder. Reproducibility of 10% is achieved in the 2–50 p.p.m. range for H_2S and in the 1 p.p.b.–1 p.p.m. range for HCN. Ninety per cent of a step change in concentration of the analyte is obtained in 1 min. and complete equilibrium is achieved in 10–15 min.

D. Turbidimetry

The analyte is scrubbed from the air sample in a liquid medium and reacts with the proper reagent to produce a solid or liquid suspension. The resultant turbidity is measured photoelectrically.

The sulfur trioxide automatic instrument devised by Crumely *et al.* (*8*) is an example of this technique. Air containing the sulfur trioxide is drawn at a constant rate through a bubbler in which it is scrubbed by an isopropyl alcohol solution supplied by an automatic pipette. The isopropyl alcohol prevents interference from SO_2 by inhibiting its oxidation to SO_3. The sulfuric acid mist that is formed is removed from the gas stream by passing the gases and mist through a sintered glass filter. The liquid retained by and drained from the filter, which now contains the sulfuric acid, is mixed with dilute barium chloride solution acidified with hydrochloric acid. This mixture then fills a light absorption cell, where the turbidity due to barium sulfate is measured photoelectrically. The sulfate solution is then drained to waste, the light absorption cell is washed with distilled water, and the cycle of operations is repeated. In this way, a determination for SO_3 is carried out every 8 min.

E. Colorimetry

After an analyte is absorbed in a suitable liquid reagent, the ensuing chemical reaction results in a color change in the solution. This change is detected photoelectrically and recorded by conventional means.

The automatic apparatus devised by Thomas *et al.* (9) for the determination of nitrogen dioxide is a good example of this principle. The analyte absorption takes place in continuously flowing liquid streams in which it contacts the air stream concurrently. The absorbing solution consists of 0.5% sulfanilic acid and 20 p.p.m. of *N*-(1-naphthyl)-ethylenediamine dihydrochloride in 14% acetic acid.

The metered gas and liquid volumes are in the ratios of 80 to 1 up to 100 to 1. The liquid, after absorption of the analyte, enters the colorimeter cell. Here the red color produced by the action of nitrous acid on the reagent is measured in a 15-cm. light absorption cell. The difference in light transmission between a reference or "zero" cell and the sample cell is recorded on a strip chart recorder.

This system can also be used to measure nitric oxide. The incoming air stream is split in two, and one of these streams is analyzed for nitrogen dioxide, as described above. The other stream is exposed to the proper concentration of ozone, potassium permanganate, or some other oxidant, to convert the nitric oxide to nitrogen dioxide, and this stream is then subjected to analysis for NO_2 in a duplicate absorber colorimeter system. The nitric oxide is then determined by difference. Helwig (*10*) has developed an instrument that uses the colorimetric method for determining atmospheric sulfur dioxide.

Figure 2 shows an instrument in which three recording colorimeters are packaged into one system, enabling some simplification in circuitry and recorder function.

Colorimetry has also been applied to automatic batch type of sampling, analysis, and recording in the Austin Dual Colorimeter (*11*). Austin designed and built an instrument of the batch type; in this a measured volume of air was reacted with a measured volume of reagent, the optical density of reacted solutions was recorded, and the solution was then automatically discarded. In effect, this principle involves conversion of manual batch sampling and analysis to automatic batch sampling, analysis, and recording.

The instrument was designed for use with two oxidant reagents: phenolphthalin and ferrous thiocyanate. Results obtained with these two reagents have been valuable in air pollution studies. The instrument records the results of five separate analyses with each of the two reagents during each hour.

The air samples are contacted with the reagents in an impinger built into a test tube-shaped absorption cell that is placed in the cellholder of a Beckman Model C colorimeter. Transmission of the reagent solution is measured before and after sampling and is automatically recorded on a strip chart recorder. The two colorimeter readings are recorded on the same strip chart in sequence. By means of critical orifices, downstream from the impingers, the air sample is metered. The flows of air and solution are controlled by actuation of solenoid valves and solenoid-operated syringe pumps in the proper sequence. A programing shaft with several cams driven by a synchronous motor automatically actuates the various syringe pumps and valves through cam-driven microswitches. For one cell and one cycle, the sequence of operation is as

FIG. 2. Automatic recorder for oxidant, nitric oxide, and nitrogen dioxide. (Courtesy of Harold Kruger Instruments.)

follows: rinsing of the cell with reagent, making up the reagent charge, recording the blank, reacting a measured air volume with the reagent, recording the resulting color, and draining the cell. Small Bunsen check valves in the fluid lines prevent reverse flow.

The reagents are made up in the form of two concentrated stock solutions for each side of the instrument. The two stock solutions are metered and diluted in the feed line to the absorption cell. In this manner, the deterioration with time of the mixed reagent solution is avoided to a great extent.

This unit was designed to give a wide selection in air-reagent ratios and hence should be applicable to other reagents. Figure 3 shows this recording colorimeter.

FIG. 3. Austin Dual Colorimeter. (Courtesy of Robert R. Austin, Consulting Chemist.)

Colorimetry has been applied to a dosimeter type analyzer by Adams *et al.* (12). The unique feature of the analyzer is a colorimeter that triggers a time stamp and refills the absorption cell upon development of a preselected photocell output equivalent to some concentration of the pollutant that has been absorbed in the reagent.

F. Fluorescence

The analyte in the air stream quenches the fluorescence induced by ultraviolet radiation in a substance (usually solid), and the resulting decrease is detected photoelectrically and recorded on a conventional strip chart recorder.

Chaiken *et al.* (*13*) initiated work on a fluoride recorder based on this principle. Filter paper strip tape was impregnated with a methyl alcohol solution of magnesium oxinate. The tape is illuminated with ultraviolet radiation in the region of 3650 Å. Fluorescence occurs in the visible light region, and this is detected by a photocell on the downstream side of the tape. A light filter, absorbing the radiation below 4500 Å, aids in detecting the fluorescence signal. When air containing gaseous fluoride is passed through the impregnated irradiation tape, the visible light produced after irradiation is markedly decreased. Thomas *et al.* (*14*) and earlier, Wiggins and St. John of Stanford Research Institute worked on this finding to produce a simplified instrument suitable for monitoring fluoride concentrations in the air in the parts per billion range. This device employs two photomultiplier tubes, which receive the fluorescent light from two adjacent areas of the tape. These areas filter a split air stream—one stream of unaltered air sample containing the analyte, and the other having been subjected to removal of the analyte. The paper is illuminated by an ultraviolet lamp through a quartz window. The fluorescent light from the paper passes through the 4500 Å light filter onto the two photomultiplier tubes. The outputs from these tubes are balanced against each other and recorded continuously on a strip chart recorder. Provision is made to advance the paper according to a preset interval schedule, or more often, if full scale readings are obtained.

G. Photometry

The air stream containing the analyte is passed through a permeable white reactive tape medium, previously impregnated with a reagent. The analyte and reagent react to produce a characteristic color, which is detected by comparing a reflection of light of suitable spectral quality with a reflection of light from tape prior to exposure to the analyte. A standard photometer can be used with two photoelectric cells in a bridge type of circuit connected with an automatic continuous balance recorder of the null type.

Schaeffer (*15*) describes such a system for the measurement of hydrogen sulfide. In this application the tape is impregnated with lead acetate which, upon reaction, converts to brown lead sulfide. At the conclusion of a preselected exposure period, the tape is advanced to expose a new section of impregnated tape.

H. Infrared Spectrometry

The nondispersive infrared measurement of trace gas concentrations, when feasible, presents an outstanding methodology for automatic instrumentation, because the technique depends on a fundamental physical property of the molecule being detected, and is nondestructive. The only drawback for widespread application is its relatively high cost.

The air sample is introduced, through suitable glass plumbing, directly into a sample cell, which serves also as the absorption cell, in the path of the infrared radiation beam. The analyte, which has one or more absorption bands in the infrared region (usually between 1 and 15 μ), attenuates the beam in proportion to its concentration.

The Lira type of instrument, devised by Mine Safety Appliances, (*16*) has applied this principle to the measurement of carbon monoxide. It consists essentially of an infrared source; a sample and filter cell; and an infrared detector, in this case a condenser microphone. Two nichrome wires provide the source of radiation. One beam traverses the sample cell, and the other, the comparison (compensator) cell. The emergent radiation is converged into a single detector cell by a beam combiner, which consists of two cylinders in the form of a V. Between the sources and the cells, a reciprocating metal slider alternately blocks the radiation to the sample cell and to the comparison cell. The amplifier is tuned so that only variations in light intensity occurring at the alternating frequency of the reciprocating slider produce an output signal. Therefore, when both beams are equal in intensity, the output is zero, there being no change in the condenser microphone capacity. When the gas to be analyzed is introduced into the sample cell, it reduces the intensity of radiation in that beam and the two beams become unequal. This sets up a signal at the condenser microphone which is amplified, rectified, and passed to a servomechanism. This does two things: it causes the pen of a recorder to move, and it causes a reduction in the voltage applied to the comparison beam source. The pen of the recorder moves until the intensity of the two beams at the detector is the same, at which point it stops and gives a measure of the concentration of the analysis component —in this case, carbon monoxide.

The use of a single detector in this instrument minimizes zero drift and gives high internal stability in the instrument.

Mine Safety Appliances (*11*) and Littman (*17*) have applied the technique to the measurement of hydrocarbons.

The dispersive infrared technique has not yet been found applicable to air-monitoring instrumentation. Perkin-Elmer *(11)* attempted to put together a system for hydrocarbon measurement at 3.4 μ. However, this development was limited by the lack of adequate filters for isolating the reference and analytical wavelengths, which is the limiting factor in this field.

I. Ultraviolet Spectrometry

The counterpart of dispersive infrared instrumentation is available in the ultraviolet region. However, very little has been done in this field because of poor specificity for the most common air pollutants. One notable exception is ozone, for which two techniques have been developed into automatic instruments.

Kruger *(18)* has developed an ultraviolet photometer for ozone, operating at a wavelength of 253.7 mμ. Ozone has a strong absorption range, extending from 220 to 310 mμ, with a peak near 265 mμ. This photometer uses a pair of 10-in. absorption cells and a single source of radiation. One cell has the air sample containing ozone; the other cell samples the same air from which ozone was removed by catalytic decomposition. The instrument is operated at high gain so that only 0.4% reduction in transmittance causes full scale deflection on the recorder (1 p.p.m.). In this range, the optical density varies inversely with the transmittance, so that the ozone concentration is read directly from a linear scale. The circuitry is arranged to record the difference signal from the two absorption cells.

Renzetti *(19)* devised an apparatus for operation directly on the atmosphere over a long atmospheric path. The advantage of this approach is that there is no handling of the air sample, thus avoiding problems of surface reactions, or of decomposition of very reactive pollutants such as ozone or nitrogen dioxide. Furthermore, Renzetti's use of several wavelengths makes possible greater discrimination against interfering absorbers.

V. The Particulate Phase

The particulate matter suspended in the atmosphere, commonly referred to as "aerosol," and of concern as a community air pollution problem, consists of liquid and solid particles less than 5 μ in diameter. Particles larger than this are normally classed as a local nuisance, since they fall out of the atmosphere in the vicinity of the source. Certain physical properties of fine particles have yielded to study by automatic instruments.

A. Light Scattering

The particle counter photometer, devised by O'Konski (*20*), is an automatic instrument that alternately measures the total light scattered at 90° by the individual particles of the aerosol, determines the size distribution by obtaining particle counts in variously sized increments (up to ten), and records these data. It has been used for particle sizes down to 0.25 μ in diameter by very careful attention to optical and electronic design. The scattered light detection system has the advantage that particles can be measured with little disturbance of the aerosol. Appropriate optics, which give highly uniform illumination and light collection, and the coaxial flow system lead to high resolving power, which is important for discriminating between particles of nearly equal sizes. Stray light is reduced to the level of that scattered by the air molecules. Thus, it was possible to combine the counter with a photometer using a common phototube and optical system. The advantage is gained in that, once the pulse amplitude versus particle size curve is established, the instrument can easily be recalibrated by reference to photometric measurements on gases. Figure 4 shows a schematic diagram

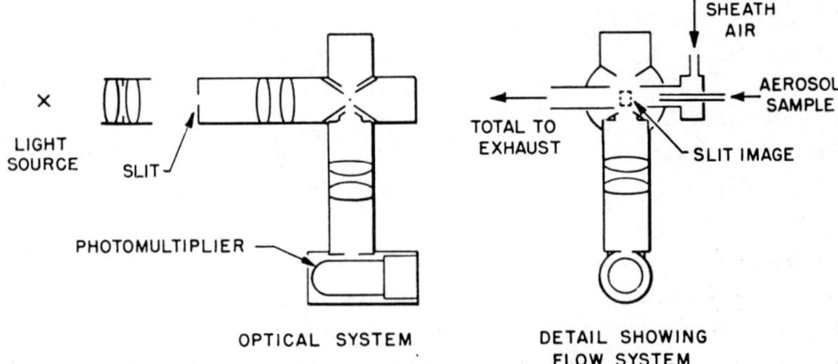

Fig. 4. Optical and flow systems of counter-photometer.

of the optical and flow systems, and Fig. 5 shows the electronic circuitry involved. Fisher *et al.* (*21*) have devised an instrument similar to the above for automatic counting and sizing of aerosol particles in the range 1 to 64 μ in diameter. Sampling at the rate of 1.8 l./min., dilution networks to limit the counting rate below 2000 particles/min., 90° light scattering, pulse amplification, and sorting in twelve channels are involved in this instrument system. Sinclair (*22*) has conceived an automatic apparatus which combines the photometric function and automatic collection of the particulate by a membrane filter. The mass concentration is measured in a dark field forward-scattering chamber over a large

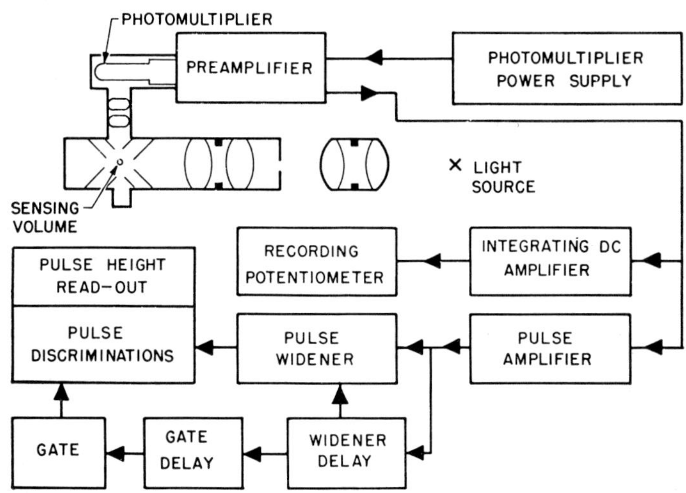

FIG. 5. Block diagram of electronic circuits.

dynamic range (1 to 100,000) by a single scale logarithmic amplifier of the photocurrent. Calibration with dioctyl phthalate droplets shows a minimum detectable limit of 10^{-3} μg./l. for 0.3 μ diameter particles up to 100 μg./l. for full scale.

B. PHOTOMETRY

Chaney (*23*) has developed an instrument (Fig. 6) for the collection by filtration of particulate matter on a roll of filter paper. This instrument records automatically the reflectance and transmittance of the deposits on the filter paper, and also the pressure drop across the paper during the sampling period, to measure the build-up on the paper. The instrument is designed to operate unattended for a period of 72 hr.

The air to be sampled is drawn through an inlet tube to a jaw mechanism, which clamps in place a 2-in. strip of Whatman No. 2 filter paper during the sampling period. A carbon vane oilless pump is used to provide the air flow, which is regulated, by means of a metering orifice to deliver 25 cu. ft./hr. at standard temperature and pressure through a 1-sq. in. area of the filter paper.

At the end of the sampling period the filter paper strip is automatically moved to the next position, and during the paper movement the particulate deposit is scanned by two photocell units successively—one for transmission and one for reflectance. The paper strip then passes through a stamp, which prints the hour and date of the sample, and is then wound on the take-up spool. The reflectance of the clean filter paper strip itself is scanned and recorded by the photocells immediately

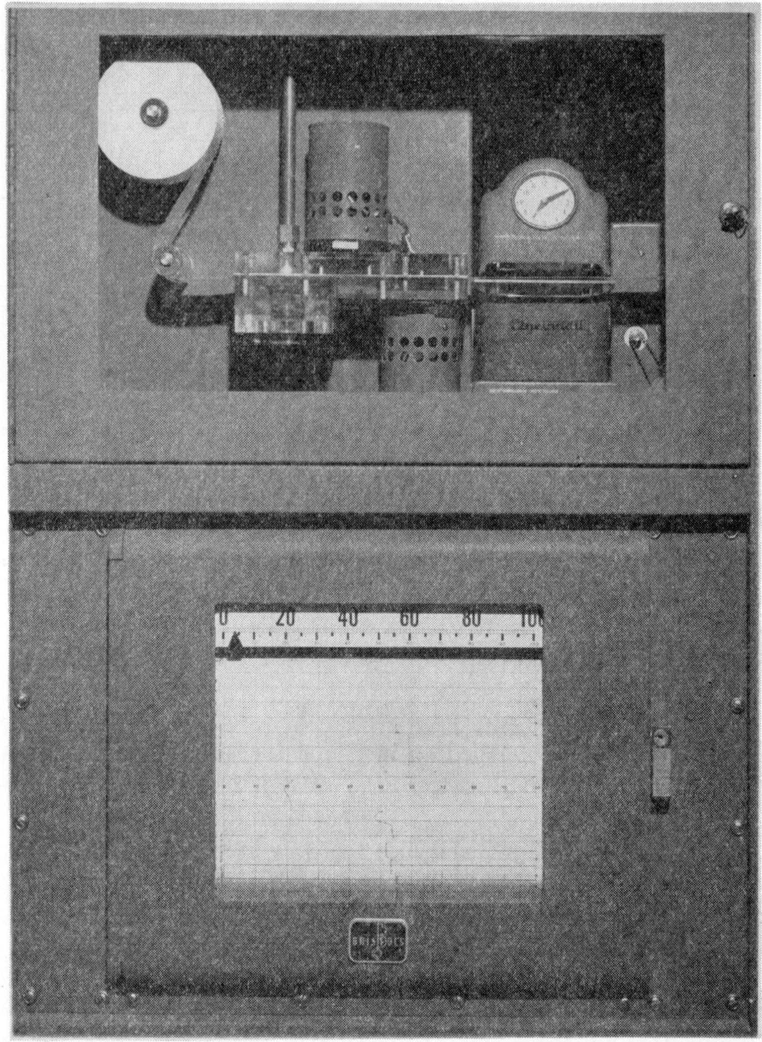

FIG. 6. Recording Auto-Sampler Model 106. (Courtesy of Albert L. Chaney Chemical Laboratories.)

preceding the reflectance and transmission measurements. The sampling frequency in general is once per hour, the actual sampling time being approximately 54 min., with 6 min. for scanning and recording the reflectance and optical transmission. The light source for the reflectance and transmission units is regulated by means of a constant voltage transformer. A d.c. source of supply for the pressure recorder and the potentiometer of the strip chart recorder is provided by means of dry cell batteries.

Nader (*24*) has devised a tape sampler of the same general type. However, he uses a Type WS microweb membrane tape which gives a more flexible instrument for the subsequent analyses. The use of the high performance, carbon vane rotary type oilless pump provides the range of sampling rate from 2.5 to 16 l. min.$^{-1}$ cm.$^{-2}$. Finally, the use of the beta gage technique renders the equipment completely automatic for making mass loading measurements in terms of micrograms per cubic meter of air.

C. Smoke Density Recorder

The basic principle involves the modulation of a light beam by the smoke particles in the air sample. Normally, the beam is projected at right angles to the air stream onto a photoelectric receiver, the output of which is proportional to the light intensity. The modulation consists of attenuation of the beam by scattering and by absorption by the particles. One must take special care to keep other sources of attenuation at a minimum, such as decrease in source energy and coatings on the optical parts. The data is presented automatically by amplifying the photocell signal to operate a strip chart recorder.

Bailey (*25*) manufactures an automatic recorder of this type for industrial types of stack application.

VI. Sophisticated Air-Monitoring Instruments

A. Dispersive Infrared Spectrophotometry

The demands of air pollution research have inspired remarkable developments in ultramicrochemical analyses, particularly for the gas phase. This has been especially true in dispersive infrared spectrometry and gas chromatography. Stephens (*26*) and his associates extended the technique of multireflection, long path, infrared absorption spectrometry to trace analyses of many organic and inorganic components of polluted atmospheres. This work led to commercial developments (*27, 28*) which have advanced the state of the art still further. It is now possible to monitor for ozone, aldehydes, classes of hydrocarbons, carbon monoxide, carbon dioxide, nitric oxide, and nitrogen dioxide in the parts-per-million concentration range in one scan of the spectrum from 2 to 14 μ. In principle, this scan can be repeated automatically every 10 to 15 min., 24 hr. a day.

B. Gas Chromatography

An admirable adjunct to the infrared method of determining trace amounts of hydrocarbons is the recording gas chromatograph. Rapid developments in this instrument field now make it possible to analyze individual hydrocarbons in the C_2 to C_5 region down to 1 p.p.h.m. in a cubic foot sample. We can look forward to its extension to the higher hydrocarbons, about C_9, or essentially all those of interest to gas phase air pollution as well as to the complete spectrum of oxygenated compounds. This capability will be achieved through research in detection systems and column materials. In particular, increased sensitivity can be expected by such developments as ionization detectors and more efficient column packings. These will also advance the feasibility of complete automation of this type of measurement system.

C. Automatic Samplers and Automatic Analyzers

Finally, it would be appropriate to mention two classes of devices, each performing a function automatically but requiring a human link. Automatic samplers (*29, 30*) for both gaseous and particulates have been developed and reduced to commercial practice for collecting up to 12 samples. Simple time programers, interchangeable gears, solenoid valves, and air pumps are combined to give preselected sampling schedules of interest to the investigator. Sampling rates are usually in two ranges, 0–10 l./min. and 0–60 l./min., with low and high vacuum pumps respectively. The samples thus collected are transported to a laboratory equipped with an automatic analyzer such as the "Analmatic" (*31*). The latter performs two functions: namely, analytical, which includes sampling, handling, and treatment of samples and measurement and recording of the results; and coordination by separate electrical or electromechanical means. Such units as dispensing and transfer pipettes for selection and delivery of aliquots, automatic titrators, recording absorptiometers, colorimeters, and other analytic instruments, as well as strip chart recorders, make up the basic system.

VII. Data Handling

The use of automatic instrumentation brings us naturally to the subject of the data handling problem. The scale of any well-designed community air pollution survey is such that very soon one accumulates vast amounts of chart paper, camera records, or the like. These raw data must be processed as part of a statistically designed experiment if they are to yield significant information. There are two methods of treating this problem:

One may subject the diurnal graphs to manual reading and recording, supported, of course, by the necessary calibration data for each instrument. An aid in this type of work is provided by the developments in the field of automatic chart readers from which the data can be punched on IBM-type cards.

A more direct method is to dispense with the chart paper and, at each instrument, reduce the data to digit form, which can then be printed or telemetered to a central recording station. Such a station could receive data from all the monitoring points of a community network, including meteorological stations, by wire or radio link. Thus, data can be presented rapidly, as well as recorded for analytical or mathematical processing.

At the final stages of data computations there are available the enormous developments in the digital computer field. This dynamic field must be periodically surveyed to ascertain the most suitable equipment for the specific problem at hand. In general, those machines developed for statistical computations will be of greatest use to air pollution data analyses (chemical, physical, and meteorological), since in such analyses basically simple mathematical manipulations are employed.

References

1. L. C. McCabe (ed.), "Air Pollution," *Proc. 1st U. S. Tech. Conf.* p. **847**. McGraw-Hill, New York, 1952.
2. Thomas Autometer, Leeds and Northrup Company, Philadelphia, Pennsylvania.
3. V. H. Regener, *Proc. Intern. Ozone Conf., Chicago, Illinois, 1956; Advances in Chem. Ser.* No. 21 (1959).
4. Atmospheric Ozone Recorder—Regener Type, Mast Development Company, Inc., Davenport, Iowa.
5. R. A. Austin Chemical Laboratories, Pasadena, California, 1959.
6. C. W. Weber and O. H. Howard, *A.M.A. Arch Ind. Health* **19,** 355–364 (1959).
7. John P. Strange, *Anal. Chem.* **29,** 1878 (1957).
8. P. H. Crumley, H. Howe, and D. S. Wilson, *J. Inst. Fuel* **31,** 378–382 (1958).
9. M. D. Thomas, J. A. MacLeod, R. C. Robbins, R. C. Goettelman, R. W. Eldridge, and L. H. Rogers, *Anal. Chem.* **28,** 1810–1816 (1956).
10. Harold L. Helwig and Chester L. Gordon, *Anal. Chem.* **30,** 1810 (1958).
11. L. H. Rogers, *Chem. Eng. Progr.* **53,** 381–384 (1957).
12. D. F. Adams, H. J. Dana, and R. K. Koppe, "Universal" Air Pollutant Analyzer, (U.S.P.H.S. Contract No. 66512), prepared for Community Air Poll. Program, S.E.C., by Inst. Technol., State College of Washington, Pullman, Wash., 20 pp.
13. S. Chaiken, T. S. Parks, and C. Glassbrook, U. S. Patent 2741544 (1956).
14. M. D. Thomas and G. A. St. John, The Fluoride Recorder, *Am. Soc. Testing Materials Spec. Tech. Publ.* No. 250 (1958).
15. W. H. Schaeffer, *Electronics* **22** (1949).
16. James L. Waters and Nelson W. Hartz, An Improved Luft-Type Infrared Gas and Liquid Analyzer. Paper presented at *Conf. of Instrument Soc. Am., Houston, Texas, 1951.*
17. Fred E. Littman and James Q. Denton, *Anal. Chem.* **28,** 945 (1956).
18. Harold Kruger Instruments, San Gabriel, California.
19. N. A. Renzetti, *Anal. Chem.* **29,** 869 (1957).
20. Chester T. O'Konski and George J. Doyle, *Anal. Chem.* **27,** 694–701 (1955).
21. M. A. Fisher, S. Katz, A. Lieberman, and N. E. Alexander, *Proc. 3rd Natl. Air Poll. Symposium, Pasadena, Calif.* pp. 112–119 (1955).

22. D. Sinclair, *Air Repair* **3,** 51 (1953).
23. A. L. Chaney, The Recording Auto-Sampler, Model 106, Chaney Chemical Laboratories, Glendale, California.
24. J. S. Nader, *J. Air Poll. Control Assoc.* **9,** 59–61 (1959).
25. Smoke Density Recorder, Bailey Meter Company Bull. No. 211-A, Cleveland, Ohio.
26. E. R. Stephens, P. L. Hanst, R. C. Doerr, and W. E. Scott, *Ind. Eng. Chem.* **48,** 1498–1504 (1956).
27. Vincent J. Coates and Robert Anacreon, Improving the Measurement of Weak Infrared Absorption Bands Using Expanded-Scale, Double-Beam Spectrophotometry. Paper presented at *Conf. on Anal. Chem. and Appl. Spectroscopy, Pittsburgh, Pennsylvania, 1957.*
28. Raymond R. Sawyer, Fred W. Behnke, and Norman I. Adams, III, The Infrared Analysis of Trace Gases Using Long-Path Gas Cell and Ordinate Expansion, *Proc. 51st Ann. Meeting Air Poll. Control Assoc., Philadelphia, Pennsylvania, 1958.*
29. Gelman Instrument Company, Chelsea, Michigan.
30. Research Appliance Company, Allison Park, Pennsylvania.
31. Analmatic (Automation in Analysis), Baird and Tatlock, London.

CHAPTER 18

The Air Pollution Survey

AUGUST T. ROSSANO, JR.*

California Institute of Technology, Pasadena, California

I. Definition and Purpose of Air Pollution Surveys

An air pollution survey may be defined as a critical examination of a given geographical area for the purpose of determining the nature, sources, extent, and effects of air pollution. Air pollution surveys are performed for a wide variety of reasons pertaining to local source problems, land usage, community air pollution control and research (*1, 2, 2a, 2b, 2c*).

Not generally considered to fall within the scope of air pollution surveys are the brief inspections performed by enforcement officials in response to nuisance complaints, or to determine compliance with local regulations. Likewise, short term investigations and consultative services limited to evaluating the performance of combustion equipment or air and gas cleaning devices do not qualify as surveys, although they serve a most useful function in efforts to mitigate air pollution.

II. Type and Scope of Surveys

A. LOCAL SOURCE PROBLEMS

Studies of local source problems usually involve specific and identifiable emission sources. An example of this type of survey is a study of

* Formerly Chief, State and Community Services, Air Pollution Engineering Research, Robert A. Taft Sanitary Engineering Center, Cincinnati, Ohio. Presently on assignment from the United States Public Health Service.

TABLE I

SELECTED LIST OF AIR POLLUTION APPRAISALS AND INVESTIGATIONS OF LIMITED SCOPE

Designation	Date	Responsible Organization	Scope	Reference
Air pollution in Poza Rica, Mexico	1950	U. S. Bureau of Mines and U. S. Public Health Service	Investigation following the Poza Rica incident. Review of symptoms, pathological findings, alleged source, and presumed cause.	*38*
Air pollution in London, England	1952	Committee of Departmental Officers and Expert Advisers, Minister of Health	Investigation into the causes of the high mortality and morbidity in London during a 2-week period in December, 1952. Information collected includes meteorological and air pollution factors, and medical statistics. Previous air pollution disasters are reviewed.	*38a, 38b*
Dust deposition in the vicinity of a power station	1952–54	Central Electricity Authority (Great Britain)	Measurement of dustfall rates in different directions from Little Barford Power Station under various meteorological and plant operating conditions.	*3*
Air pollution in New South Wales	1953	New South Wales Department of Public Health, Australia	Measurement of dustfall by means of station networks in Sydney, Newcastle, and Port Kembla.	*27*
Air pollution in the vicinity of Portland, Oregon	1956	Stanford Research Institute (Menlo Park, Calif.)	The air pollution potential of the Portland area is determined from calculated estimates of emissions under specified meteorological conditions.	*12*
Air pollution in St. Bernard, Ohio	1956	U. S. Public Health Service in cooperation with the Cincinnati Bureau of Air Pollution Control and Heating Inspection	One-month concentrated study of sulfur dioxide, oxides of nitrogen, hydrogen sulfide, suspended particulates, and selected weather factors at one station in a suburb of Cincinnati, Ohio. Results explained in terms of wind direction and speed.	*21*
Atmospheric pollution in Milan, Italy	1956	Milan University Institute of Hygiene with	Measurements of sulfur dioxide, carbon monoxide, carbon dioxide, hydrogen sulfide, chlorine,	*22*

		the cooperation of the Health Office of the City Council	fluorine, ammonia, oxides of nitrogen, and suspended particulates with respect to location, season, topography, and other factors.	
An aerometric survey of the city of Honolulu, Hawaii	1956–57	Truesdail Laboratories, Inc. (Los Angeles, Calif.) at the request of the Board of Health of the territory of Hawaii	Measurement of aldehydes, carbon monoxide, hydrocarbons, oxidants, oxides of nitrogen, sulfur dioxide, and particulate matter during 2-week periods of differing weather conditions in September and January. Correlation of pollution with weather, time of day, and location.	*19*
State-wide air pollution appraisals:				
Washington	1956			
Connecticut	1956	U. S. Public Health Service in cooperation with the individual state departments of public health and air pollution control boards	Evaluation of the current status and future outlook of air pollution based largely on existing data on such factors as population, fuel usage, industrial activity, waste disposal practices, topography, and meteorology.	*6–11*
Tennessee	1957			
Texas	1958			
New York	1958			
North Carolina	1959			
Pennsylvania	1959			
Minnesota	1961			*11a*
Florida	1961			*11b*
Community-wide air pollution appraisals:				
Steubenville, Ohio	1956	U. S. Public Health Service in cooperation with local public health or air pollution agency	Same as for state-wide air pollution appraisals.	*13–16b*
Portland, Oregon	1956			
Denver, Colo.	1957			
Birmingham, Ala.	1958			
Charleston, S. C.	1959			
Hamilton, Ohio	1960			
Bi-state study	1957–59	Illinois Department of Public Health and Indiana State Board of Health and Purdue University	A study of the sources, nature and extent of air pollution in the Chicago metropolitan area. This study was preceded by an Illinois State study in 1956 by the Illinois Department of Public Health.	*11c* *51*

TABLE I (*Continued*)

Designation	Date	Responsible Organization	Scope	Reference
Air pollution in El Paso, Texas	1957–59	El Paso City-County Health Unit	A two-year study to obtain data on type, extent, source, and effects of air pollution in the El Paso area.	*23a*
Air pollution in Phoenix, Arizona	1958	Arizona State Department of Health with the assistance of the U. S. Public Health Service	Diurnal sampling for 7 consecutive days at one location for oxidants, nitrogen dioxide, sulfur dioxide, carbon monoxide, and suspended particulates. These data are related to visibility and wind speed.	*20*
Pollutants in Mexico City	1959	Laboratory of Industrial Hygiene Department of Health, Mexico	Measurements at two stations for suspended particulates, sulfur dioxide, and oxidants. Correlation of pollutant data with meteorology, topography, and industrial activity and time of day.	*24*
Air pollution in Tucson, Arizona	1959	Arizona State Department of Health with the assistance of the U. S. Public Health Service	Essentially similar to the Phoenix study.	*23*
Air pollution in Roseburg, Oregon	1960	Oregon State Sanitary Authority	A six-month study using nine stations gathering data on particle fallout and suspended particulates within or near Roseburg, Oregon.	*24a*
Air pollution in Medford, Oregon	1960	Oregon State Sanitary Authority	A six-month study using a total of ten stations gathering data on dustfall, suspended particulates, oxides of nitrogen, carbon monoxide, sulfur dioxide, and meteorologic variables within or near Medford, Oregon.	*24b*

the air, water, vegetation, and possibly animal life in the vicinity of a phosphate fertilizer plant, aluminum reduction plant, or steel mill to determine the extent to which particulate and gaseous pollutants from such a source affect the local ecology. A study of the concentrations of sulfur dioxide and particulates from an isolated coal-burning electric power plant or metal refinery may be conducted to obtain data on the range of influence of such a source, or the efficiency of its air pollution control measures (*3, 3a, 3b*).

B. Site Selection Surveys

A practice which unfortunately is only infrequently followed is the air pollution survey of an area prior to the selection of a site for the construction of a new industry. The proper use of land in an era of expanding technological and population growth requires imaginative and thoughtful community planning and zoning. While such a practice cannot guarantee freedom from future air pollution difficulties, it does provide an opportunity to prevent the unnecessary creation of obviously undesirable situations and possibly litigation. In such studies due regard is given to local meteorology, topography, real estate values, and future growth trends. Of significant importance is data on existing sources, receptors, and air pollutant concentrations (*3c–g*).

C. Area Surveys

1. *Appraisals*

Area surveys cover a wide spectrum of types. At one end are appraisals involving little or no air sampling, but rather mainly based on analyses of available pertinent technical data and information. The objectives of such appraisals are to determine the current status of air pollution in a community or group of communities, to estimate future potential for air pollution intensification, and to offer broad recommendations for prevention or abatement (*4*).

The survey findings and recommendations are based on available facts and figures on population and population trends, industrial activity, fuel consumption for space heating and power, automotive usage, waste disposal practices, agricultural activity, as well as local and regional topography and climatology. Within recent years several such appraisals have been made on a community and statewide basis by Federal, State, local, and private organizations (*5–16b*). Table I lists these as well as other types of air pollution investigations of limited scope, indicating their location, date, scope, and responsible organization.

In general, community-wide appraisals require one to two man-weeks

TABLE II

Selected List of Major Air Pollution Surveys

Designation	Date	Responsible organization	Scope	References
Chicago smoke abatement survey	1911–15	City of Chicago	Comprehensive study of the causes and effects of air pollution in Chicago with emphasis on coal smoke, particularly from railroads. Smoke abatement recommendations are made.	*25a*
Selby smelter study	1913–14	U. S. Bureau of Mines	Fifteen-month investigation, by a special commission, of the dust and gaseous emissions from a large lead smelter in Solano County, California. Study included stack and atmospheric sampling, vegetation and soil analyses, effects on humans, livestock, and plants, and control recommendations.	*3b*
Smoke abatement in Grafton, West Virginia	1924	U. S. Bureau of Mines	Smoke, airborne solids, sootfall, etc., in a coal-burning railroad center.	*25b*
Smoke abatement in Salt Lake City, Utah	1926	U. S. Bureau of Mines	Study of coal consumption and air quality in terms of airborne solids, sootfall, oxides of sulfur, nitrogen and carbon, chlorine, sulfuric acid, and ammonia. Data are related to meteorology, location, and time of year. Recommendations are offered.	*25c*
Air pollution in the Meuse Valley, Belgium	1930	Committee of experts appointed by the King's attorney at Liège	An investigation following the Meuse Valley air pollution disaster of December, 1930. A compilation of medical observations and opinions, meteorological information, data on chemical composition of dustfall, and estimates of sulfur dioxide, and other emissions as potential causes.	*36, 36a*

New York City air pollution survey	1935–37	Department of Health, New York City	Relation of fuel usage to air pollution, sootfall, atmospheric, dust counts, airborne bacteria measurements.	*25d*
Leicester air pollution study	1937–39	Atmospheric Research Committee of Department of Scientific and Industrial Research (Great Britain)	Study of the distribution, dispersal, and character of atmospheric pollution. Measurements of suspended and deposited dust, sulfur dioxide, and ultraviolet light, and meteorological factors.	*26*
Trail smelter study (British Columbia)	1938–40	Arbitral Tribunal of the governments of Canada and the United States	Source study of smelter. Comprehensive program of air sampling for sulfur dioxide, meteorological investigation, and effects of sulfur dioxide on vegetation.	*25*
Air pollution in Donora, Pennsylvania	1948–49	U. S. Public Health Service	A 5-month intensive investigation following the Donora crisis. Included medical interviews and examinations, epidemiological studies, air sampling, and analysis of gases and particulates, source evaluations, and meteorological investigations.	*37*
Air pollution in the Kanawha Valley, West Virginia	1950–51	West Virginia Department of Public Health assisted by the Kettering Laboratory (Cincinnati, Ohio) and the U. S. Public Health Service	A 19-month study of air pollution sources and airborne concentrations of oxides of nitrogen and sulfur, aldehydes, fluorides, ammonia, hydrogen sulfide, chlorine, particulates, as well as sootfall. Sampling done at a total of 28 locations by mobile units and fixed stations.	*25e*
Air pollution in the Detroit-Windsor area	1950–60	Technical Advisory Board on Air Pollution of the International Joint Commission of Canada and the United States	A long-term study of the sources, concentrations, and effects of air pollution in the Detroit area, with recommendations for a legal control program on a local and international level.	*34*

TABLE II (*Continued*)

Designation	Date	Responsible organization	Scope	References
Air pollution in the vicinity of Louisville, Kentucky	1952–53	Battelle Memorial Institute (Columbus, Ohio) under the sponsorship of the Rubbertown Industrial Group	Measurement of particulate and gaseous pollutants by means of a mobile laboratory over a period of about 1½ years. Estimates of industrial sources.	*28*
The Sarnia survey	1953–54	Ontario Research Foundation with the support of six major industrial firms	Measurement of dustfall, sulfur dioxide, and airborne particulates at several fixed and one mobile sampling stations. Correlation with meteorological variables.	*29*
Los Angeles Basin aerometric survey	1954	Air Pollution Foundation (San Marino, Calif.) in cooperation with the Los Angeles County Air Pollution Control District	Continuous sampling and analysis for eight pollutants at ten stations, August through November. Estimation of degree and frequency of eye irritation and vegetation damage. Meteorological measurements. Dispersion studies aloft using a blimp.	*30*
Atmospheric pollution in Pretoria, South Africa	1955	National Physical Research Laboratory, Council for Scientific and Industrial Research, Union of South Africa	A 2-year study to determine degree of pollution in the city. Smoke, sulfur dioxide, and dustfall were measured at six fixed stations. Results are related to fuel usage and season, and compared with data from Chattanooga, Tennessee.	*18*
The special air pollution study of Louisville and Jefferson County, Kentucky	1956–58	U. S. Public Health Service in cooperation with several other federal agencies as well as state and local health and air pollution agencies	A 2-year comprehensive study which included detailed source studies, emission inventory, and continuous air sampling at six network stations and mobile samplers. Measurements include airborne particulates, soiling, sulfur dioxide, hydrocarbons, auto exhaust, and several other gases, odor and human response, material deterioration,	*32*

			airborne bacteria, climatology, and meteorological variables at nine stations. Recommendations for abatement are offered.	
The Houston air pollution survey	1956–58	Southwest Research Institute (San Antonio, Texas) under the sponsorship of the Houston Chamber of Commerce	Air sampling for sulfur compounds, oxidants, carbon monoxide, particulates, and other selected pollutants, and vegetation survey by means of mobile laboratory. Study of meteorological factors.	*31*
New York-New Jersey interstate air pollution survey	1957	Interstate Sanitation Commission (New York, New Jersey, and Connecticut) in cooperation with the Public Health Service	Summary of the history as well as findings of earlier surveys of the area. Limited gas sampling. Tracer studies of interstate air movement. Appraisal of damage to vegetation, property, and health. Meteorological, climatological, and visibility studies. Review of the legislative aspects.	*33*
Nashville air pollution study	1958–59	Vanderbilt University for the medical phase and Robert A. Taft Sanitary Engineering Center for the engineering phase	A joint one-year medical-engineering study of air pollution in a typical coal-burning midwest community. Study of relationship between air pollution and public health with emphasis on combustion products of coal. Detailed morbidity, mortality, clinical, and autopsy studies. Extensive aerometric, meteorological, and source investigation.	*35*

of field observations with about three or four man-months of either prior or subsequent data collection and computation. Areas as large as a state require about nine man-months of field work and a similar amount of time for questionnaire and data analysis.

2. *Small-Scale Intensive Investigations*

Another type of survey which is less demanding in terms of manpower and time, but involves a considerable amount of air sampling and analysis is the intensive small-scale investigation limited in geographical scope and time (*17–24b*). This type seeks to demonstrate the general patterns and levels of pollution by sampling continuously for selected gases and solids at a few locations in a community for a period of one to several weeks. Such surveys provide order-of-magnitude figures of levels and fluctuations of pollutant concentrations, and serve as a useful device for focusing the attention of the community on its growing problem. This type of survey can frequently be used to advantage in training or orienting new personnel.

3. *Community Air Pollution Surveys*

At the other end of the spectrum is the large-scale technical air pollution study of a community, or a part of a community, involving a considerable amount of field and laboratory activities over a period of one or more years (*25–34*). Table II lists major air pollution surveys in this category. The objective of this type of survey is to develop a sounder understanding of the magnitude, origin, causes, and effects of air pollution, and ultimately to recommend effective action for abatement.

Such a study requires considerable resources in terms of technical staff, equipment, and facilities. The data is obtained largely by actual field measurements and observations relating to source sampling, atmospheric sampling, meteorology, and manifested effects.

D. Research Studies

In the present state of knowledge concerning atmospheric pollution a most important function of a survey is that which falls under the broad category of research. Though impressive progress has been made in recent years, there still exists a considerable lack of understanding of the fundamental mechanisms and processes involved in the formation, intensification, and attenuation of air pollution and its undesirable effects. It must be recognized that past community air pollution studies have substantially increased our knowledge of the basic concepts of air pollution even though their prime objective was to develop control measures. The recently completed Nashville Community Air Pollution Study provides a rare example of a survey conducted solely in the interest of research (*35*). Many more research-oriented air pollution surveys are needed to provide answers and explanations for the many complex problems inherent in the air pollution phenomenon.

Investigations of the air pollution disasters which occurred in Liège, Belgium (*36, 36a*), Donora, Pennsylvania (*37*), Poza Rica, Mexico (*38*), and London, England (*38a, 38b*) represent special research investigations performed immediately after the episodes in an effort to uncover fundamental facts concerning the nature, extent, and causative factors involved.

III. The Community Air Pollution Survey

Of all the types of surveys described above, the comprehensive community air pollution surveys generally require the greatest amount of effort, time, and funds. This is because of their intrinsically broad coverage with regard to variety and frequency of measurements, geographical extent, and duration. A typical community-wide air pollution survey may cover all or a major portion of some large city, and may depend on a considerably extensive network of air-sampling and meteorologic stations operated on a frequent, if not continuous, schedule, supplemented by mobile air-monitoring facilities. In addition the survey may include a determination of the principal pollutant sources with an estimate of their emission rates.

Other pertinent considerations include climatologic and topographic factors, as well as an evaluation of effects of pollution on the human. Such surveys may extend over a period of one or more years, and require the services of many professional disciplines including physics, chemistry, mathematics, biology, applied sciences, and engineering.

A guiding principle in developing a community air pollution survey is the pursuit of answers to such questions as:

(a) *What* are the pollution levels with respect to time and place?
(b) *Why* do these levels vary?
(c) *Which* undesirable environmental effects are produced?
(d) *Where* does the pollution come from?
(e) *How* can the problem be solved?

The details of planning, design, and execution of surveys vary since each must be tailored to the specific needs, requirements, and resources of the area involved. Nevertheless, there are some considerations which are in a sense fundamental. All of the major activities relating to community air pollution surveys can be classified into three separate phases —Planning and Development, Operations, Evaluation and Report.

A. Planning and Development

This phase involves reconnaissance of the situation to size up the magnitude and nature of the problem, as well as the interests and resources of the community (*39*). The individual or organization selected to make the survey then reaches an agreement with official representatives of the community or the sponsoring group on the purpose and scope of the proposed study, cost and duration, type of final report, and administrative or policy matters. Where several participating groups are involved it is advisable to spell out in writing these terms as well as conditions of participation, responsibility, and authority. Since community studies are complex and expensive operations subject to public opinions and pressures, it is recommended that a clear understanding among interested parties be achieved at the earliest possible time. Insofar as it is feasible, the general public should be kept informed initially and throughout the study.

The next step in this preliminary phase is the systematic and logical development of a detailed plan of study which specifies the broad objectives, the individual projects, the organization, including the classification and grades of professional and subprofessional personnel, the requirements for laboratory and office space, scientific and technical equipment and supplies, field facilities, and transportation.

B. Operations

The actual execution of the various field and laboratory operations and projects which relate to the collection of information, and the performance of the many technical measurements and observations, represents the operations phase. In general, the survey consists of the following five activities with appropriate modifications and emphasis to suit individual needs:

1. *Air Pollutant Source Measurements*

Knowledge of the types and rates of emissions is fundamental to any study of community air pollution (*40*). An accurate appraisal of the entire problem of an area must take into account the interrelation between air pollution sources, mechanisms of atmospheric transport and diffusion, and undesirable effects on animate and inanimate objects.

There are at least seven ways in which air pollution source information is useful:

(a) It helps determine the type of the air-sampling and air-analysis program to be utilized in an area-wide survey.

(b) It helps to interpret results of air sampling in terms of both air composition and fluctuations in such composition.

(c) It helps to explain observed undesirable effects.

(d) It helps to establish the relative contribution of each major source.

(e) It provides a basis for determining the type of control program needed in a community as well as modifications which may be necessary from time to time. This applies to both engineering control on a local source basis as well as legal control on an area-wide basis.

(f) From the research standpoint, source data are necessary for constructing mathematical models of the atmosphere in a given location for purposes of estimating its air pollution potential, or predicting the atmospheric concentrations of specific pollutants.

(g) Intimate knowledge of sources, present and future, is an important factor in the establishment of emission standards as well as in planning and zoning.

It must be stressed that, while knowledge of emission sources is fundamental to an understanding of the nature, causes, and effects of air pollution in a given community, air pollution source information per se is definitely limited in its value. In other words, data on quantities of a pollutant emitted in one area are not necessarily directly relatable to the situation in another area. For instance, a given emission rate of a gas may be responsible for a serious problem in a specific location. The same emission rate applied to another area with differing meteorological, topographic, social, and economic conditions may produce only a barely perceptible effect.

The systematic collection and collation of detailed information concerning the air pollution emissions in a given area are referred to as an emission inventory (*41*). To be of greatest use, such an inventory should contain as much information as possible on the *types* of sources as well as their contributions in terms of the *composition* and *rates of discharge* of the individual pollutants. This should be supplemented by information on the number and geographical distribution of sources, description of process, raw materials, and control measures.

The choice of units of expression in an emission inventory is immaterial as long as the system is consistent, realistic, and relatable to the particular air pollution condition or effect in question (*42*). Emissions are commonly reported in terms of weight of pollutant per unit of time.

Such an inventory should be kept current not only so that the effectiveness of the local control program can be periodically evaluated, and if necessary modified, but also because of the changing character of pollution sources in a rapidly expanding technological society.

2. *Meteorological and Topographic Studies*

A thorough study of the local climatology, meteorology, and topography is essential for defining the air flow patterns which in large measure control the rate of intensification and attenuation of air pollution in the locality (*43*). Climatologic information is a necessary requirement for the proper design of air-sampling and observation networks used in area-wide studies. Forecasts are needed for certain field activities such as intensive air sampling during specified weather conditions.

Meteorologic parameters provide a rational basis upon which to select, from a large number of collected air samples, those to be given detailed analytical treatment. Perhaps the most important use of meteorology in an air pollution survey is in correlating weather factors with air-sampling and allied data to permit reasonable interpretation of air quality measurements in terms of source and atmospheric variables.

Tracer studies in which fluorescent, radioactive, or other type of tracer material is released into the air at air pollutant emission points provide excellent means for studying the behavior of pollutants under specified weather and source conditions (*44*).

3. *Air Sampling and Analysis*

A thorough and accurate record of air quality is of fundamental importance in a survey. This not only includes information on the particulate and gaseous content of the air but also knowledge of the variations and fluctuations in pollutant concentrations with respect to time and space. Time considerations include diurnal, seasonal, and long-range trends and patterns, while spatial factors involve comparisons of pollutant concentrations on the basis of their horizontal and vertical distribution. In large studies it is desirable to use an air-sampling network in and around the area of interest. The design of such a network will depend on the local conditions as well as resources; however, its configuration should take into account the sources, receptors, and local climatology.

The network of sampling stations employed in the Aerometric Survey of Los Angeles is shown in Fig. 1 (*30*). It does not conform to any specific geometric pattern, the sites having been selected on the basis of typical surface wind trajectories for the season during which the study was conducted.

The Louisville air pollution study networks are shown in Fig. 2 (*32*). Unlike the Los Angeles study, the air-sampling network is laid out according to a pattern consisting of two concentric circles around the major presumed sources. The selection of location of individual stations on this network was determined on the basis of topography and surface wind movements as well as sources and receptors.

The aerometric network employed on the Nashville study is shown in Fig. 3 (*35a–h*). It is noted that this network possesses a high degree of

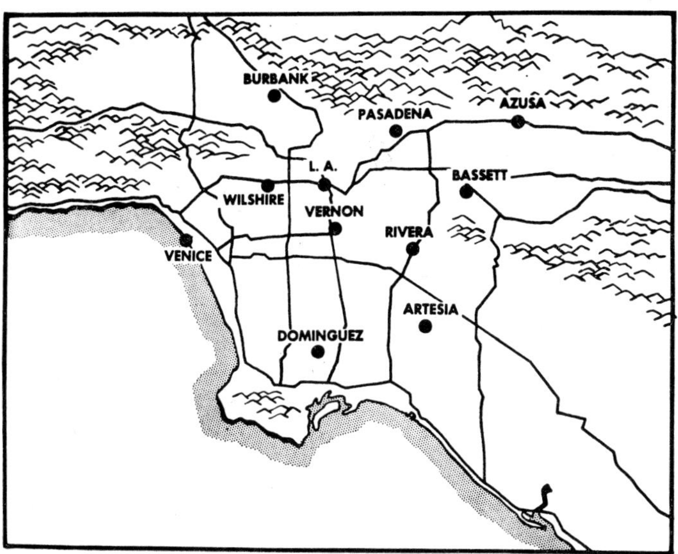

FIG. 1. Network of sampling stations. Los Angeles Aerometric Survey. (Courtesy of the Air Pollution Foundation.)

symmetry, and contains a much greater number of stations than the two previously discussed networks. Basically, it represents a triangulation pattern superimposed upon a circular grid system having its geometric center at the center of the city.

A total of 119 stations are situated at apexes of equilateral triangles having sides 0.87 mi. in length. Thus no ground location is further than about a half mile from the nearest observation station.

In these three surveys measurements were made on a full-time basis ranging from continuous to monthly intervals, depending upon the particular pollutant or effect measured. Table III summarizes the sampling schedule used in the Nashville study.

The type and frequency of air sampling likewise depend on local considerations. In general, the value of air-sampling results will be maximum if the network stations are fixed and operate simultaneously and continuously every day including weekends and holidays with the shortest practicable sampling period. Intensive physical and chemical analyses are performed only on samples selected on some rational basis. This system permits efficient use of limited analytic facilities since more thorough examination of significant samples is possible.

The fixed air sampling network should be supplemented by mobile stations built in suitable vehicles to cover areas outside the network, and to enable more intensive sampling of selected areas during periods of

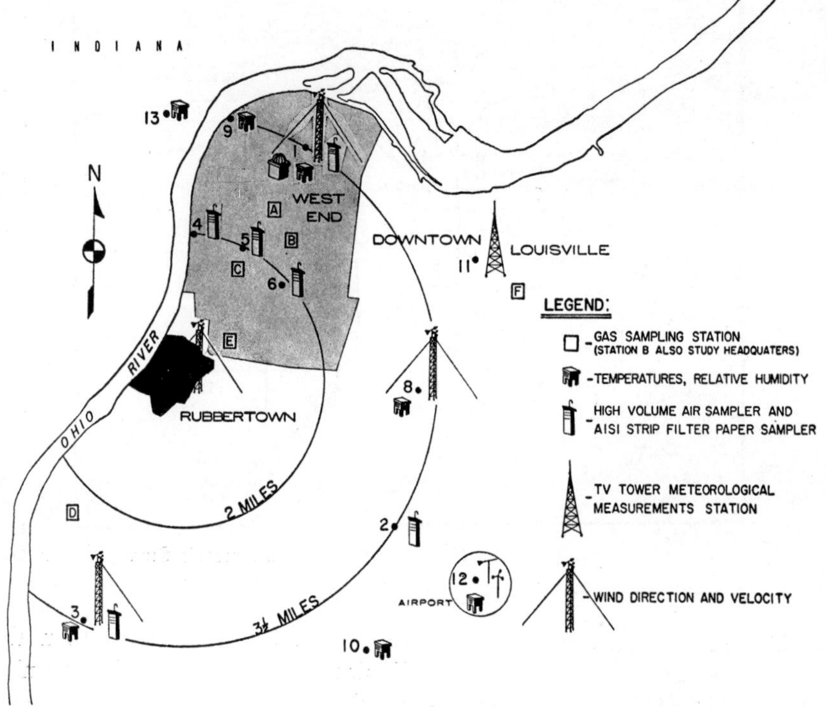

FIG. 2. Air-sampling network and meteorological observation network. Special Air Pollution Study of Louisville and Jefferson County, Kentucky. (Courtesy of the U. S. Public Health Service.)

special interest. For obtaining samples vertically through the air mass it may be necessary to employ towers, fixed-wing piloted airplanes, radio-controlled airplanes, helicopters, or captive balloons.

The type of shelter used at each station and the facilities and equipment for obtaining a sample should be such as to insure the collection of representative samples.

In the Louisville study the stations were standardized as to shape, size, construction, and height above ground. A typical station is shown in Fig. 4.

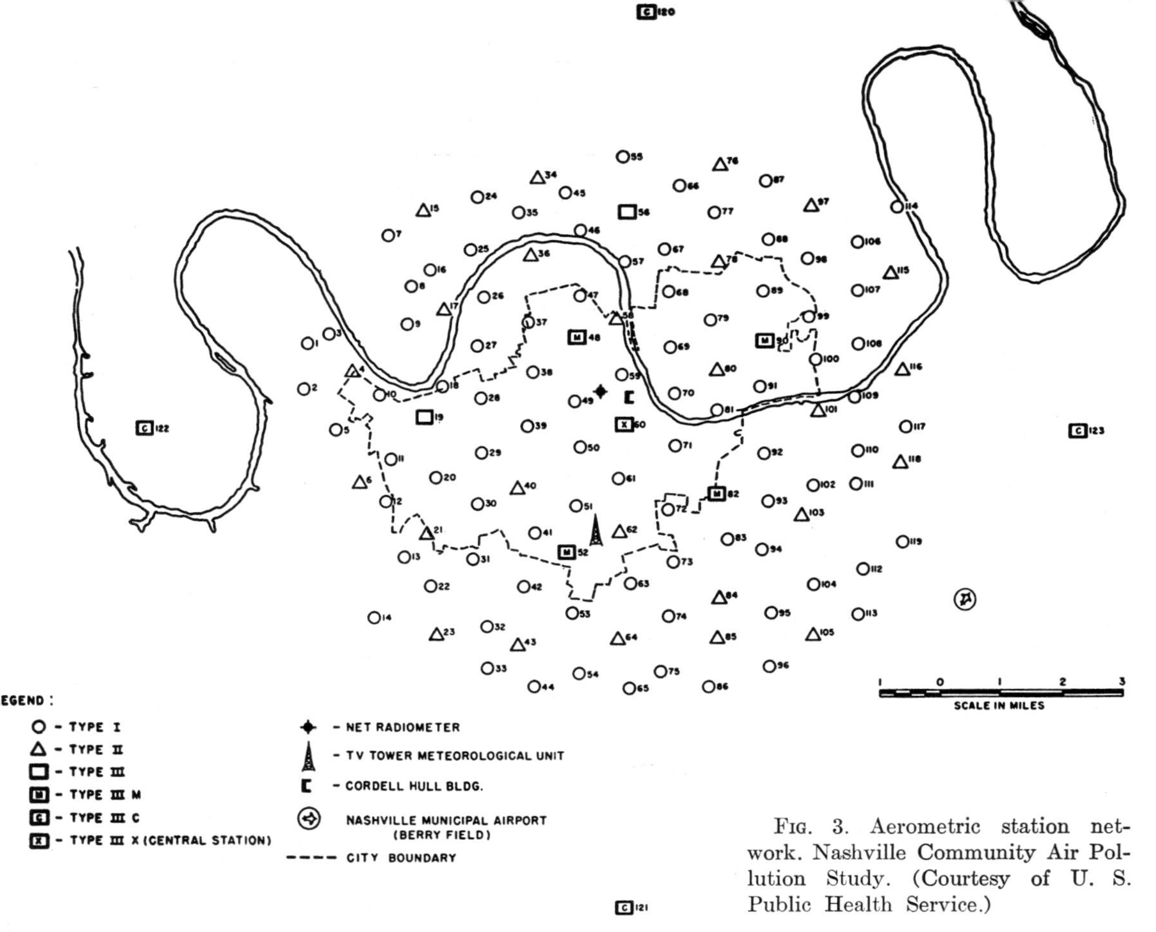

FIG. 3. Aerometric station network. Nashville Community Air Pollution Study. (Courtesy of U. S. Public Health Service.)

TABLE III
SUMMARY OF ROUTINE AEROMETRIC PROGRAM: NASHVILLE AIR POLLUTION STUDY[a]

Station	Number of stations	Measurements made	Equipment	Frequency of measurement	Analyses made	Analytical method	Remarks
Type I	87	Dustfall	Plastic dustfall collectors—wet bottom	1—30 day sample per month	Weight of water insoluble matter	Filter contents of collector, dry, and weigh	Sampling equipment mounted on utility poles
		Sulfur dioxide	Lead peroxide candle	1—30 day sample per month	Sulfur trioxide determined as sulfate	Barium chloride method for sulphate; gravimetric	
Type II	25	Measurements made at Type I stations also made at all Type II stations					
		Soiling (Suspended particulate)	Sampling train of filter paper, bubbler, trap, orifice, and pump	1—24 hour sample per day	Change in light transmission through filter paper	Photometric	Sampling equipment mounted on utility poles
		Sulfur dioxide		1—24 hour sample per day	Sulfur dioxide	West and Gaeke method	Laboratory analyses made using Technicon Autoanalyzer
		Total wind movement	Airways Weather Bureau #402 Odometer	1—24 hour total per day	Total wind movement per 24 hour period	Automatic counter read daily	Sensing elements about 33 feet above ground
Type III	2	Measurements made at Type I and Type II stations also made at all Type III stations					Dustfall also analyzed for water soluble; benzene soluble; other combustible; ash
		Suspended particulate	High volume filter paper sampler	1—24 hour sample per day	All samples—total weight of particulate matter	Gravimetric	Benzene extracts of many samples fractionated and used for animal studies of possible carcinogenicity
					One sample in ten—further analyses made for total organic; nitrate; and sulfate	As used in U.S. Public Health Service National Air Sampling Network	
		Soiling (Suspended particulate)	AISI strip filter paper sampler	12—2 hour or 6—4 hour samples per day	Change in light transmission through filter paper	Photometric	2 hour samples in high pollution seasons; 4 hour samples in low pollution seasons
		Sulfur dioxide	Automatic sequential sampler with midget bubblers	12—2 hour samples per day	Sulfur dioxide	West and Gaeke method	Atmospheric air filtered before passing through bubbler. Laboratory analyses made using Technicon Autoanalyzer

Type III M	4	Measurements made at Type III stations also made at all Type III M stations					
		Wind speed; wind direction	Beckman and Whitley Model K 100 wind system	Continuous strip chart record	Wind speed—average; maximum; and minimum hourly wind direction—average; highest veering and backing direction—all hourly	Strip chart observation and data reduction	Sensing elements about 33 feet above ground. Fifth highest veering and backing direction used August 1958 through January 1959
		Temperature; relative humidity	Friez Hygrothermograph Model 594	Continuous strip chart record	Average hourly values taken from charts	Strip chart observation and data reduction	Instrument in Weather Bureau Cotton Region type shelter
Type III C	4	Measurements made at Type III stations were made at all Type III C stations except that two-hourly sulfur dioxide measurements were *not* made					
Type III X (Central Station)	1	Measurements made at Type III stations amde also at the Type III X station					
		Sulfur Dioxide	Thomas Autometer	Continuous strip chart record	Sulfur dioxide	Change in electrolytic conductivity of hydrogen peroxide–sulfuric acid absorbing solution	
		Nitrogen dioxide	Kruger Model 73 Atmosphere Analyzer	Continuous strip chart record	Nitrogen dioxide	Automatically recorded colorimetric analysis based on method described by Saltzman	Nitric oxide channel of recorder not operated successfully
		Oxidant			Oxidant	Automatically recorded colorimetric analysis based on neutral KI reaction	
		Carbon monoxide	M.S.A. Luft type non-dispersive infrared analyzer	Continuous strip chart record	Carbon monoxide	Absorption of infrared radiation converted to electrical output signal	
		Suspended particulate matter collected	Positive displacement pump; sheets of membrane filter media	Sampler run continuously. Each filter used 2–4 weeks	Particulate matter mechanically removed for use as collected		Collected material used for animal studies of possible carcinogenicity
Cordell Hull Building	1	Visual range	Human observer	0900 and 1500 CST daily		Visibility of certain objects at known distances away was noted	
		Photographs	Camera	0900 and 1500 CST Daily		Appraisal of degree of haze as shown on pictures	Picture taken in three compass directions
		Incoming radiation	Instrument Corp. Actinometer	Continuous strip chart record	Average hourly total incoming radiation	Instrument operates on a differential heating principle	

TABLE III (*Continued*)

Station	Number of stations	Measurements made	Equipment	Frequency of measurement	Analyses made	Analytical method	Remarks
Television Tower	1	Upper air wind speed; wind direction	Bendix-Friez Aerovane	Continuous strip chart record	Same as at Type III M stations	Same as at Type III M stations	Sensing units at 251.5 and 501.5 feet above ground—recorder at ground level
Downtown park area	1	Net radiation	Suomi Economical Net Radiometer	Four times per minute-recorded	Net radiation. (Difference between incoming solar and sky radiation and outgoing terrestrial radiation)	Output of thermopiles recorded	Located in small park area near downtown area near Cordell Hull Building
U.S. Weather Bureau Airport Station Berry Field	1	Upper air winds	Pilot balloons and rawinsonde	4 per day at 0600; 1200; 1800; and 2400 CST	Wind speed and direction at specified levels		Pilot balloons at 1200 and 2400 CST; Rawinsonde at 0600 and 1800 CST
		Sunshine	Marvin Sunshine Recorder	Continuous strip chart record	Minutes of sunshine each hour	Instrument is a differential air thermometer	Other measurements usually made at USWB first order stations are available
		Upper air temperature; pressure; relative humidity	Radiosonde units	0600 and 1800 CST daily	Temperature, relative humidity, and pressure in upper air		

[a] Courtesy of U.S. Public Health Service.

The Nashville study made use of several standardized types of stations, as shown in Figs. 5 through 7.

In addition to routine network sampling, provision should be made for the collection of special samples such as freeze-out and evacuated

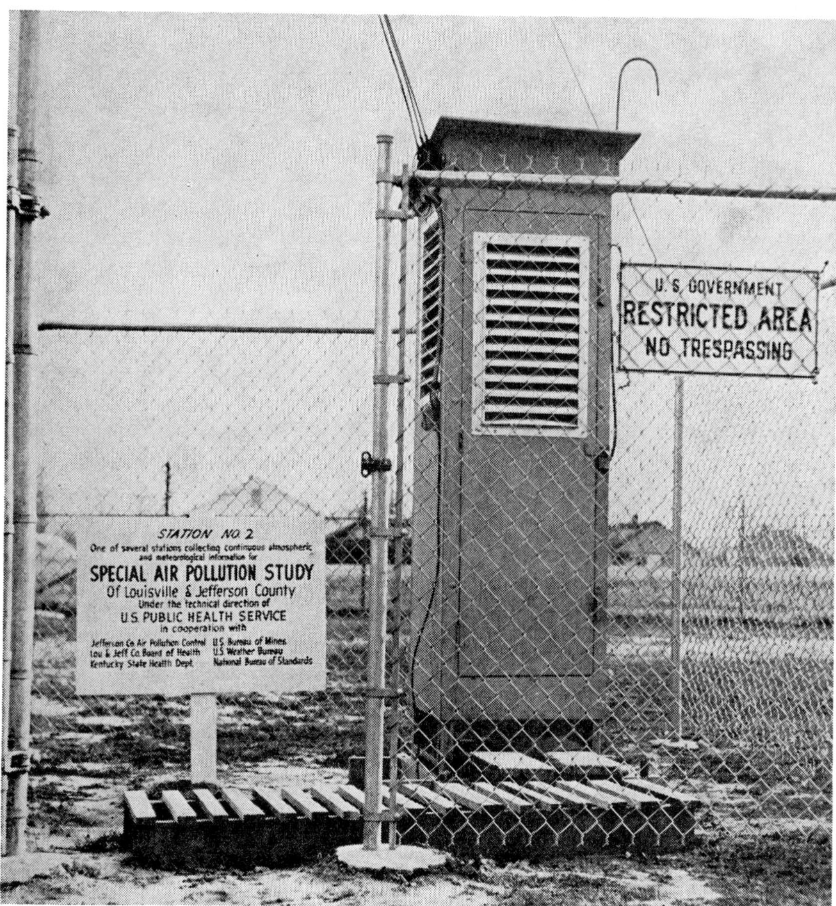

FIG. 4. Standardized type of air-sampling station used in the Special Air Pollution Study of Louisville and Jefferson County, Kentucky. (Courtesy of the U. S. Public Health Service.)

container samples for hydrocarbons and auto exhaust, and greased slides or impactors for chemical, physical, or morphological identification of particulates.

It is to be expected that as modern technology continues to diversify, new classes of pollutants will attract greater attention than they do at present. At least two nonchemical type agents will come under closer scrutiny in future air pollution surveys. One of these encompasses the biological organisms, concerning which too little is known regarding their role and significance in the community atmosphere.

The other includes the radioactive materials which are expected to assume greater hygienic importance in an era of increasing production

FIG. 5. Type I station showing mounting of dustfall and lead peroxide instruments. Nashville Community Air Pollution Study. (Courtesy of the U. S. Public Health Service.)

and use of radioactive isotopes in industry, medicine, agriculture, and research. The expanding utilization of stationary and mobile nuclear reactors, as well as the testing of nuclear weapons, gives added importance to the need for measurement of airborne radioactivity.

4. *Measurements of Effects*

Except for purely research reasons, most area-wide air pollution surveys are initiated because a problem was thought to exist. The existence of a problem in turn implies the existence of an undesirable effect such as reduced visibility and haze; irritation of the eyes or respiratory tract; obnoxious odors; damage to vegetation, livestock, property, or health; or other untoward effect (*45, 45a*). An air pollution survey therefore must seek to identify and evaluate the undesirable effects and relate them to air quality and source. In this manner the cause and effect relationships are clarified, and the way is opened for the development of a rational basis for control and abatement of the problem.

Most of the air pollution effects lend themselves to relatively simple physical or chemical mensuration such as visibility reduction or cor-

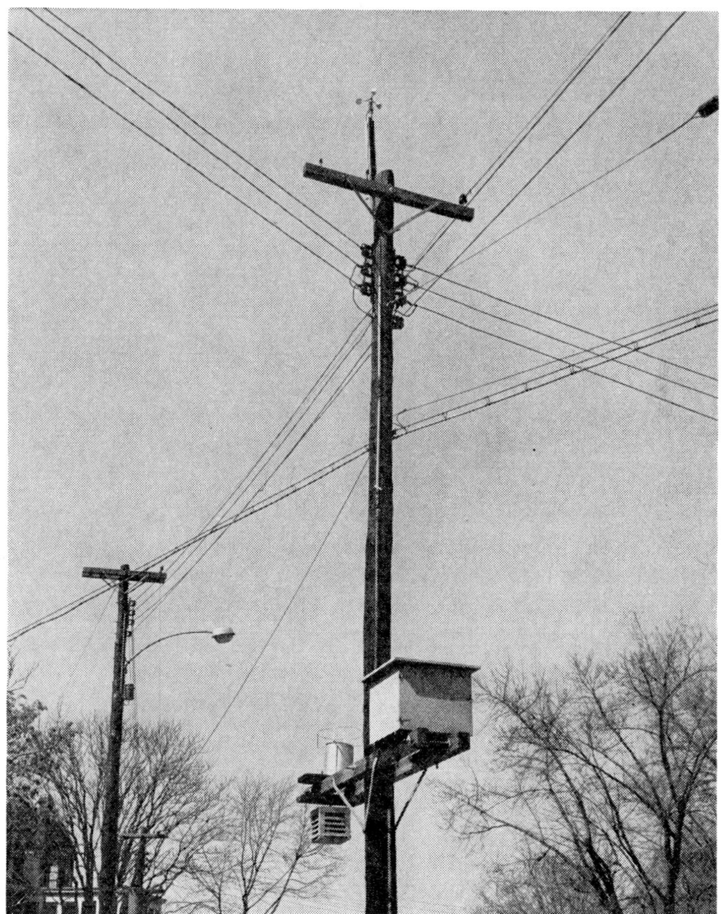

FIG. 6. Type II station showing the mounting of dustfall and lead peroxide instruments, as well as shelter for housing filter paper and sulfur dioxide sampling equipment and counter for the wind odometer shown at top of the pole. Nashville Community Air Pollution Study. (Courtesy of the U. S. Public Health Service.)

rosion rate. Others, such as the health effects, are not easily assayed since they represent long-term and not easily demonstrated changes in biological systems. Still other effects, such as odors, are difficult to quantitate because of the subjective nature of the human response.

Present state of knowledge makes measurement of these types of effects difficult, but progress towards better identification and quantitation is encouraging, and hopefully research will soon provide more reliable methods for this very important aspect of air pollution.

FIG. 7. Type III station showing dustfall and lead peroxide equipment on a cross arm of the pole; sensing elements for wind-measuring equipment at top of pole, and walk-in shelter at ground for housing wind registers and equipment for sampling total particulates, soiling, sulfur dioxide, nitrogen dioxide, oxidants, and carbon monoxide. Nashville Community Air Pollution Study. (Courtesy of the U. S. Public Health Service.)

Of intense interest in some localities is the economic effects of air pollution (*46*). Accordingly, a survey may include measurements of at least the more important of these effects. The corrosion of metals, deterioration of fabrics, damage to paint, and soiling of laundry, merchandise, and interior furnishings represent substantial economic losses to the individuals as well as commercial and industrial organizations of the typically urban society. The relationship of air pollution to these damaging effects can in itself be a subject of major study. Nevertheless, a reasonable effort to appraise the pertinent economic effects is a necessary part of community air pollution studies. A few relatively simple survey techniques already exist and more will undoubtedly be developed as interest in this area grows.

5. *Photographic Studies*

The use of photographic techniques in an air pollution survey has not been sufficiently explored. Applications of photography include the documentation of visible air pollution manifestations such as decreased visibility; specific emission sources such as smokestacks, and their range of influence under varying weather conditions; and type and degree of damage to vegetation, materials of construction, and paints.

Ground and aerial observations are useful in correlating visible pollution with physical, chemical, and biological measurements. Reconnaissance from the ground and the air is an aid in designing a network of sampling and observation stations, and in planning sampling schedules.

A very impressive tool in air pollution studies is time lapse photography for the diurnal study of sources, character, and rate of development of urban air pollution. New photomicrographic techniques using three-dimensional color photography greatly facilitate the identification of suspended and deposited particulates and their relation to known emission sources.

6. *Analysis of Data*

It is readily apparent that the routine handling and reduction of the voluminous data and information collected during a comprehensive study constitute a formidable task. Advice of and consultation with statistical analysts, familiar with modern methods of data processing, should be sought early in the planning and design stage to insure the development of a realistic and efficient system for the collection and reduction of raw data. Decisions on selection of data-handling methods as well as on many of the specific types of correlative analyses should be made at this stage. Advantageous use should be made of electronic calculators and computer programing (*47–50*).

7. *Public Relations and Information*

It must be stressed that at the very outset of the study, and at frequent intervals during the study, the general public should be kept closely informed on the purpose and progress of the study through the medium of press, radio, television, and addresses to local organizations.

Photographic records of pertinent developments during the study not only provide a useful documentary but also furnish graphic material for press releases and for the final report.

C. Evaluation and Report

This is one of the most challenging aspects of the study, since it includes the difficult task of analyzing what may be voluminous data, interpreting the findings, and formulating a logical conclusion. After this, appropriate recommendations must be developed, and finally all this must be reported in a clear, understandable and systematic manner. Perhaps the greatest difficulty in arriving at definite conclusions lies in the inherent complexity of air pollution, the incomplete state of knowledge in this field, and limitations in survey methods and techniques. These factors very frequently make firm and irrefutable statements most difficult.

Recommendations likewise are often difficult to make, since in many areas of air pollution control adequate abatement measures are virtually nonexistent or economically burdensome. An example of the latter is the problem of sulfur dioxide from burning of sulfur-bearing coal for generation of electric power. Huge quantities of oxides of sulfur are so produced, especially in our midwest and eastern communities, and yet there is no practicable method for removal of sulfur dioxide from stack gases. The only choice is switching to other fuels or low sulfur coal. The former may not be feasible, since the economy of the region may be based on production of coal. To bring in coal of lower sulfur content or oil or gas may not only upset the local economy but also raise the cost of power.

This is typical of the perplexing situations encountered in drafting a set of recommendations for correction or abatement. A reasonable course to follow in such circumstances is to present a thorough evaluation of the benefits and disadvantages of the various solutions of choice, since in the final analysis it is up to the community to decide the ultimate course of action.

The next step is the preparation of the final report. The importance of submitting a clear, concise, attractive, and easily understood report is not always apparent to technical people who are accustomed to dealing mainly with other professional persons and to reading the technical literature. It must be remembered that invariably the report will be put in the hands of intelligent but nevertheless nontechnical persons. These may include mayors, city managers, county judges, boards of aldermen, company presidents, and citizens who eventually will have to make decisions on a course of action. The content of the report must be made intelligible to them, or much of the effort of the study may have been wasted.

In the case of publicly financed surveys, of sufficient magnitude, a formal presentation of the report to the leading local government officials in the presence of invited representatives from industry, civic organizations, press, and radio may have a beneficial effect on its general acceptance. Equally important is an appropriate announcement at the completion of a privately supported community survey.

IV. Summary

In sum, the air pollution survey in general concerns itself with a systematic study of a considerable segment of the environment to define the interrelationship of sources of pollution, atmospheric and geographic parameters, and measurable manifestations—in order to evaluate the character and magnitude of an existing problem, to estimate the potential for future worsening, or to obtain the knowledge and understanding necessary for developing preventive and corrective measures.

The design, development, and execution of the survey demand the imaginative application of many skills and professional disciplines. The objectives and purposes must be made clear from the outset and strictly adhered to throughout the course of the survey, particularly in the final stages of interpretation and reporting of the findings.

References

1. L. C. McCabe (ed.), "Air Pollution," *Proc. 1st U. S. Tech. Conf.* pp. 117, 408, 822. McGraw-Hill, New York, 1952.
2. W. L. Faith, "Air Pollution Control." Wiley, New York, 1959.
2a. W. L. Faith, The air pollution survey, *Ind. Wastes* **2,** 4 (1957).
2b. Sampling procedures and measuring equipment. *In* "Air Pollution Abatement Manual," Chapter 6. Manufacturing Chemists Assoc., Washington, D. C., 1952.
2c. P. L. Magill, F. R. Holden, and C. Ackley (eds.), "Air Pollution Handbook." McGraw-Hill, New York, 1956.
3. G. England *et al.,* A survey of dust deposition in the neighborhood of a power station, *J. Inst. Fuel* **30,** 511 (1957).
3a. Atmospheric Emissions from Petroleum Refineries. *Public Health Serv. Publ.* No. 763 (1960).
3b. J. A. Holmes, E. C. Franklin, and R. A. Gould, Report of the Selby Smelter Commission. *U. S. Bur. Mines Bull.* No. 98 (1915).
3c. J. Z. Holland, Meteorological survey of the Oak Ridge Area. Atomic Energy Commission Report No. ORO-99. Oak Ridge, Tennessee, 1953.
3d. A. H. Rose, Jr., *et al.,* "Report on Air & Water Pollution Studies Related to Proposed Petroleum Refinery for Sand Island, Oahu, Territory of Hawaii." Taft Sanitary Engineering Center, Cincinnati, Ohio, 1955.
3e. D. H. Pack *et al.,* "Meteorological Survey of the PWR Site at Shippingport, Pennsylvania." U. S. Weather Bureau, Washington, D. C., 1957.

3f. G. A. DeMarrais, "The Engineering Climatology of the National Reactor Test Station," Idaho Operations Office Report IDO-12004. Atomic Energy Commission, Idaho Falls, Idaho, 1958.

3g. O. C. Compton, "Comparison of Fluorine Levels in Groups before and after Aluminum Factory Operations in the Dalles Area." Oregon State College, Corvallis, Oregon, 1960.

4. D. M. Keagy, P. A. Kenline, E. R. Hendrickson, and R. O. McCaldin, Methodology for evaluating the air pollution problems of a state, *J. Air Poll. Control. Assoc.* **8,** 153 (1958).

5. E. R. Hendrickson, D. M. Keagy, and R. L. Stockman, "Evaluation of Air Pollution in the State of Washington," Report of a Cooperative Survey. Robert A. Taft Sanitary Engineering Center, Cincinnati, Ohio, 1956.

6. R. O. McCaldin and P. A. Kenline, "Air Pollution in Connecticut," Report of a Cooperative Survey. Robert A. Taft Sanitary Engineering Center, Cincinnati, Ohio, 1957.

7. P. A. Kenline, "Appraisal of Air Pollution in Tennessee," Report of a Cooperative Survey. Robert A. Taft Sanitary Engineering Center, Cincinnati, Ohio, 1957.

8. O. Paganini, M. D. High, and P. A. Kenline, "Appraisal of Air Pollution in Texas," Report of a Cooperative Survey. Texas Dept. of Health, Austin, Texas, 1958.

9. New York State Air Pollution Control Board, "A Review of Air Pollution in New York State." Albany, New York, 1958.

9a. C. S. Maneri and W. H. Megonnell, "Comprehensive area surveys in New York State," *J. Air Poll. Control Assoc.* **10,** 374 (1960).

10. B. C. Blakeney and M. D. High, "Cleaner Air for North Carolina, Report of a Cooperative Survey." North Carolina State Board of Health, Raleigh, North Carolina, 1959.

11. D. M. Anderson and V. H. Sussman, "Pure Air for Pennsylvania." Pennsylvania Dept. of Health, Harrisburg, Pennsylvania, 1960.

11a. Minnesota Dept. of Public Health, "An Appraisal of Air Pollution in Minnesota." Minneapolis, Minnesota, 1961.

11b. C. I. Harding *et al.*, "A Report on Florida Air Resources." Florida State Board of Health, Jacksonville, Florida, 1961.

11c. Illinois Department of Public Health, Indiana State Board of Health, and Purdue University, "Report on Bi-State Study of Air Pollution in the Chicago Metropolitan Area," 1957–1959.

12. Stanford Research Institute, "Air Pollution in the Vicinity of Portland, Oregon," Final Report. Menlo Park, California, 1956.

13. J. J. Schueneman and S. M. Rogers, "The Air Pollution Problem in Steubenville, Ohio." Robert A. Taft Sanitary Engineering Center, Cincinnati, Ohio, 1956.

14. J. J. Schueneman, "The Air Pollution Problem in Portland, Oregon." Robert A. Taft Sanitary Engineering Center, Cincinnati, Ohio, 1956.

15. J. J. Schueneman, "The Denver Area Air Pollution Problem." Robert A. Taft Sanitary Engineering Center, Cincinnati, Ohio, 1957.

16. D. M. Keagy and J. J. Schueneman, "Air Pollution in the Birmingham, Alabama, Area." Robert A. Taft Sanitary Engineering Center, Cincinnati, Ohio, 1958.

16a. P. A. Kenline, "Air Pollution in Charleston, South Carolina," Tech. Report A 60-6. Robert A. Taft Sanitary Engineering Center, Cincinnati, Ohio, 1960.

16b. P. A. Kenline, "Air Pollution in Hamilton, Ohio," Tech. Report A 60-8. Robert A. Taft Sanitary Engineering Center, Cincinnati, Ohio, 1960.
17. M. Moriguchi *et al.,* Atmospheric pollution in Tokyo district, *Papers Meteorol. Geophys. (Tokyo)* **7,** 271 (1956).
18. E. C. Halliday and S. Kemeny, Atmospheric pollution in a South African city, *Air Poll. Control Assoc. News* **5,** 3–5 (1957).
19. Truesdail Laboratories, Inc., "An Aerometric Survey of the City of Honolulu 1956–1957" Report for Board of Health, Territory of Hawaii. Los Angeles, California, 1957.
20. Arizona State Dept. of Health, "Air Pollution in Phoenix, Arizona," Report No. 1 on Air Pollution. Phoenix, Arizona, 1958.
21. E. C. Tabor and J. E. Meeker, "Air Pollution in St. Bernard, Ohio," Tech. Report A 58–5. Robert A. Taft Sanitary Engineering Center, Cincinnati, Ohio, 1958.
22. A. Giovanardi and E. Grosso, Investigation of atmospheric pollution in the city of Milan, *Nuovi ann. igiene e microbiol.* **9** (1958).
23. Arizona State Dept. of Health, "Air Pollution in Tucson, Arizona," Report No. 2 on Air Pollution. Phoenix, Arizona, 1959.
23a. M. D. Hornedo and J. H. Tillman, "Air Pollution in El Paso, Texas Area." El Paso City-County Health Unit, El Paso, Texas, 1957–1959.
24. H. Bravo, Variation of different pollutants in the atmosphere of Mexico City, *J. Air Poll. Control Assoc.* **10,** 447 (1960).
24a. Oregon State Sanitary Authority "Report on Air Pollution Conditions in and Around Roseburg, Oregon." Portland, Oregon, 1960.
24b. Oregon State Sanitary Authority "The Air Pollution Problem in Medford, Oregon." Portland, Oregon, 1960.
25. U. S. Dept. Interior, Report submitted to the trail smelter arbitral tribunal. R. S. Dean and R. E. Swain, *U. S. Bur. Mines Bull.* **453** (1944).
25a. A Committee of the Chicago Association of Commerce, "Smoke Abatement and Electrification of Railway Terminals in Chicago." Rand McNally, Chicago, Illinois, 1915.
25b. U. S. Dept. of Commerce, Smoke-abatement investigation at Grafton, W. Va., O. Monnett and L. R. Hughes, *U. S. Bur. Mines Tech. Paper* **338** (1924).
25c. U. S. Dept. of Commerce, Smoke-abatement investigations at Salt Lake City, Utah, O. Monnett, G. St. J. Perrott, and H. W. Clark, *U. S. Bur. Mines Bull.* **254** (1926).
25d. A. C. Stern, L. Buchbinder, and J. Siegel, Report of the New York City air pollution survey, *Heating, Piping Air Conditioning,* July, August, Sept., and Oct.–Nov. (1945).
25e. West Virginia Dept. of Health, "Atmospheric Pollution of the Great Kanawha River Valley Industrial Area, West Virginia." Bur. of Ind. Hyg., Charleston, West Virginia, 1952.
26. Great Britain, Dept. of Sci. and Ind. Research, "Atmospheric Pollution in Leicester—A Scientific Survey," Atmospheric Research Tech. Paper No. 1. His Majesty's Stationery Office, London, 1945.
27. J. L. Sullivan, "A Report of a Survey of Air Pollution in New South Wales." Division of Ind. Hyg., N. S. W. Dept. of Public Health, Sidney, Australia, 1953.
28. J. E. Yocum, I. M. Saslaw, S. Chapman, and R. L. Richardson, "Research Investigations of Air Pollution in the Vicinity of Louisville, Kentucky," Summary Report to Rubbertown Industrial Group. Battelle Memorial Institute, Columbus, Ohio, 1954.

29. B. C. Newbury, The Sarnia survey: Action without compulsion, *1st Intern. Congr. on Air Pollution, Am. Soc. Mech. Engrs., New York* Paper 55-APC-4 (1955).
30. N. A. Renzetti (ed.), "An Aerometric Survey of the Los Angeles Basin, August–November, 1954" Report No. 9. Air Pollution Foundation, San Marino, California, 1955.
31. Southwest Research Institute, "Air Pollution Survey of the Houston Area," Tech. Report No. 4, Summary Report, Phase I. San Antonio, Texas, 1957.
32. Public Health Service, "The Air Over Louisville—Summary of a Joint Report." Robert A. Taft Sanitary Engineering Center, Cincinnati, Ohio, 1958.
33. Interstate Sanitation Commission, "Smoke and Air Pollution, New York-New Jersey." New York, 1958.
34. International Joint Commission (Canada and United States), "Air Pollution in the Detroit-Windsor Area." Report of the Technical Advisory Board on Air Pollution, 1960.
35. L. D. Zeidberg, J. J. Schueneman, P. A. Humphrey, and R. A. Prindle, Air pollution and health; General description of a study in Nashville, Tennessee. *J. Air Poll. Control Assoc.* **11,** 289 (1961).
35a. Air Pollution Foundation, "Wind Trajectory Studies of the Movement of Polluted Air in Los Angeles Basin," Tech. Report No. 11. Los Angeles, California, 1956.
35b. J. Cholak *et al.,* "The Lead Content of the Atmosphere." Kettering Laboratory, University of Cincinnati, Cincinnati, Ohio, 1960.
35c. Air Pollution Control District, Los Angeles County, "Emissions of Oxides of Nitrogen from Stationary Sources in Los Angeles County, California." Reports Nos. 1 & 2. 1960.
35d. R. A. Brief *et al.,* Lead, carbon monoxide and traffic. *J. Air Pollution Control Assoc.* **10,** 384 (1960).
35e. "Airborne Particulate Emissions from Cotton Ginning Operations," Tech. Report A60-5. Robert A. Taft Sanitary Engineering Center, Cincinnati, Ohio, 1960.
35f. "Air Pollution Aspects of the Iron & Steel Industry," Taft Sanitary Engineering Center, Cincinnati, Ohio, 1961.
35g. R. L. Chass *et al.,* "Total air pollution emissions in Los Angeles County. *J. Air Poll. Control Assoc.* **10,** 351 (1960).
35h. Air Pollution Control District, Los Angeles County, "Emissions to the Atmosphere from Petroleum Refineries in Los Angeles County," Final Report No. 9. Los Angeles, California.
36. J. Firket, Sur les causes des accidents survenus dans la vallée de la Meuse lors des brouillards de décembre, 1930. *Bull. acad. roy. méd. Belg.* **11,** 683 (1931).
36a. J. Mage and G. Batta, Results of the investigation into the cause of the deaths which occurred in the Meuse valley during the fogs of December, 1930. *Chim. & ind. (Paris)* **27,** 961 (1932).
37. H. H. Schrenk, H. Heimann, G. D. Clayton, W. M. Gafafer, and H. Wexler, "Air Pollution in Donora, Pennsylvania," Public Health Bulletin No. 306. U. S. Public Health Service, Washington, D. C., 1949.
38. L. C. McCabe and G. D. Clayton, Air pollution by hydrogen sulfide in Poza Rica, Mexico. *Arch. Ind. Hyg. and Occupational Med.* **6,** 199 (1952).
38a. P. Drinker, Air Pollution and the London Fog of December, 1952. *Arch. Ind. Hyg. Occupational Med.* **9** (1954).

38b. Ministry of Health, "Mortality and Morbidity During the London Fog of December, 1952," Report No. 95. Her Majesty's Stationery Office, London, 1954.

39. A. T. Rossano, Jr., The joint city, county, state and federal study of air pollution in Louisville, Kentucky, *J. Air Poll. Control Assoc.* **6,** 176 (1956).

40. A. T. Rossano, Jr., Sources of community air pollution, *Interdiscipl. Conf. on Atmospheric Poll., Am. Meteorol. Soc., Santa Barbara, 1959.*

41. A. T. Rossano, Jr., and N. E. Schell, Procedures for making and inventory of air pollution emissions, *J. Air Poll. Control Assoc.* **8,** 147 (1958).

42. F. P. Terraglio, J. P. Sheehy, and R. M. Manganelli, Recommended units of expression for air pollution, *J. Air Poll. Control Assoc.* **8,** 220 (1958).

43. J. M. Leavitt *et al.,* Design and interim meteorological evaluation of a community network for meteorological and air quality measurements, *J. Air Poll. Control Assoc.* **7,** 211 (1957).

44. W. H. Megonnell, "Interstate Atmospheric Transport of Tracer Particles in the New York-New Jersey Metropolitan Area," Report to the Interstate Sanitation Commission. Robert A. Taft Sanitary Engineering Center, Cincinnati, Ohio, 1958.

45. R. E. Swain, Smoke and fume investigation, *Ind. Eng. Chem.* **41,** 2384 (1949).

45a. J. H. Ludwig, The effects of air contaminants upon a community, *Trans. 47th Natl. Safety Congr. and Exposition, Chicago, Illinois* p. 55 (1959).

46. R. I. Larsen, Air pollution damage to paint, *Am. Paint J.* **42,** 94 (1957).

47. E. K. Harris and E. C. Tabor, Statistical considerations related to the planning and operation of a national air sampling network, *Proc. 49th Ann. Meeting Air Poll. Control Assoc., Buffalo, New York* p. 35–1 (1956).

48. A. C. Stern, Application of electronic processing to air quality data. *Proc. Semi-Ann. Tech. Conf. Air Poll. Control Assoc., San Francisco, Calif.* p. 93–105 (1957).

49. A. C. Stern and C. E. Zimmer, "National Air Sampling Network Program Manual for the IBM 650 Computer." Robert A. Taft Sanitary Engineering Center, Cincinnati, Ohio, 1958.

50. R. I. Larsen, A method for determining source reduction required to meet air quality standards, *J. Air Poll. Control Assoc.* **11,** 71 (1961).

51. Illinois Department of Public Health, "Something in the Air: A Report on Air Pollution in Illinois." Springfield, Illinois, 1956.

APPENDIX I

Characteristics of Particles and Particle Dispersoids

CHARACTERISTICS OF PARTICLES AND PARTICLE DISPERSOIDS

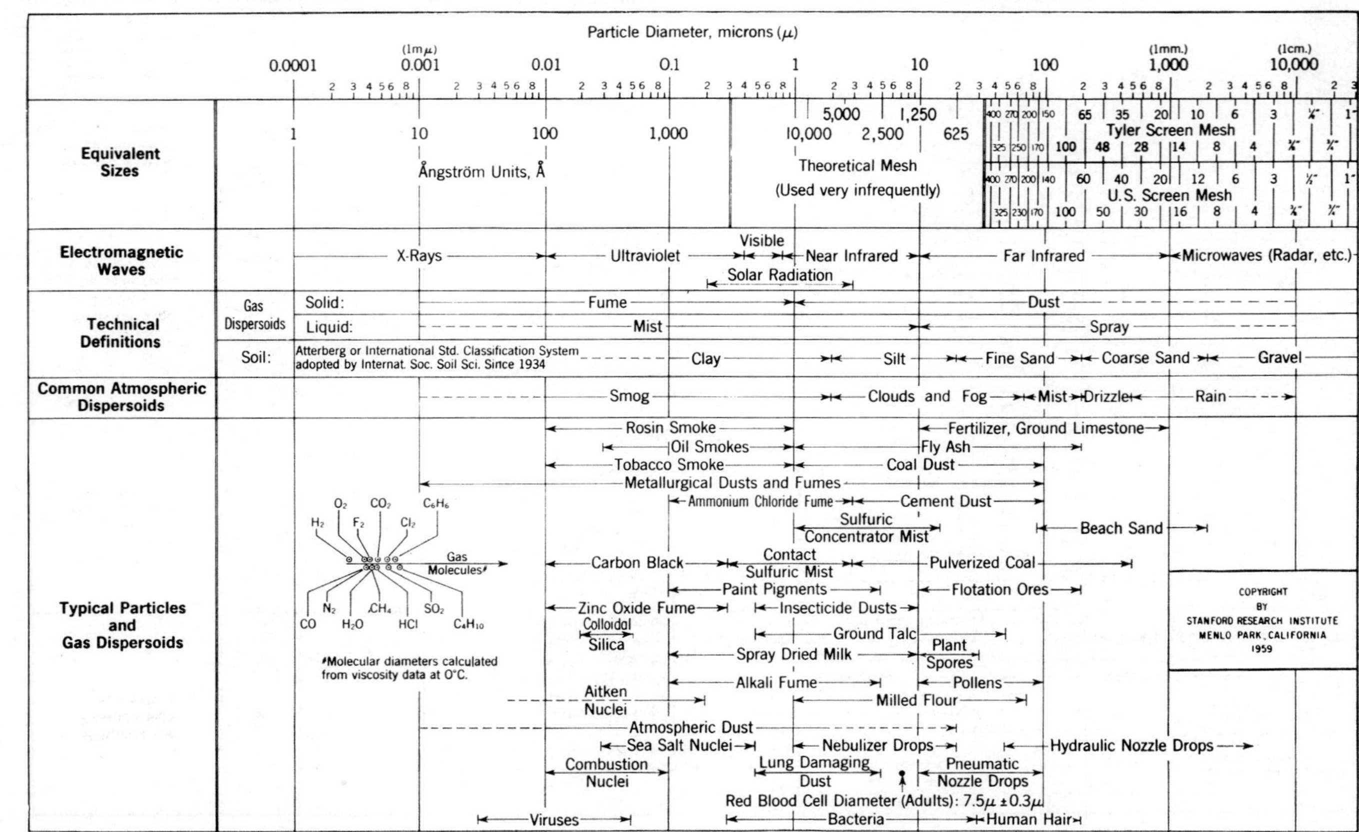

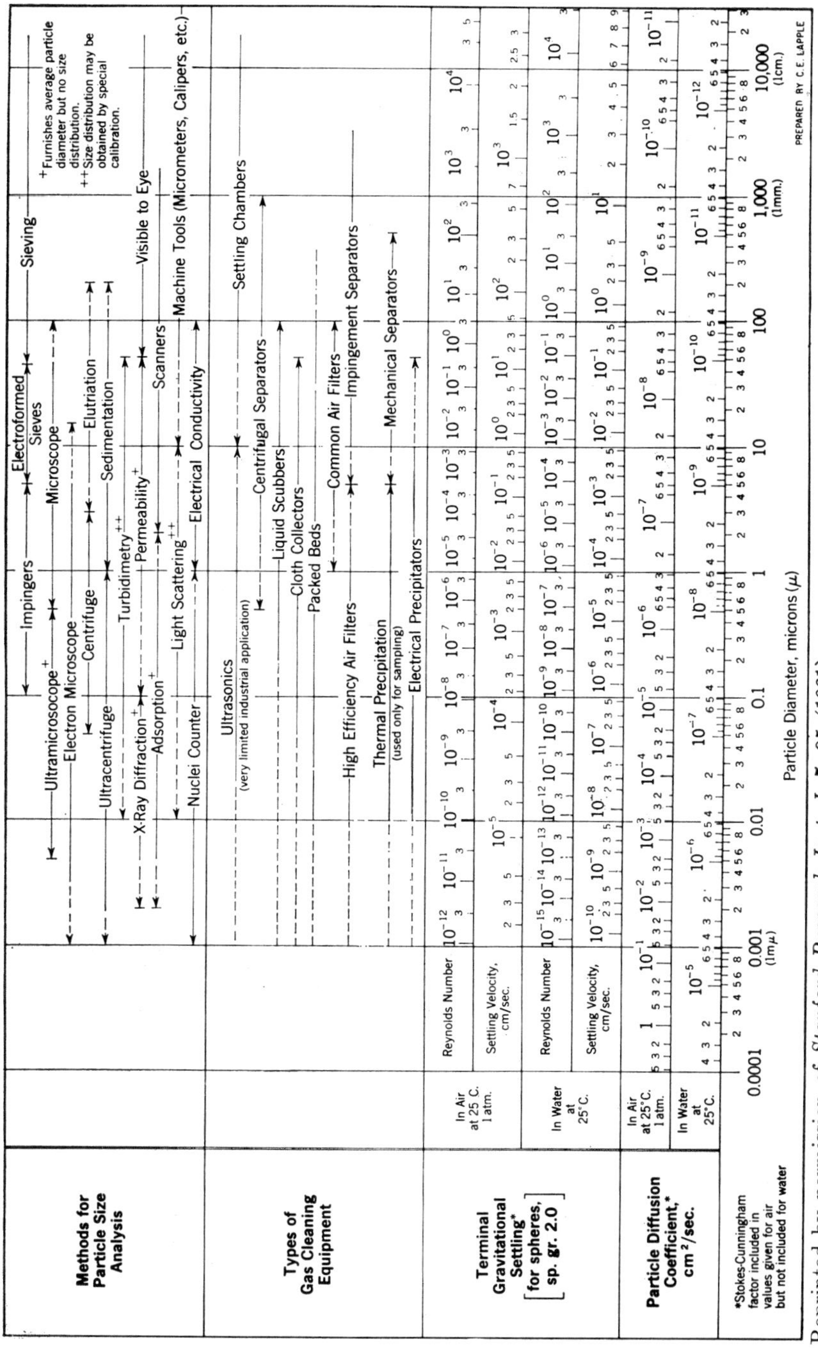

Methods for Particle Size Analysis

Impingers — Electroformed Sieves — Sieving
Ultramicroscope+ — Microscope
Electron Microscope
Centrifuge — Elutriation
Ultracentrifuge — Sedimentation
Turbidimetry++
X-Ray Diffraction+ — Permeability+ — Visible to Eye
Adsorption+ — Scanners
Light Scattering++ — Machine Tools (Micrometers, Calipers, etc.)
Nuclei Counter — Electrical Conductivity

+Furnishes average particle diameter but no size distribution.
++Size distribution may be obtained by special calibration.

Types of Gas Cleaning Equipment

Ultrasonics (very limited industrial application) — Settling Chambers
Centrifugal Separators
Liquid Scubbers
Cloth Collectors
Packed Beds
Common Air Filters
High Efficiency Air Filters — Impingement Separators
Thermal Precipitation (used only for sampling) — Mechanical Separators
Electrical Precipitators

Terminal Gravitational Settling* [for spheres, sp. gr. 2.0]

In Air at 25 C. 1 atm. — Reynolds Number: 10^{-12} 10^{-11} 10^{-10} 10^{-9} 10^{-8} 10^{-7} 10^{-6} 10^{-5} 10^{-4} 10^{-3} 10^{-2} 10^{-1} 10^{0} 10^{1} 10^{2} 10^{3} 10^{4}

In Air at 25 C. 1 atm. — Settling Velocity, cm/sec.: 10^{-5} 10^{-4} 10^{-3} 10^{-2} 10^{-1} 10^{0} 10^{1} 10^{2} 10^{3}

In Water at 25°C. — Reynolds Number: 10^{-15} 10^{-14} 10^{-13} 10^{-12} 10^{-11} 10^{-10} 10^{-9} 10^{-8} 10^{-7} 10^{-6} 10^{-5} 10^{-4} 10^{-3} 10^{-2} 10^{-1} 10^{0} 10^{1} 10^{2} 10^{3} 10^{4}

In Water at 25°C. — Settling Velocity, cm/sec.: 10^{-10} 10^{-9} 10^{-8} 10^{-7} 10^{-6} 10^{-5} 10^{-4} 10^{-3} 10^{-2} 10^{-1} 10^{0} 10^{1}

Particle Diffusion Coefficient,* cm²/sec.

In Air at 25°C. 1 atm.: 1 10^{-1} 10^{-2} 10^{-3} 10^{-4} 10^{-5} 10^{-6} 10^{-7} 10^{-8} 10^{-9} 10^{-10} 10^{-11}

In Water at 25°C.: 10^{-5} 10^{-6} 10^{-7} 10^{-8} 10^{-9} 10^{-10} 10^{-11} 10^{-12}

*Stokes-Cunningham factor included in values given for air but not included for water

Particle Diameter, microns (μ): 0.0001 · 0.001 (1mμ) · 0.01 · 0.1 · 1 · 10 · 100 · 1,000 (1mm.) · 10,000 (1cm.)

PREPARED BY C. E. LAPPLE

Reprinted by permission of *Stanford Research Inst. J.* **5,** 95 (1961).

AUTHOR INDEX

Numbers in parentheses are reference numbers and are included to assist in locating the reference where the authors' names are not mentioned in the text. Numbers in italics refer to the page on which the reference is listed.

A

B

C

D

H

L

M

N

Y

Z

SUBJECT INDEX

C

P

Y

Z

HETERICK MEMORIAL LIBRARY
628.53 S83 v.1
Stern, Arthur Cecil/Air pollution
onuu
3 5111 00139 0024